W9-BLV-832

F. X. Leyendecker
UNCLE SAM AT WAR
April 14, 1917

Lester Railk
SWEETHEARTS
September 6, 1919

Ruth Eastman
FLAPPER
April 30, 1927

Lawson Wood
MONKEYS
June 4, 1932

COLLIER'S

ONCE A WEEK

FICTION · FACT · SENSATION · WIT · HUMOR · NEWS

H. BROWN, DES.

VOL. I.	P. F. COLLIER, PROPRIETOR, Nos. 104 to 110 Attorney Street, N. Y.	NEW YORK, APRIL 28, 1888.	TERMS: $2.70 per Year. Seven Cents per Copy.	No. 1.

"I'LL HAVE NO SUCH PAUPER FOR A SON-IN-LAW!" SAID THE JUDGE, WITH A SNEER.—See "In the Dead of Night," p. 2.

First cover of *Collier's Once a Week*, April 28, 1888

COLLIER'S WEEKLY

AN ILLUSTRATED JOURNAL

Vol. XV.—No. 21.

NEW YORK, SEPTEMBER 19, 1895.

TERMS:—$6.50 PER YEAR.
Including Library and Premium Volumes.
In Canada, $7.50. (See page 2.)

THE GREAT INTERNATIONAL YACHT RACE.—THE YACHTS CROSSING THE LINE.

First cover of *Collier's Weekly*, September 19, 1895

F. X. Leyendecker
San Francisco Earthquake
May 5, 1906

Edward Penfield
Automobile
October 12, 1907

Edward Penfield
George Washington
February 22, 1908

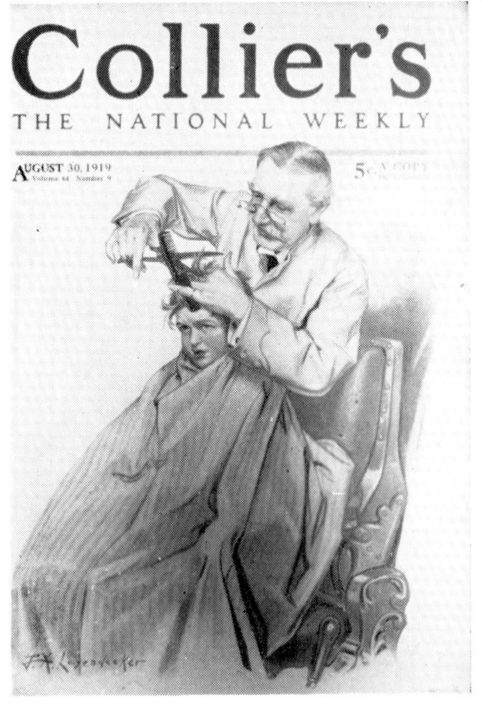

F. X. Leyendecker
Boy's Haircut
August 30, 1919

Charles Dana Gibson
GIBSON GIRL
October 30, 1920

Frederick Stanley
HUMOR
February 25, 1922

Francis Tipron Hunter
PATHOS
February 9, 1929

Maxfield Parrish
MODEL
May 11, 1929

Lawson Wood
MONKEYS
May 9, 1931

Lawson Wood
MONKEYS
August 4, 1934

Arthur Szyk
HITLER
March 28, 1942

Ronald McLeod
EISENHOWER AT WAR
September 25, 1943

Hugh Laidman
CONVERTED LST
September 1, 1945

Chesley Bonestell
HIROSHIMA, U.S.A.
August 5, 1950

Howell Conant
PRINCESS GRACE
January 4, 1957—*Collier's* last cover

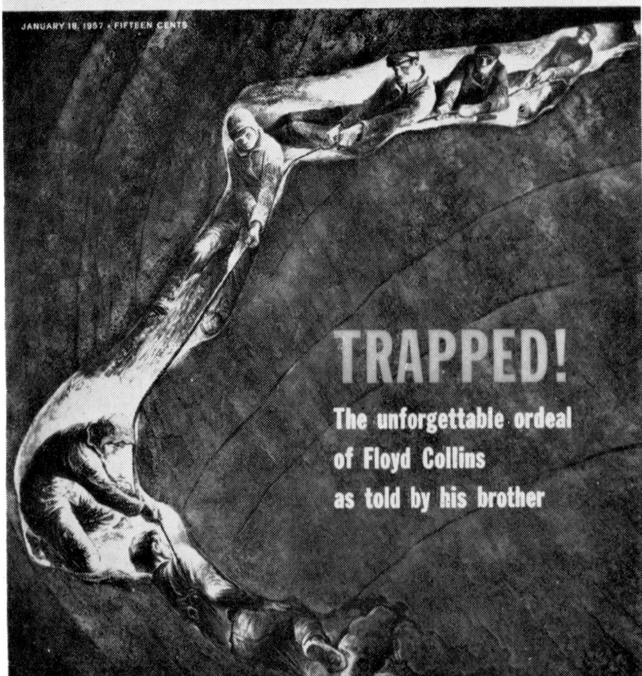

Lynd Ward
FLOYD COLLINS
Dated January 18, 1957—the "unborn" cover which never appeared on the newsstands

A Cavalcade of Collier's

A Cavalcade of Collier's

Edited by
Kenneth McArdle

A. S. BARNES & COMPANY, INC. · NEW YORK

Library of Congress Catalog Card Number: 59-12209

Printed in the United States of America

Acknowledgments

The editor wishes to thank the following for permission to reprint in this anthology the articles and stories listed below:

General Omar N. Bradley, for "What You Owe Your Country," copyright 1949 by Omar N. Bradley.

Brandt & Brandt, for "The Odor of Sanctity," by Stephen Vincent Benét, copyright 1926 by Stephen Vincent Benét, copyright 1954 by Rosemary Carr Benét; for "After Three Years," by Dana Burnet, copyright 1929, 1957 by Dana Burnet; for "The End of the Story," by John P. Marquand, copyright 1929, 1957 by John P. Marquand.

The Chase Manhattan Bank as Trustee of the Estate of Alfred Damon Runyon, for "The Three Wise Guys," copyright 1933 by Damon Runyon.

The Estate of Louis Bromfield, for "The Wedding Dress," by Louis Bromfield, copyright 1925 by the Crowell-Collier Publishing Company.

Pat Frank, for "They Think of Everything," copyright 1940 by Pat Frank.

Frank Harvey, for "Terror at Webb's Landing," copyright 1956 by Frank Harvey.

Alfred Hitchcock, for "Lifeboat," copyright 1943 by Alfred Hitchcock.

MacKinlay Kantor, for "Miracle from Heaven," copyright 1943 by the Crowell-Collier Publishing Company.

Mrs. Ring Lardner, for "Reporter's Diary," by Ring W. Lardner, copyright 1917 by Ring W. Lardner.

Harold Matson Company, for "Long Distance Call," by Jack Finney, copyright 1948 by Jack Finney; for "Hornblower and His Majesty," by C. S. Forester, copyright 1940 by the Crowell-Collier Publishing Company.

Harold Ober Associates, Inc., for "Four and Twenty Blackbirds," by Agatha Christie, for "The Last Kiss," by F. Scott Fitzgerald, copyright 1949 by Frances Scott Fitzgerald Lanahan; for "Freshman," by Corey Ford, copyright 1931 by the Crowell-Collier Publishing Company.

Robert O'Brien, for "San Francisco: April 18, 1906," copyright 1956 by Robert O'Brien.

Paul R. Reynolds and Son, for "The Zayat Kiss," by Sax Rohmer, copyright 1913 by the Crowell-Collier Publishing Company; for "The Challenge," by William R. Scott, copyright 1950 by the Crowell-Collier Publishing Company.

Rinehart and Company, Inc., for "Contents of the Dead Man's Pocket," from *The Third Level,* by Jack Finney, copyright 1956, 1957 by Jack Finney.

Mrs. Ad Schulberg, for "Love, Action, Laughter," by Budd Schulberg, copyright 1938 by Budd Schulberg.

Francis Cardinal Spellman, for "Prayer for Children," copyright 1944 by the New York Foundling Hospital.

Rogers Terrill, for "The Trap," by Howard Bloomfield, copyright 1947 by Howard Bloomfield.

Gene Tunney, for "A Man Must Fight," copyright 1932 by James Joseph Tunney.

A. Watkins, Inc., for "Five Desperate Hours in Cabin 56," by Cornelius Ryan, copyright 1956 by Cornelius Ryan; for "Crossing the Last Frontier," by Wernher von Braun, copyright 1952 by Wernher von Braun.

P. G. Wodehouse and Scott Meredith Literary Agency, Inc., for "Disentangling Old Duggie," copyright 1912, 1940 by P. G. Wodehouse.

The editor's appreciation is also extended to the following artists for permission to reproduce their cartoons in this volume:

Bo Brown; Irwin Caplan; Richard Decker; Eric Ericson; James Montgomery Flagg; Rube Goldberg; Gerald Green; Ned Hilton; Stan Hunt; Al Kaelin; Reamer Keller; Hank Ketcham; Ted Key; Bill King; Lawrence Lariar; Earle Levenstein; George Lichty; Charles E. Martin; Frank B. Modell; Virgil Partch; Charles Pearson; Irving Roir; Adolph Schus; George Shellhase; Otto Soglow; Herb Williams; Rowland Wilson; and Bernard Wiseman.

For Mary

For Mary

Introduction

COLLIER'S MAGAZINE (b. 1888, d. 1957) spanned the lifetime of an average man. As a matter of fact, its passing was more like a death in the family than the collapse of an institution to us who worked for it. I think some of this feeling must have been shared by its readers. For a magazine or a newspaper comes into the home as a kind of guest, and pays its keep by telling stories, passing along information, cracking jokes, and behaving pretty much as a human being—even to the point of getting emotional as people do, and being opinionated about politics and the high cost of living.

Collier's had such a living personality—more volatile and changeable than many of its contemporaries, but human even in its frailties.

Yet I discovered, when the time came to raise a decently inscribed memorial to this venerable old character, that none of us who were around at the end really knew *Collier's* very well. Even those whose memories went back farthest—like Walter Davenport and Bill Chenery—had known *Collier's* only in its middle and later years. There was a long and storied past—the salad days—of which only scattered episodes had been catalogued. The whole story could be found only in the long rows of fat and dog-eared bound volumes, and it was there I turned for the essence of this book.

The journey through the thousands of pages took several months. It was an exciting, and rewarding, trip of a kind few find the time to make nowadays and more should.

For here was an American cavalcade, not told with the ponderous impersonality of the average historian, but drawn vividly from life by alert eyewitness reporters.

And what reporters they were!

There was Richard Harding Davis, at home on the Rue de la Paix or a bluff overlooking the Korean plain watching the Japanese turn back and destroy the cream of the Czar's legions.

There was Jack London, telegraphing his word-picture of a catastrophe so immense that it defied even his great talents—the destruction of San Francisco in April, 1906.

There was the dashing young British aristocrat covering the Boer War who got caught by the enemy, managed a hair-raising escape, and survived to leave his bold mark upon world history and world literature—Winston S. Churchill.

There was towering Leo Tolstoy, dourly and majesically defying Russia's arrogant princes, and accurately foretelling the downfall that was to open the way to the even more terrible scourge of world communism.

Here placid Lizzie Borden sat for a word portrait as the State of Massachusetts tried her for hacking her parents to death with an ax. Here John L. Sullivan spoke the appropriate words of a fallen monarch.

Here a long succession of Presidents—Cleveland and Taft and Hoover and the Roosevelts—came to plead their causes or to record their philosophy. Here Andrew

Carnegie spoke out with startling candor against the inheritance of great wealth; here Mr. Dooley and Booth Tarkington ventilated the swollen egos of the political mighty, and William Allen White wrote warmly of the West he helped to build.

So the parade went on, as the automobile grew from a ridiculed gas-buggy to set all America on wheels; as the Wright Brothers' secretive venture at Kitty Hawk opened the air age; as the last of the Indian wars and the charge up San Juan Hill waxed large in the public fancy, and waned before the titanic struggles of Verdun and the Marne and the Argonne.

History is a fusion of events and the men who make them and record them. Here came Babe Ruth and baseball . . . Benchley and Scott Fitzgerald and prohibition and the jazz age . . . Dion O'Bannion and Al Capone and the gangster era . . . Franklin Roosevelt and Harry Hopkins and the New Deal . . . Hitler and Chamberlain and Dwight Eisenhower and Omar Bradley and again Winston Churchill, in that prophetic Spring of 1939, growling, "Let the tyrant criminals bomb!"

Then, as a restless peace returned, came the prophets of the atomic age, the outriders of the spacemen, and Heartbreak Ridge and the *Andrea Doria* and a little boy named Bobby Cain, making a new kind of history at Clinton, Tennessee. Much of it is here; much is omitted to permit a volume that is, at the very least, portable. But enough could be included to provide an unusual set of footnotes to history.

As to fiction, almost no writer of consequence through the whole seventy-year span of the magazine failed to show up, sooner or later, in *Collier's.*

Fiction styles, like automobiles and women's dresses, change rapidly. Some of the most renowned of the old-time fiction writers wouldn't find their way out of the editor's slush-box today. Stephen Crane wrote the splendid *Red Badge of Courage;* his short stories, in my opinion, are atrocious. Henry James, giant among nineteenth-century novelists, seems to me to have had an exasperating trick in his shorter works of getting the reader so hopelessly involved that it was hard to keep hero and villain clearly assorted.

Yet the best writing is timeless, and much of the best found its way into *Collier's.* H. G. Wells wrote as well in 1900 as twenty years later. Indeed, even before the turn of the century he was indulging a genius for future-gazing (*The War of the Worlds*) that was still in high gear a third of a century later in *The Shape of Things to Come.* And Bernard Shaw, in those turn-of-the-century days of the young *Collier's,* was an established dramatist just on the verge of his heyday. Few better examples of his famous wit can be found than the brief letter to the editors of *Collier's* in 1908 indignantly returning a $1,000 bonus payment for his short story, "Aerial Football—The New Game."

In sifting through the fiction from Wells, Shaw, and Bret Harte to Wodehouse and Rohmer, Runyon and Kantor, I used one main criterion—the story itself. The manners piece, the drawing-room piece, the sweetness-and-light story generally got the back of the hand from *Collier's* action-loving editors. They liked adventure, excitement, mystery, violence, and fun; that is what they gave their audiences; that is what I have passed along here.

There was more to the contents and the character of *Collier's,* of course, than the sum total of its articles and its fiction. *Collier's* built its prestige and its circulation with bare knuckles and a fighting heart. Looking back, it seems to me that *Collier's* at its fightingest was usually *Collier's* at its best.

Just after the turn of the century, *Collier's* began looking around, like a young bull-terrier, for objects of combat. They were plentiful. It took out after the Beef Trust, the Sugar Trust, the Oil Trust, the Insurance Trust, William Randolph Hearst, liquor, patent medicines, child labor, the haphazard food labelers, and any other handy targets. By the early 'teens it had a dozen crusades running simultaneously. Sometimes it gave the opponents an inning or two—as when it let Arthur Brisbane write an accolade about Hearst in the midst of its lambasting of "The Yellow Press." But it never backed away from a good fight and, in this particular case, went on to broaden the target area to envelop practically all the newspapers in the country.

Sued for libel occasionally, threatened often, it gave enthusiastic—even gleeful—publicity to the threats and the suits, meanwhile hooting its derision and trumpeting the charges anew. A Colonel W. D. Mann, proprietor of a journal called *Town Topics*, attacked President Roosevelt's daughter. In an editorial *Collier's* declared that Colonel Mann's standing among the people was and ought to be "somewhat worse than that of an ordinary forger, horse-thief, or second-story man." Colonel Mann wrote that the article was "most grossly libelous of myself," and said he would hold the distributors of the piece responsible "to the full extent of the law."

Replied *Collier's* editorially: "Colonel Mann, of course, is indulging in a feeble bluff. If we can goad him into daylight, the happier we. Fancy him in Court, putting into figures the injury to his fair name, and inviting us to prove the justice of our opinion!"

The case did get into court, the defendants won, and *Collier's* dramatically proclaimed the victory as a triumph of Right.

Collier's was right a good part of the time; one of its most impressive and far-reaching triumphs was forcing the adoption of the country's first pure food and drug laws, which resulted principally from *Collier's* years-long hammering at the widespread practice of false and misleading labeling of processed foods and patent medicines.

Of perhaps less lasting value was *Collier's* interminable crusade against the saloons and the brewers, certainly one of the factors in the ultimate adoption of the Volstead Act. But the ink was hardly dry on the Prohibition law when *Collier's* leaped to the opposite side and declared the Noble Experiment an abomination and a breeder of evils far worse than those it sought to cure. *Collier's* became one of the few nationwide voices to share importantly and equally in the credit for both Prohibition and Repeal. The magazine—like so many people given to violent emotions—was seldom on an even keel for very long.

Launched by Mr. Peter Fenley Collier on April 28, 1888, *Collier's* offered a potpourri of "Fiction, Fact, Sensation, Wit, Humor, and News" that created an instant stir on the national journalistic scene. P. F. Collier's son Robert succeeded the founder as controlling voice, and helped set the magazine on a course that built circulation rapidly through a succession of newsmaking crusades that prompted competitors and foes to brand *Collier's* as "yellow" as the "Yellow Press" it perennially attacked.

Reporters Will Irwin, Frederick Palmer, Richard Harding Davis, and Samuel Hopkins Adams probably contributed most to establishing *Collier's* as an important national institution. Finley Peter Dunne's "Mr. Dooley" and Conan Doyle's "Sherlock Holmes" helped spread its fame and popularity. Editors Norman Hapgood and Mark Sullivan gave it editorial vigor and direction in its early years.

Circulation boomed toward the million mark in the middle 'teens. Superb coverage of World War I by Ring Lardner, William Slavens McNutt and Fred Palmer (with an occasional diapason note by Churchill) helped continue the upward trend. Advertising grew with circulation, and by January, 1920, the magazine was over one hundred pages in size and circulation was into the second million.

Then came an almost catastrophic nose-dive—for reasons involving changes of editors and a spectacular decline of editorial vitality. The issue of April 16, 1921, was down to twenty-eight pages, and the pre-Christmas issue of December 10 carried a total of six and a half pages of advertising, of which two were non-revenue "house" ads.

It took a swift transfusion of dollars to keep *Collier's* alive. The editorial format was shaken up, along with the staff, and editors Richard Walsh and Loren Palmer managed to get it back on a proper track.

In 1925 a battery of talent including Octavus Roy Cohen, Zona Gale, Rupert Hughes, and Sophie Kerr was assembled to create and perfect a novel literary form —the "short-short story"—which became a kind of *Collier's* trade-mark for all the years to come.

That was the year that William Ludlow Chenery came over from the *New York Telegram* to become *Collier's* editor, a position he held until he moved up to publisher in 1943. Bill Chenery and his managing editor Charles Colebaugh gave *Collier's* its solidest period of growth and editorial development. They built up a distinguished staff—Quentin Reynolds, Walter Davenport, T. R. Ybarra, Kyle Crichton, and Ken Littauer—and brought in Damon Runyon and a host of able cartoonists to spice up the content. Steering a liberal course in tune with the times, they dug beneath the grist of the news for material of significance dealing with the main issues of the day.

But Colebaugh died, Chenery retired, and in the years following World War II *Collier's* contracted a second illness from which it never recovered. Times and tastes shifted faster than *Collier's* could, or would, change. Profit-taking and tight editorial budgets sapped the magazine's vitality while precious years were consumed as the magazine flopped about searching for a new soul and a new reason for being. Editors came and went. Sensational experiments were tried and fizzled. *Life* and *Look*, each with a fresh editorial approach, came up steadily and finally pushed the thrashing *Collier's* into the hapless position of No. 4 in a field of four—trailing *Life*, the *Saturday Evening Post*, and *Look* in circulation, advertising volume, and influence in the mass-market field.

When Editor-in-Chief Paul C. Smith brought in his new team in 1954, it was—most people said—too late. With whatever authority I may claim as *Collier's* last editor, I would add that the time we consumed learning our job was time that could not at that stage be spared. Had we known at the beginning what we knew at the end there might still be a *Collier's*. We gave it all the time and energy we had, and it wasn't enough.

But we tried.

There was never a staff that gave more dedicated effort to salvaging a foundering magazine than the one that finally went down with the ship. Often stretching the working day into sixteen or eighteen hours, we toiled over our failing patient, diagnosed, fought over the diagnoses, brain-stormed, argued, sweated, and finally came up with what I still believe to have been the right remedy. We decided the magazine needed a new, modern look . . . "big" stories . . . warm, human stories . . . greater appeal to women . . . more color, more photos . . . a finer grade of fiction than we had been using. And we set out to get them.

But turning a magazine around is a ponderous proposition like turning a battleship around in its own water. We didn't really get under way with a totally new magazine until the late spring of 1956. At that point we stopped the circulation sag, then went into a steady climb that added over half a million readers in the last eight months of the magazine's existence. Then—with circulation at an all-time peak, but with advertisers still holding back to see whether this was just another flash in the pan—we found ourselves without enough money to meet the payroll and the paper bills, and credit sources shut off. On December 14—eleven days before Christmas of 1956—management decided finally that *Collier's* had to fold. A stunned staff received the word, the final issue of January 4, 1957, was put on the presses, *Collier's* died, and its people scattered to look for other jobs.

How do you write an obituary for a magazine? Not, I think, by seeking out culprits, or dreaming of what might have been had the patient recovered. In a vigorous lifetime of seventy years, *Collier's* gave the American people a full measure of "fiction, fact, sensation, wit, humor and news"—that was its starting mission and *Collier's* accomplished it.

It gave its readers a great deal and it gave its own people, perhaps, even more—an opportunity to make life a little pleasanter, a little more meaningful for others, and by that means, a little more rewarding for themselves. None of that dies with a magazine.

KENNETH MCARDLE

Contents

Covers

(The Following *Collier's* covers appear as a group at the front of this volume)

Color Plates

Monochrome Plates

Cartoons

(Cartoons by the following artists appear as a group after page 558)

Who Killed the Bordens?

Julius Chambers

On August 4, 1892, Fall River, Massachusetts, leaped to national prominence as the scene of one of the most grisly and baffling crimes of modern times—the murder of wealthy Andrew J. Borden and his wife. Here is the story of the murder, and the subsequent arrest of Andrew Borden's stepdaughter, Lizzie—whose name is still celebrated in the annals of crime.

September 10, 1892

A MYSTERIOUS DOUBLE MURDER IN DAYlight. A case of circumstantial evidence. A celebrated case—one that must take high rank among the criminal trials of this century—is the Borden murder, at Fall River.

Fall River was of no importance whatever to the Commonwealth of Massachusetts, or to the country at large, until the war. The Rebellion made Fall River; it developed its great mills and cotton industry, and it has now become a city of considerable population, busy during the day with the hum of spindles and other machinery, and teeming with millhands after working hours. On August 4th, it acquired a new claim to national consideration. Just about noon of that day an alarm was given that a close-fisted, hardheaded old man, of Irish descent, but of Yankee pertinacity, Andrew J. Borden, and his wife, had been found murdered at their home on Second street. The dead man was known to almost everybody in the city. He was a large holder of real estate, and the next street below the house of the crime bore his name. He had many tenants, and the first natural assumption was that the murders had been committed for gain.

A very unfortunate series of circumstances occurred. It was the day of a police picnic, and nearly every man on the force was absent. Marshal Hilliard, the chief of the department, was in the village, but did not reach the scene of the crime until three o'clock in the afternoon! When the crime was reported at the police station, a watchman was sent to investigate. During the delay, before any thoroughly competent and experienced detective officer reached the place, sufficient time had elapsed for an assassin to have escaped and for all traces of the murder to be removed.

The family consisted of Mr. Borden, his wife, who was a second wife, and two stepdaughters, Lizzie and Emma Borden. A brother of Mr. Borden's first wife, John V. Morse, had been visiting the family from the West, but was apparently absent at the time of the crime. Emma Borden was absent in the southern part of the State of Massachusetts, and had not been near the house for several days. The details of the crime are particularly harrowing. Lizzie, the elder daughter, had been ill for two days. Mr. Borden, his wife and Mr. Morse had breakfasted at half-past eight, and at 8:45 Mr. Morse had left the house. Mrs. Borden then assisted the servant, Bridget Sullivan, in clearing away the dishes, and after ordering her to wash the windows had gone to her room upstairs.

While the servant was engaged in finishing her dishes, Lizzie Borden appeared from her room on the second floor, declined to eat any breakfast because of her illness, and began to iron some handkerchiefs that she had washed on a previous day. During this time a conversation of almost frivolous character, relating to a sale of shop dry goods announced in one of the morning papers, was carried on between the two young women. The maid-of-all-work then went outside with her brushes and cleansed the windows, as she had been ordered by the lady of the house. The servant did not see Mr. Borden at that time, or Mrs. Borden. While she was so engaged, Lizzie claims that Mr. Borden entered the sitting-room and stretched himself upon the sofa to take a nap, as was his custom. At five minutes of eleven—time is paramount in this narrative—Bridget completed her work on the windows, re-entered the kitchen and announced that she was going upstairs to rest awhile, as was also her rule. Bridget had considerable trouble in opening the kitchen door, and used a vulgar expression that caused Lizzie, who was within hearing distance, to laugh hilariously. (If I could have heard that laugh I believe I would know whether or not this was a hysterical or morbid crime!) During Bridget's presence in the kitchen, Lizzie stated that her stepmother had told her of the receipt of a letter from a sick friend who desired that she should visit her, and added that she supposed her stepmother had gone in response to the call. (First suspicious statement.) (If that letter be in existence or its writer can be found, it will save the life of Lizzie Borden. Once a Week will pay *Five Hundred Dollars* for that letter and its author!)

Immediately after the servant's departure for her bedchamber, Lizzie Borden claims to have gone to the stable in search of some lead to be used as sinkers for a fishingline. (Second suspicious statement.) On the way to the barn she gathered some pears and ate them during her search. She claims to have been absent twenty minutes. On her return to the house she was heard to scream, and was seen at the side door in plain sight of a neighbor's dwelling, and called for assistance: "Come, quickly! Get a doctor! My father's been murdered!" The servant was also called immediately by Lizzie Borden and dispatched for a physician. In a very few moments the house was filled with neighbors and people who had been passing on the streets. Many of the persons in the house during the first ten minutes were strangers whose identity has been utterly lost.

Mr. Borden was found lying on a sofa, his face and neck hacked with a hatchet or some sharp instrument to such an extent as to render the countenance almost unrecognizable. He had apparently been rendered senseless at one blow, because he had not struggled. Although the blood was widely scattered and many of the large veins of the head and neck had been severed, he rested in the position that a man would occupy who was in sound slumber. Lizzie Borden advised the first comers to search the house for her mother, repeating the story previously mentioned about the letter, but advising that a search be made for her. (Third suspicious act.) The neighbor first called hastened upstairs and found Mrs. Borden lying on her face in her bedroom in a pool of blood, her arms crossed complacently under her, the back of her head beaten into pulp. Blood had spattered the walls and the furniture. The dwelling was a charnel house. It seemed incredible that anybody could have committed the two horrible crimes without being literally deluged in human gore. Though Lizzie Borden's clothes were unspotted, the cool and collected manner of the girl made a bad impression at once, and caused her to become an object of suspicion.

Dr. Bowen, who lived across the street, was the first physician on the ground. He was a friend of the family, and at once interested himself in the search for the murderer. Marshal Hilliard and the detectives made a thorough search of the house late in the afternoon, but the house had been crowded with people for three hours. They found in the cellar three hatchets or small axes, more or less rusty, that appeared to contain spots of blood. They searched every room in the house without finding any evidence of the presence of the murderer. Suspicion still closed about the daughter of the family, and, although she was not arrested until one week later she was placed under espionage. Her clothes were taken from her, and, together with the axes, were given to Professor Wood, of Harvard University, for microscopical examination. To anticipate, it may be said that after three weeks' scrutiny, Professor Wood announces, under oath, that he is unable to find any blood spots whatever upon the axes or upon the clothing of the Borden girl. Some white hairs, adhering to the head of an ax, were supposed to furnish a clew of the greatest importance; but Professor Wood unequivocably swears that those hairs are not human hairs. Science is inexorable. It destroys the backbone of the charges against the prisoner! Those white hairs would have hanged the prisoner fifty years ago.

During the time that the house was in commotion, the uncle, John V. Morse, returned to dinner, as he had been invited to do by Mr. Borden. He added his modicum of testimony to what had already been given by the servant and by the suspected daughter. It was very slight, and amounted to little more than a statement that Mr. Borden had urged him to return in time for the noonday meal. He stated that he had seen Mrs. Borden at breakfast, and confirmed the statement of Lizzie that she (Lizzie) had not been present at the meal. Further he said nothing.

Practically, that is all that is known about this curious crime at this hour! Two horrible murders have been committed in broad daylight, the mother apparently having been killed one hour and a half before the father, and no witnesses have been found who saw any stranger enter or leave the Borden house or grounds after the moment in which Mr. Morse, accompanied by Mr. Borden, separated from his host at the front gate. This interval between the two murders makes the mystery all the greater! It is fixed by Dr. Bowen, who first examined the bodies, and who swears that Mrs. Borden had been dead fully an hour and a half to two hours before her husband was killed; whereas, the body of Mr. Borden was quite warm and the blood was still flowing from the gaping wounds. These facts would indicate that Mrs. Borden was killed and that the murderer lingered about the house, his or her clothes a mass of blood, for an hour and a half with the horrible purpose in mind of finishing the head of the family—a purpose which was thoroughly carried out.

The reader has now in his possession all the known facts relating to the crime itself—all that has been ascertained after three days of secret inquisition, in which the suspect was questioned without the presence of counsel; after three weeks of scientific investigation by the cleverest experts; after a week's legal inquiry before Judge Blaisdell, and after a month's persistent and tireless search on the part of several able detectives and thirty-odd shrewd and experienced newspaper reporters! Many side issues have been started by the sleuths of the law, the stomachs of the murdered people have been carefully analyzed upon the assertion that poison had been attempted before murder was done, and a drug clerk has sworn that Lizzie Borden attempted to purchase prussic acid at his shop for the avowed purpose of killing insects in a sealskin cape that she carried upon her arm. As no poison was found in the stomachs, I do not discuss the poison theory at all.

The police started with the assumption that Lizzie Borden is guilty. They have exhausted every clew, every ingenious theory, and they have not fastened the chain of circumstantial evidence irrevocably about her. It is true that she has made contradictory statements. I never have been accused of murder and my parents never were found brutally hacked to pieces in the home of my childhood; but I have seen with my own eyes a man afterward conclusively proven to be innocent suddenly charged with murdering a friend and confronted with the most damning circumstantial evidence of his guilt, and I never beheld a more pitiable exhibition of terror than that man made. He stuttered and stammered, was unable to recollect where he had left his friend on the night of the murder, made a number of the most damaging admissions—even confessed to a quarrel—and yet he was not guilty. (To be specific, I refer to the Dieterly case in Philadelphia, about 1884.) I did not see Lizzie Borden until I beheld her in the courtroom, as I shall hereafter describe her; but I now know her to be a familiar type of the New England woman who has passed the age of youth and has become confirmed in the ways of maidenhood; whose friends are few and have generally been selected from girls beneath her social sphere; a girl of originally even mind, warped by strong religious emotions and sterner creeds. The foremost figure in this certainly celebrated case, guilty or innocent, will go down in criminal history as a woman of remarkable nerve and self-control. To my mind, every equivocation that may be detected in her statements or her testimony before the secret inquiry will be strong evidence of her innocence. The facts that no blood was found upon her clothing, the utter absence of motive, the statement, *yet uncontradicted*, that her mother had received a letter calling her away, the previous good-character of the girl, her education and foreign travel, and, above all, the fact that no quarrel had occurred between the mother and stepdaughter for several years, all taken together, constitute very strong presumptive evidence of innocence.

I spent a day looking up the history of this young woman—I have said young, but she is no longer a girl, because she confesses under oath to the age of thirty-two. She has been an orphan for twenty-nine and a half years—in other words, she does not remember her mother, and has been reared up as motherless children usually are. The other daughter, Emma, cannot be much younger. She certainly is thirty. She is a woman of entirely different type. Her face is without serious expression, even in the terrible situation that confronts her sister and the calamity that has overtaken her family. She appears to be a woman who has never had a practical idea; her cheeks are flabby with fat, her lips are full and pouty, her eyes are shy and distrustful—indeed, hers is one of those baby faces that we sometimes see in a crowd that cause us to wonder what their possessors find to live for. It is very certain that she has never been any use to this world and has never had much use for it.

Lizzie Andrew Borden, not "Elizabeth," is a different type of a woman. She was graduated at the ward school, and I hunted up the teacher who for several years instructed her. I learned that Miss Borden had been a quick scholar; that, even while in school, she was much given to religious thoughts; that she had a fairly good voice, quite uncultivated; that she had been raised without much care from her parents; had always been a lonely girl, with few friends and companions at school; that she had drifted along through her educational course without any aim, never having felt a necessity of preparation for the earning of a future livelihood, and absolutely without any desire for marriage. While her sister may be a woman with some passion, Lizzie would never be suspected of it. She has a cold, gray eye, thin, almost bloodless, lips, and is wanting in personal attraction of any kind. So far as I am able to ascertain, after careful inquiry, she never had a lover and her hand was never asked in marriage. It would be a matter of the greatest importance to know all about this poor girl's private life—I say it without any morbid feeling of curiosity, but purely in the interest of justice and of American womanhood. The police have intimated undue familiarity between Lizzie and her uncle, but remembering the character of the girl and her strong religious instincts, I am loath to even consider the subject. As to old man Morse, I confess frankly that I would hate to meet him in a dark alley. He certainly has a very cruel and hardened face, and I think it would be very proper to make serious inquiry regarding his past history in that part of the far West from which he comes. I say this without any prejudice to Mr. Morse, because his alibi is apparently complete. Apropos, the early life of Mr. Borden should be inquired into. I learn that he was quite a "sporting man" when he lived in Troy twenty-odd years ago and had a curious reputation.

The unsolved factor in the case is Bridget Sullivan, a tall, well-formed and rather comely girl of Irish birth but of considerable American experience, who came to Fall River about two years and a half ago from a situation in Newport, where she is still remembered. I visited her former employers, and they speak well of her. I studied her on the witness stand for five hours, under the most searching cross-examination by Colonel Adams, a very clever lawyer. She did not contradict herself, and carefully avoided entanglement in many of the shrewdly conceived plans of her interrogator. She appeared to be telling the truth, and her evidence disclosed the social condition of the Borden house more completely than any bare statement of facts could have done. It showed while the Bordens were wealthy, even in a rich community, they lived in a poverty-stricken way—unworthy of a common workman's family. The fare of that household on the day of the crime was enough to beget murder! The breakfast consisted of bananas and cold mutton. The midday meal, which was never eaten, was to have consisted of broth made from the scraps of the breakfast and more cold mutton, not even pie, or cheese, or coffee. Heaven knows what supper was to have been! And yet the head of that family was worth a quarter of a million dollars.

If we have to deal with a psychological murder it is with one that will become memorable in American criminal annals for all time. As I suggested, had the laugh of Lizzie Borden at a time that must have been after her stepmother's death and before her father's killing been heard that morning by an ear that is trained to the detection of mental alienation, her guilt or innocence would not be a matter of conjecture. I regret very much the secretiveness which the family physician chooses to manifest regarding the previous physical condition of Miss Borden. She has no appearance of hysteria, never has manifested any of the symptoms thereof, so far as I am able to find by inquiry among her acquaintances; but it is only true to say that her women acquaintances have been largely among shop girls and fellow Sunday-school attendants who are not shrewd observers or experienced regarding the physical ills of a celibate life. I mean to say, in as delicate a manner as I possibly can, that I shall look forward to the recurrence of the 4th of September with considerable curiosity. A psychologist like Charcot, of Paris; Bucknell, of London; Hammond, of Washington, or Mitchell, of Philadelphia, ought to grapple with this theory of temporary emotional insanity. Since the testimony of Professor Wood it would appear that the weapon with which the murder was committed has not been found! There is a closet in the yard which, I believe, has not yet been searched, but it is incredible to assume that the murderer, after chopping his two victims to death, would carry away the bloodstained ax or hatchet. It was supposed that the axes would play a startling part in the tragedy, but the testimony of Professor Wood has annihilated their importance. I have been told of an inquiry, pursued night and day for more than a week, that apparently traced one of the hatchets to the house of an evicted tenant of the late Mr. Borden; but when we are told that the murders must have been done with an ax or hatchet, that bloodstains upon wood or iron cannot be removed by a superficial washing, and, thirdly, that none of these weapons contains the slightest bloodstain, the axes found in the Borden cellar must be dismissed from all further consideration in the case.

The corner-stone of the prosecution against Lizzie Borden has been that it would have been impossible for a stranger to have entered or left the house or grounds without being seen by neighbors or workmen in the adjoining yard. Supplied with the details that are offered, this assertion seems plausible enough; but the homestead is surrounded by several bits of open ground, abuts upon an alleyway and adjoins what may be technically termed a *cul de sac*. This last place is behind the barn. Down the middle of the Borden lot extends a close grape arbor, through which anybody can walk, in daylight, without being visible from the house. To settle that question beyond dispute, after consulting the deputy marshal, I walked up Second street and entered the Borden grounds, passed to the right of the house down through the grape arbor, then behind the barn, crossed the low fence without difficulty into the pear orchard of Dr. Chagnon, then traversed the orchard to the corner adjoining the front end of Kelley's barn, passed over that fence into the street, came around and entered Dr. Chagnon's front gate, rang his door bell, sent my card to his associate and secured permission to explore his grounds. Did so. Then re-entered the Borden property, over the fence, at the corner adjoining the rear end of Kelley's barn. I then crossed behind the house, examined the exterior of the Borden barn, which was securely closed. I observed that no driveway led to it, indeed there was no gate; saw that the straw in the manger, as seen through the window, had not been moved; came out through the front gate at the footway that leads to the side door, and, so far as can be surmised, I was not seen by anybody—not even the old housekeeper or Mr. Morse, who were in the dwelling, as I subsequently ascertained. There are at least half a dozen places along the back fence that could be scaled by a child without danger.

If the murder were committed by a stranger, there would be no difficulty whatever in his escape, no matter how many people were about the building at the time. Why the Borden sisters and their friends should advance the theory that the murderer walked out through the front gate, I cannot understand.

After spending two hours in the neighborhood of the property, I am quite willing to wager any reasonable sum of money that the Borden grounds can be entered at any hour of the day or night, without detection, by anyone familiar with the locality.

Now let us visit the court.

The entrance to the police court in which the inquiry was progressing is reached through a narrow and forbidding little alley. The building is of white stone, cut in large blocks, and is as grim a structure as ever prisoner entered. Crowded to the foot of the stairs, it would not be an easy thing to gain access did I not bear a letter from Superintendent Byrnes, of New York, to Marshal Hilliard. That is a passport anywhere, and, in less time than it takes to write it, I am ensconced alongside the plump and pretty stenographer, Miss White, within ten feet of the witness on the stand, and an equal distance from the prisoner—facing both. I can see every face in the quaint old court room—an apartment eighty feet deep by sixty in width—with its plaster-cracked ceiling and dust-incrusted walls. On the east side is the judge's bench. Magistrate Blaisdell is red in the face as a lobster, and wears his long locks of gray hair brushed behind his ears so that they fall about his neck and connect with the tuft of white beard on his chin. He looks tough; but his firmly closed mouth indicates that, no matter how he looks, he feels first-rate. Clerk of the Court Leonard resembles a St. Jerome, from a canvas of one of the old masters.

Miss White stops rolling her chubby little hand across the paper, and glares at me with her big, round eyes. Just beyond her is the witness-box. All witnesses in Massachusetts stand while giving testimony. Bridget Sullivan is testifying, clinging to the railing with her hands, and she recalls Hester Pryne on the pillory. Her evidence is expected to be highly important to the prisoner, and the steel-gray eyes of Lizzie Borden fasten their gaze upon her. Just at my left sits District Attorney Knowlton, short, fat and forty. His neck is thick as his voice, and his massive head is framed by a shock of reddish-brown hair and closely trimmed whiskers. Across a narrow table from him stands Lawyer Adams, of Boston, senior counsel for the defense, tall, straight, dark of feature and hair. He is quick, nervous, keen and resolute. Every line in his strong face shows determination. The interests of his client have his entire attention. Mr. Jennings, the home attorney for the Borden girl, is actively taking notes. He is a small, slender and excitable man, with a face full of anxiety. I wonder what secrets in this case he carries! Adams may be the brainy man of the defense, but Jennings is true as oak.

Within a foot of the place where Mr. Adams is standing sits the prisoner. Her nose is her best feature. The chin is not pleasant and the high cheek-bones destroy any suggestion of beauty. Her coolness and self-mastery are superb! She doesn't stare about, but looks before her naturally. The profile of her face gives a very different idea of the woman from that inspired by contemplating her visage as a whole. She is thinking deeply. What about? If innocent, I'd venture that she's lamenting her inability to participate in the latest sale of three-cent calico. Miss Borden is dressed in a neat blue serge suit, and when she throws the shawl from her shoulders discloses considerable *embonpoint*. Flat-chested women of Massachusetts have been in trouble before, and I rather expected to find that Lizzie Borden belonged to the class. But, she doesn't. The preliminary trial closed on Thursday, September 1st, and although it was a foregone conclusion that the prisoner would be held for the Grand Jury, the last in the cycle of Thursdays left the mystery unsolved. The important events in this case have all happened on Thursday. Mr. Borden and his wife were murdered on Thursday forenoon, August 4th; Lizzie Borden was arrested on Thursday, August 11th. On the same day the autopsy on the unburied bodies was made, and by order of the attorney-general of the State the heads of the butchered couple were cut off and taken by the local medical examiner for probable exhibition in court. A week later, Thursday, August 18th, the preliminary trial began, and ended September 1st, with a judicial finding of "probably guilty." The Grand Jury will meet in November.

To sum up: Beyond the slight discrepancies in her statements, Lizzie Borden has not even been seriously incriminated by a Star Chamber inquisition lasting three days, and a public trial continuing for a week.

If she be the murderess, thorough premeditation and preparation for the slaughter (in view of the entire obliteration of all incriminating evidences of the act) must be conceded.

If the murders were done with one of the axes found in the cellar, she must have boiled it thoroughly, and quite as thoroughly dried it, after the crimes and before it was replaced in the cellar. The handle inside the ax would have been swollen for days. The fact was that the ax heads were loose on the helves!

She must have utterly, and in some way yet wholly unexplained even by theory, destroyed every vestige of clothing she wore at the time. In view of Bridget Sullivan's testimony, she must have killed her stepmother before she came downstairs and was seen by the servant, must have destroyed the clothing as necessitated by that crime, and subsequently taken her father's life without in any way again getting bespattered with blood. If she did that and laughed, that laugh must have made the imps in hell shudder!

Bridget Sullivan, a level-headed and observing young woman, says Miss Lizzie did not change her clothes. She makes it quite clear that the prisoner would not have had sufficient time to do so before she gave the alarm. All the ashes in the stoves were carefully removed and not less carefully examined and analyzed. They did not contain the slightest trace of woolen or cotton fiber! If Lizzie Borden hid the clothing under the hay in the loft of the barn until it could be removed by an accomplice, Mrs. Churchill should have seen her carry it from the house to that outbuilding. (If that barn loft was not carefully searched that afternoon, Marshall Hilliard cannot escape censure; every wisp of hay should have been removed and examined.)

If Lizzie Borden did not strike the blows, who did? Eh! that's the position of the police.

And it's a very awkward question to be asked.

The crime bears every evidence of an insane or morbid act. It is crowned with the cunning of madness; it is gorged with wanton butchery. Le Chourineur, of Le Tapis-Franc, would not have gloated over blood more than the Borden murderer must have done. He or she literally must have wallowed in it.

Who killed the Bordens, then? I answer: Somebody temporarily insane—a human creature whose heart grew gleeful as the blows did fall and the blood did spurt. The murder was a maniac's carnival.

Whoever killed Lizzie Borden, the all-male Superior Court jury sitting in New Bedford, Bristol County, ruled that it wasn't Lizzie. After hearing testimony for two weeks and a final, melodramatic query from the chief defense counsel ("To find her guilty you must believe she is a fiend. Gentlemen, does she look it?") the jury acquitted her.

The Fall of King John

A Staff Reporter

Here is the round-by-round account of one of the great ring battles of history —fought September 7, 1892, in New Orleans between World's Heavyweight Champion John L. Sullivan and the contender, James J. Corbett. After twenty-one punishing rounds, King John fell—to his own stunned surprise ("Say, am I licked? Did that young fellow do that?") and the consternation of the worshipful followers who had come to believe him something more than mortal.

September 10, 1892

THE CHOLERA WAS FORGOTTEN FOR twenty-four hours! Hamburg and the New York quarantine took second place in importance, throughout the "civilized" world, to New Orleans. The Olympic Club House was the center of American thought. Had not a Harvard professor, at the center of American culture, examined and expatiated on the splendid manly qualities of the then champion of the world! The undeniable fact that no event in the history of this country since the shooting of Garfield has commanded such universal interest must be the excuse of Once a Week for printing this page. It is demanded as a matter of record and as a part of the history of our era. This is the Athletic Age!

John Lawrence Sullivan, since 1882 champion pugilist of the world, was defeated in twenty-one rounds at New Orleans, on September 7th, by James John Corbett, a young Californian, aged twenty-six. The fall of "King John" was a crushing surprise to four-fifths of the people of this country; it was a crushing blow to the sporting fraternity that had supported the champion at odds of three and four to one on. It was a dreadful misfortune to Sullivan, because it abruptly ends his career as pugilist, actor and swell. It was the first defeat he had ever met, though he has been twenty-one times in the ring. (Fatal number; three times seven!)

The battle was fought under the Marquis of Queensbury rules. The official time of the fight was one hour and twenty-one minutes and forty-five seconds. These rules, always considered favorable to Sullivan, compel the contestants to fight for three consecutive minutes, with one minute's rest between rounds, a man going down must rise and take more punishment within ten seconds or lose the fight. Sullivan never once leveled his right. He fought himself to a standstill in his efforts to get at his skillful antagonist. Seven thousand men saw the fight. Sullivan took all of Corbett's blows gamely. In a short, manly speech he called attention to the fact that an American had beaten him. His swollen lips moved, but no sound came from them. Finally his voice came back, and in that hoarse, bellowing tone so well known to his opponents, he made his speech.

"Gentlemen," he began, "it is the old, old story—the story of a young man against an old one. There are gray hairs in my head and I should have known better." There was a break in the big fellow's hoarse voice, but he gulped down his feeling and continued: "I can only say that I am glad that the championship is to remain in America. That is all I've got to say."

When the two men entered the twenty-foot ring they appeared very confident. Professor Duffy made a close examination of Sullivan to see whether he wore plasters. He found none. Then the men shook hands and returned to their corners. As time was called the men advanced to the center simultaneously.

Round First—The champion leads with the left; Corbett dodges; again he leads and misses, Corbett dancing around him. Sully tries a rush, but without avail. The crowd hisses. Sullivan looks vicious. He tries again, first at the head, then at the body. He does not land. Corbett still dancing. Sullivan tries to corner him, but Jim slipped out handily, laughing all the time. Gong; not a blow struck.

Round Second—Sullivan still the aggressor. Again he makes a useless left lead. At last John taps lightly, then rushes. They clinch. A rapid exchange. Corbett lands twice with left, first on head, then on stomach. Sully upper cuts once with left, but lightly. Sullivan gets his right in on Jim's shoulder and gets a right on the stomach as bell rings.

Round Third—John looks wicked. John tries for the stomach with right, but fails to land; gets in two light ones with left on shoulder. Corbett lands two hard ones with right on John's body. They clinch again, and after the break Corbett is in three times on Sully's stomach, and then swings a left stinger on John's ear. Just as round ends John lands lightly on Jim's shoulder with his left.

Round Fourth—Sullivan misses the left again and again. John gets in a light left on body. John tries to corner Jim repeatedly, but fails. Sully makes a vicious right-hand swing. He misses and catches Jim's left on the head. Corbett lands both hands on Sullivan's head as round ends. Corbett laughs tantalizingly every time John misses.

Round Fifth—Jim jabs Sullivan on the nose with the left; Sully lands his first hard one with left on Corbett's chest, then John makes a frightful swinging miss which nearly took him off his feet. Sparring prettily now. First blood for Corbett. John's nose bleeding profusely; Corbett rushing him and banging him right and left. Both glaring at each other, but Corbett's stock is away up. Sully had all the worst of the round. Wild cheers for Corbett.

Round Sixth—John up smiling. He lands lightly with left; John misses with right; wind sparring; Corbett plants left on stomach, then gets in left on John's jaw, then another socker with left on the nose. Sully sends a bad left, which only slaps Corbett; Corbett gets in three times, right, left and right again. Jim closes up to Sully; Corbett gets in another lefter as bell rings.

Round Seventh—Sully lands a left-hander on Corbett's ribs. Corbett gets left in on John's stomach. Sully lands twice lightly on the head, and gets three straight jabs on his bleeding nose again. Jim hits the champion again with right. His work is wonderfully clever. Corbett backs John to ropes; hits him right and left out in the middle of the ring. Corbett lands with right again as bell rings.

Round Eighth—Sully looks none the worse for his punishment. Sully lands left on stomach. Corbett the aggressor. John misses a left-hand swing, but lands with right on ear, then Corbett gets in twice and clinches. A vicious exchange follows, Corbett keeping away from Sully's right. He lands left twice on John's breadbasket, but blows don't seem to phase John. Corbett lands with left on the ear, cross-counters with right, and lands left on John's ribs and round ends.

Round Ninth—Both fresh as ever. John lands with left twice on Jim's shoulder, Jim gets in a good left swing on John's breast. John tries to tap him, then lands on Jim's chest, getting in one on the ear and one on the nose in return. Corbett lands twice on Sully's nose, then they clinch, exchanging light ones as they come together. John mutters something as he gets a wicked one from Corbett on the stomach. John gets his right in with some effect, but gets it right and left in the rally at end of round.

Round Ten—Corbett looks anxious and John is determined. John misses his left-hand lead. He led again and landed on Jim's breast. Jim returns the compliment by smashing John on the ribs. Jim lands lightly and stops neatly a straight left-hander. It is a great fight so far. Sully rises and Jim meets him with two pokes on the nose. They spar beautifully as bell rings.

Round Eleven—Jim taps Sully lightly with right, then gets a stinger from John's right on body. Both wary. Jim gets a crusher on John's neck with his right, then runs in and smashes Sully twice, getting away unscratched. He gets in two more jabs on John's nose. Sully lands on Corbett's stomach. Corbett quick as a cat. He jumped in and landed two smashers on the champion's ribs as the round ends.

Round Twelve—Jim jabs with left again, catching Sully in the stomach. He repeats the dose twice, then skips lightly away. John lands a fine one with the right one on the chest, and gets a thump on the neck from Jim, which sounded all over the house. Jim jabs twice again in the body, then lands his right on Sully's shoulder. John chases him around ring. Jim stops, wheels and pokes in a good one on John's neck. Corbett ducks in time to avoid a right swing which would have settled him, as round ended.

Round Thirteen—Corbett up first. He dodges John's left handily. No signs of suffering on either side yet. Sparring for an opening. John slaps Corbett on the ribs with the left and smiles. Corbett scores a miss with the left. John is anxious to hurry matters. He receives a left on the face. Just as bell rings he manages to land a light tap on Jim's head.

Round Fourteen—Sully leads and lands with left, then they exchange fine ones. Corbett landed with left, John with right. Jim gets in again twice on John's neck, then jabs him with left on nose and smiles at him. Both get in solid lefts on the body. Jim jabs again and lands on Sully's nose. Then the champion gets in on Jim's face, but receives two stingers in return. Both sparring as the gong sounds.

Round Fifteen—John forcing Corbett. Jim lands twice, and is nearly floored by John's right. John is bleeding from the mouth now. The 'Frisco boy taps John repeatedly and slips away. Jim gets in again with left on the head, then gets a resounding bang from John's right on the body. Jim jabs twice on John's stomach. Sully gets in again on Jim's chest, but gets a right-hand smash in the stomach which sounded like a bass drum. Cheers for Corbett.

Round Sixteen—Sullivan rushing. They counter with the left on the start. Sully tries his left on the head, but Jim throws it off with his shoulder. John tries the killing right, but is short. Jim lands on Sully's neck with left, and gets in again on stomach three times. A moment later he hits John at will, then jumps away. Jim gets in two more on John's nose, then a clinch follows. Jim gets in again with a straight right and they laugh at each other. Cries of foul on the last clinch, but Jim shakes his head.

Round Seventeen—Sullivan is breathing hard. He misses his right, but lands on Corbett's head lightly with his left. Again he lands the right, somewhat short, but Jim's ribs felt it. John smashes Jim on the face with left and evokes applause. Corbett lands with his left again on John's ribs; Sullivan with right on the body. They play for an opening. Bell rings.

Round Eighteen—Not a sign of a mark on Corbett. Sully comes up slowly, but looks good for an hour yet. Fine rally. Sully lands with left on Jim's neck, and delivers two rapid stomach blows later. Jim then jabs John on the nose, and repeats the dose a moment later. At last John gets in that "awful right." It catches Corbett on the breast. Then Jim puts in two light ones. John lands again with his right. Corbett looks mad now, and punches John twice with his right. Jim again sends in the right, and Sully's head flies back from the force. Time. Corbett's blows are delivered with rapidity of lightning.

Round Nineteen—Both come up quickly; Sully lands a stunner with left on face, getting a light return from Jim's right. John doing the leading now; his lips are swollen; Corbett looks pale. Twice again, like a flash, Jim lands on the ribs, then left and right on Sully's face. Jim lands right on stomach, then left on John's ribs, and Jim banging him right and left.

Round Twenty—Sully puffing. Jim cool as a cucumber. John cautiously determined. Short exchange. Sully is caught off his guard and is banged right and left to the ropes. He is puffing awfully. Sully tries the right unsuccessfully, then gets jabbed in the face and is floored. Jim goes in again left and right. John looks tired. Corbett on him again and banging him against the ropes. The call of time saves John, apparently.

Round Twenty-one and Last—Sullivan came from his corner in the same shape that he had shown for a dozen rounds before. He had the same cross expression on his face, and seemed to be strong as at any time during that period. He continued to do the "edging in," and Corbett followed his original tactics of "edging away." This sort of trade was not going on very long—not more than ten seconds—when Corbett jumped back, rushed forward, hit John on the nose, and John was dazed. Corbett went at him further, and the same old nose was again smashed.

John looked astounded, and Corbett jumped back with the merry smile of a schoolboy with a big apple. Suddenly he returned to the fray, and, before Sullivan knew what was the meaning of the Californian's happy look, he got a crack on the side of the head that made him close his eyes. With this Corbett was on top of him in no time. Left hand on one side of the head and right hand on the other. Poor John L. Sullivan became an unconscious, beaten man. He staggered about on his pins for a second or so, and while displaying this fatal weakness Corbett went at him again. A right on the ear and a left on the jaw settled the business and the championship.

The last blow sent Sullivan to the floor with a thump, the second time in all his long career as a fighter that he had ever been knocked down. But he was down this time for good. It was a clean and clever knockout blow. Sullivan doubled up his legs as though in pain, but in another instant seemed to collect his senses and made an effort to rise. He failed in that, and tried the second time, with the same result. He was knocked out, pure and simple.

When the ten seconds were over Sullivan failed to respond, and Corbett was declared the winner. Then Sullivan asked in a weak voice: "Say, am I licked? Did that young fellow do it?"

His seconds sorrowfully admitted that that was the case.

A Cure for Love

H. G. Wells

When Orson Welles created his famous panic with his radio broadcast of a fictional Martian invasion in 1938, he was merely dramatizing a novel written nearly half a century earlier by Herbert George Wells, called The War of the Worlds. *Historian, social philosopher, and novelist, H. G. Wells was a resourceful, if not always wholly accurate, prober of the future, as he demonstrates in this short story.*

May 20, 1899

THE EXCELLENT MR. MORRIS WAS AN Englishman, and he lived in the days of Queen Victoria the Good. He was a prosperous and very sensible man; he read the "Times" and went to church, and as he grew toward middle age an expression of quiet contented contempt for all who were not as himself settled on his face. He was one of those people who do everything that is right and proper and sensible with inevitable regularity. He always wore just the right and proper clothes, steering the narrow way between the smart and the shabby, always subscribed to the right charities, just the judicious compromise between ostentation and meanness, and never failed to have his hair cut to exactly the proper length.

Everything that it was right and proper for a man in his position to possess, he possessed; and everything that it was not right and proper for a man in his position to possess, he did not possess.

And among other right and proper possessions, this Mr. Morris had a wife and children. They were the right sort of wife, and the right sort and number of children, of course; nothing imaginative or highly flighty about any of them, so far as Mr. Morris could see; they wore perfectly correct clothing, neither smart nor hygienic nor faddy in any way, but just sensible; and they lived in a nice sensible house in the later Victorian sham Queen Anne style of architecture, with sham half-timbering of chocolate-painted plaster in the gables, Lincrusta Walton sham carved oak panels, a terrace of terra cotta to imitate stone, and cathedral glass in the front door. His boys went to good solid schools, and were put to respectable professions; his girls, in spite of a fantastic protest or so, were all married to suitable, steady, oldish young men with good prospects. And when it was a fit and proper thing for him to do so, Mr. Morris died. His tomb was of marble, and, without any art nonsense or laudatory inscription, quietly imposing—such being the fashion of his time.

He underwent various changes according to the accepted custom in these cases, and long before this story begins his bones even had become dust, and were scattered to the four quarters of heaven. And his sons and his grandsons and his great-grandsons and his great-great-grandsons, they too were dust and ashes, and were scattered likewise. It was a thing he could not have imagined, that a day would come when even his great-great-grandsons would be scattered to the four winds of heaven. If any one had suggested it to him he would have resented it. He was one of those worthy people who take no interest in the future of mankind at all. He had grave doubts, indeed, if there was any future for mankind after he was dead. It seemed quite impossible and quite uninteresting to imagine anything happening after he was dead. Yet the thing was so, and when even his great-great-grandson was dead and decayed and forgotten, when the sham half-timbered house had gone the way of all shams, and the "Times" was extinct, and the silk hat a ridiculous antiquity, and the modestly imposing stone that had been sacred to Mr. Morris had been burned to make lime for mortar, and all that Mr. Morris had found real and important was sere and dead, the world was still going on, and people were still going about it, just as heedless and impatient of the Future, or, indeed, of anything but their own selves and property, as Mr. Morris had been.

And, strange to tell, and much as Mr. Morris would have been angered if any one had foreshadowed it to him, all over the world there were scattered a multitude of people, filled with the breath of life, in whose veins the blood of Mr. Morris flowed. Just as some day the life which is gathered now in the reader of this very story may also be scattered far and wide about this world, and mingled with a thousand alien strains, beyond all thought and tracing.

And among the descendants of this Mr. Morris was one almost as sensible and clear-headed as his ancestor. He had just the same stout, short frame as that ancient man of the nineteenth century from whom his name of Morris—he spelled it Mwres—came; he had the same half-contemptuous expression of face. He was a prosperous person, too, as times went, and he disliked the "new-fangled," and bothers about the future and the lower classes, just as much as the ancestral Morris had done. He did not read the "Times" indeed, he did not know there ever had been a "Times"—that institution had foundered somewhere in the intervening gulf of years; but the phonograph machine, that talked to him as he made his toilet of a morning, might have been the voice of a reincarnated Blowitz when it dealt with the world's affairs. This phonographic machine was the size and shape of a Dutch clock, and down the front of it were electric barometric indicators, and an electric clock and calendar, and automatic engagement reminders, and where the clock would have been was the mouth of a trumpet. When it had news the trumpet gobbled like a turkey, "Galloop, galloop," and then brayed out its message as, let us say, a trumpet might bray. It would tell Mwres in full, rich, throaty tones about the overnight accidents to the omnibus flying machines that plied around the world, the latest arrivals at the fashionable resorts in Tibet, and of all the great monopolist company meetings of the day before, while he was dressing. If Mwres did not like hearing what it said, he had only to touch a stud, and it would choke a little and talk about something else.

Of course his toilet differed very much

from that of his ancestor. It is doubtful which would have been the more shocked and pained to find himself in the clothing of the other. Mwres would certainly have sooner gone forth to the world stark naked than in the silk hat, frock coat, gray trousers and watch-chain that had filled Mr. Morris with sombre self-respect in the past. For Mwres there was no shaving to do: a skilful operator had long ago removed every hair-root from his face. His legs he incased in pleasant pink and amber garments of an air-tight material, which with the help of an ingenious little pump he distended so as to suggest enormous muscles. Above this he also wore pneumatic garments beneath an amber silk tunic, so that he was clothed in air and admirably protected against sudden extremes of heat or cold. Over this he flung a scarlet cloak with its edge fantastically curved. On his head, which had been skilfully deprived of every scrap of hair, he adjusted a pleasant little cap of bright scarlet, held on by suction and inflated with hydrogen, and curiously like the comb of a cock. So his toilet was complete; and, conscious of being soberly and becomingly attired, he was ready to face his fellow-beings with a tranquil eye.

This Mwres—the civility of "Mr." had vanished ages ago—was one of the officials under the Wind Vane and Waterfall Trust, the great company that owned every wind wheel and waterfall in the world, and which pumped all the water and supplied all the electric energy that people in these latter days required. He lived in a vast hotel near that part of London called Seventh Way, and had very large and comfortable apartments on the seventeenth floor. Households and family life had long since disappeared with the progressive refinement of manners; and indeed the steady rise in rents and land values, the disappearance of domestic servants, the elaboration of cookery, had rendered the separate domicile of Victorian times impossible, even had any one desired such a savage seclusion. When his toilet was completed he went toward one of the two doors of his apartment—there were doors at opposite ends, each marked with a huge arrow pointing one one way and one the other—touched a stud to open it, and emerged on a wide passage, the centre of which bore chairs and was moving at a steady pace to the left. On some of these chairs were seated gayly dressed men and women. He nodded to an acquaintance—it was not in those days etiquette to talk before breakfast—and seated himself on one of these chairs, and in a few seconds he had been carried to the doors of a lift, by which he descended to the great and splendid hall in which his breakfast would be automatically served.

It was a very different meal from a Victorian breakfast. The rude masses of bread needing to be carved and smeared over with animal fat before they could be made palatable, the still recognizable fragments of recently killed animals, hideously charred and hacked, the eggs torn ruthlessly from beneath some protesting hen—such things as these, though they constituted the ordinary fare of Victorian times, would have awakened only horror and disgust in the refined minds of the people of these latter days. Instead were pastes and cakes of agreeable and variegated design, without any suggestion in color or form of the unfortunate animals from which their substance and juices were derived. They appeared on little dishes sliding out upon a rail from a little box at one side of the table. The surface of the table, to judge by touch and eye, would have appeared to a nineteenth-century person to be covered with fine white damask, but this was really an oxidized metallic surface, and could be cleaned instantly after a meal. There were hundreds of such little tables in the hall, and at most of them were other latter-day citizens singly or in groups. And as Mwres seated himself before his elegant repast, the invisible orchestra, which had been resting during an interval, resumed and filled the air with music.

But Mwres did not display any great interest either in his breakfast or the music; his eye wandered incessantly about the hall, as though he expected a belated guest. At last he rose eagerly and waved his hand, and simultaneously across the hall appeared a tall dark figure in a costume of yellow and olive green. As this person, walking amid the tables with measured steps, drew near, the pallid earnestness of his face and the unusual intensity of his eyes became apparent. Mwres reseated himself and pointed to a chair beside him.

"I feared you would never come," he said. In spite of the intervening space of time, the English language was still almost exactly the same as it had been in England under Victoria the Good. The invention of the phonograph and suchlike means of recording sound, and the gradual replacement of books by such contrivances, had not only saved the human eyesight from decay, but had also by the establishment of a sure standard arrested the process of change in accent that had hitherto been so inevitable.

"I was delayed by an interesting case," said the man in green and yellow. "A prominent politician—ahem!—suffering from overwork." He glanced at the breakfast and seated himself. "I have been awake for forty hours."

"Eh dear!" said Mwres: "fancy that! You hypnotists have your work to do."

The hypnotist helped himself to some attractive amber-colored jelly. "I happen to be a good deal in request," he said modestly.

"Heaven knows what we should do without you."

"Oh! we're not so indispensable as all that," said the hypnotist, ruminating the flavor of the jelly. "The world did very well without us for some thousands of years. Two hundred years ago even—not one! In practice, that is. Physicians by the thousand, of course—frightfully clumsy brutes for the most part, and following one another like sheep—but doctors of the mind, except a few empirical flounderers, there were none."

He concentrated his mind on the jelly.

"But were people so sane—?" began Mwres.

The hypnotist shook his head. "It didn't matter then if they were a bit silly or faddy. Life was so easy-going then. No competition worth speaking of—no pressure. A human being had to be very lopsided before anything happened. Then, you know they clapped 'em away in what they called a lunatic asylum."

"I know," said Mwres. "In these confounded historical romances that every one is listening to, they always rescue a beautiful girl from an asylum or something of the sort. I don't know if you attend to that rubbish."

"I must confess I do," said the hypnotist. "It carries one out of one's self to hear of those quaint, adventurous, half civilized days of the nineteenth century, when men were stout and women simple. I like a good swaggering story before all things. Curious times they were, with their smutty railways and puffing old iron trains, their rum little houses and their horse vehicles. I suppose you don't read books?"

"Dear, no!" said Mwres, "I went to a modern school and we had none of that old-fashioned nonsense. Phonographs are good enough for me."

"Of course," said the hypnotist, "of course"; and surveyed the table for his next choice. "You know," he said, helping himself to a dark-blue confection that promised well, "in those days our business was scarcely thought of. I dare say if any one had told them that in two hundred years' time a class of men would be entirely occupied in impressing things upon the memory, effacing unpleasant ideas, controlling and overcoming instinctive but undesirable impulses, and so forth, by means of hypnotism, they would have refused to believe the thing possible. Few people knew that an order made during a mesmeric trance, even an order to forget or an order to desire, could be given so as to be obeyed after the trance was over. Yet there were men alive then who could have told them the thing was as absolutely certain to come about as—well, the transit of Venus."

"They knew of hypnotism, then?"

"Oh dear, yes! They used it—for painless dentistry and things like that! This blue stuff is confoundedly good: what is it?"

"Haven't the faintest idea," said Mwres, "but I admit it's very good. Take some more."

The hypnotist repeated his praises, and there was an appreciative pause.

"Speaking of these historical romances," said Mwres, with an attempt at an easy, off-hand manner, "brings me—ah—to the matter I—ah—had in mind when I asked you—when I expressed a wish to see you." He paused and took a deep breath.

The hypnotist turned an attentive eye upon him, and continued eating.

"The fact is," said Mwres, "I have a—in fact a—daughter. Well, you know I have given her—ah—every educational advantage. Lectures—not a solitary lecturer of ability in the world but she has had a telephone direct—dancing, deportment, conversation, philosophy, art criticism . . ." He indicated catholic culture by a gesture of his hand. "I had intended her to marry a very good friend of mine—Bindon of the Lighting Commission—plain little man, you know, and a bit unpleasant in some of his ways, but an excellent fellow really—an excellent fellow."

"Yes," said the hypnotist, "go on. How old is she?"

"Eighteen."

"A dangerous age. Well?"

"Well: it seems that she has been indulging in these historical romances—excessively. Excessively. Even to the neglect of her philosophy. Filled her mind with unutterable nonsense about soldiers who fight—what is it?—Etruscans?"

"Egyptians."

"Egyptians—very probably. Hack about with swords and revolvers and things—bloodshed galore—horrible!—and about young men on torpedo catchers who blow up—Spaniards, I fancy—and all sorts of irregular adventurers. And she has got it into her head that she must marry for Love, and that poor little Bindon—"

"I've met similar cases," said the hypnotist. "Who is the other young man?"

Mwres maintained an appearance of resigned calm. "You may well ask," he said. "He is"—and his voice sank with shame—"a mere attendant upon the stage on which the flying-machines from Paris alight. He has—as they say in the romances—good looks. He is quite young and very eccentric. Affects the antique—he can read and write! So can she. And instead of communicating by telephone, like sensible people, they write and deliver—what is it?"

"Notes?"

"No—not notes. . . . Ah—poems."

The hypnotist raised his eyebrows. "How did she meet him?"

"Tripped coming down from the flying-machine from Paris—and fell into his arms. The mischief was done in a moment!"

"Yes?"

"Well—that's all. Things must be stopped. That is what I want to consult you about. What must be done? What *can* be done? Of course I'm not a hypnotist; my knowledge is limited. But you—?"

"Hypnotism is not magic," said the man in green, putting both arms on the table.

"Oh, precisely! But still—!"

"People cannot be hypnotized without their consent. If she is able to stand out against marrying Bindon, she will probably stand out against being hypnotized. But if once she can be hypnotized—even by somebody else—the thing is done."

"You can—?"

"Oh, certainly! Once we get her amenable, then we can suggest that she *must* marry Bindon—that that is her fate; or that the young man is repulsive, and that when she sees him she will be giddy and faint, or any little thing of that sort. Or if we can get her into a sufficiently profound trance we can suggest that she should forget him altogether—"

"Precisely."

"But the problem is to get her hypnotized. Of course no sort of proposal or suggestion must come from you—because no doubt she already distrusts you in the matter."

The hypnotist leaned his head upon his arm and thought.

"It's hard a man cannot dispose of his own daughter," said Mwres irrelevantly.

"You must give me the name and address of the young lady," said the hypnotist, "and any information bearing upon the matter. And, by the by, is there any money in the affair?"

Mwres hesitated.

"There's a sum—in fact, a considerable sum—invested in the Patent Road Company. From her mother. That's what makes the thing so exasperating."

"Exactly," said the hypnotist. And he proceeded to cross examine Mwres on the entire affair.

It was a lengthy interview.

And meanwhile "Elizebeθ Mwres," as she spelled her name, or "Elizabeth Morris," as a nineteenth-century person would have put it, was sitting in a quiet waiting-place beneath the great stage upon which the flying-machine from Paris descended. And beside her sat her slender, handsome lover, reading her the poem he had written that morning while on duty upon the stage. When he had finished they sat for a time in silence; and then, as if for their special entertainment, the great machine that had come flying through the air from America that morning rushed down out of the sky.

At first it was a little oblong, faint and blue amid the distant fleecy clouds; and then it grew swiftly large and white, and larger and whiter, until they could see the separate tiers of sails, each hundreds of feet wide, and the lank body they supported, and at last even the swinging seats of the passengers in a dotted row. Although it was falling it seemed to them to be rushing up the sky, and over the roof-spaces of the city below its shadow leaped toward them. They heard the whistling rush of the air about it and its yelling siren, shrill and swelling, to warn those who were on its landing-stage of its arrival. And abruptly the note fell down a couple of octaves, and it had passed, and the sky was clear and void, and she could turn her sweet eyes again to Denton at her side.

Their silence ended; and Denton, speaking in a little language of broken English that was, they fancied, their private possession—though lovers have used such little languages since the world began—told her how they too would leap into the air one morning out of all the obstacles and difficulties about them, and fly to a sunlight city of delight he knew of in Japan, half-way about the world.

She loved the dream, but she feared the leap; and she put him off with "Some day, dearest one, some day," to all his pleading that it might be soon; and at last came a shrilling of whistles, and it was time for him to go back to his duties on the stage. They parted—as lovers have been wont to part for thousands of years. She walked down a passage to a lift, and so came to one of the streets of that latter-day London, all glazed in with glass from the weather, and with incessant moving platforms that went to all parts of the city. And by one of these she returned to her apartments in the Hotel for Women where she lived, the apartments that were in telephonic communication with all the best lecturers in the world. But the sunlight of the flying stages was in her heart, and the wisdom of all the best lecturers in the world seemed folly in that light.

She spent the middle part of the day in the gymnasium, and took her midday meal with two other girls and their common chaperone—for it was still the custom to have a chaperone in the case of motherless girls of the more prosperous classes. The chaperone had a visitor that day, a man in green and yellow, with a white face and vivid eyes, who talked amazingly. Among other things, he fell to praising a new historical romance that one of the great popular story-tellers of the day had just put forth. It was, of course, about the spacious times of Queen Victoria; and the author, among other pleasing novelties, made a little argument before each section of the story, in imitation of the chapter headings of the old-fashioned books: as, for example, "How the Cabmen of Pimlico stopped the Victoria Omnibuses, and of the Great Fight in Palace Yard," and "How the Piccadilly Policeman was slain in the midst of his Duty." The man in green and yellow praised this innovation. "These pithy sentences," he said, "are admirable. They show at a glance those headlong, tumultuous times, when men and animals jostled in the filthy streets, and death might wait for one at every corner. Life was life then! How great the world must have seemed then! How marvellous! There were still parts of the world absolutely unexplored. Nowadays we have almost abolished wonder, we lead lives so trim and orderly that courage, endurance, faith, all the noble virtues seem fading from mankind."

And so on, taking the girls' thoughts with him, until the life they led, life in the vast and intricate London of the twenty-second century, a life interspersed with soaring excursions to every part of the globe, seemed to them a monotonous misery compared with the dædal past.

At first Elizabeth did not join in the conversation, but after a time the subject became so interesting that she made a few shy interpolations. But he scarcely seemed to notice her as he talked. He went on to describe a new method of entertaining people. They were hypnotized, and then suggestions were made to them so skilfully that they seemed to be living in ancient times again. They played out a little romance in the past as vivid as reality, and when at last they awakened they remembered all they had been through as though it were a real thing.

"It is a thing we have sought to do for years and years," said the hypnotist. "It is practically an artificial dream. And we know the way at last. Think of all it opens out to us—the enrichment of our experience, the recovery of adventure, the refuge it offers from this sordid, competitive life in which we live! Think!"

"And you can do that!" said the chaperone eagerly.

"The thing is possible at last," the hypnotist said. "You may order a dream as you wish."

The chaperone was the first to be hypnotized, and the dream, she said, was wonderful, when she came to again.

The other two girls, encouraged by her enthusiasm, also placed themselves in the hands of the hypnotist and had plunges into the romantic past. No one suggested that Elizabeth should try this novel entertainment; it was at her own request at last that she was taken into that land of dreams where there is neither any freedom of choice nor will. . . .

And so the mischief was done.

One day, when Denton went down to that quiet seat beneath the flying stage, Elizabeth was not in her wonted place. He was disappointed, and a little angry. The next day she did not come, and the next also. He was afraid. To hide his fear from himself, he set to work to write sonnets for her when she should come again. . . .

For three days he fought against his dread by such distraction, and then the truth was before him clear and cold, and would not be denied. She might be ill, she might be dead; but he would not believe that he had been betrayed. There followed a week of misery. And then he knew she was the only thing on earth worth having, and that he must seek her, however hopeless the search, until she was found once more.

He had some small private means of his own, and so he threw over his appointment on the flying stage, and set himself to find this girl who had become at last all the world to him. He did not know where she lived, and little of her circumstances; for it had been part of the delight of her girlish romance that he should know nothing of her, nothing of the difference of their station. The ways of the city opened before him east and west, north and south. Even in Victorian days London was a maze, that little London with its poor four millions of people; but the London he explored, the London of the twenty-second century, was a London of thirty million souls. At first he was energetic and headlong, taking time neither to eat nor sleep. He sought for weeks and months, he went through every imaginable phase of fatigue and despair, over-excitement and anger. Long after hope was dead, by the sheer inertia of his desire he still went to and fro, peering into faces and looking this way and that, in the incessant ways and lifts and passages of that interminable hive of men.

At last chance was kind to him, and he saw her.

It was in a time of festivity. He was hungry; he had paid the inclusive fee and had gone into one of the gigantic dining-places of the city; he was pushing his way among the tables and scrutinizing by mere force of habit every group he passed.

He stood still, robbed of all power of motion, his eyes wide, his lips apart. Elizabeth sat scarcely twenty yards away from him, looking straight at him. Her eyes were as hard to him, as hard and expressionless and void of recognition, as the eyes of a statue.

She looked at him for a moment, and then her gaze passed beyond him.

Had he had only her eyes to judge by he might have doubted if it was indeed Elizabeth, but he knew her by the gesture of her hand, by the grace of a wanton little curl that floated over her ear as she moved her head. Something was said to her, and she turned, smiling tolerantly, to the man beside her, a little man in foolish raiment knobbed and spiked like some odd reptile with pneumatic horns—the Bindon of her father's choice.

For a moment Denton stood white and wild-eyed; then came a terrible faintness, and he sat before one of the little tables. He sat down with his back to her, and for a time he did not dare to look at her again. When at last he did, she and Bindon and two other people were standing up to go. The others were her father and her chaperone.

He sat as if incapable of action until the four figures were remote and small, and then he rose up possessed with the one idea of pursuit. For a space he feared he had lost them, and then he came upon Elizabeth and her chaperone again in one of the streets of moving platforms that intersected the city. Bindon and Mwres had disappeared.

He could not control himself to patience. He felt he must speak to her forthwith, or die. He pushed forward to where they were seated, and sat down beside them. His white face was convulsed with half-hysterical excitement.

He laid his hand on her wrist. "Elizabeth?" he said.

She turned in unfeigned astonishment. Nothing but the fear of a strange man showed in her face.

"Elizabeth," he cried, and his voice was strange to him: "dearest—you *know* me?"

Elizabeth's face showed nothing but alarm and perplexity. She drew herself away from him. The chaperone, a little gray-headed woman with mobile features, leaned forward to intervene. Her resolute bright eyes examined Denton. "*What* do you say?" she asked.

"This young lady," said Denton—"she knows me."

"Do you know him, dear?"

"No," said Elizabeth in a strange voice, and with a hand to her forehead, speaking almost as one who repeats a lesson. "No, I do not know him. I *know*—I do not know him."

"But—but . . . Not know me! It is I—Denton. Denton! To whom you used to talk. Don't you remember the flying stages? The little seat in the open air? The verses—"

"No," cried Elizabeth—"no. I do not know him. I do not know him. There is something . . . But I don't know. All I know is that I do not know him." Her face was a face of infinite distress.

The sharp eyes of the chaperone flitted to and fro from the girl to the man. "You see?" she said, with the faint shadow of a smile. "She does not know you."

"I do not know you," said Elizabeth. "Of that I am sure."

"But, dear—the songs—the little verses—"

"She does not know you," said the chaperone. "You must not . . . You have made a mistake. You must not go on talking to us after that. You must not annoy us on the public ways."

"But—" said Denton, and for a moment his miserably haggard face appealed against fate.

"You must not persist, young man," protested the chaperone.

"*Elizabeth!*" he cried.

Her face was the face of one who is tormented. "I do not know you," she cried, hand to brow. "Oh, I do not know you!"

For an instant Denton sat stunned. Then he stood up and groaned aloud.

He made a strange gesture of appeal toward the remote glass roof of the public way, then turned and went plunging recklessly from one moving platform to another, and vanished amid the swarms of people going to and fro thereon. The chaperone's eyes followed him, and then she looked at the curious faces about her.

"Dear," asked Elizabeth, clasping her hand, and too deeply moved to heed observation, "who was that man? Who *was* that man?"

The chaperone raised her eyebrows. She spoke in a clear, audible voice. "Some half-witted creature. I have never set eyes on him before."

"Never?"

"Never, dear. Do not trouble your mind about a thing like this."

And soon after this the celebrated hypnotist who dressed in green and yellow had another client. The young man paced his consulting-room, pale and disordered. "I want to forget," he cried. "I *must* forget."

The hypnotist watched him with quiet eyes, studied his face and clothes and bearing. "To forget anything—pleasure or pain—is to be, by so much—*less*. However, you know your own concern. My fee is high."

"If only I can forget—"

"That's easy enough with you. You wish it. I've done much harder things. Quite recently. I hardly expected to do it: the thing was done against the will of the hypnotized person. A love affair too—like yours. A girl. So rest assured."

The young man came and sat beside the hypnotist. His manner was a forced calm. He looked into the hypnotist's eyes. "I will tell you. Of course you will want to know what it is. There was a girl. Her name was Elizabeth Mwres. Well . . ."

He stopped. He had seen the instant surprise on the hypnotist's face. In that instant he knew. He stood up. He seemed to dominate the seated figure by his side. He gripped the shoulder of green and gold. For a time he could not find words.

"*Give her me back!*" he said at last. "Give her me back!"

"What do you mean?" gasped the hypnotist.

"Give her me back."

"Give whom?"

"Elizabeth Mwres—the girl—"

The hypnotist tried to free himself; he rose to his feet. Denton's grip tightened.

"Let go!" cried the hypnotist, thrusting an arm against Denton's chest.

In a moment the two men were locked in a clumsy wrestle. Neither had the slightest training—for athleticism, except for exhibition and to afford opportunity for betting, had faded out of the earth—but Denton was not only the younger but the stronger of the two. They swayed across the room, and then the hypnotist had gone down under his antagonist. They fell together. . . .

Denton leaped to his feet, dismayed at

his own fury; but the hypnotist lay still, and suddenly from a little white mark where his forehead had struck a stool shot a hurrying band of red. For a space Denton stood over him irresolute, trembling.

A fear of the consequences entered his gently nurtured mind. He turned toward the door. "No," he said aloud, and came back to the middle of the room. Overcoming the instinctive repugnance of one who had seen no act of violence in all his life before, he knelt down beside his antagonist and felt his heart. Then he peered at the wound. He rose quietly and looked about him. He began to see more of the situation.

When presently the hypnotist recovered his senses, his head ached severely, his back was against Denton's knees and Denton was sponging his face.

The hypnotist did not speak. But presently he indicated by a gesture that in his opinion he had been sponged enough. "Let me get up," he said.

"Not yet," said Denton.

"You have assaulted me, you scoundrel!"

"We are alone," said Denton, "and the door is secure."

There was an interval of thought.

"Unless I sponge," said Denton, "your forehead will develop a tremendous bruise."

"You can go on sponging," said the hypnotist sulkily.

There was another pause.

"We might be in the Stone Age," said the hypnotist. "Violence! Struggle!"

"In the Stone Age no man dared to come between man and woman," said Denton.

The hypnotist thought again.

"What are you going to do?" he asked sulkily.

"While you were insensible I found the girl's address on your tablets. I did not know it before. I telephoned. She will be here soon. Then—"

"She will bring her chaperone."

"That is all right."

"But what—? I don't see. What do you mean to do?"

"I looked about for a weapon also. It is an astonishing thing how few weapons there are nowadays, if you consider that in the Stone Age men owned scarcely anything *but* weapons. I hit at last upon this lamp. I have wrenched off the wires and things, and I hold it so." He extended it over the hypnotist's shoulders. "With that I can quite easily smash your skull. I *will*—unless you do as I tell you."

"Violence is no remedy," said the hypnotist, quoting from the "Modern Man's Book of Moral Maxims."

"It's an undesirable disease," said Denton.

"Well?"

"You will tell that chaperone you are going to order the girl to marry that knobby little brute with the red hair and ferrety eyes. I believe that's how things stand?"

"Yes—that's how things stand."

"And, pretending to do that, you will restore her memory of me."

"It's unprofessional."

"Look here! If I cannot have that girl I would rather die than not. I don't propose to respect your little fancies. If anything goes wrong you shall not live five minutes. This is a rude makeshift of a weapon, and it may quite conceivably be painful to kill you. But I will. It is unusual, I know, nowadays, to do things like this—mainly because there is so little in life that is worth being violent about."

"The chaperone will see you directly she comes—"

"I shall stand in that recess. Behind you."

The hypnotist thought. "You are a determined young man," he said, "and only half civilized. I have tried to do my duty to my client, but in this affair you seem likely to get your own way. . . ."

"You mean to deal straightly?"

"I'm not going to risk having my brains scattered in a petty affair like this."

"And afterward?"

"There is nothing a hypnotist or doctor hates so much as a scandal. I at least am no savage. I am annoyed. . . . But in a day or so I shall bear no malice. . . ."

"Thank you. And now that we understand each other, there is no necessity to keep you sitting any longer on the floor."

Triangle of Death

W. J. Carney

The final bloody and heroic chapters of the winning of the West were still fresh in the memories of many Americans as the nineteenth century ended, and the most dramatic of these chapters were those battles fought to the last man. Among the superb fictional recreations of such a battle is Frank Norris's A Memorandum of Sudden Death *(Page 37). And among the graphic personal accounts of such a battle is this recollection by a former corporal of Cavalry, who just missed being a member of the detachment of Custer's force whose fate he describes here.*

November 24, 1900

THE OVERLAND STAGE BROUGHT TEMPOrary addition to the officers at Fort Sedgwick, Colorado; a young lieutenant fresh from West Point named Kidder. His first appointment was to the Seventh Cavalry, that was now scouting along the Republican River. Though only several days' ride from the fort, just where they were was not known. Custer was in command, and had been driving the Indians toward the upper forts; yet the whole country was alive with Sioux and Cheyennes. When Lieutenant Kidder arrived there was but one troop of cavalry and three companies of infantry at Fort Sedgwick. A request to General Potter for an escort to accompany him to his regiment was refused on the ground that so small a party as the general could then afford to give him could not possibly get through. Even then Troop M of the Second Cavalry was under marching orders to leave the fort next day on a scouting expedition toward the Black Hills. Just as the troop was all ready to start an order to postpone the trip was handed to Captain Mix. This was Kidder's opportunity. He begged so hard to go that the general at last consented.

At first General Potter ordered Captain Mix to detail twelve of the best men in his company as Kidder's escort. For noncommissioned officers the captain selected Sergeant A. T. Carrick, late Police Judge of Baltimore, and myself as the corporal, leaving the rest to us. Carrick picked five men, and I the other five. Carrick chose Christian Felto, William Curry, William Humphrey, John Lawlor, and Herman Smidth; mine were Michael Healey, William Floyd, Michael Growman, Alonzo Defo, and Michael Connell. An hour before starting Sergeant Close and Corporal Haynes were substituted for Carrick and myself. This was at the special request of Close and Haynes who had brothers in the Seventh and wished to see them. They were green men, having had no experience whatever in Indian warfare, nor had either ever been on the prairies. They had lately come to us from the exhibition or dandy company, at Carlisle Barracks, then head rendezvous for recruits. It was said that both had influence with their superior officers. It must have been so, for after joining our company they retained their sergeant and corporal stripes, something unheard of before, as they had been given those stripes without seeing any active service whatever. Not having been promoted for gallantry in the field, no one could say whether they were brave or not, as no one ever saw them tried. Still, they may have been, and no doubt were, brave men. But Sergeant Carrick was a brave, experienced man; many times tried and proven; a very brave, good soldier. I say nothing against Close and Haynes, except that they were green and did lots of things neither Carrick nor myself would have done; camping in a hollow, allowing all the men to go in bathing at once, and going through a hostile Indian country as if on a picnic. When found, the party was twenty-five miles south of where they should have been. It was fourteen men with no one in authority that knew the country, the ways of the enemy, or even active service. Though the scout and the men were old Indian fighters, this counted for nothing, as their lips were sealed by an iron discipline. It is one of the evils of the discipline of the regular army that no private, no matter what the danger nor how incompetent the officer, can even offer a suggestion; and these men, scarred in many an Indian battle, were held silent under green officers. Theory commanded Experience. This long explanation is given that the results may be better understood.

They had for a guide Red Bead, a full-blooded Sioux Indian chief. This Red Bead was head chief of the tribe of Indians that made such a gallant fight against the Eleventh Ohio Volunteer Cavalry on Laramie plains in 1865. The Ohio men were outnumbered six to one, and were nearly all killed, Major English escaping with a few of his men. After this fight, or massacre, Red Bead came into Fort Laramie alone and surrendered. He made a vow never again, except in self-defence, to take arms against the pale-face. When the government became satisfied that he was honest in his desire to leave the life of the savage and become the friend of the white man, this old Indian was made a government scout. He was now to guide Kidder and his escort in their search for Custer. It was a beautiful summer's evening, and as the little party drew up in line in front of the adjutant's office their comrades came down to bid them good-by. They were not to leave until dusk; as it was considered safer to travel at night and rest in some ravine during the day. In this way they could avoid being seen by the Indians, who were travelling north and west. At last the order came; a grip of the hand and they rode away. We could see the glimmer of the big brass buckles on their sling belts as they slowly worked their way up the steep bluffs behind the fort; and we watched to catch a last glimpse of them as they went up and over the crest. It was nearly dark as they waved their last farewell on top of this high hill. The rest of this story I gathered from Pawnee Killer himself, an old Indian, who, like Red Bead, afterward became civilized and a friend to the whites. He was the chief in command during the events I am about to describe, and from his lips we learned the sad, sad facts.

For some unaccountable reason the officers did not keep to their first and better plan of marching by night and resting by day. On the second day out, the white men, all unknown to them, had been sighted by an Indian runner. From that moment their every move was being watched by the scouts of Pawnee Killer, who, with a band of some three hundred warriors, kept in the background ready to spring at the first good chance. Lieutenant Kidder and his escort had been travelling three days when they arrived at Beaver Creek. It was late in the afternoon. The men were hot and dusty, and had been without water for thirty-six hours, so, upon beholding this clear, cold stream, camp was made and the whole party prepared to go in swimming. Just over the hill behind them, silent on their horses, crouched three hundred Indians. If Lieutenant Kidder had been longer on the frontier he would not have allowed all his men to go into the water at once with none to guard. The scout could not speak much English, was evidently ignored, and the sergeant must have been asleep to permit it. They seemed to throw all caution to the winds, and nearly all stripped and plunged in.

The chance had come. A swelling, shaking roar of coming hoofs, and over the hill came a wave of red. Down the slope, in a swirling cloud of dust, burst an avalanche of shrieking, shooting Indians. Over the camp and away they went, sending showers of arrows into the naked whites. Two white men were hit, but not disabled. The water protected the rest. From the creek they rushed for their horses, to secure them from stampeding. The camp was in wild confusion; but after the excitement of the surprise was over the men settled down to business and began pumping the lead into the redskins without mercy. Each man was armed with a seven-shot Spencer carbine, and a Remington six-shooter, and had two hundred rounds of ammunition. Besides this there were two thousand rounds carried by the pack mule. There were plenty of cartridges. At the time of the attack Red Bead was about five hundred yards away from camp, creeping up a ravine to get a shot at a bunch of antelope. He was hidden in a clump of sage brush, and from there watched the fighting going on down in the bottom. How to dash in and out, strike and get away, or circle around, not stand and fight, is the Indian way of battle. Again came the savages, tearing through the camp. The lieutenant and two of the men were killed, but eleven remained. One now ran from horse to horse, and after leading each animal to the place he wanted him, shot him down. In this way he quickly made good breastworks. Dead Indians were piled up with the horses, forming a triangle. Behind this they now prepared to sell their lives. As the redskins came, first from one side, then from another, the white men crawled over and among the dead horses. In this way they had fair protection, until the attack began from both sides at once. After the first two or three charges the fine shooting of the regulars cooled the Indians' ardor, and, just out of range, they commenced circling the little camp, endeavoring to waste its fire. One of the Indians, to show his bravery, rode close to the besieged men, threw himself alongside his running pony, fired from under the horse's neck, and got away safely. But the second time, growing more bold, he came closer. A shot from the little fort brought down his pony, and, before he could find shelter, another one laid him out. The Indians now made every effort to get the body of the dead warrior. It proved a good bait for the white men, for in the attempt to bring off their dead six savages were brought down. It is a part of the Indian religion not to leave dead or wounded in the hands of the enemy, and to recover them the living risk their lives with religious recklessness. The fight had been going on a little over an hour when the Indians discovered Red Bead. They started for him. The brave old fellow made them pay dear for his scalp. He might have been able to make his peace with those of his own tribe, but instead he fought like a demon until out of ammunition. He had only what was contained in his belt when he started to stalk the antelope. Whether or not he took his own life with his last cartridge is not known, but he was dead when they got to him. Around his body lay one hundred and fifty empty shells. For the men within the triangle there now could be but little hope; the one chance left was for some hunting or scouting party to be attracted by the firing and come to their aid, or an hour would end it. This was but one chance in a thousand, for at that time the Beaver Creek country was a wild, trackless place, not a human within fifty miles. Hope had been centered on Red Bead and died with him.

Help could come only from within or above. From the brow of the hill to the timber along the creek is four hundred yards. The dead lieutenant made the fatal mistake of pitching camp on the slope half way between. The hill commanded the camp. The attack changed. Though armed mostly with bows, yet the Indians had perhaps twenty "heap smoke sticks," as the Indian told me long afterward. But even from two hundred yards an Indian arrow is dangerous; and at half this distance it is more deadly than the cavalryman's revolver. Almost all of the redskins now gathered in the timber just across the creek below the camp. From safety here they sent up clouds of arrows, sticking into the carcass fort. All unsuspecting, and seeking cover from that shower of death, the remaining poor fellows behind the breastworks jumped to the side facing the hill. The Indians in the timber gave the signal. Instantly ten or more of the fiends came over the hill and fired into their backs. This seemed to end the struggle, as there was no sign of life in what now appeared to be the triangle of death. After waiting a little the red devils began to cautiously approach, but when within one hundred yards three shots were fired and three more savages went to the happy hunting grounds. The whole three hundred Indians now made a dash for the brave defenders of the death heap, but were met by a stream of shots. Indians in those days were not used to going against repeating rifles, and with the Spencer seven-shooter in the hands of three such experienced men the redskins were led to think they were targets for a dozen sharpshooters. With one cartridge in the breech and seven in the magazine, these three men sent twenty-four bullets into the red ranks so quickly that it drove them back. But the end was not far off. Weeks later we found nothing but their skeletons. When the party on the hill attacked again the three remaining cavalrymen shook hands, stood up and delivered their fire as if on skirmish drill. Three against three hundred. The red demons were coming at them from all sides. There was no hope. The white men were now firing from revolvers, one in each hand. Suddenly one of them received an arrow in the breast, but he did not fall. His comrade reached over and pulled it out. Then he sank to his knees, lay over on the heap of dead, fired another shot, tried to raise his hand again, but fell, rolled over, and lay still. Only two were left. Soon one of them staggered and fell against his comrade, who lifted him tenderly and laid him down, dead. Finding himself alone, the last man looked wildly around on the bloody, ghastly heaps of dead men and horses, looked out and all over the plains. He did not seem to realize that his enemies had stopped shooting. He walked to the left of the pile of dead to where the lieutenant lay, stooped down, and peered into his face. Then he came back to where he had stood, and where his last comrade fell. Kneeling down, he turned the dead man's head and looked at his face. Then he stood up, and for the first time noticed that the Indians were closing in on him, and that the arrows had stopped. He ran quickly from body to body, picked up and hurriedly examined their revolvers. Some he kept, others he dropped. When through he had four. He stepped to a dead horse, no doubt his own, and, putting his foot on its side, began to shoot. The Indians wanted to get him alive, for torture. He knew this. They dodged here and there; and when they thought he had fired his last shot closed in on him. He dropped both revolvers, and with folded arms stood waiting. With a yell of triumph they rushed at him. The one in the lead was a big, hideous-looking warrior, a chief in a white-feathered war bonnet. When the Indian was within ten feet the soldier stooped and grabbed the two revolvers. The savage leaped for his victim, but the white man put a bullet between the eyes of the Indian, who threw up his hands and plunged forward, dead. Then the soldier fired the last shot into his own brain and fell across the pile of dead men in the triangle of death.

What Americans Think About the Boer War

Winston Spencer Churchill

When Winston Spencer Churchill came to America to lecture in 1900, he was twenty-six years old, a decorated soldier with service in India and Cuba, and a young politician of considerable prominence and promise. He came, however, as a practitioner of his most steadfast trade—publicist and champion of close relationship between the two great English-speaking peoples. He came in particular to temper a certain animosity felt by the Americans against the British in their war against the Dutch settlers of two South African republics, the Orange Free State and the Transvaal. Churchill had not only covered the Boer war as a correspondent, he had been captured by the Boers, made a sensational escape, and, at this writing, was serving his first term in Parliament. Much of the philosophy, as well as the style, of the latter-day Churchill will be found in this report, written for Collier's *almost forty years before the mightiest war in history brought him to his Finest Hour. And in the closing paragraph will be found a prophecy, since fulfilled.*

January 26, 1901

Before I sailed from England proposing to lecture in the United States, people who understood American opinion, or who said they understood American opinion—I wonder if any one man can gauge the opinion, at a given moment, of eighty millions spread over a continent?—declared that I should meet a warm reception.

"They are all bitter pro-Boers over there," they said.

But I have always believed that in a free country every one, even an alien, has a right to form his own opinion and express the same to as many as care to listen. Nevertheless, it was with feelings of considerable trepidation that I appeared before my first American audience.

It was in Philadelphia itself—the City of the Messenger Boy. A concourse of something like three thousand people had gathered in a spacious and magnificent theatre. The chairman made a few neutral observations, retired from the stage and left me alone with America. I had arranged some slides for the magic lantern, which would enable the audience to express and me to learn their feelings as early as possible.

Several pictures of Boer commandoes and the portrait of Mr. Reitz were passed with indifference, but when General Louis

Botha's portrait was flashed upon the screen the applause was sudden and loud. So far as I could tell, about three-fifths of the audience were politely hostile. I said that they were quite right to cheer a gallant and patriotic man fighting against heavy odds, that whenever I had shown Louis Botha's picture in England it had always been received with cheers, and that they ought to know that the British felt no rancor nor any bitterness whatever against the Boers for their brave resistance and respected every honorable enemy.

At this the audience thawed perceptibly, and I then took occasion to observe that we British hoped that we should not be found less steadfast and enduring in support of our cause than were our stubborn antagonists, whereat the pro-British section of the audience raised a lively counter-cheer; and, matters having thus been established on a friendly basis all round, I proceeded to the end of my address with a most indulgent and attentive audience.

Since then I have spoken in many towns throughout the Eastern States. Opinion in the audiences has varied from Philadelphia, which was as I have described, to Boston, where a regular demonstration was made in favor of the British cause.

The great hall was crowded in every part and at least a dozen Union Jacks were waved by enthusiastic people. Across the platform were drawn up fifty gentlemen of the British Veteran's Corps in uniform, with their Crimean and Mutiny medals glittering, and a sprinkling of American volunteers returned from serving in the Light Horse in South Africa relieved the black and white of evening dress with the familiar color of khaki.

Naturally I took rather a bolder line under these encouragements, for although an honest man should always sing the same song—his country's cause—sometimes it is wise to sing it in a different key.

The only unpleasant incident which I have had was in New York, where my agent, without my knowledge, printed, without their consent, the names of several prominent pro-Boers as forming part of a reception committee. These gentlemen, to whom I am glad to have an opportunity of offering all apologies, were very properly indignant and wrote to say so in the newspapers. This affair in no way affected the success of my New York lecture, for I found there a very large, though rather silent, audience, who heard me with patience to the end.

So much for experiences; let me try to reach some conclusion. What is the true opinion of the United States upon the Boer war and her attitude toward Great Britain? It seems presumptuous for any one to answer such a question after the study only of a month; but an invitation to pronounce must always be accepted as an excuse for doing so.

A large minority of the people of the United States sympathize with the Boers. To my mind that is very natural. If a man has detached sympathies curling about idly in the air, like the tentacles of an octopus, he will probably fasten them on to the first object of sympathy which may come along.

The British Empire, although anxious for the respect of the United States, stands in no immediate need of sympathy from any one.

On the other hand, the Boers and their sad position, the prolonged and marvellous resistance which, all untrained or taught only by the cunning of the frontiersman, they are making for the sake of preserving their own independence and their own Dutch flag, must attract the interest and the admiration of sentimental people, particularly of those folk who give and are in a position to give their sentiments free play, untrammelled by vulgar and prosaic facts. I am frank to admit that I should sympathize with the Boers, if I were not an Englishman and had not visited South Africa.

There is a great volume of academic sympathy for the Boers in this country, but whatever practical strength it possesses arises from the comparatively small nucleus of bitter and irreconcilable anti-British feeling, which has always marred, and may for a long time mar, the good understanding which ought to exist between Great Britain and the United States.

Upon the other hand, I rejoice to find that Great Britain has many firm friends in the United States. There is the Englishman who has made America his home and has become a citizen, but who, for all his loyalty to the land of his adoption, cherishes a deep affection for the land of his birth. There is the American whose ancestors have lived for so many generations on American soil that, despite political cataclysms and the inevitable changes of time, he looks back, with the kinship of race and law, and bridges the ocean which divides the New World from the Old and links the traditions of an ancient kingdom with the hope of a growing republic. There is the naval officer—one that I met had fought in Manila Bay—who tells me, with the usual intolerance of the fighting man, that whenever they enter port and see the white ensign above the British man-of-war they know they will find "somebody fit to speak to." There is the ordinary humdrum man of good sense who knows that neither Britain nor the United States has anything to gain from friction and ill-temper, and that both they and the world itself will benefit from their concord and co-operation. And, lastly, there is the candid cynic—there are such in every country—the man who likes to tell the truth, particularly the unpleasant truth, to his countryman and who sardonically observes that the position in the Philippine Islands is not the best place in the world from which to throw stones at the British policy in South Africa.

I have always found it easy to make up my mind on questions about which I know very little; but the more facts one learns, the more difficult it is to come to a decision. Now in the busy whirl of modern life and the limitless field of modern thought it is not possible for an ordinary man to know much about the political questions of countries other than his own. That is the reason why we can form such decided opinions upon them. I am far from saying that these opinions are not of use and value. I believe that British and American opinion may react upon one another as a most healthy corrective to both countries.

In the work of healing the wounds of war in South Africa, in drawing the greatest measure of good from a great misfortune, there is room for the friends of all parties to co-operate; and in that work the attention of the United States—not necessarily their praise, but their friendly and temperate criticism—may, indeed must, exert a valuable and effective influence. But let us, above all things, criticise each other with restraint. No nation pays any attention to the criticism of a foreign power unless it is moderate. It is merely treated as abuse, perfectly futile unless supported by cannon. For this reason, and also because we cannot take more than a superficial view of other people's affairs, the case for moderation claims alike from policy and justice the support of practical men.

I have found this attitude of tolerance, of desire to hear both sides and all sides, very frequent among the Americans of every class that I have met. Several prominent pro-Boers whose private friendship I have long enjoyed, others whom I only knew by name, came to hear what I had to say. I must confess that they went away friendly but unconverted. But I find in American audiences as a whole a great measure of this judicial quality, which is, after all, one of the main distinctions between a civilized man and a cannibal—the wish to find out the real truth instead of merely to strengthen established convictions.

American audiences are, moreover, very good-natured, quick to appreciate a joke, even if turned against themselves; most kind, patient and reasonable. Of course, I never have had the opportunity of addressing a meeting of working men on this side of the Atlantic. It is a pleasure, perhaps, to come; but, so far as may be judged from a limited, though very recent, experience, it seems that an American audience is much harder to convince than a similar gathering in Great Britain, but much easier to persuade.

I have tried to show in what degrees American opinion is divided upon the Boer war: a large minority of academic Boer sympathizers around a small but implacable nucleus of Anglophobes on the one hand; and, upon the other, a great mass of phlegmatic opinion and the many forces actively friendly to Great Britain.

But we must not mislead ourselves as to the practical strength of pro-Boer sympathy in America. To whatever side they may attach themselves upon this question, Americans are not greatly stirred by it. They do not care much either way. The world lives so fast nowadays that the cry for something new interrupts the closing acts of the greatest dramas. The United States have looked away from South Africa and are busy with their own concerns, and nothing which can arise out of the sentiments the Boer war has excited is likely to impair the good relations which have so long existed with Great Britain.

I have never been an advocate of the Anglo-American alliance. Such an idea, however attractive, is far removed from practical politics—almost as far removed as the idea of an Anglo-American war. There are mighty forces silently at work on both sides of the Atlantic to join the two peoples with bonds of friendship and sympathy. But alliances arise out of the interests, not out of the sentiments, of nations. An alliance founded on sentiment alone would not be worth the paper upon which it was written. It would be a draft on a bank which had closed its doors.

It is not the interest of the United States, certainly it is not the interest of Great Britain, to become involved in the foreign politics of another power pursuing different objects from an entirely different point of view. Perhaps the day will come when the tie of common interest will be added to the other ties which join, as no communities of such magnitude have been joined before, the two greatest powers of the modern world.

As the United States gradually expands her sphere of action beyond the shores of America and takes her place among the nations she will find new opportunities of profiting by the good offices of England; and some day a common danger and a common cause may array in appalling battle-line the incalculable energies of the Anglo-Saxon family. But for the present, and as far into the future as we can see, the watchword of wise men of either nation must be "Friendship, not Alliance." The tragic episode of the South African war and any irritation it may have excited in the United States will not disturb this kind of relationship.

A Memorandum of Sudden Death

Frank Norris

Frank Norris's brilliant talent had already produced McTeague *(1892)*, The Octopus *(1901) and several other notable novels when this story appeared. Ironically, a memorandum of Norris's own sudden death at the age of thirty-two, appeared in* Collier's *just ten months later—November, 1902. Several of his most memorable works, including* The Pit, *were published after his death.*

January 11, 1902

THE MANUSCRIPT OF THE ACCOUNT THAT follows belongs to a harnessmaker in Albuquerque, Juan Tejada by name, and he is welcome to whatever of advertisement this notice may bring him. He is a good fellow, and his patented martingale for stage horses may be recommended. I understand he got the manuscript from a man named Bass, or possibly Bass left it with him for safe-keeping. I know that Tejada has some things of Bass's now—things that Bass left with him last November: a mess-kit, a lantern, and a broken theodolite—a whole saddlebox full of contraptions. I forgot to ask Tejada how Bass got the manuscript, and I wish I had done so now, for the finding of it might be a story itself. The probabilities are that Bass simply picked it up page by page off the desert, blown about the spot where the fight occurred and at some little distance from the bodies. Bass, I am told, is a bone-gatherer by profession, and one can easily understand how he would come across the scene of the encounter in one of his tours into Western Arizona. My interest in the affair is impersonal, but none the less keen. Though I did not know young Karslake, I knew his stuff—as everybody still does, when you come to that. For the matter of that, the mere mention of his pen-name, "Anson Qualtraugh," recalls at once to thousands of the readers of a certain world-famous monthly magazine of New York articles and stories he wrote for it while he was alive; as, for instance, his admirable descriptive work called "Traces of the Aztecs on the Mogolon Mesa," in the October number of 1890. Also, in the January issue of 1892 there are two specimens of his work, one signed Anson Qualtraugh and the other Justin Blisset. Why he should have used the Blisset signature I do not know. It occurs only this once in all his writings. In this case it is signed to a very indifferent New Year's story. The Qualtraugh "stuff" of the same number is, so the editor writes to me, a much shortened transcript of a monograph on "Primitive Methods of Moqui Irrigation," which is now in the archives of the Smithsonian. The admirable novel, "The Peculiar Treasure of Kings," is of course well known. Karslake wrote it in 1888-89, and the controversy that arose about the incident of the third chapter is still—sporadically and intermittently—continued.

The manuscript that follows now appears, of course, for the first time in print, and I acknowledge herewith my obligations to Karslake's father, Mr. Patterson Karslake, for permission to publish.

I have set the account down word for word, with all the hiatuses and breaks that by nature of the extraordinary circumstances under which it was written were bound to appear in it. I have allowed it to end precisely as Karslake was forced to end it, in the middle of a sentence. God knows the real end is plain enough and was not far off when the poor fellow began the last phrase that never was to be finished.

The value of the thing is self-apparent. Besides the narrative of incidents it is a simple setting forth of a young man's emotions in the very face of violent death. You will remember the distinguished victim of the guillotine, a lady, who on the scaffold begged that she might be permitted to write out the great thoughts that began to throng her mind. She was not allowed to do so, and the record is lost. Here is a case where the record is preserved. But Karslake, being a young man not very much given to introspection, his work is more a picture of things seen than a transcription of things thought. However, one may read between the lines; the very breaks are eloquent, while the break at the end speaks with a significance that no words could attain.

The manuscript in itself is interesting. It is written partly in pencil, partly in ink (no doubt from a fountain pen), on sheets of manila paper torn from some sort of long and narrow account-book. In two or three places there are smudges where the powder-blackened finger and thumb held the sheets momentarily. I would give much to own it, but Tejada will not give it up without Bass's permission, and Bass has gone to the Klondike.

As to Karslake himself. He was born in Raleigh, in South Carolina, in 1868, studied law at the State University, and went to the Bahamas in 1885 with the members of a government coast survey commission. Gave up the practice of law and "went in" for fiction and the study of the ethnology of North America about 1887. He was unmarried.

The reasons for his enlisting have long been misunderstood. It was known that at the time of his death he was a member of B troop of the Sixth Regiment of United States Cavalry, and it was assumed that because of this fact Karslake was in financial difficulties and not upon good terms with his family. All this, of course, is untrue, and I have every reason to believe that Karslake at this time was planning a novel of military life in the Southwest, and, wishing to get in closer touch with the *milieu* of the story, actually enlisted in order to be able to write authoritatively. He saw no active service until the time when his narrative begins. The year of his death is uncertain. It was in the spring probably of 1896, in the twenty-eighth year of his age.

There is no doubt he would have become in time a great writer. A young man of twenty-eight who had so lively a sense of the value of accurate observation and so eager a desire to produce, that in the very face of death he could faithfully set down a description of his surroundings, actually laying down the rifle to pick up the pen, certainly was possessed of extraordinary faculties.

"They came in sight early this morning just after we had had breakfast and had broken camp. The four of us—'Bunt,' 'Idaho,' Estorijo and myself—were jogging on to the southward and had just come up out of the dry bed of some water hole—the alkali was white as snow in the crevices—when Idaho pointed them out to us, three to the rear, two on one side, one on the other and—very far away—two ahead. Five minutes before, the desert was as empty as the flat of my hand. They seemed literally to have *grown* out of the sagebrush. We took them in through my field-glasses and Bunt made sure they were an outlying band of Hunt-in-the-Morning's bucks. I had thought, and so had all of us, that the rest of the boys had rounded up the whole of the old man's hostiles long since. We are at a loss to account for these fellows here. They seem to be well mounted.

"We had a council of war from the saddle without halting, but there seemed very little to be done—but to go right along and wait for developments. At about eleven we found water—just a pocket in the bed of a dried stream—and stopped to water the ponies. I am writing this during the halt.

"We have one hundred and sixteen rifle cartridges. Yesterday was Friday, and all day, as the newspapers say, 'the situation remained unchanged.' We expected surely that the night would see some rather radical change, but nothing happened, though we stood watch and watch till morning. Of yesterday's eight only six are in sight and we believe that the other two have gone off to bring up reserves. We now have two to the front, one on each side, and two to the rear, all far out of rifle range. [*The following paragraph is in an unsteady script and would appear to have been written in the saddle. The same peculiarity occurs from time to time in the narrative, and occasionally the writing is so broken as to be illegible.*]

"On again after breakfast. It is about eight-fifteen. The other two have come back—without 'reserves,' thank God. Very possibly they did not go away at all, but were hidden by a dip in the ground. I cannot see that any of them are nearer. I have watched one to the left of us steadily for over half an hour and I am sure that he has not shortened the distance between himself and us. What their plans are Hell only knows, but this silent, persistent escorting tells on the nerves. I do not think I am afraid—as yet. It does not seem possible but that we will ride into La Paz at the end of the fortnight exactly as we had planned, meet Greenock according to arrangements and take the stage on to the railroad. Then next month I shall be in San Antonio and report at headquarters. Of course, all this is to be, of course; and this business of to-day will make a good story to tell. It's an experience—good 'material.' Very naturally I cannot now see how I am going to get out of this [*the word "alive" has here been erased*], but of course I *will*. Why 'of course'? I don't know. Maybe I am trying to deceive myself. Frankly, it looks like a situation insoluble; but the solution will surely come right enough in good time.

"Eleven o'clock.—No change.

"Two-thirty P.M.—We are halted to tighten girths and to take a single swallow of the canteens. One of them rode in a wide circle from the rear to the flank, about ten minutes ago, conferred a moment with his fellow, then fell back to his old position. He wears some sort of red cloth or blanket. We reach no more water till day after to-morrow. But we have sufficient. Estorijo has been telling funny stories en route.

"Four o'clock P.M.—They have closed up perceptibly, and we have been debating about trying for one of them with Idaho's Winchester. No use; better save the ammunition. It looks . . . [*the next words are undecipherable, but from the context they would appear to be "as if they would attack tonight"*] . . . we have come to know certain of them now by nicknames. We speak of the Red One, or the Little One, or the One with the Feather, and Idaho has named a short thickset fellow on our right 'Little Willie.' By God, I wish something would turn up—relief or fight. I don't care which. How Estorijo can cackle on, reeling off his senseless, pointless funny stories is beyond me. Bunt is almost as bad. They understand the fix we are in, I *know*, but how they can take it so easily is the staggering surprise. I feel that I am as courageous as either of them, but levity seems horribly inappropriate. I could kill Estorijo joyfully.

"Sunday morning.—Still no developments. We were so sure of something turning up last night that none of us pretended to sleep. But nothing stirred. There is no sneaking out of the circle at night. The moon is full. A jack-rabbit could not have slipped by them unseen last night.

"Nine o'clock (in the saddle).—We had coffee and bacon as usual at sunrise; then on again to the southeast just as before. For half an hour after starting the Red One and two others were well within rifle-shot, nearer than ever before. They had worked in from the flank. But before Idaho could get a chance at them they dipped into a shallow arroyo, and when they came out on the other side were too far away to think of shooting.

"Ten o'clock.—All at once we find there are nine instead of eight; where and when this last one joined the band we cannot tell. He wears a sombrero and army trousers, but the upper part of his body is bare. Idaho calls him 'Half-and-half.' He is riding a— They're coming.

"Later.—For a moment we thought it was the long-expected rush. The Red One—he had been in the front—wheeled quick as a flash and came straight for us, and the others followed suit. Great Heavens, how they rode! We could hear them yelling on every side of us. We jumped off our ponies and stood behind them, the rifles across the saddles. But at four hundred yards they all pivoted about and cantered off again leisurely. Now they follow us as before—three in the front, two in the rear, and two on either side. I do not think I am going to be frightened when the rush does come. I watched myself just now. I was excited, and I remember Bunt saying to me, 'Keep your shirt on, m'son'; but I was not afraid of being killed. Thank God for that! It is something I've long wished to find out, and now that I know it I am proud of it. Neither side fired a shot. I was not afraid. It's glorious. Estorijo is all right.

"Sunday afternoon, one-thirty.—No change. It is unspeakably hot.

"Three-fifteen.—The One with the Feather is walking, leading his pony. It seems to be lame. [*With this entry Karslake ended page five, and the next page of the manuscript is numbered seven. It is very probable, however, that he made a mistake in the numerical sequence of his pages, for the narrative is continuous, and, at this point at least, unbroken. There does not seem to be any sixth page.*]

"Four o'clock.—Is it possible that we are to pass another night of suspense? They certainly show no signs of bringing on the crisis, and they surely would not attempt anything so late in the afternoon as this. It is a relief to feel that we have nothing to fear till morning, but the tension of watching all night long is fearful.

"Later.—Idaho has just killed the Little One.

"Later.—Still firing.

"Later.—Still at it.

"Later, about five.—A bullet struck within three feet of me.

"Five-ten.—Still firing.

"Seven-thirty P.M., in camp.—It happened so quickly that it was all over before I realized. We had our first interchange of shots with them late this afternoon. The Little One was riding from the front to the flank. Evidently he did not think he was in range—nor did any of us. All at once Idaho tossed up his rifle and let go without aiming—or so it seemed to me. The stock was not at his shoulder before the report came. About six seconds after the smoke had cleared away we could see the Little One begin to lean backward in the saddle, and Idaho said grimly, 'I guess I got *you*.' The Little One leaned further and further till suddenly his head dropped back between his shoulderblades. He held to his pony's mane with both hands for a long time and then all at once went off feet first. His legs bent under him like putty as his feet touched the ground. The pony bolted.

"Just as soon as Idaho fired the others closed right up and began riding around us at top speed, firing as they went. Their aim was bad as a rule, but one bullet came very close to me. At about half-past five they drew off out of range again and we made camp right where we stood. Estorijo and I are both sure that Idaho hit the Red One, but Idaho himself is doubtful, and Bunt did not see the shot. I could swear that the Red One all but went off his pony. However, he seems active enough now.

"Monday morning.—Still another night without attack. I have not slept since Friday evening. The strain is terrific. At daybreak this morning, when one of our ponies snorted suddenly, I cried out at the top of my voice. I could no more have repressed it than I could have stopped my blood flowing; and for half an hour afterward I could feel my flesh crisping and pringling, and there was a sickening weakness at the pit of my stomach. At breakfast I had to force down my coffee. They are still in place, but now there are two on each side, two in the front, two in the rear. The killing of the Little One seems to have heartened us all wonderfully. I am sure we will get out—somehow. But oh! the suspense of it.

"Monday morning, nine-thirty.—Under way for over two hours. There is no new development. But Idaho has just said that they seem to be edging in. We hope to reach water to-day. Our supply is low, and the ponies are beginning to hang their heads. It promises to be a blazing hot day. There is alkali all to the west of us, and we just commence to see the rise of ground miles to the southward that Idaho says is the San Jacinto Mountains. Plenty of water there. The desert hereabout is vast and lonesome beyond words; leagues of sparse sagebrush, leagues of leper-white alkali, leagues of baking gray sand, empty, heat-ridden, the abomination of desolation; and always—in whichever direction I turn my eyes—always, in the midst of this pale-yellow blur, a single figure in the distance, blanketed, watchful, solitary, standing out sharp and distinct against the background of sage and sand.

"Monday, about eleven o'clock.—No change. The heat is appalling. There is just a—

"Later.—I was on the point of saying that there was just a mouthful of water left for each of us in our canteens when Estorijo and Idaho both at the same time cried out that they were moving in. It is true. They are within rifle range, but do not fire. We, as well, have decided to reserve our fire until something more positive happens.

"Noon.—The first shot—for to-day—from the Red One. We are halted. The shot struck low and to the left. We could see the sand spout up in a cloud just as though a bubble had burst on the surface of the ground.

"They have separated from each other, and the whole eight of them are now in a circle around us. Idaho believes the Red One fired as a signal. Estorijo is getting ready to take a shot at the One with the Feather. We have the ponies in a circle around us. It looks as if now at last this was the beginning of the real business.

"Later, twelve thirty-five.—Estorijo missed. Idaho will try with the Winchester as soon as the One with the Feather halts. He is galloping toward the Red One.

"All at once, about two o'clock, the fighting began. This is the first let-up. It is now—God knows what time. They closed up suddenly and began galloping about us in a circle, firing all the time. They rode like madmen. I would not have believed that Indian ponies could run so quickly. What with their yelling and the incessant crack of their rifles and the thud of their ponies' feet our horses at first became very restless, and at last Idaho's mustang bolted clean away. We all stood to it as hard as we could. For about the first fifteen minutes it was hot work. The Spotted One is hit. We are certain of that much, though we do not know whose gun did the work. My poor old horse is bleeding dreadfully from the mouth. He has two bullets in the stomach and I do not believe he can stand much longer. They have let up for the last few moments, but are still riding around us, their guns at 'ready.' Every now and then one of us fires, but the heat shimmer has come up over the ground since noon and the range is extraordinarily deceiving.

"Three-ten.—Estorijo's horse is down, shot clean through the head. Mine has gone long since. We have made a rampart of the bodies.

"Three-twenty.—They are at it again, tearing around us incredibly fast, every now and then narrowing the circle. The bullets are striking everywhere now. I having no rifle do what I can with my revolver, and try to watch what is going on in front of me and warn the others when they press in too close on my side. [*Karslake nowhere accounts for the absence of his carbine. That a U. S. trooper should be without his gun while traversing a hostile country is a fact difficult to account for.*]

"Three-thirty.—They have winged me—through the shoulder. Not bad, but it is bothersome. I sit up to fire, and Bunt gives me his knee on which to rest my right arm. When it hangs it is painful.

"Quarter to four.—It is horrible. Bunt is dying. He cannot speak, the ball having gone through the lower part of his face, but back, near the neck. It happened through his trying to catch his horse. The animal was struck in the breast and tried to bolt. He reared up, backing away, and as we had to keep him close to us to serve as a bulwark Bunt followed him out from the little circle that we formed, his gun in one hand, his other gripping the bridle. I suppose every one of the eight fired at him simultaneously, and down he went. The pony dragged him a little ways still clutching the bridle, then fell itself, its whole weight rolling on Bunt's chest. We have managed to get him in and to secure his rifle, but he will not live. None of us knows him very well. He only joined us about a week ago, but we all liked him from the start. He never spoke of himself, so we cannot tell much about him. Idaho says he has a wife in Torreon, but that he has not lived with her for two years; they did not get along well together, it seems. This is the first violent death I have ever seen, and it astonishes me to note how *unimportant* it seems. How little anybody cares—after all. If I had been told of his death—the details of it, in a story or in the form of fiction—it is easily conceivable that it would have impressed me more with its importance than the actual scene has done. Possibly my mental vision is scaled to a larger field since Friday, and as the greater issues loom up one man more or less seems to be but a unit—more or less—in an eternal series. When he was hit he swung back against the horse, still holding by the rein. His feet slid from under him, and he cried out, 'My *God!*' just once. We divided his cartridges between us and Idaho passed me his carbine. The barrel was scorching hot.

"They have drawn off a little and for fifteen minutes, though they still circle us slowly, there has been no firing. Forty cartridges left. Bunt's body (I think he is dead now) lies just back of me, and already the gnats—I can't speak of it.

[*Karslake evidently made the next few entries at successive intervals of time but neglected in his excitement to note the exact hour as above. We may gather that "They" made another attack and then repeated the assault so quickly that he had no chance to record it properly. I transcribe the entries in exactly the disjointed manner in which they occur in the original. The reference to the "fire" is unexplainable.*]

"I shall do my best to set down exactly what happens and what I do and think, and what I see.

"The heat-shimmer spoiled my aim, but I am quite sure that either

"This last rush was the nearest. I had started to say that though the heat-shimmer was bad, either Estorijo or myself wounded one of their ponies. We saw him stumble.

"Another rush—

"Our ammunition

"Only a few cartridges left.

"The Red One like a whirlwind only fifty yards away

"We fire separately now as they sneak up under cover of our smoke.

"We put the fire out. Estorijo— [*It is possible that Karslake had begun here to chronicle the death of the Mexican.*]

"I have killed the Spotted One. Just as he wheeled his horse I saw him in a line with the rifle sights and let him have it squarely. It took him straight in the breast. I could *feel* that shot strike. He went down like a sack of lead weights. By God, it was superb!

"Later.—They have drawn off out of range again, and we are allowed a breathing spell. Our ponies are either dead or dying, and we have dragged them around us to form a barricade. We lie on the ground behind the bodies and fire over them. There are twenty-seven cartridges left.

"It is now mid-afternoon. Our plan is to stand them off if we can till night and then to try an escape between them. But to what purpose? They would trail us so soon as it was light.

"We think now that they followed us without attacking for so long because they were waiting till the lay of the land suited them. They wanted—no doubt—an absolutely flat piece of country, with no depressions, no hills or streambeds in which we could hide, but which should be high upon the edges, like an amphitheatre. They would get us in the centre and occupy the rim themselves. Roughly, this is the bit of desert which witnesses our 'last stand.' On three sides the ground swells, a very little—the rise is not four feet. On the third side it is open, and so flat that even lying on the ground as we do we can see (leagues away) the San Jacinto hills—'from whence cometh no help.' It is all sand and sage, forever and forever. Even the sage is sparse—a bad place even for a coyote. The whole is flagellated with an intolerable heat and—now that the shooting is relaxed—oppressed with a benumbing, sodden silence—the silence of a primordial world. Such a silence as must have brooded over the Face of the Waters on the Eve of Creation—desolate, desolate, as though a colossal, invisible pillar—a pillar of the Infinitely Still, the Pillar of Nirvana—rose forever into the empty blue, human life an atom of microscopic dust crushed under its basis, and at the summit God Himself. And I find time to ask myself why, at this of all moments of my tiny life-span, I am able to write as I do, registering impressions, keeping a finger upon the pulse of the spirit. But oh! if I had time now—time to write down the great thoughts that do throng the brain. They are there, I feel them, know them. No doubt the supreme exaltation of approaching death is the stimulus that one never experiences in the humdrum business of the day-to-day existence. Such mighty thoughts! Unintelligible, but if I had time I could spell them out, *and how I could write then!* I feel that the whole secret of Life is within my reach; I can almost grasp it; I seem to feel that in just another instant I can see it all plainly, as the archangels see it all the time, as the great minds of the world, the great philosophers, have seen it once or twice, vaguely—a glimpse here and there, after years of patient study. Seeing thus I should be the equal of the gods. But it is not meant to be. There is sacrilege in it. I almost seem to understand why it is kept from us. But the very reason of this withholding is in itself a part of the secret. If I could only, only set it down!—for whose eyes? Those of a wandering hawk? God knows. But never mind. I should have spoken—once; should have said the great Word for which the World since the evening and the morning of the First Day has listened. God knows. God knows. What a whirl is this? Monstrous incongruity. Philosophy and fighting troopers. The Infinite and dead horses. There's humor for you. The Sublime takes off its hat to the Ridiculous. Send a cartridge clashing into the breech and speculate about the Absolute. Keep one eye on your sights and the other on Cosmos. Blow the reek of burned powder from before you so you may look over the edge of the abyss of the Great Primal Cause. Duck to the whistle of a bullet and commune with Schopenhauer. Perhaps I am a little mad. Perhaps I am supremely intelligent. But in either case I am not understandable to myself. How, then, be understandable to others? If these sheets of paper, this incoherence, is ever read, the others will understand it about as much as the investigating hawk. But none the less be it of record that I, Karslake, SAW. It reads like Revelations: 'I, John, saw.' It is just that. There is something apocalyptic in it all. I have seen a vision, but cannot—there is the pitch of anguish in the impotence—bear record. If time were allowed to order and arrange the words of description, this exaltation of spirit, in that very space of time, would relax, and the describer lapse back to the level of the average again before he could set down the things he saw, the things he thought. The machinery of the mind that could coin the great Word is automatic, and the very force that brings the die near the blank metal supplies the motor power of the reaction before the impression is made. . . . I stopped for an instant, looking up from the page, and at once the great vague Panorama faded. I lost it all. Cosmos has dwindled again to an amphitheatre of sage and sand, a vista of distant purple hills, the shimmer of scorching alkali, and in the middle distance there, those figures, blanketed, beaded, feathered, rifle in hand.

"But for a moment I stood on Patmos.

"The Ridiculous jostles the elbow of the Sublime and shoulders it from place as Idaho announces that he has found two more cartridges in Estorijo's pockets.

"They rushed again. Eight more cartridges gone. Twenty-one left. They rush in this manner—at first the circle, rapid beyond expression, one figure succeeding the other so swiftly that the dizzied vision loses count and instead of seven of them there appear to be seventy. Then suddenly, on some indistinguishable signal, they contract this circle, and through the jets of powder-smoke Idaho and I see them whirling past our rifle-sights not one hundred yards away. Then their fire suddenly slackens, the smoke drifts by, and we see them in the distance again, moving about us at a slow canter. Then the blessed breathing spell, while we peer out to know if we have killed or not, and count our cartridges. We have laid the twenty-one loaded shells that remain in a row between us, and after our first glance outward to see if any of them are down, our next is inward at that ever-shrinking line of brass and lead. We do not talk much. This is the end. We know it now. All of a sudden the conviction that I am to die here has hardened within me. It is, all at once, absurd that I should ever have supposed that I was to reach La Paz, take the east-bound train and report at San Antonio. It seems to me that I *knew*, weeks ago, that our trip was to end thus. I knew it—somehow—in Sonora last month, while we were waiting orders, and I tell myself that if I had only stopped to really think of it I could have foreseen the whole of to-day's bloody business.

"Later.—The Red One got off his horse and bound up the creature's leg. One of us hit him evidently. A little higher, it would have reached the heart. Our aim is ridiculously bad—the heat-shimmer—

"Later.—Idaho is wounded. This last time, for a moment, I was sure the end had come. They were within revolver range and we could feel the vibration of the ground under their ponies' hoofs. But suddenly they drew off. I have looked at my watch; it is four o'clock.

"Four o'clock—Idaho's wound is bad—a long, raking furrow in the right fore-arm. I bind it up for him, but he is losing a great deal of blood and is very weak.

"They seem to know that we are only two by now, for with each rush they grow bolder. The slackening of our fire must tell them how scant is our ammunition.

"Later.—This last was magnificent. The Red One and one other with lines of blue paint across his cheek galloped right at us. Idaho had been lying with his head and shoulders propped against the neck of his dead pony. His eyes were shut, and I thought he had fainted. But as he heard them coming he struggled up, first to his knees and then to his feet—to his full height—dragging his revolver from his hip with his left hand. The whole right arm swung useless. He was so weak that he could only lift the revolver half way—could not get the muzzle up. But though it sagged and dropped in his grip, he *would* die fighting. When he fired, the bullet threw up the sand not a yard from his feet, and then he fell on his face across the body of the horse. During the charge I fired as fast as I could, but evidently to no purpose. They must have thought that Idaho was dead, for so soon as they saw him getting to his feet they sheered their horses off and went by on either side of us. I have made Idaho comfortable. He is unconscious; have used the last of the water to give him a drink. He does not seem—

"They continue to circle us. Their fire is incessant, but very wild. So long as I keep my head down I am comparatively safe.

"Later.—I think Idaho is dying. It seems he was hit a second time when he stood up to fire. Estorijo is still breathing; I thought him dead long since.

"Four-ten.—Idaho gone. Twelve cartridges left. Am all alone now.

"Four twenty-five.—I am very weak. [*Karslake was evidently wounded sometime between ten and twenty-five minutes after four. His notes make no mention of the fact.*] Eight cartridges remain. I leave my library to my brother, Walter Patterson Karslake; all my personal effects to my parents, except the picture of myself taken in Baltimore in 1897, which I direct to be [*the next lines are undecipherable*] . . . at Washington, D. C., as soon as possible. I appoint as my literary

"Four forty-five.—Seven cartridges. Very weak and unable to move lower part of my body. Am in no pain. They rode in very close. The Red One is— An intolerable thirst—

"I appoint as my literary executor my brother, Patterson Karslake. The notes on 'Coronado in New Mexico' should be revised.

"My death occurred in Western Arizona, April fifteenth, at the hands of a roving band of Hunt-in-the-Morning's bucks. They have—

"Five o'clock.—The last cartridge gone.

"Estorijo still breathing. I cover his face with my hat. Their fire is incessant. Am much weaker. Convey news of death to Patterson Karslake, care of Corn Exchange Bank, New York City.

"Five-fifteen — about. — They have ceased firing, and draw together in a bunch. I have four cartridges left [*see conflicting note dated five o'clock*], but am extremely weak. Idaho was the best friend I had in all the Southwest. I wish it to be known that he was a generous, openhearted fellow, a kindly man, clean of speech, and absolutely unselfish. He may be known as follows: Sandy beard, long sandy hair, scar on forehead, about six feet one inch in height. His real name is James Monroe Herndon; his profession that of government scout. Notify Mrs. Herndon, Trinidad, New Mexico.

"The writer is Arthur Staples Karslake,

dark hair, height five feet eleven, body will be found near that of Herndon.

"Luis Estorijo, Mexican—

"Later.—Two more cartridges.

"Five-thirty.—Estorijo dead.

"It is half-past five in the afternoon of April fifteenth. They followed us from the eleventh—Friday—till to-day. It will

[*The MS. ends here.*]

Mr. Dooley Guesses About Women

Finley Peter Dunne

Out of Chicago near the turn of the Century came the newspaperman Finley Peter Dunne and his brain-child, Martin Dooley. Dunne wrote sharp, straight-faced editorials for Collier's, *but it was Mr. Dooley—modeled from a Chicago bartender and editorializing from that unique vantage point—who carried himself and his maker to lasting fame. Dunne died in 1936, but Mr. Dooley lives on and on as the source of needle-sharp Gaelic quotes about almost everything.*

February 28, 1903

"I HAVE TO TALK ABOUT WOMEN," SAID Mr. Dooley. "Do ye know annything about thim?"

"Nawthin'," said Mr. Hennessy. "I've been livin' with wan so long that she looks like me, but she's as much iv a gamble to me now as she iver was. I know what she'll do. She'll do what I tell her to do if she plazes. But I can niver more thin guess what she's thinkin' about."

"Well," said Mr. Dooley, "women is sthrange crathers. I niver pretinded to larn thim. I can tell be th' cut iv a man's coat or his whiskers, be th' way he walks, be his attichood at th' bar, be a light wurrud spoke in jest or a heavy wurrud in anger, be a glance at th' side iv his face as he passes a lookin'-glass, what kind iv a man he is. Wan thing I'll always bet on—he ain't much diff'rent fr'm any other man. If I want to get a line on what he'd do in case iv fire, I ask mesilf what I wud do in case iv fire. I, mesilf, am ivry man. Barrin' iddycation an' th' business we're in, th' King iv England, th' Impror iv Russhya, Kaiser Wilhelm th' Busy, Teddy Rosenfelt, J. Pierpont Morgan, th' Prince iv Siam an' Martin Dooley is all out iv th' same peck measure. If I know mesilf, I know thim all. King, czar, potintate, doctor, lawyer, merchant, thief, rich man, poor man, beggar man, congressman—they're all me with betther or worse clothes. They'se a kind iv a Martin Dooley down shootin' bears an' coons in th' swamps iv Mississippi; they'se another cockin' up his heels at Windsor Castle; they'se a Martin Dooley iv some sort on ivry throne iv Europe, an' ivry ash heap in Canal Shtreet. I don't say all men ar-re brothers. All men are ME. Th' little tape line that I use f'r mesilf is long enough an' acc'rate enough to measure anny man in th' wurruld, an' if it happens that I'm ladlin' out red impeeryalism at tin cints th' glass instead iv breakin' stone at Joliet or frinds in Wall Shtreet, it's because I started th' way I did.

"But whin it comes to sizin' up th' ladies,

Gawd bless thim an' tache thim their places, I hang up th' rule, th' compass an' th' tape line, an' go be guess an' be luck. In dalin' with women a man mus' play entirely be ear. They'se a good manny men that'll tell ye they know all about thim. Almost anny young unmarrid man between eighteen an' twinty-wan cud map a woman out f'r ye as plain as State Shtreet. He has her mind an' her sowl charted an' he takes a squint at th' north star, f'r he wud disdain to steer be annything less, sets his coorse, ties down th' tiller an' goes to sleep. He wakes up in th' roarin' forties wrecked on an iceberg.

"See young Terence Riordan comin' out iv th' front dure iv Callahan's house with his chin in th' air an' his hat cocked over his ear. Is there annything about women that he don't know, from Claypathry to Carrie Nation? Divvle th' thing. He's taken his degree. Women is mental arithmetic f'r him. He does sums about thim in his head. All ye have to do to win a woman, says Terence Riordan, is to look like Terence Riordan. As f'r Ellen Callahan that he's keepin' comp'ny with among others, he's got her intelleck figured out to decimals. He knows ivrything about her except th' wan thing I see fr'm me window, that whin gallant Terence Riordan wint out through th' front dure steppin' high, Ellen Callahan wint out th' back dure to meet Larry Hannigan an' go to a moonlight excursion.

"Bimeby Terence will marry her, f'r she has him nailed to th' flure now, not be her own charms but be his fine opinyon iv himself. Whin I see thim together an' he's lookin' into thim eyes iv hers that say so much an' mane so diff'rent, I know he's thinkin': 'I can read ivry thought in her mind. She's thinkin' how gr-reat I am an' how good, what a handsome head iv hair I have, how that mole alongside me nose sets off me vivid complexion. Her thrust an' confidence in me is ra-aly sad. Th' poor, little mis'rable thing, I must reward her with me distinguished s'ciety f'r life.' An' manetime down in her heart is th' moonlight excursion an' th' pitcher iv Hannigan with no job but a mandolin. Terence'll niver find it. Whin he gets to be forty he'll suspict it, whin he gets to be fifty he'll quit thryin' to find out, an' whin he gets to be sixty he'll wish he'd had th' mandolin an' Hannighan th' job. Wise is he who says: 'I on'y know yisterdah. I must look out to-morrah.' Whin he's young it's simple, whin he's middle-aged it's a problem an' whin he's old, he's solved it a thousan' times in a thousan' diff'rent ways an' still he don't know th' answer.

"It's forty year since I see ye dancin' a hornpipe at ye'er weddin'. F'r forty year ye've been studyin' th' charackter iv th' lady iv ye'er choice, an' her own. How manny times d'ye put down th' pa-aper an' look acrost th' table an' say: 'Who's that sthrange, quare woman acrost fr'm me? I call her Mrs. Hinnissy, but who th' divvle is she? What do I know about her or her about me?' They'se thirty inches iv oilcloth between ye an' eighty million miles an' I don't know how many years iv diff'rence. Ye know about as much iv her as ye know iv th' sun. Ye know whin she gets up in th' mornin' an' whin she sinks to rest at night. An' thin again, p'raps ye don't. An' she knows less about ye. Over her knittin' needles she's sayin': 'I wondher who me frind is, th' ol'la-ad with th' naked head an' th' neck like a plumber's file. He's a sthrange crather. He's got a logical mind. He can tell at a glance where a ca'ar is goin' to, he always faces for'ard whin he gets off th' platform, he ain't afraid iv mice, cows or ghosts. What sort iv iddycated pig is he?'

"Some time arly in his life ivry man writes a book entitled 'All there is to know about women in wan volume, thirteen pages, includin' a biography an' pitchers iv th' author.' Afther a while he puts in wan iv thim little tags that always goes at th' end iv a book iv acc'rate information: 'E-eratum: In th' foregoin' volume, on pages wan to tin, f'r "is" read "is not," an' f'r "is not" read "is." On th' other pages wheriver "is" or "is not" appears, substichoot "maybe" or "p'raps" or "th' Lord on'y knows." ' Whin a man tells ye that he knows about women, don't ast him anny questions in th' higher mathymatics iv th' fair sect. Ast him how a woman sticks a hat-pin into her head without killin' hersilf, why she always smoothes her dhress down whin she stand in front iv a fire, an' why she on'y ates whin there ar-re men ar-round. A woman will load in ivrything in sight if a kind an' manly eye is watchin' her wurruk, but whin she's with other women she takes a cup iv tay an' a pickle. Why is it? If th' expert don't know that, how can he expict us to believe he knows about th' gr-reater things? If he don't know addition, how can he know compound fractions?

"It's th' same with th' gr-reatest an' th' laste iv us. Th' more we know iv men, th' less we know iv th' conthrary sect. Take that ol' boy Socrates that Hogan talks about. There was a man that was as wise as a mountain or an ol' elephant. He knew more thin I think I know. Men wint hundherds iv miles to hear him talk. He ladled out wisdom an' information be th' bucketful to wan an' all. He niver tur-rned a sthranger fr'm th' dure without givin' him a full meal iv knowledge. But whin it come to handlin' an ordhinry, plain wife or termygant, as th' wurrud is in Greek, he cud get pints fr'm a bridge tinder. He had such a tough game iv it that whin th' authorities suggested that th' dhrinks was on th' state, he dhrained his cup iv pizen with a wink iv th' eye an' said: 'Don't be sorry f'r me, boys, I'm not going home to-night.'

"I guess about thim. I guess they don't live in th' same wurruld as men. It seems to be th' same wurruld but it ain't th' same at all. It's a wurruld where all th' clocks ar-re wrong an' where they'se no such thing as distance. It's peopled with ghosts, dhressmakers an' princes. Th' other day I r-read in th' pa-aper that a German prince has advertised f'r an American girl, white preferred, who wud be willin' to exchange three millyon dollars f'r th' opporchunity to bear th' proud but thirsty name iv Prince Otto Finkelstein Zum Rathskeller, an' later on ye'll see that Prince Otto, who is known among his frinds as Fink, has borrowed a coat an' come over on a tank steamer to wed wan iv Cincinnati's fairest belles. Why does she do it? There ar-re plinty iv American men around who wud take her in spite iv the money. To show that they loved her for hersilf alone they'd agree to spind the fortune in a year. Anny wan iv thim cud tell her that Prince Otto is on'y a German afther all. In th' happy home life at Rathskeller he laves th' prince part iv his nature out iv dures if it isn't hung up at a pawnshop, an' is plain Otto who loves noodles in a thick soup and uses a pocket comb on his whiskers afther dinner.

"But she don't see it that way. They ain't annything in th' books she's read that teaches her that th' object iv a fair young American heiress' life is to be led up to th' big jump be th' champeen prune preserver iv th' wurruld. I stand by th' American man. He's a fine fellow. He may be short iv wurruk on polite convarsation, but he can shoe a horse. As a mannyfacthrer iv soap, bottles, hair-ile, steel billets an' spring matthresses he has th' effete Europeen away to th' bad. He has circled th' globe with canned meat an' in faroff Ind, as the sayin' goes, his pitcher is on th' labels iv th' talcum powdher an' th' pork an' beans ready to eat. How is it possible that anny wan cud prefer a decayin' sign iv nobility who wuddn't know th' diff'rence between short rib sides an' number two hard winter wheat? Alonzo Blinks is a good man. At the daily meetin' in the quick-lunch room he's th' life iv th' party. If his pants bags at th' knee, he has a heart iv oak. If a glance at his boot gives ye at wanst an outline map iv his big toe, he can figure out interest in his head. Sthrange that such an int'lectual light shud not be able to put th' fortune iv th' fair wan into his business.

"But I guess th' fact is that Alonzo has niver got himsilf into th' fair wan's coorse iv readin'. He's devoted his life to makin' himsilf th' hayro iv Dun an' Bradsthreet, but thim two gran' wurruks iv modhren chivalree an' romance have niver been taken out iv th' Dope Lovers' Libry be Gladys. Whin he was exhibitin' his charms to Dun an' Bradsthreet he wud have been betther employed if he'd thried to stand in with the author iv 'Whin Knighthood wus in Flower.' All her happy little life Gladys has been thryin' to cash in a fairy dhream an' here it comes. She marries a man who can get on a horse without chloryformin' it, an' be Hivins, Hinnissy, I'm not so sure she's iver as sorry f'r it as I wud be if I was makin' a Foorth of July oration. She'll find out in time that th' on'y coort he's familyar with is th' polis coort, that th' ancesthral mansion is th' county jail an' Prince Otto's father th' Gran' Jook runs a bus line f'r a hotel. Th' on'y raison he didn't hook up in Germany was because he was rayfused be th' daughter iv a butcher that he cheated in a horse thrade. But Gladys will niver be ra-aly sorry. She'll niver come to as long as thy'se wan iv her counthrywomen without a title on th' face iv Europe. She'll soon be through with Otto, who will nobly dhrink himsilf to death, but at eighty-five she'll be expictin' another prince to come around an' fit a glass slipper on her fut. An' she'd expect it if th' entire output iv the glass wurruks iv Pittsburg was rayquired f'r th' shoe. F'r ivry free-bor-rn American lady, Hinnissy, is a bor-rn aristocrat to her finger tips. She don't want to be th' akel iv anny man. Nature niver intended her f'r th' grocery business. She bends on'y to a king or a pauper. She is th' mos' loyal subjick in the wurruld, an' th' best nurse. If Alonzo Blinks knew his business he'd ayether call on her with a gilt crown on his head or break his leg on th' fron dure step. In ayether case he'd stand a chance.

"Is there wan law f'r men an' another f'r women? says the lady who had bad luck in a play I wanst see. No, sir. They'se wan law f'r men an' no law f'r women. Th' laws ar-re made be men, f'r men, who ar-re taught to think in sthraight lines, while a woman thinks ar-round a corner and over the tops iv houses. Don't lave us tache thim anny iv th' foolish things we've got to know. They don't believe in idees, theries or argymint. They believe in persons. If th' baldheaded Columbus showed thim be his chart an' log that he'd discovered America they'd say: 'I don't believe that odjous man iver discovered annything.' But if Padarooski tol' thim he did they'd belive it without a doubt. Women will stand by a murdhrer or a safe-blower not because they don't think he done it but because crime ain't a crime whin it's committed be th' right party. Facts ain't annything to thim; they regard argymint as an old worn out way iv gettin' annywhere, like an engineer wud look at a stage coach. They don't believe in figures or, at laste, in other people's figures. Don't argye with thim. Ye can't convince thim iv annything onless ye hol' their hands. Take thim firmly be th' fingers an' tell thim what ye want thim to believe. P'raps they'll say: 'He has nice hair. He must be right.' "

"Well," said Mr. Hennessy, "f'r a man that don't know annything about th' subjick ye've had a good dale to say."

"Th' raison I've said so much," replied Mr. Dooley, "is that I know so little. Be Hivins, whin I think iv how little I know I'm surprised at me own modhration."

Mr. Dooley on the White House Expense Account

April 14, 1908

"I SEE BE TH' PA-APERS," SAID MR. DOOLEY, "that me frind Tiddy Rosenfelt is in throuble."

"What's th' matther?" asked Mr. Hennessy. "Has he been run over be a thrust?"

"No," said Mr. Dooley. "He's been vilatin' th' principle iv dimmycratic simplicity an' has turned in an expinse account that may cost him his job. I don't blame th' poor lad. He didn't know anny betther. But he'd ought to've ast some wan. Almost annybody in Wash'nton cud have tol' him th' thraditions iv Jeffersonyan simplicity. Ye see, Hinnissy, in th' beginnin' George Wash'nton wasn't very simple. Whin he wint up to th' White House he rode in a goold coach and was followed be wan thousan' naygurs in uniform. If George had had his way he'd 've started in as king an' wurruked up fr'm that. But whin Thomas Jefferson come in he played th' other end iv th' game. He rode up to th' White House on a horse an' hitched th' horse to a post in front an' wint in an' kicked a hole in a plush sofy left be George Wash'nton. 'Where will we stable ye'er horse, ye'er majisty?' ast wan iv th' sarvants. 'In th' house,' said Thomas Jefferson. 'Anny place that is good enough f'r me is good enough f'r me horse,' he says. 'An',' he says, 'call me Tom hereafther,' he says, 'ye varlet,' he says. So iver afther th' prisidint rode up to th' White House on a horse till it come to Grover Cleveland's time, whin th' horses sthruck an' he wint up in a carredge.

"Up to this day ivry prisidint in th' White House has lived as become his station, that is, Hinnissy, very badly. Foreign noblemen long unaccustomed to lookin' upon th' currant wine whin it was red within th' cup come out iv th' White House with their hands on their stomach. Th' first lady iv th' land cut th' hair iv th' first childher iv th' land with her own fair hands an' th' first gintleman in th' land was often to be seen wurrukin' th' wringer on Mondahs. They wasn't a man howiver humble that wint to th' White House an' didn't feel at home or worse. They was a corjal welcome f'r wan an' all in that hospitable mansion. But whin Teddy Rosenfelt come in he changed all that. Th' first thing he done was to make over th' White House. Up to his time th' White House was a place where anny gintleman cud live but wudden't if there was a hotel handy. But it wasn't good enough f'r this jood. He changed it around, this mansion full iv th' best thraditions of our governmint an' ivry other kind of thraditions, this sacred ol' hen-coop where a cinchry iv statesmen had come an' gone—he changed it round to suit th' idees iv archytecture in New York. He put th' coal cellar on th' roof, th' kitchen in th' threasury departmint an' arranged it so that guests enthered through th' laundhry an' proceeded up through th' ash chute to a pint where they was picked up be an autymatic disthributor and disthributed—th' leg in the east room, th' ar-rms in th' west room, an' so on. Before he wint at it th' White House looked like a handsome calcimined packin' case with windows cut in f'r Gin'ral Miles to lave by. Afther this jood prisidint got through with it it looked as though th' packin' case had taken Tiddy's advice an' raised a large fam'ly iv soap boxes, tea caddies an' little ice chests. In this palace he lives like a king an' onaisy lies th' head that wears a crown.

"But that ain't th' worst iv it. Whin he got to Wash'nton he found that this counthry had become a wurruld power. Th' difference between a wurruld power an' an ordhinry back-yard power is that it costs money to be a wurruld power. If ye're jus' a power ye can take ye'er meals in ye'er shirt sleeves, but if ye're a wurruld power ye have to take ye'er bath in a swallow-tail coat. Th' prisidint iv th' United States cud lock th' dure at sivin' o'clock, pull off his coat, sind wan iv th' childher f'r his slippers an' go to sleep in front iv th' fire with th' avnin' paper over his head. Not so th' prisidint iv a wurruld power. He spinds th' day appintin' eighth-class fourth-class postmasthers, shakin' hands with naygurs, annihilatin' th' thrusts again an' again, settlin' affairs in Vinzwala, Macydonya, Bolgahrya an' Chiny. At sivin o'clock he goes to th' dure with Epaminondas Guff (colored) an' thin hurries to his room where he hurls himsilf into th' new uniform iv th' prisidint iv th' United States, a dhress suit. He has hardly time to get th' soap out iv his ears whin th' dure bell rings an' he runs down th' stairs to rayceive th' ambassadure fr'm Cochin Chiny. D'ye know what wud happen if he wasn't on th' dure mat ready to take th' ambassadure fr'm Cochin Chiny be th' ear with wan hand an' rub th' top iv his head with th' other, which is th' officyal for-rm iv salutation in Cochin Chiny? Ye don't? Well, I'll tell ye. It wud mane WAR, Hinnissy. Grogan, who was a good deal in Wash'nton in Finerty's day, tells me that this counthry was wanst on th' very verge iv war with Pattygonya because Grover Cleveland butted th' ambassadure from Pattygonya in th' stomach, mistakin' him f'r th' ambassadure fr'm Beloochystan. As it is there ar-re twinty-four thrained assistant sicrities iv state, disguised as waithers to tip off to th' prisidint how to rayceive th' ambassadures. Each iv these here handicappers knows to a pinnyweight how many guns each ambassadure carries an' it's well 'tis so, f'r I cudden't tell ye how horrible it wud be if th' ambassadure fr'm Rooshya got to th' vittles befure th' ambasandure fr'm England.

Las' year be mistake th' wife iv th' Turkish ambassadure enthered th' room out iv her turn. They were put out be th' waither but not in time to prevint th' allied powers fr'm bombardin' Constantinople.

"So it is at dinner. In th' ol' days befure we was a wurruld power ivrybody come up in a bunch an' set down in a hurry. It was: 'Pass th' butther,' 'Let me give ye a chunk iv th' dark meat,' 'Lo Hing Fang, can't I help ye to th' part that wint over th' fence las'?' 'I'll thank ye, ma'am, f'r another cup iv tay,' 'Won't ye thry a bit iv this leg?' 'No, thanks, I've quite a sufficiency,' an' so on. But now no wan talks excipt in his odrher. First, th' prisidint, thin th' ambassadure fr'm Rooshya, thin all th' wives iv all th' ambassadures at wanst, an' so on down th' right an' up th' left. It's no use hurlin' plain American food at these ambassadures an' hopin' it will take. Th' las' time th' presidint give a dish iv buckwheat cakes to th' British ambassadure he rose fr'm th' table an' cried in ringin' tones: 'It is needless to inform ye that this is war.' Th' raysult was th' Vinzwalan throuble. No, sir, no johnny cake f'r these proud souls. In front iv each ambassadure mus' be placed th' typical naytional dish: a box iv candles an' a glass iv sulphuric acid f'r th' Rooshyan, a veal an' ham pie an' a small ninety-pound loaf iv English bread f'r th' Englishman, two live chickens an' a shark's fin f'r th' Chinnyman, a mud pie f'r th' Pattgonyan, an' so on.

"All this takes money, Hinnissy, an' where does it come fr'm? Out iv my pocket an' ye'er's, me boy. It's you an' me that's payin' f'r this here oryental splindhor. I'm with th' la-ad that got up in Congress th' other day an' give it to him good. 'Fellow mimbers,' he says, 'th' time has come whin we mus' decide whether this nation founded be Wash'nton, Lincoln an' U. S. Grant shall go on as it was or some other way which I blush to repeat. Gintlemen,' he says, 'in th' White House there is a man who if we nominate him victhry will perch—excuse me, I mane there is a man in th' White House who is rapidly turnin' this counthry into an oryental dispotism,' he says. 'Th' dhreams iv Zum Zallam, th' Pershan prince, could not akel th' splindhor iv th' magnificint palace which rears its rear toward th' monymint to th' matchless Wash'nton. Here he lives in a state iv luxury that baffles description although I must say th' archytecture is rocky. Where ar-re our thraditions? Where th' Jeffersonyan simplicity iv th' arly days iv th' raypublic? I hold in me hand a docymint that must appal ivry lover iv his counthry. It is an expinse account fr'm th' White House. I will not r-read th' sickenin' details, but I will recite a few iv th' monsthrous items. Gas fixtures, eight dollars! Clanin' an' repairin' house afther the rayciption to Congress, thirty dollars! Soap, eighteen dollars! Soap eighteen dollars. Need I say more? Need I go on? Gintlemen, I see th' las' bulwark swept fr'm beneath th' feet iv dimmycratic govermint an' tumblin' on its devoted head. I see all this vast edifice or fabric iv our nation's pride disappear as at th' touch iv a wizard's hand. As in a dhream, I behold wan be wan th' monymints to th' heroes iv th' past crumblin' into dust an' in their place rise th' pomp iv kings an' th' hoarse cries iv clangin' retinooes. Gintlemen, th' dice is cast. Th' doom iv dimmocracy is writ in thim three wurruds: Soap, eighteen dollars! Soap, eighteen dollars. Eighteen dollars f'r soap! Ere another ides—what d'ye say, boy? A tillyphone fr'm th' White House? What time d'ye say? Eight o'clock? Tell Misther Corteloo I'll be there at a quarther past five. As I was sayin', gintlemen, th' doom iv th' ol' ordher is sealed. I regret it but p'raps 'tis f'r th' best. We have become a gr-reat wurruld power an' nawthin' is too good f'r us. If th' chief exicutive impulsively wants to mop himsilf ivry day let us charge it as a fault iv th' heart rather thin th' head. It ill becomes us as a nation to intercept our chief magistrate at th' threshold iv th' bath room an' with a feigned sincerity bid him go thus fur an' no further. I move we give him what he wants. I will now ask th' attintion iv th' house to th' bill appropriatin' ninety-three millyon dollars toward widenin', deepenin', enlargin', discoverin', irrigatin' an' otherwise improvin' Milkweed River or Creek, that flighty mud or, I should say, mighty flood that surges down or will surge down with a little help to meet th' haughty Slew, watherin' or manin' to, th' fer-tile plans, th' smilin' valleys, th' frownin' mountain peaks, th' wavin' cor-rn fields, th' little school houses, th' graves where lie our honored tombstones an' th' conthractors of my congressyonal disthrict.' "

"What d'ye raly think iv it?" asked Mr. Hennessy.

"I ra-aly think this," said Mr. Dooley, "that annybody who don't expict to be prisidint ought to fight to make th' prisidint live on fourteen dollars a month. But bein' that I'm lookin' forward to th' day whin th' foolish Constitution will be changed so that a good American who happened to be bor-rn in th' County Roscommon will be illegible f'r prisidint, I'd like to be sure that there were a few hams in th' cellar."

"It's conthry to Jeffersonyan simplicity," said Mr. Hennessy.

"I believe in Jeffersonyan simplicity," said Mr. Dooley, "but I don't want to be a Jeffersonyan simpleton."

The Adventure of the Dancing Men

A. Conan Doyle

Sir Arthur Conan Doyle (1859-1930) was a serious historical novelist as well as the creator of Sherlock Holmes, the most famous detective ever to spring from pen of man. But the names Doyle and Holmes became indivisible in the public mind—so much so that when Doyle, in a kind of despair, finally sent Holmes hurtling to certain death in the abyss of Reichenbach Fall, he couldn't keep him dead for long. Revived in a new series for Collier's *called* "The Return of Sherlock Holmes," *the detective plunged into a new cycle of adventures that continued to the eve of World War I. This is one of the first stories of the "Return" series.*

December 5, 1903

Holmes had been seated for some hours in silence with his long, thin back curved over a chemical vessel in which he was brewing a particularly malodorous product. His head was sunk upon his breast, and he looked from my point of view like a strange, lank bird, with dull gray plumage and a black top-knot.

"So, Watson," said he suddenly, "you do not propose to invest in South African securities?"

I gave a start of astonishment. Accustomed as I was to Holmes's curious faculties, this sudden intrusion into my most intimate thoughts was utterly inexplicable.

"How on earth do you know that?" I asked.

He wheeled round upon his stool with a steaming test-tube in his hand, and a gleam of amusement in his deep-set eyes.

"Now, Watson, confess yourself utterly taken aback," said he.

"I am."

"I ought to make you sign a paper to that effect."

"Why?"

"Because in five minutes you will say that it is all so absurdly simple."

"I am sure that I shall say nothing of the kind."

"You see, my dear Watson"—he propped his test-tube in the rack and began to lecture with the air of a professor addressing his class—"it is not really difficult to construct a series of inferences, each dependent upon its predecessor and each simple in itself. If, after doing so one simply knocks out all the central inferences and presents one's audience with the starting-point and the conclusion, one may produce a startling, though possibly a meretricious, effect. Now, it was not really difficult, by an inspection of the groove between your left forefinger and thumb, to feel sure that you did *not* propose to invest your small capital in the gold fields."

"I see no connection."

"Very likely not; but I can quickly show you a close connection. Here are the missing links of the very simple chain: 1. You had chalk between your left finger and thumb when you returned from the club last night. 2. You put chalk there when you play billiards to steady the cue. 3. You never play billiards except with Thurston. 4. You told me four weeks ago that Thurston had an option on some South African property which would expire in a month, and which he desired you to share with him. 5. Your checkbook is locked in my drawer, and you have not asked for the key. 6. You do not propose to invest your money in this manner."

"How absurdly simple!" I cried.

"Quite so!" said he, a little nettled. "Every problem becomes very childish when once it is explained to you. Here is an unexplained one. See what you can make of that, friend Watson." He tossed a sheet of paper upon the table and turned once more to his chemical analysis.

I looked with amazement at the absurd hieroglyphics upon the paper.

"Why, Holmes, it is a child's drawing," I cried.

"Oh, that's your idea!"

"What else should it be?"

"That is what Mr. Hilton Cubitt of Ridling Thorpe Manor, Norfolk, is very anxious to know. This little conundrum came by the first post, and he was to follow by the next train. There's a ring at the bell, Watson. I should not be very much surprised if this were he."

A heavy step was heard upon the stairs, and an instant later there entered a tall, ruddy, clean-shaven gentleman, whose clear eyes and florid cheeks told of a life led far from the fogs of Baker Street. He seemed to bring a whiff of his strong, fresh, bracing, east-coast air with him as he entered. Having shaken hands with each of us, he was about to sit down when his eye rested upon the paper with the curious markings, which I had just examined and left upon the table.

"Well, Mr. Holmes, what do you make of these?" he cried. "They told me that you were fond of queer mysteries, and I don't think you can find a queerer one than that. I sent the paper on ahead so that you might have time to study it before I came."

"It is certainly rather a curious production," said Holmes. "At first sight it would appear to be some childish prank. It consists of a number of absurd little figures dancing across the paper upon which they are drawn. Why should you attribute any importance to so grotesque an object?"

"I never should, Mr. Holmes. But my wife does. It is frightening her to death. She says nothing, but I can see terror in her eyes. That's why I want to sift the matter to the bottom."

Holmes held up the paper so that the sunlight shone full upon it. It was a page torn from a notebook. The markings were done in pencil, and ran in this way:

Holmes examined it for some time, and then, folding it carefully up, he placed it in his pocketbook.

"This promises to be a most interesting and unusual case," said he. "You gave me a few particulars in your letter, Mr. Hilton Cubitt, but I should be very much obliged if you would kindly go over it all again for the benefit of my friend, Dr. Watson."

"I'm not much of a story-teller," said our visitor, nervously clasping and unclasping his great strong hands. "You'll just ask me anything that I don't make clear. I'll begin at the time of my marriage last year; but I want to say first of all that, though I'm not a rich man, my people have been at Ridling Thorpe for a matter of five centuries, and there is no better-known family in the County of Norfolk. Last year I came up to London for the Jubilee, and I stopped at a boarding-house in Russell Square, because Parker, the vicar of our parish, was staying in it. There was an American young lady there—Patrick was the name—Elsie Patrick. In some way we became friends, until before my month was up I was as much in love as a man could be. We were quietly married at a registry office, and we returned to Norfolk a wedded couple. You'll think it very mad, Mr. Holmes, that a man of a good old family should marry a wife in this fashion, knowing nothing of her past or of her people; but if you saw her and knew her it would help you to understand.

"She was very straight about it, was Elsie. I can't say that she did not give me every chance of getting out of it if I wished to do so. 'I have had some very disagreeable associations in my life,' said she: 'I wish to forget all about them. I would rather never allude to the past, for it is very painful to me. If you take me, John, you will take a woman who has nothing that she need be personally ashamed of; but you will have to be content with my word for it, and to allow me to be silent as to all that passed up to the time when I became yours. If these conditions are too hard, then go back to Norfolk and leave me to the lonely life in which you found me.' It was only the day before our wedding that she said those very words to me. I told her that I was content to take her on her own terms, and I have been as good as my word.

"Well, we have been married now for a year, and very happy we have been. But about a month ago, at the end of June, I saw for the first time signs of trouble. One day my wife received a letter from America. I saw the American stamp. She turned deadly white, read the letter, and threw it into the fire. She made no allusion to it afterward, and I made none, for a promise is a promise; but she has never known an easy hour from that moment. There is always a look of fear upon her face—a look as if she were waiting and expecting. She would do better to trust me. She would find that I was her best friend. But until she speaks I can say nothing. Mind you, she is a truthful woman, Mr. Holmes, and whatever trouble there may have been in her past life it has been no fault of hers. I am only a simple Norfolk squire, but there is not a man in England who ranks his family honor more highly than I do. She knows it well, and she knew it well before she married me. She would never bring any stain upon it—of that I am sure.

"Well, now I come to the queer part of my story. About a week ago—it was the Tuesday of last week—I found on one of the window-sills a number of absurd little dancing figures, like these upon the paper. They were scrawled with chalk. I thought that it was the stable-boy who had drawn them, but the lad swore he knew nothing about it. Anyhow, they had come there during the night. I had them washed out, and I only mentioned the matter to my wife afterward. To my surprise she took it very seriously, and begged me if any more came to let her see them. None did come for a week, and then yesterday morning I found this paper lying on the sundial in the garden. I showed it to Elsie, and down she dropped in a dead faint. Since then she has looked like a woman in a dream, half dazed, and with terror always lurking in her eyes. It was then that I wrote and sent the paper to you, Mr. Holmes. It was not a thing that I could take to the police, for they would have laughed at me, but you will tell me what to do. I am not a rich man; but if there is any danger threatening my little woman I would spend my last copper to shield her."

He was a fine creature, this man of the old English soil, simple, straight, and gentle, with his great, earnest blue eyes and broad, comely face. His love for his wife and his trust in her shone in his features. Holmes had listened to his story with the utmost attention, and now he sat for some time in silent thought.

"Don't you think, Mr. Cubitt," said he, at last, "that your best plan would be to make a direct appeal to your wife, and to ask her to share her secret with you?"

Hilton Cubitt shook his massive head.

"A promise is a promise, Mr. Holmes. If Elsie wished to tell me she would. If not, it is not for me to force her confidence. But I am justified in taking my own line—and I will."

"Then I will help you with all my heart. In the first place, have you heard of any strangers being seen in your neighborhood?"

"No."

"I presume that it is a very quiet place. Any fresh face would cause comment?"

"In the immediate neighborhood, yes. But we have several small watering-places not very far away. And the farmers take in lodgers."

"These hieroglyphics have evidently a meaning. If it is a purely arbitrary one it may be impossible for us to solve it. If, on the other hand, it is systematic, I have no doubt that we shall get to the bottom of it. But this particular sample is so short that I can do nothing, and the facts which you have brought me are so indefinite that we have no basis for an investigation. I would suggest that you return to Norfolk, that you keep a keen lookout, and that you take an exact copy of any fresh dancing men which may appear. It is a thousand pities that we have not a reproduction of those which were done in chalk upon the window-sill. Make a discreet inquiry also as to any strangers in the neighborhood. When you have collected some fresh evidence come to me again. That is the best advice which I can give you, Mr. Hilton Cubitt. If there are any pressing fresh developments I shall be always ready to run down and see you in your Norfolk home."

The interview left Sherlock Holmes very thoughtful, and several times in the next few days I saw him take his slip of paper from his notebook and look long and earnestly at the curious figures inscribed upon it. He made no allusion to the affair, however, until one afternoon a fortnight or so later. I was going out when he called me back.

"You had better stay here, Watson."

"Why?"

"Because I had a wire from Hilton Cubitt this morning—you remember Hilton Cubitt, of the dancing men? He was to reach Liverpool Street at one-twenty. He may be here at any moment. I gather from his wire that there have been some new incidents of importance."

We had not long to wait, for our Norfolk squire came straight from the station as fast as a hansom could bring him. He was looking worried and depressed, with tired eyes and a lined forehead.

"It's getting on my nerves, this business, Mr. Holmes," said he, as he sank, like a wearied man, into an armchair. "It's bad enough to feel that you are surrounded by unseen, unknown folk, who have some kind of design upon you; but when, in addition to that, you know that it is just killing your wife by inches, then it becomes as much as flesh and blood can endure. She's wearing away under it—just wearing away before my eyes."

"Has she said anything yet?"

"No, Mr. Holmes, she has not. And yet there have been times when the poor girl has wanted to speak, and yet could not quite bring herself to take the plunge. I have tried to help her; but I dare say I did it clumsily, and scared her off from it. She has spoken about my old family, and our reputation in the country, and our pride in our unsullied honor, and I always felt it was leading to the point; but somehow it turned off before we got there."

"But you have found out something for yourself?"

"A good deal, Mr. Holmes. I have several fresh dancing-men pictures for you to examine, and, what is more important, I have seen the fellow."

"What, the man who draws them?"

"Yes, I saw him at his work. But I will tell you everything in order. When I got back after my visit to you, the very first thing I saw next morning was a fresh crop of dancing men. They had been drawn in chalk upon the black wooden door of the tool-house, which stands beside the lawn in full view of the front windows. I took an exact copy, and here it is." He unfolded a paper and laid it upon the table. Here is a copy of the hieroglyphics:

"Excellent!" said Holmes. "Excellent! Pray continue."

"When I had taken the copy I rubbed out the marks: but two mornings later a fresh inscription had appeared. I have a copy of it here."

Holmes rubbed his hands and chuckled with delight.

"Our material is rapidly accumulating," said he.

"Three days later a message was left scrawled upon paper, and placed under a pebble upon the sundial. Here it is. The characters are, as you see, exactly the same as the last one. After that I determined to lie in wait; so I got out my revolver and I sat up in my study, which overlooks the lawn and garden. About two in the morning I was seated by the window, all being dark save for the moonlight outside, when I heard steps behind me, and there was my wife in her dressing-gown. She implored me to come to bed. I told her frankly that I wished to see who it was who played such absurd tricks upon us. She answered that it was some senseless practical joke, and that I should not take any notice of it.

" 'If it really annoys you, John, we might go and travel, you and I, and so avoid this nuisance.'

" 'What, be driven out of our own house by a practical joker?' said I. 'Why, we should have the whole county laughing at us.'

"'Well, come to bed,' said she, 'and we can discuss it in the morning.'

"Suddenly, as she spoke, I saw her white face grow whiter yet in the moonlight, and her hand tightened upon my shoulder. Something was moving in the shadow of the tool-house. I saw a dark, creeping figure which crawled round the corner and squatted in front of the door. Seizing my pistol I was rushing out, when my wife threw her arms round me and held me with convulsive strength. I tried to throw her off, but she clung to me most desperately. At last I got clear, but by the time I had opened the door and reached the house the creature was gone. He had left a trace of his presence, however, for there on the door was the very same arrangement of dancing men which had already twice appeared, and which I have copied on that paper. There was no other sign of the fellow anywhere, though I ran all over the grounds. And yet the amazing thing is that he must have been there all the time, for when I examined the door again in the morning he had scrawled some more of his pictures under the line which I had already seen."

"Have you that fresh drawing?"

"Yes; it is very short, but I made a copy of it, and here it is."

Again he produced a paper. The new dance was in this form:

"Tell me," said Holmes—and I could see by his eyes that he was much excited—"was this a mere addition to the first, or did it appear to be entirely separate?"

"It was on a different panel of the door."

"Excellent! This is far the most important of all for our purpose. It fills me with hopes. Now, Mr. Hilton Cubitt, please continue your most interesting statement."

"I have nothing more to say, Mr. Holmes, except that I was angry with my wife that night for having held me back when I might have caught the skulking rascal. She said that she feared I might come to harm. For an instant it had crossed my mind that perhaps what she really feared was that *he* might come to harm, for I could not doubt that she knew who this man was and what he meant by these strange signals. But there is a tone in my wife's voice, Mr. Holmes, and a look in her eyes which forbid doubt, and I am sure that it was indeed my own safety that was in her mind. There's the whole case, and now I want your advice as to what I ought to do. My own inclination is to put half-a-dozen of my farm lads in the shrubbery, and when this fellow comes again to give him such a hiding that he will leave us in peace for the future."

"I fear it is too deep a case for such simple remedies," said Holmes. "How long can you stay in London?"

"I must go back to-day. I would not leave my wife alone at night for anything. She is very nervous and begged me to come back."

"I dare say you are right. But if you could have stopped I might possibly have been able to return with you in a day or two. Meanwhile you will leave me these papers, and I think it is very likely that I shall be able to pay you a visit shortly and to throw some light upon your case."

Sherlock Holmes preserved his calm professional manner until our visitor had left us, although it was easy for me, who knew him so well, to see that he was profoundly excited. The moment that Hilton Cubitt's broad back had disappeared through the door my comrade rushed to the table, laid out all the slips of paper containing dancing men in front of him, and threw himself into an intricate and elaborate calculation.

For two hours I watched him as he covered sheet after sheet of paper with figures and letters, so completely absorbed in his task that he had evidently forgotten my presence. Sometimes he was making progress and whistled and sang at his work; sometimes he was puzzled, and would sit for long spells with a furrowed brow and a vacant eye. Finally he sprang from his chair with a cry of satisfaction, and walked up and down the room rubbing his hands together. Then he wrote a long telegram upon a cable form. "If my answer to this is as I hope, you will have a very pretty case to add to your collection, Watson," said he. "I expect that we shall be able to go down to Norfolk tomorrow, and to take our friend some very definite news as to the secret of his annoyance."

I confess that I was filled with curiosity, but I was aware that Holmes liked to make his disclosures at his own time and in his own way; so I waited until it should suit him to take me into his confidence.

But there was a delay in that answering telegram, and two days of impatience followed, during which Holmes pricked up his ears at every ring of the bell. On the evening of the second there came a letter from Hilton Cubitt. All was quiet with him, save that a long inscription had appeared that morning upon the pedestal of the sundial. He inclosed a copy of it, which is here reproduced:

Holmes bent over this grotesque frieze for some minutes, and then suddenly sprang to his feet with an exclamation of surprise and dismay. His face was haggard with anxiety.

"We have let this affair go far enough," said he. "Is there a train to North Walsham to-night?"

I turned up the time-table. The last had just gone.

"Then we shall breakfast early and take the very first in the morning," said Holmes. "Our presence is most urgently needed. Ah! here is our expected cablegram. One moment, Mrs. Hudson; there may be an answer. No, that is quite as I expected. This message makes it even more essential that we should not lose an hour in letting Hilton Cubitt know how matters stand, for it is a singular and a dangerous web in which our simple Norfolk squire is entangled."

So, indeed, it proved, and as I come to the dark conclusion of a story which had seemed to me to be only childish and bizarre, I experience once again the dismay and horror with which I was filled. Would that I had some brighter ending to communicate to my readers, but these are the chronicles of fact, and I must follow to their dark crisis the strange chain of events which for some days made Ridling Thorpe Manor a household word through the length and breadth of England.

We had hardly alighted at North Walsham and mentioned the name of our destination when the station-master hurried toward us.

"I suppose that you are the detectives from London?" said he.

A look of annoyance passed over Holmes's face.

"What makes you think such a thing?"

"Because Inspector Martin from Norwich has just passed through. But maybe you are the surgeons. She's not dead—or wasn't by last accounts. You may be in time to save her yet—though it be for the gallows."

Holmes's brow was dark with anxiety.

"We are going to Ridling Thorpe Manor," said he, "but we have heard nothing of what has passed there."

"It's a terrible business," said the stationmaster. "They are shot, both Mr. Hilton Cubitt and his wife. She shot him and then herself—so the servants say. He's dead and her life is despaired of. Dear, dear, one of the oldest families in the County of Norfolk, and one of the most honored."

Without a word Holmes hurried to a carriage, and during the long seven miles' drive he never opened his mouth. Seldom have I seen him so utterly despondent. He had been uneasy during all our journey from town, and I had observed that he had turned over the morning papers with anxious attention; but now this sudden realization of his worst fears left him in a blank melancholy. He leaned back in his seat, lost in gloomy speculation.

Yet there was much around us to interest us, for we were passing through as singular a countryside as any in England, where a few scattered cottages represented the population of to-day, while on every hand enormous square-towered churches bristled up from the flat, green landscape and told of the glory and prosperity of old East Anglia. At last the violet rim of the German Ocean appeared over the green edge of the Norfolk coast, and the driver pointed with his whip to two old brick and timber gables which projected from a grove of trees. "That's Ridling Thorpe Manor," said he.

As we drove up to the porticoed front door I observed in front of it, beside the tennis lawn, the black tool-house and the pedestalled sundial with which we had such strange associations. A dapper little man, with a quick, alert manner and a waxed mustache, had just descended from a high dogcart. He introduced himself as Inspector Martin of the Norfolk Constabulary, and he was considerably astonished when he heard the name of my companion.

"Why, Mr. Holmes, the crime was only committed at three this morning. How could you hear of it in London and get to the spot as soon as I?"

"I anticipated it. I came in the hope of preventing it."

"Then you must have important evidence of which we are ignorant, for they were said to be a most united couple."

"I have only the evidence of the dancing men," said Holmes. "I will explain the matter to you later. Meanwhile, since it is too late to prevent this tragedy, I am very anxious that I should use the knowledge which I possess in order to ensure that justice be done. Will you associate me in your investigation, or will you prefer that I should act independently?"

"I should be proud to feel that we were acting together, Mr. Holmes," said the inspector earnestly.

"In that case I should be glad to hear the evidence and to examine the premises without an instant of unnecessary delay."

Inspector Martin had the good sense to allow my friend to do things in his own fashion, and contented himself with carefully noting the results. The local surgeon, an old, white-haired man, had just come down from Mrs. Hilton Cubitt's room, and he reported that her injuries were serious, but not necessarily fatal. The bullet had passed through the front of her brain, and it would probably be some time before she could regain consciousness. On the question of whether she had been shot or had shot herself he would not venture to express any decided opinion. Certainly the bullet had been discharged at very close quarters. There was only the one pistol found in the room, two barrels of which had been emptied. Mr. Hilton Cubitt had been shot through the heart. It was equally conceivable that he had shot her and then himself, or that she had been the criminal, for the revolver lay upon the floor midway between them.

"Has he been moved?" asked Holmes.

"We have moved nothing except the lady. We could not leave her lying wounded upon the floor."

"How long have you been here, doctor?"

"Since four o'clock."

"Any one else?"

"Yes, the constable here."

"And you have touched nothing?"

"Nothing."

"You have acted with great discretion. Who sent for you?"

"The housemaid, Saunders."

"Was it she who gave the alarm?"

"She and Mrs. King, the cook."

"Where are they now?"

"In the kitchen, I believe."

"Then I think we had better hear their story at once."

The old hall, oak-panelled and high-windowed, had been turned into a court of investigation. Holmes sat in a great, old-fashioned chair, his inexorable eyes gleaming out of his haggard face. I could read in them a set purpose to devote his life to this quest until the client whom he had failed to save should at last be avenged. The trim Inspector Martin, the old, gray-headed country doctor, myself, and a stolid village policeman made up the rest of that strange company.

The two women told their story clearly enough. They had been aroused from their sleep by the sound of an explosion, which had been followed a minute later by a second one. They slept in adjoining rooms, and Mrs. King had rushed in to Saunders. Together they had descended the stairs. The door of the study was open and a candle was burning upon the table. Their master lay upon his face in the centre of the room. He was quite dead. Near the window his wife was crouching, her head leaning against the wall. She was horribly wounded, and the side of her face was red with blood. She breathed heavily, but was incapable of saying anything. The passage, as well as the room, was full of smoke and the smell of powder. The window was certainly shut and fastened upon the inside. Both women were positive upon the point. They had at once sent for the doctor and for the constable. Then, with the aid of the groom and the stable-boy, they had conveyed their injured mistress to her room. Both she and her husband had occupied the bed. She was clad in her dress—he in his dressing-gown, over his night clothes. Nothing had been moved in the study. So far as they knew there had never been any quarrel between husband and wife. They had always looked upon them as a very united couple.

These were the main points of the servants' evidence. In answer to Inspector Martin, they were clear that every door was fastened upon the inside, and that no one could have escaped from the house. In answer to Holmes, they both remembered that they were conscious of the smell of powder from the moment that they ran out of their rooms upon the top floor. "I commend that fact very carefully to your attention," said Holmes to his professional colleague. "And now I think that we are in a position to undertake a thorough examination of the room."

The study proved to be a small chamber, lined on three sides with books, and with a writing-table facing an ordinary window, which looked out upon the garden. Our first attention was given to the body of the unfortunate squire, whose huge frame lay stretched across the room. His disordered dress showed that he had been hastily aroused from sleep. The bullet had been fired at him from the front, and had remained in his body after penetrating the heart. His death had certainly been instantaneous and painless. There was no powder-marking either upon his dressing-gown or on his hands. According to the country surgeon, the lady had stains upon her face, but none upon her hand.

"The absence of the latter means nothing, though its presence may mean everything," said Holmes. "Unless the powder from a badly fitting cartridge happens to spurt backward, one may fire many shots without leaving a sign. I would suggest that Mr. Cubitt's body may now be removed. I suppose, doctor, you have not recovered the bullet which wounded the lady?"

"A serious operation will be necessary before that can be done. But there are still four cartridges in the revolver. Two have been fired and two wounds inflicted, so that each bullet can be accounted for."

"So it would seem," said Holmes. "Perhaps you can account also for the bullet which has so obviously struck the edge of the window?"

He had turned suddenly, and his long, thin finger was pointing to a hole which had been drilled right through the lower window-sash about an inch above the bottom.

"By George!" cried the inspector. "How ever did you see that?"

"Because I looked for it."

"Wonderful!" said the country doctor. "You are certainly right, sir. Then a third shot has been fired, and therefore a third person must have been present. But who could that have been and how could he have got away?"

"That is the problem which we are now about to solve," said Sherlock Holmes. "You remember, Inspector Martin, that when the servants said that on leaving their rooms they were at once conscious of a smell of powder, I remarked that the point was an extremely important one?"

"Yes, sir; but I confess I did not quite follow you."

"It suggested that at the time of the firing the window as well as the door of the room had been open. Otherwise the fumes of powder could not have been blown so rapidly through the house. A draught in the room was necessary for that. Both door and window were only open for a very short time, however."

"How do you prove that?"

"Because the candle has not guttered."

"Capital!" cried the inspector. "Capital!"

"Feeling sure that the window had been open at the time of the tragedy, I conceived that there might have been a third person in the affair, who stood outside this opening and fired through it. Any shot directed at this person might hit the sash. I looked, and there, sure enough, was the bullet mark!"

"But how came the window to be shut and fastened?"

"The woman's first instinct would be to

shut and fasten the window. But, halloa! what is this?"

It was a lady's hand-bag which stood upon the study table—a trim little hand-bag of crocodile-skin and silver. Holmes opened it and turned the contents out. There were twenty fifty-pound notes of the Bank of England, held together by an india-rubber band—nothing else.

"This must be preserved, for it will figure in the trial," said Holmes, as he handed the bag with its contents to the inspector. "It is now necessary that we should try to throw some light upon this third bullet, which has clearly, from the splintering of the wood, been fired from inside the room. I should like to see Mrs. King, the cook, again.

"You said, Mrs. King, that you were awakened by a *loud* explosion. When you said that, did you mean that it seemed to you to be louder than the second one?"

"Well, sir, it wakened me from my sleep, and so it is hard to judge. But it did seem very loud."

"You don't think that it might have been two shots fired almost at the same instant?"

"I am sure I couldn't say, sir."

"I believe that it was undoubtedly so. I rather think, Inspector Martin, that we have now exhausted all that this room can teach us. If you will kindly step round with me, we shall see what fresh evidence the garden has to offer."

A flower-bed extended up to the study window, and we all broke into an exclamation as we approached it. The flowers were trampled down, and the soft soil was imprinted all over with footmarks. Large, masculine feet they were, with peculiarly long, sharp toes. Holmes hunted about among the grass and leaves like a retriever after a wounded bird. Then, with a cry of satisfaction, he bent forward and picked up a little brazen cylinder.

"I thought so," said he; "the revolver had an ejector, and here is the third cartridge. I really think, Inspector Martin, that our case is almost complete."

The country inspector's face had shown his intense amazement at the rapid and masterful progress of Holmes's investigation. At first he had shown some disposition to assert his own position; but now he was overcome with admiration and ready to follow without question wherever Holmes led.

"Whom do you suspect?" he asked.

"I'll go into that later. There are several points in this problem which I have not been able to explain to you yet. Now that I have got so far I had best proceed on my own lines, and then clear the whole matter up once and for all."

"Just as you wish, Mr. Holmes, so long as we get our man."

"I have no desire to make mysteries, but it is impossible at the moment of action to enter into long and complex explanations. I have the threads of this affair all in my hand. Even if this lady should never recover consciousness, we can still reconstruct the events of last night and ensure that justice be done. First of all I wish to know whether there is any inn in this neighborhood known as 'Elrige's'?"

The servants were cross-questioned, but none of them had heard of such a place. The stable-boy threw a light upon the matter by remembering that a farmer of that name lived some miles off in the direction of East Ruston.

"Is it a lonely farm?"

"Very lonely, sir."

"Perhaps they have not heard yet of all that happened here during the night?"

"Maybe not, sir."

Holmes thought for a little and then a curious smile played over his face.

"Saddle a horse, my lad," said he. "I shall wish you to take a note to Elrige's Farm."

He took from his pocket the various slips of the dancing men. With these in front of him he worked for some time at the study-table. Finally he handed a note to the boy, with directions to put it into the hands of the person to whom it was addressed, and especially to answer no questions of any sort which might be put to him. I saw the outside of the note, addressed in straggling, irregular characters, very unlike Holmes's usual precise hand. It was consigned to Mr. Abe Slaney, Elrige's Farm, East Ruston, Norfolk.

"I think, inspector," Holmes remarked, "that you would do well to telegraph for an escort, as, if my calculations prove to be correct, you may have a particularly dangerous prisoner to convey to the county jail. The boy who takes this note could no doubt forward your telegram. If there is an afternoon train to town, Watson, I think we should do well to take it, as I have a chemical analysis of some interest to finish, and this investigation draws rapidly to a close."

When the youth had been despatched with the note, Sherlock Holmes gave his instructions to the servants. If any visitor were to call asking for Mrs. Hilton Cubitt no information should be given as to her condition, but he was to be shown at once into the drawing-room. He impressed these points upon them with the utmost earnestness. Finally he led the way into the drawing-room with the remark that the business was now out of our hands, and that we must while away the time as best we might until we could see what was in store for us. The doctor had departed to his patients, and only the inspector and myself remained.

"I think that I can help you to pass an hour in an interesting and profitable manner," said Holmes, drawing his chair up to the table, and spreading out in front of him the various papers upon which were recorded the antics of the dancing men. "As to you, friend Watson, I owe you every atonement for having allowed your natural curiosity to remain so long unsatisfied. To you, inspector, the whole incident may appeal as a remarkable professional study. I must tell you first of all the interesting circumstances connected with the previous consultations which Mr. Hilton Cubitt has had with me in Baker Street." He then shortly recapitulated the facts which have already been recorded. "I have here in front of me these singular productions, at which one might smile had they not proved themselves to be the forerunners of so terrible a tragedy. I am fairly familiar with all forms of secret writings, and am myself the author of a trifling monograph upon the subject, in which I analyze one hundred and sixty separate ciphers; but I confess that this is entirely new to me. The object of those who invented the system has apparently been to conceal that these characters convey a message, and to give the idea that they are the mere random sketches of children.

"Having once recognized, however, that the symbols stood for letters, and having applied the rules, which guide us in all forms of secret writings, the solution was easy enough. The first message submitted to me was so short that it was impossible for me to do more than to say with some confidence that the symbol stood for

E. As you are aware, E is the most common letter in the English alphabet, and it predominates to so marked an extent that even in a short sentence one would expect to find it most often. Out of fifteen symbols in the first message four were the same, so it was reasonable to set this down as E. It is true that in some cases the figure was bearing a flag, and in some cases not, but it was probable from the way in which the flags were distributed that they were used to break the sentence up into words. I accepted this as a hypothesis, and noted as standing for E.

"But now came the real difficulty of the inquiry. The order of the English letters after E is by no means well marked, and any preponderance which may be shown in an average of a printed sheet may be reversed in a single short sentence. Speaking roughly, T, A, O, I, N, S, H, R, D, and L is the numerical order in which letters occur; but T, A, O, and I are very nearly abreast of each other, and it would be an endless task to try each combination until a meaning was arrived at. I therefore waited for fresh material. In my second interview with Mr. Hilton Cubitt he was able to give me two other short sentences and one message, which appeared—since there was no flag—to be a single word. Here are the symbols. Now, in the single word I have already got the two E's coming second and fourth in a word of five letters. It might be 'sever,' or 'lever,' or 'never.' There can be no question that the latter as a reply to an appeal is far the most probable, and the circumstances pointed to its being a reply written by the lady. Accepting it as correct, we are now able to say that the symbols stand respectively for N, V, and R.

"Even now I was in considerable difficulty, but a happy thought put me in possession of several other letters. It occurred to me that if these appeals came, as I expected, from someone who had been intimate with the lady in her early life, a combination which contained two E's with three letters between might very well stand for the name 'ELSIE.' On examination I found that such a combination formed the termination of the message, which was three times repeated. It was certainly some appeal to Elsie. In this way I had got my L, S, and I. But what appeal could it be? There were only four letters in the word which preceded 'Elsie,' and it ended in E. Surely the word must be 'COME.' I tried all other four letters ending in E, but could find none to fit the case. So now I was in possession of C, O, and M, and I was in a position to attach the first message once more, dividing it into words and putting dots for each symbol which was still unknown. So treated, it worked out in this fashion:

.M .ERE . . E SL . NE .

Now the first letter *can* only be A, which is a most useful discovery, since it occurs no fewer than three times in this short sentence, and the H is also apparent in the second word. Now it becomes:

AM HERE A . E SLANE .

Or, filling in the obvious vacancies in the name:

AM HERE ABE SLANEY.

I had so many letters now that I could proceed with considerable confidence to the second message, which worked out in this fashion:

A . ELRI . ES.

Here I could only make sense by putting T and G for the missing letters, and supposing that the name was that of some house or inn at which the writer was staying."

Inspector Martin and I had listened with the utmost interest to the full and clear account of how my friend had produced results which had led to so complete a command over our difficulties.

"What did you do then, sir?" asked the inspector.

"I had every reason to suppose that this Abe Slaney was an American, since Abe is an American contraction, and since a letter from America had been the starting-point of all the trouble. I had also every cause to think that there was some criminal secret in the matter. The lady's allusions to her past and her refusal to take her husband into her confidence both pointed in that direction. I therefore cabled to my friend, Wilson Hargreave, of the New York Police Bureau, who has more than once made use of my knowledge of London crime. I asked him whether the name of Abe Slaney was known to him. Here is his reply: 'The most dangerous crook in Chicago.' On the very evening upon which I had his answer Hilton Cubitt sent me the last message from Slaney. Working with known letters it took this form:

ELSIE . RE . ARE TO MEET THY GO.

The addition of a P and a D completed a message which showed me that the rascal was proceeding from persuasion to threats, and my knowledge of the crooks of Chicago prepared me to find that he might very rapidly put his words into action. I at once came to Norfolk with my friend and colleague, Dr. Watson, but, unhappily, only in time to find that the worst had already occurred."

"It is a privilege to be associated with you in the handling of a case," said the inspector warmly. "You will excuse me, however, if I speak frankly to you. You are only answerable to yourself, but I have to answer to my superiors. If this Abe Slaney, living at Elrige's, is indeed the murderer, and if he has made his escape while I am seated here, I should certainly get into serious trouble."

"You need not be uneasy. He will not try to escape."

"How do you know?"

"To fly would be a confession of guilt."

"Then let us go to arrest him."

"I expect him here every instant."

"But why should he come?"

"Because I have written and asked him."

"But this is incredible, Mr. Holmes! Why should he come because you have asked him? Would not such a request rather rouse his suspicions and cause him to fly?"

"I think I have known how to frame the letter," said Sherlock Holmes. "In fact, if I am not very much mistaken, here is the gentleman himself coming up the drive."

A man was striding up the path which led to the door. He was a tall, handsome, swarthy fellow, with a Panama hat, a bristling black beard, and a great, aggressive hooked nose, clad in a suit of gray flannel, and flourishing a cane as he walked. He swaggered up the path as if the place belonged to him, and we heard his loud, confident peal at the bell.

"I think, gentlemen," said Holmes quietly, "that we had best take up our position behind the door. Every precaution is necessary when dealing with such a fellow. You will need your handcuffs, inspector. You can leave the talking to me."

We waited in silence for a minute—one of those minutes which one can never forget. Then the door opened and the man stepped in. In an instant Holmes clapped a pistol to his head and Martin slipped the handcuffs over his wrists. It was all done so swiftly and deftly that the fellow was helpless before he knew that he was attacked. He glared from one to the other of us with a pair of blazing black eyes. Then he burst into a bitter laugh.

"Well, gentlemen, you have the drop on me this time. I seem to have knocked up against something hard. But I came here in answer to a letter from Mrs. Hilton Cubitt. Don't tell me that she is in this? Don't tell me that she helped to set a trap for me?"

"Mrs. Hilton Cubitt was seriously injured and is at death's door."

The man gave a hoarse cry of grief which rang through the house.

"You're crazy!" he cried fiercely. "It was he that was hurt, not she. Who would have hurt little Elsie? I may have threatened her, God forgive me, but I would not have touched a hair of her pretty head. Take it back—you! Say that she is not hurt!"

"She was found badly wounded by the side of her dead husband."

He sank with a deep groan on to the settee and buried his face in his manacled hands. For five minutes he was silent. Then he raised his face once more, and spoke with the cold composure of despair.

"I have nothing to hide from you, gentlemen," said he. "If I shot the man he had his shot at me, and there's no murder in that. But if you think I could have hurt that woman, then you don't know either me or her. I tell you there was never a man in this world loved a woman more than I loved her. I had a right to her. She was pledged to me years ago. Who was this Englishman that he should come between us? I tell you that I had the first right to her, and that I was only claiming my own."

"She broke away from your influence when she found the man that you are," said Holmes sternly. "She fled from America to avoid you, and she married an honorable gentleman in England. You dogged her and followed her and made her life a misery to her in order to induce her to abandon the husband whom she loved and respected in order to fly with you, whom she feared and hated. You have ended by bringing about the death of a noble man and driving his wife to suicide. That is your record in this business, Mr. Abe Slaney, and you will answer for it to the law."

"If Elsie dies I care nothing what becomes of me," said the American. He opened one of his hands and looked at a note crumpled up in his palm. "See here, mister," he cried, with a gleam of suspicion in his eyes, "you're not trying to scare me over this, are you? If the lady is hurt as bad as you say, who was it that wrote this note?" He tossed it forward on to the table.

"I wrote it to bring you here."

"You wrote it? There was no one on earth outside the Joint who knew the secret of the dancing men. How came you to write it?"

"What one man can invent another can discover," said Holmes. "There is a cab coming to convey you to Norwich, Mr. Slaney. But, meanwhile, you have time to make some small reparation for the injury you have wrought. Are you aware that Mrs. Hilton Cubitt has herself lain under grave suspicion of the murder of her husband, and that it was only my presence here and the knowledge which I happened to possess which has saved her from the accusation? The least that you owe her is to make it clear to the whole world that she was in no way, directly or indirectly, responsible for his tragic end."

"I ask nothing better," said the American. "I guess the very best case I can make for myself is the absolute naked truth."

"It is my duty to warn you that it will be used against you," cried the inspector, with the magnificent fair-play of the British criminal law.

Slaney shrugged his shoulders.

"I'll chance that," said he. "First of all, I want you gentlemen to understand that I have known this lady since she was a child. There were seven of us in a gang in Chicago, and Elsie's father was the boss of the Joint. He was a clever man, was old Patrick. It was he who invented that writing, which would pass as a child's scrawl unless you just happened to have the key to it. Well, Elsie learned some of our ways; but she couldn't stand the business, and she had a bit of honest money of her own, so she gave us all the slip and got away to London. She had been engaged to me, and she would have married me, I believe, if I had taken over another profession; but she would have nothing to do with anything on the cross. It was only after her marriage to this Englishman that I was able to find out where she was. I wrote to her, but got no answer. After that I came over, and, as letters were no use, I put my messages where she could read them.

"Well, I have been here a month now. I lived in that farm, where I had a room down below, and could get in and out every night, and no one the wiser. I tried all I could to coax Elsie away. I knew that she read the messages, for once she wrote an answer under one of them. Then my temper got the better of me, and I began to threaten her. She sent me a letter then, imploring me to go away and saying that it would break her heart if any scandal should come upon her husband. She said that she would come down when her husband was asleep at three in the morning, and speak with me through the end window, if I would go away afterward and leave her in peace. She came down and brought money with her, trying to bribe me to go. This made me mad, and I caught her arm and tried to pull her through the window. At that moment in rushed the husband with his revolver in his hand. Elsie had sunk down upon the floor, and we were face to face. I was heeled also, and I held up my gun to scare him off and let me get away. He fired and missed me. I pulled off almost at the same instant, and down he dropped. I made away across the garden, and as I went I heard the window shut behind me. That's God's truth, gentlemen, every word of it, and I heard no more about it until that lad came riding up with a note which made me walk in here, like a jay, and give myself into your hands."

A cab had driven up while the American had been talking. Two uniformed policemen sat inside. Inspector Martin rose and touched his prisoner on the shoulder.

"It is time for us to go."

"Can I see her first?"

"No, she is not conscious. Mr. Sherlock Holmes, I only hope that if ever again I have an important case I shall have the good fortune to have you by my side."

We stood at the window and watched the cab drive away. As I turned back my eye caught the pellet of paper which the prisoner had tossed upon the table. It was the note with which Holmes had decoyed him.

"See if you can read it, Watson," said he with a smile.

It contained no word, but this little line of dancing men:

"If you use the code which I have explained," said Holmes, "you will find that it simply means, 'Come here at once.' I was convinced that it was an invitation which he would not refuse, since he could never imagine that it could come from any one but the lady. And so, my dear Watson, we have ended by turning the dancing men to good when they have so often been the agents of evil, and I think that I have fulfilled my promise of giving you something unusual for your notebook. Three-forty is our train, and I fancy we should be back in Baker Street for dinner."

. . . .

Only one word of epilogue. The American, Abe Slaney, was condemned to death at the winter assizes at Norwich; but his penalty was changed to penal servitude in consideration of mitigating circumstances, and the certainty that Hilton Cubitt had fired the first shot. Of Mrs. Hilton Cubitt I only know that I have heard that she recovered entirely, and that she still remains a widow, devoting her whole life to the care of the poor and to the administration of her husband's estate.

A Presidential Epigram

F. A. Emery

A phrase that has since become a permanent part of the American language came into being in 1903. Here's how it happened.

December 26, 1903

THERE IS A NEW SLOGAN IN THE POLICY of the Administration. President Roosevelt has used it twice, at Evanston, Illinois, a year or two ago, and again during his trip through the West last spring. Now it has appeared again in the form of a placard posted at the entrance to the private office of "Tama Jim" Wilson, the Secretary of Agriculture. It is not original with the President, however, at is was handed down from the race of hardy Scotchmen whose blood flows in Secretary Wilson's veins. This is the watchword, printed in bold type and conspicuously posted by Secretary Wilson's direction:

"Speak softly, carry a big stick and you will go far in a day."—Theodore Roosevelt.

The Original of Sherlock Holmes

Dr. Harold Emery Jones

Sir Arthur Conan Doyle has, himself, named Dr. Joseph Bell, consulting surgeon at the Royal infirmary, Edinburgh, as the original model of that fictional master of deduction, Mr. Sherlock Holmes. Here a fellow medical student of Doyle's describes the surgeon whose imaginary counterpart outlived his own fame.

January 9, 1904

When it was known that Dr. Conan Doyle had decided on bringing Sherlock Holmes back to the land of the living, a number of his admirers were fearful lest the author wreck his own reputation and destroy the interesting and unique character of Sherlock Holmes, by attempting what was seemingly an impossibility or, at any rate, an absurdity. Conan Doyle's friends, however, had supreme confidence in his ability to revivify Sherlock Holmes in an artistic and natural manner. After "The Adventure of the Empty House," admirers and friends could not but exclaim in unison: "How simple! How plausible! How clever!"

The great mystery, which has as yet never been cleared up, is whether Holmes ever really existed. Is Holmes merely the creation of Doyle's ingenious brain? Or is there really an individual who is the living embodiment of Sherlock Holmes?

Conan Doyle is essentially an Edinburgh product. He was born there. His medical studies were pursued in that ancient city of medical lore. His father was a well-known artist. He himself was the nephew of the famous Dicky Doyle, and his grandfather was the celebrated caricaturist John Doyle, known to the public as H. B. So the author had, to say the least, a heritage of promise. His first literary venture was as editor of a school magazine in Germany, where he was sent to receive his early education. Prior to that he had attended a private school in England. Leaving Germany, he returned to Edinburgh, where he entered the university for the purpose of studying medicine.

To a man of Doyle's alertness, memory, and imagination, this training was invaluable. It was in the infirmary wards at Edinburgh, in the dispensaries, and in the out-patient department that he first encountered that subtle and wonderful character who is now world-renowned, the original of the great detective, Sherlock Holmes.

All Edinburgh medical students remembered Joseph Bell—Joe Bell—as they called him. Always alert, always up and doing, nothing ever escaped that keen eye of his. He read both patients and students like so many open books. His diagnosis was almost never at fault.

One would never dream, by looking through "Who's Who" (in England), that the person described as follows is the original of the great detective, Sherlock Holmes:

"Joseph Bell, M.D., F.R.C.S., Edinburgh; consulting Surgeon to the Royal Infirmary and Royal Hospital for Sick Children. Member of University Court, Edinburgh University; born in Edinburgh in the year 1837. The eldest son of Benjamin Bell, Surgeon, and of Cecilia Craigie. Married to Edith Katherine, daughter of the Honorable James Erskine Murray. Went through the ordinary course of a Hospital Surgeon at Edinburgh Royal Infirmary, from Dresser to Senior Surgeon and Consulting Surgeon. Twenty-three years (1873-96) editor of the 'Edinburgh Medical Journal.' "

Yet he is the original Sherlock Holmes —the Edinburgh medical students' ideal— who could tell patients their habits, their occupations, nationality, and often their names, and who rarely, if ever, made a mistake. Oftentimes he would call upon one of the students to diagnose the cases for him. Telling the House Surgeon to usher in a new patient, he delighted in putting the deductive powers of the student to the test, with results generally amusing, except to the poor student victim himself.

This is Conan Doyle's description of Joseph Bell: "He would sit in the patients' waiting-room, with a face like a Red Indian, and diagnose the people as they came in, before even they opened their mouths. He would tell them their symptoms, and would even give them details of their past life, and he would hardly ever make a mistake."

What Edinburgh student of Conan Doyle's student years can fail to recognize in the stoic-faced professor, Joe Bell, the "king of deduction"?

"What is the matter with this man, sir?" he suddenly inquired of a trembling student. "Come down, sir, and look at him! No! You mustn't touch him. Use your eyes, sir! Use your ears, use your brain, your bump of perception, and use your powers of deduction."

After looking at the patient, the embryonic Holmes blurted out: "Hip-joint disease, sir!"

"Hip-nothing!" Bell retorted. "The man's limp is not from his hip, but from his foot, or rather from his feet. Were you to observe closely, you would see that there are slits, cut by a knife, in those parts of the shoes where the pressure of the shoe is greatest against the foot. The man is a sufferer from corns, gentlemen, and has no hip trouble at all. He has not come here to be treated for corns, gentlemen. We are not chiropodists. His trouble is of a much more serious nature. This is a case of chronic alcoholism, gentlemen. The rubicund nose, the puffed, bloated face, the bloodshot eyes, the tremulous hands and twitching face muscles, with the quick, pulsating temporal arteries, all show this. These deductions, gentlemen, must, however, be confirmed by absolute and concrete evidence. In this instance my diagnosis is confirmed by the fact of my seeing the neck of a whiskey-bottle protruding from the patient's right-hand coat pocket.

"From close observation and deduction, gentlemen, you can make a correct diagnosis of any and every case. However, never neglect to ratify your deductions, to substantiate your diagnosis with the stethoscope, and by other recognized and every-day methods of diagnosis."

Of another patient he would say: "Gentlemen, we have here a man who is either a cork-cutter or a slater. If you will only use your eyes a moment you will be able to define a slight hardening—a regular callous, gentlemen—on one side of his forefinger, and a thickening on the outside of his thumb, a sure sign that he follows the one occupation or the other."

Or again: "Gentlemen, a fisherman! You will notice that, though this is a very hot summer's day, the patient is wearing top-boots. When he sat on the chair they were plainly visible. No one but a sailor would wear top-boots at this season of the year. The shade of tan on his face shows him to be a coast-sailor, and not a deep-sea sailor—a sailor who makes foreign lands. His tan is that produced by one climate, a 'local tan,' so to speak. A knife scabbard shows beneath his coat, the kind used by fishermen in this part of the world. He is concealing a quid of tobacco in the furthest corner of his mouth and manages it very adroitly indeed, gentlemen. The summary of these deductions shows that this man is a fisherman. Further, to prove the correctness of these deductions, I notice several fishscales adhering to his clothes and hands, while the odor of fish announced his arrival in a most marked and striking manner."

On one occasion he called upon a student to diagnose a case. The student made a miserable failure of it.

"Get out your notebook, man," said Bell, "and see whether you can't express your thoughts that way." Then, turning to the class, the Professor continued: "The gentleman has ears and he hears not, eyes and he sees not! You come from Wales, don't you, sir?"—again turning to the poor victim—"I thought so! A man who says 'silling' for shilling, who rattles his R's, who has a peculiar, rough, broad accent like yours, sir, is not a Scotchman. You are not an Irishman! You are not an Englishman! Your speech 'smacks of Wales.' And to clinch the matter, gentlemen"—once more addressing the class—"when I asked Mr. Edward Jones—that is his name, gentlemen—to transfer his thoughts to paper, he nervously pulled out his notebook, and, to his chagrin, with it a letter. Mr. Jones endeavored to palm the letter, gentlemen; but he is evidently a little out of training at present, as he blundered most beautifully. The postmark shows that the letter was posted yesterday morning at Cardiff. The address was written by a female—undoubtedly Mr. Jones's sweetheart—for the very sight of it caused our friend to blush furiously. It was addressed to Mr. Edward Jones! Now, gentlemen! Cardiff is in South Wales, and the name Jones proclaims our friend a Welshman."

According to Doyle, Bell's faculty of deduction was at times highly dramatic. "Ah," he would say to one of the patients, "you are a soldier, and a non-commissioned officer at that. You have served in Bermuda. Now how do I know that, gentlemen? Because he came into the room without even taking his hat off, as he would go into an orderly room. He was a soldier. A slight, authoritative air, combined with his age, shows that he was a non-commissioned officer. A rash on his forehead tells me he was in Bermuda and subject to a certain rash known only there."

Bell was as full of dry humor and satire, and he was as jealous of his reputation, as the detective Sherlock Holmes ever thought of being.

One day, in the lecture theatre, he gave the students a long talk on the necessity for the members of the medical profession cultivating their senses—sight, smell, taste, and hearing. Before him on a table stood a large tumbler filled with a dark, amber-colored liquid.

"This, gentlemen," announced the Professor, "contains a very potent drug. To the taste it is intensely bitter. It is most offensive to the sense of smell. Yet, as far as the sense of sight is concerned—that is, in color—it is no different from dozens of other liquids.

"Now I want to see how many of you gentlemen have educated your powers of perception. Of course, we might easily analyze this chemically, and find out what it is. But I want you to test it by smell and taste; and, as I don't ask anything of my students which I wouldn't be willing to do myself, I will taste it before passing it round."

Here he dipped his finger in the liquid, and placed it in his mouth. The tumbler was passed round. With wry and sour faces the students followed the Professor's lead. One after another tasted the vile decoction; varied and amusing were the grimaces made. The tumbler, having gone the round, was returned to the Professor.

"Gentlemen," said he, with a laugh, "I am deeply grieved to find that not one of you has developed this power of perception, which I so often speak about; for if you had watched me closely, you would have found that, while I placed my forefinger in the medicine, it was the middle finger which found its way into my mouth."

These methods of Bell impressed Doyle greatly at the time. The impression made was a lasting one.

But, while Joseph Bell is the original Sherlock Holmes, another Edinburgh professor "had a finger in the pie," so to speak.

While Joseph Bell gave Doyle the idea of the character Holmes, the man who, unknowingly perhaps, influenced Doyle in adapting that character to the detection of crime, was Sir Henry Little-John.

"Little-John," as the students all called him, was the Police Surgeon and the Medical Officer of Health to the City of Edinburgh. He was also Lecturer on Forensic Medicine and Public Health at the Royal College of Surgeons.

No teacher ever took a greater interest in his students than did Sir Henry. He not only lectured to "his boys"—as he always spoke of them—in the lecture-room, but he took them to the city slaughterhouses, and to the reservoirs which supply Edinburgh with water. Here he would explain the why and the wherefore of hygiene. As Police Surgeon he had unlimited liberties and unequaled facilities for the study of crime and criminals. It was a common but interesting sight to see the dapper Sir Henry Little-John, little both in stature and name, walking along the street with a crowd of medical students trailing along behind. His lectures on crime and criminals were always entertaining and instructive, as they were generally straightforward statements of personal experiences.

While Bell was lecturing deduction and perception into Doyle's receptive and imaginative brain, Sir Henry Little-John was giving Doyle material for his detective stories.

Whenever a mysterious or suspected murder was perpetrated, Sir Henry loved to ferret out the criminals and clear up the crime. He always gave expert medical evidence in the law courts, and, being Police Surgeon, of necessity testified for the Crown on behalf of the prosecution.

It was a red-letter day for Edinburgh medical students when Sir Henry was due in the witness-box. How they flocked around the courthouse, and how they fought to gain an entrance! Even standing-room was at a premium on these occasions; one and all were anxious to hear their "Little-John" testify. For Sir Henry never got the worst of the argument. He was never entrapped by the smartest of lawyers, and never disconcerted by the severest of cross-examinations.

One case, out of hundreds of a similar kind, will exemplify his knowledge of criminals and crime, and show his readiness of repartee.

A woman was charged with the poisoning of her husband. Arsenic had been found in the stomach of the dead man. The prosecution failed, however, to prove that the woman had purchased arsenic. As the law in the British Isles is very explicit and severe in its restriction of the sale of poisons, and at all times is strictly enforced, the defence made much of the failure of the prosecution to prove the purchasing of the arsenic. No poison in class A—in which class arsenic is placed—can be bought at any chemist's shop unless the sale is entered in the Government Poison Book—a book kept specially for that purpose. The signatures of vender, buyer, and a witness, known to both parties, must be attached. No record of the sale of arsenic could be found in any of the city druggists' establishments. Sir Henry's attention was called to this fact by the attorney for the defence.

"So you found arsenic in the stomach of the deceased?" inquired the lawyer.

"I did," answered Sir Henry, in his usual quick and decided manner.

"But where could the arsenic have been procured?" questioned the attorney. "We have no record of the sale!"

"Why," retorted Little-John scornfully, "there is enough arsenic in the room where the man slept to poison a small army, right at hand, on the very walls of the room itself. The green wall-paper, with which the walls of the room are covered, is saturated with arsenic."

"True, perhaps," replied the man of law, "but surely the defendant is not sufficiently versed in chemistry—she is certainly not well enough educated—to understand the process of extracting arsenic from wall-paper, even if the wall-paper contains arsenic—which is very, very doubtful."

"Some women's intuition is greater than certain men's knowledge," answered Sir Henry, pointedly and dryly.

The cross-examining lawyer immediately ceased his questioning. The woman later admitted her crime, and Little-John again scored.

The University, with its associations, with its antiquity, with the respect and affection shown professors by students, with the unlimited trouble taken by professors with the students, and the general atmosphere and environments of both the University and Edinburgh itself, had undoubtedly an influence upon Conan Doyle's literary work, and a potent influence at that.

Out of Paradise

E. W. Hornung

Hardly less famous in his day than Sherlock Holmes was Raffles, the Amateur Cracksman. However, E. W. Hornung (1866-1921) created a character quite different from that devised by his brother-in-law, Dr. Arthur Conan Doyle. Holmes, a man of highest conscience, strove for law and justice. Raffles was a rogue out for adventure and illicit profit—but a fascinating rogue. Between Holmes and Raffles, Collier's *held a pair of circulation-builders so potent that the* Saturday Evening Post *finally turned in self-defense to G. K. Chesterton for a rival series, "The Adventures of Father Brown."*

December 10, 1904

If I must tell more tales of Raffles, I can but go back to our earliest days together, and fill in the blanks left by discretion in existing annals. In so doing I may indeed fill some small part of an infinitely greater blank, across which you may conceive me to have stretched my canvas for a first frank portrait of my friend. The whole truth can not harm him now. I shall paint in every wart. Raffles was a villain, when all is written; it is no service to his memory to gloze the fact; yet I have done so myself before to-day. I have omitted whole heinous episodes. I have dwelt unduly on the redeeming side. And this I may do again, blinded even as I write by the gallant glamor that made my villain more to me than any hero. But at least there shall be no more reservations, and as an earnest I shall make no further secret of the greatest wrong that even Raffles ever did me.

I pick my words with care and pain, loyal as I still would be to my friend, and yet remembering as I must those Ides of March when he led me blindfold into temptation and crime. That was an ugly office, if you will. It was a moral bagatelle to the treacherous trick he was to play me a few weeks later. The second offence, on the other hand, was to prove the less serious of the two against society, and might in itself have been published to the world years ago. There have been private reasons for my reticence. The affair was not only too intimately mine, and too discreditable to Raffles. One other was involved in it, one dearer to me than Raffles himself, one whose name shall not even now be sullied by association with ours.

Suffice it that I had been engaged to her before that mad March deed. True, her people called it "an understanding," and frowned even upon that, as well they might. But their authority was not direct; we bowed to it as an act of politic grace; between us, all was well but my unworthiness. That may be gauged when I confess that this was how the matter stood on the night I gave a worthless check for my losses at baccarat, and afterward turned to Raffles in my need. Even after that I saw her sometimes. But I let her guess that there was more upon my soul than she must ever share, and at last I had written to end it all. I remember that week so well! It was the close of such a May as we have never had since, and I was too miserable even to follow the heavy scoring in the papers! Raffles was the only man who could get a wicket up at Lord's and I never once went to see him play. Against Yorkshire, however, he helped himself to a hundred runs as well; and that brought Raffles round to me on his way home to the Albany.

"We must dine and celebrate the rare event," said he. "A century takes it out of one at my time of life; and you, Bunny, you look quite as much in need of your end of a worthy bottle. Suppose we make it the Café Royal, and eight sharp? I'll be there first to fix up the table and the wine."

And at the Café Royal I incontinently told him of the trouble I was in. It was the first he had ever heard of my affair, and I told him all, though not before our bottle had been succeeded by an imperial pint of the same exemplary brand. Raffles heard me out with grave attention. His sympathy was the more grateful for the tactful brevity with which it was indicated rather than expressed. He only wished that I had told him of this complication in the beginning; as I had not, he agreed with me that the only course was a candid and complete renunciation. It was not as though my divinity had a penny of her own, or I could earn an honest one. I had explained to Raffles that she was an orphan, who spent most of her time with an aristocratic aunt in the country, and the remainder under the repressive roof of a pompous politician in Palace Gardens. The aunt had, I believed, still a sneaking softness for me, but her illustrious brother had set his face against me from the first.

"Hector Carruthers," murmured Raffles, repeating the detested name with his clear cold eye on mine. "I suppose you haven't seen much of him?"

"Not a thing for ages," I replied. "I was at the house two or three days last year, but they've neither asked me since nor been at home to me when I've called. The old beast seems a judge of men!"

And I laughed bitterly in my glass.

"Nice house?" said Raffles, glancing at himself in his silver cigarette-case.

"Top shelf," said I. "You know the houses in Palace Gardens, don't you?"

"Not so well as I should like to know them, Bunny."

"Well, it's the best of the lot, and a perfect museum inside. The old ruffian is as rich as Crœsus. It's the palace of a prince."

"What about the window fastenings?" asked Raffles, casually.

I recoiled from the open cigarette-case that he proffered as he spoke. Our eyes met; and in his there was that starry twinkle of mirth and mischief, that sunny beam of audacious devilment, which had been my undoing two months before, which was to undo me as often as he chose until the chapter's end. Yet for once I withstood its glamor; for once I turned aside that luminous glance with front of steel. There was no need for him to voice his plans. I read them all between the strong lines of his smiling, eager face. And I pushed back my chair in the equal eagerness of my own resolve.

"Not if I know it!" said I. "A house I've dined in—a house I've seen *her* in—a house where *she* stays by the month together! Don't put it into words, Raffles, or I'll get up and go."

"You mustn't do that before the coffee and liqueur," said Raffles, laughing. "Have a small Sullivan first: it's the royal road to a cigar. And now let me observe that your scruples would do you honor if old Carruthers still lived in the house in question."

"Do you mean to say he doesn't?"

Raffles struck a match and handed it first to me. "I mean to say, my dear Bunny, that Palace Gardens knows the very name no more. You began by telling me you had heard nothing of these people all this year. That's quite enough to account for our little misunderstanding. I was thinking of the house, and you were thinking of the people in the house."

"But who are they, Raffles? Who has taken the house, if old Carruthers has moved, and how do you know that it is still worth a visit?"

"In answer to your first question, Lord Lochmaben," replied Raffles, blowing bracelets of smoke toward the ceiling. "You look as though you had never heard of him; but as the cricket and racing are the only parts of your paper that you condescend to read, you can't be expected to keep track of all the peers created in your time. Your other question is not worth answering. How do you suppose that I know these things? It's my business to get to know them, and that's all there is to it. As a matter of fact, Lady Lochmaben has just as good diamonds as Mrs. Carruthers ever had; and the chances are that she keeps them where Mrs. Carruthers kept hers, if you could enlighten me on that point."

As it happened, I could, since I knew from his niece that it was one on which Mr. Carruthers had been a faddist in his time. He had made quite a study of the cracksman's craft, in a resolve to circumvent it with his own. I remembered myself how the ground floor windows were elaborately bolted and shuttered, and how the doors of all the rooms opening upon the square inner hall were fitted with extra Yale locks at an unlikely height, not to be discovered by one within the room. It had been the butler's business to turn and to collect all these keys before retiring for the night. But the key of the safe in the study was supposed to be in the jealous keeping of the master of the house himself. That safe was in its turn so ingeniously hidden that I never should have found it for myself. I well remember how one who showed it to me (in the innocence of her heart) laughed as she assured me that even her little trinkets were solemnly locked up in it every night. It had been let into the wall behind one end of the bookcase expressly to preserve the barbaric splendor of Mrs. Carruthers; without a doubt these Lochmabens would use it for the same purpose; and in the altered circumstances I had no hesitation in giving Raffles all the information he desired. I even drew him a rough plan of the ground floor on the back of my menu card.

"It was rather clever of you to notice the kind of locks on the inner doors," he remarked as he put it in his pocket. "I suppose you don't remember if it was a Yale on the front door as well?"

"It was not," I was able to answer quite promptly. "I happen to know because I once had the key when—when we went to a theatre together."

"Thank you, old chap," said Raffles sympathetically. "That's all I shall want from you, Bunny, my boy. There's no night like to-night!"

It was one of his sayings when bent upon his worst. I looked at him aghast. Our cigars were just in blast, yet already he was signaling for his bill. It was impossible to remonstrate with him until we were both outside in the street.

"I'm coming with you," said I, running my arm through his.

"Nonsense, Bunny!"

"Why is it nonsense? I know every inch of the ground, and since the house has changed hands, I have no compunction. Besides, 'I have been there' in the other sense as well; once a thief, you know! In for a penny, in for a pound!"

It was ever my mood when the blood was up. But my old friend failed to appreciate the characteristic, as he usually did. We crossed Regent Street in silence. I had to catch his sleeve to keep a hand in his inhospitable arm.

"I really think you had better stay away," said Raffles as we reached the other curb. "I've no use for you this time."

"Yet I thought I had been so useful up to now?"

"That may be, Bunny, but I tell you frankly I don't want you to-night."

"Yet I know the ground, and you don't! I tell you what," said I: "I'll come just to show you the ropes, and I won't take a pennyweight of the swag."

Such was the teasing fashion in which he invariably prevailed upon me; it was delightful to note how it caused him to yield in his turn. But Raffles had the grace to give in with a laugh, whereas I too often lost my temper with my point.

"You little rabbit!" he chuckled. "You shall have your share, whether you come or not; but, seriously, don't you think you might remember the girl?"

"What's the use?" I groaned. "You agree there is nothing for it but to give her up. I am glad to say I saw that for myself before I asked you, and wrote to tell her so on Sunday. Now it's Wednesday, and she hasn't answered by line or sign. It's waiting for one word from her that's driving me mad!"

"Perhaps you wrote to Palace Gardens?"

"No, I sent it to the country. There's been time for an answer, wherever she may be."

We had reached the Albany, and halted with one accord at the Piccadilly portico, red cigar to red cigar.

"You wouldn't like to go and see if the answer's in your rooms?" he asked.

"No. What's the good? Where's the point in giving her up if I'm going to straighten out when it's too late? It *is* too late, I *have* given her up, and I *am* coming with you!"

The hand that bowled the most puzzling ball in England (once it found its length) descended on my shoulder with surprising promptitude.

"Very well, Bunny! That's finished; but your blood be on your own pate if evil comes of it. Meanwhile we can't do better than turn in here till you have finished your cigar as it deserves, and topped up with such a cup of tea as you must learn to like if you hope to get on in your new profession. And when the hours are small enough, Bunny, my boy, I don't mind admitting I shall be very glad to have you with me."

I have a vivid memory of the interim in his rooms. I think it must have been the first and last of its kind that I was called upon to sustain with so much knowledge of what lay before me. I passed the time with one restless eye upon the clock, and the other on the Tantalus which Raffles ruthlessly declined to unlock. He admitted that it was like waiting with one's pads on; and in my slender experience of the game of which he was a world's master, that was an ordeal not to be endured without a general quaking of the inner man. I was, on the other hand, all right when I got to the metaphorical wicket; and half the surprises that Raffles sprung on me were doubtless due to his early recognition of the fact.

On this occasion I fell swiftly and hopelessly out of love with the prospect I had so gratuitously embraced. It was not only my repugnance to enter that house in that way, which grew upon my better judgment as the artificial enthusiasm of the evening evaporated from my veins. Strong as that repugnance became, I had an even stronger feeling that we were embarking on an important enterprise far too much upon the spur of the moment. The latter qualm I had the temerity to confess to Raffles; nor have I often loved him more than when he freely admitted it to be the most natural feeling in the world. He assured me, however, that he had had my Lady Lochmaben and her jewels in his mind for several months; he had sat behind them at first nights, and long ago determined what to take and to reject; in fine, he had only been waiting for those topographical details which it had been my chance privilege to supply. I now learned that he had numerous houses in a similar state upon his list; something or other was wanting in each case in order to complete his plans. In that of the Bond Street jeweler it was a trusty accomplice; in the present instance, a more intimate knowledge of the house. And lastly this was a Wednesday night, when the tired legislator gets early to his bed.

How I wish I could make the whole world see and hear him, and smell the smoke of his beloved Sullivan, as he took me into these the secrets of his infamous trade! Neither look nor language would betray the infamy. As a mere talker, I shall never listen to the like of Raffles on this side of the sod; and his talk was seldom garnished by an oath, never in my remembrance by the unclean word. Then he looked like a man who had dressed to dine out, not like one who had long since dined; for his curly hair, though longer than another's, was never untidy in its length; and these were the days when it was still far from white. Nor were there many lines as yet upon the smooth and mobile face; and its frame was still that dear den of disorder and good taste, with the carved bookcase, the dresser, and chests of still older oak, and the Wattses and Rossettis hung anyhow on the walls.

It must have been one o'clock before we drove in a hansom as far as Kensington Church, instead of getting down at the gates of our private road to ruin. Constitutionally shy of the direct approach, Raffles was further deterred by a ball in full swing at the Empress Rooms, whence potential witnesses were pouring between dances into the cool deserted street. Instead he led me a little way up Church Street, and so through the narrow passage into Palace Gardens. He knew the house as well as I did. We made our first survey from the other side of the road. The house was not quite in darkness; there was a dim light over the door, a brighter one in the stables, further back from the road.

"That's a bit of a bore," said Raffles. "The ladies have been out somewhere—

trust them to spoil the show! They would get to bed before the stable folk, but insomnia is the curse of their sex and our profession. Somebody's not home yet; that will be the son of the house; but he's a beauty, who may not come home at all."

"Another Alick Carruthers," I murmured, recalling the one I liked least of all the household as I remembered it.

"They might be brothers," rejoined Raffles, who knew all the loose fish about town. "Well, I'm not sure that I shall want you after all, Bunny."

"Why not?"

"If the front door's only on the latch, and you're right about the lock, I shall walk in as though I were the son of the house myself."

And he jingled the skeleton that he carried on a chain as honest men carry their latchkeys.

"You forget the inner doors and the safe."

"True. You might be useful to me there. But I still don't like leading you in where it isn't absolutely necessary, Bunny."

"Then let me lead you," I answered, and forthwith marched across the broad, secluded road, with the great houses standing back on either side in their ample gardens, as though the one opposite belonged to me. I thought Raffles had stayed behind, for I never heard him at my heels, yet there he was when I turned round at the gate.

"I must teach you the step," he whispered, shaking his head. "You shouldn't use your heel at all. Here's a grass border for you: walk it as you would the plank! Gravel makes a noise, and flower-beds tell a tale. Wait—I'm going to carry you across this!"

It was the sweep of the drive, and in the dim light from above the door, the soft gravel, plowed into ridges by the night's wheels threatened an alarm at every step. Yet Raffles, with me in his arms, crossed the zone of peril softly as the pard.

"Shoes in your pocket—that's the beauty of pumps!" he whispered on the step; his light bunch tinkled faintly; a couple of keys he stooped and tried, with the touch of a humane dentist; the third let us into the porch. And as we stood together on the mat, as he was gradually closing the door, a clock within chimed a half-hour in fashion so thrillingly familiar to me that I caught Raffles by the arm. My half-hours of happiness had flown to just such chimes! I looked wildly about me in the dim light. Hat-stand and oak settee belonged equally to my past. And Raffles was smiling in my face as he held the door wide for my escape.

"You told me a lie!" I gasped in whispers.

"I did nothing of the sort," he replied. "The furniture's the furniture of Hector Carruthers, but the house is the house of Lord Lochmaben. Look here!"

He had stooped, and was smoothing out the discarded envelope of a telegram. "Lord Lochmaben," I read in pencil by the dim light; and the case was plain to me on the spot. My friends had let their house, furnished, as anybody but Raffles would have explained to me in the beginning.

"All right," I said. "Shut the door."

And he not only shut it without a sound, but drew a bolt that might have been sheathed in rubber.

In another minute we were at work upon the study door, I with the tiny lantern and the bottle of rock-oil, he with the brace and the largest bit. The Yale lock he had given up at a glance. It was placed high up in the door, feet above the handle, and the chain of holes with which Raffles had soon surrounded it were bored on a level with his eyes. Yet the clock in the hall chimed again, and two ringing strokes resounded through the silent house before we gained admittance to the room.

Raffle's next care was to muffle the bell on the shuttered window (with a silk handkerchief from the hat-stand) and to prepare an emergency exit by opening first the shutters and then the window itself. Luckily it was a still night, and very little wind came in to embarrass us. He then began operations on the safe, revealed by me behind its folding screen of books, while I stood sentry on the threshold. I may have stood there for a dozen minutes, listening to the loud hall clock, and to the gentle dentistry of Raffles in the mouth of the safe behind me, when a third sound thrilled my every nerve. It was the equally cautious opening of a door in the gallery overhead.

I moistened my lips to whisper a word of warning to Raffles. But his ears had been as quick as mine, and something longer. His lantern darkened as I turned my head; next moment I felt his breath upon the back of my neck. It was now too late even for a whisper, and quite out of the question to close the mutilated door. There we could only stand, I on the threshold, Raffles at my elbow, while one carrying a candle crept down the stairs.

The study door was at right angles to the lowest flight, and just to the right of one alighting in the hall. It was thus impossible for us to see who it was until the person was close abreast of us; but by the rustle of the gown we knew that it was one of the ladies, and dressed just as she had come from theatre or ball. Insensibly I drew back as the candle swam into our field of vision: it had not traversed many inches when a hand was clapped firmly but silently across my mouth.

I could forgive Raffles for that, at any rate! In another breath I should have cried aloud; for the girl with the candle, the girl in her ball-dress at dead of night, the girl with the letter for the post, was the last girl on God's wide earth whom I should have chosen thus to encounter—a midnight intruder in the very house where I had been reluctantly received on her account!

I forgot Raffles. I forgot the new and unforgivable grudge I had against him now. I forgot his very hand across my mouth, even before he paid me the compliment of removing it. There was the only girl in all my world: I had eyes and brains for no one and for nothing else. She had neither seen nor heard us, had looked neither to the right hand nor the left. But a small oak table stood on the opposite side of the hall; it was to this table that she went. On it was one of those boxes in which one puts one's letters for the post; and she stooped to read by her candle the times at which this box was cleared.

The loud clock ticked and ticked. She was standing at her full height now, her candle on the table, her letter in both hands, and in her downcast face a sweet and pitiful perplexity that drew the tears to my eyes. Through a film I saw her open the envelope so lately sealed, and read her letter once more, as though she would have altered it a little at the last. It was too late for that; but of a sudden she plucked a rose from her bosom, and was pressing it in with her letter when I groaned aloud.

How could I help it? The letter was for me: of that I was as sure as though I had been looking over her shoulder. She was as true as tempered steel; there were not two of us to whom she wrote and sent roses at dead of night. It was her one chance of writing to me. None would know that she had written. And she cared enough to soften the reproaches I had richly earned with a red rose warm from her own warm heart. And there, and there was I, a common thief who had broken in to steal! Yet I was unaware that I had uttered a sound until she looked up, startled, and the hands behind me pinned me where I stood.

I think she must have seen us, even in the dim light of the solitary candle. Yet not a sound escaped her as she peered courageously in our direction; neither did one of us move; but the hall clock went on and on, every tick like the beat of a drum to bring the house about our ears, until a minute must have passed as in some breathless dream. And then came the awakening —with such a knocking and a ringing at the front door as brought all three of us to our senses on the spot.

"The son of the house!" whispered Raffles in my ear, as he dragged me back to the window he had left open for our escape. But as he leaped out first a sharp cry stopped me at the sill. "Get back! Get back! We're trapped!" he cried; and in the single second that I stood there, I saw him fell one officer to the ground, and dash across the lawn with another at his heels. A third came running up to the window. What could I do but dash back into the house? And there in the hall I met my lost love face to face.

Till that moment she had not recognized me. I ran to catch her as she all but fell. And my touch repelled her into life, so that she shook me off, and stood gasping. "You, of all men! You, of all men!" until I could bear it no more, but broke again for the study window. "Not that way—not that way!" she cried in an agony at that. Her hands were upon me now. "In there, in there!" she whispered, pointing and pulling me to a mere cupboard under the stairs, where hats and coats were hung, and it was she who shut the door on me with a sob.

Doors were already opening overhead, voices calling, voices answering, the alarm running like wildfire from room to room. Soft feet pattered in the gallery and down the stairs about my very ears. I do not know what made me put on my own shoes as I heard them, but I think that I was ready and even longing to walk out and give myself up. I need not say what and who it was that alone restrained me. I heard her name. I heard them crying to her as though she had fainted. I recognized the detested voice of my *bête noir*, Alick Carruthers, thick as might be expected of the dissipated dog, yet daring to stutter out her name. And then I heard, without catching, her low reply; it was in answer to the somewhat stern questioning of quite another voice; and from what followed I knew that she had never fainted at all.

"Upstairs, miss, did he? Are you sure?"

I did not hear her answer. I conceived her as simply pointing up the stairs. In any case, about my very ears once more, there now followed such a patter and tramp of bare and booted feet as renewed in me a base fear for my own skin. But voices and feet passed over my head, went up and up, higher and higher; and I was wondering whether or not to make a dash for it, when one light pair came running down again, and in very despair I marched out to meet my preserver, looking as little as I could like the abject thing I felt.

"Be quick!" she cried in a harsh whisper, and pointed peremptorily to the porch.

But I stood stubbornly before her, my heart hardened by her hardness, and perversely indifferent to all else. And as I stood I saw the letter she had written, in the hand with which she pointed, crushed into a ball.

"Quickly!" She stamped her foot. "Quickly—*if you ever cared!*"

This in a whisper, without bitterness, without contempt, but with a sudden wild entreaty that breathed upon the dying embers of my poor manhood. I drew myself together for the last time in her sight. I turned, and left her as she wished—for her sake, not for mine. And as I went I heard her tearing her letter into little pieces, and the little pieces falling on the floor.

Then I remembered Raffles, and could have killed him for what he had done. Doubtless by this time he was safe and snug in the Albany: what did my fate matter to him? Never mind; this should be the end between him and me as well; it was the end of everything, this dark night's work! I should go and tell him so. I should jump into a cab and drive there and then to his accursed rooms. But first I must escape from the trap in which he had been so ready to leave me. Yet on the very steps I gave up the thought. They were searching the shrubberies between the drive and the road; a policeman's lantern kept flashing in and out among the laurels, while a young man in evening clothes directed him from the gravel sweep. It was this young man whom I must dodge, but at my first step in the gravel he wheeled round, and it was Raffles himself.

"Hulloa!" he cried. "So you've come up to join the dance as well! Had a look inside, have you? You'll be better employed in helping to draw the cover in front here. It's all right, officer—only another gentleman from the Empress Rooms!"

And we made a brave show of assisting in the futile search until the arrival of more police, and a broad hint from an irritable sergeant, gave us an excellent excuse for going off arm-in-arm. But it was Raffles who had thrust his arm through mine. I shook him off as we left the scene of shame behind.

"My dear Bunny!" he exclaimed. "Do you know what brought me back?"

I answered savagely that I neither knew nor cared.

"I had the very devil of a squeak for it," he went on. "I did the hurdles over two or three garden walls, but so did the flyer who was on my tracks, and he drove me back into the straight and down to High Street like any lamplighter. If he had only had the breath to sing out it would have been all up with me then; as it was, I pulled off my coat the moment I was round the corner, and took a ticket for it at the Empress Rooms."

"I suppose you had one for the dance that was going on," I growled. Nor would it have been a coincidence for Raffles to have had a ticket for that or any other entertainment of the London season.

"I never asked what the dance was," he returned. "I merely took the opportunity of revising my toilet, and getting rid of that rather distinctive overcoat, which I shall call for now. They're not too particular at such stages of such proceedings, but I've no doubt I should have seen some one I knew if I had gone right in. I might even have had a turn if I had been less uneasy about you, Bunny."

"It was like you to come back to help me out," said I. "But to lie to me, and to inveigle me with your lies into that house of all houses—that was not like you, Raffles —and I never shall forgive it or you!"

Raffles took my arm again. We were near the High Street gates of Palace Gardens, and I was too miserable to resist an advance which I meant never to give him an opportunity to repeat.

"Come, come, Bunny, there wasn't much inveigling about it," said he. "I did my level best to leave you behind, but you wouldn't listen to me."

"If you had told me the truth I should have listened fast enough," I retorted. "But what's the use of talking? You can boast of your own adventures after you bolted. You don't care what happened to me."

"I cared so much that I came back to see."

"You might have spared yourself the trouble! The wrong had been done. Raffles—Raffles—don't you know who she was?"

It was my hand that gripped his arm once more.

"I guessed," he answered, gravely enough even for me.

"It was she who saved me, not you," I said. "And that is the bitterest part of all!"

Yet I told him that part with a strange sad pride in her whom I had lost, through him, forever. As I ended we turned into High Street; in the prevailing stillness, the faint strains of the band reached us from the Empress Rooms; and I hailed a crawling hansom as Raffles turned that way.

"Bunny," said he, "it's no use saying I'm sorry. Sorrow adds insult in a case like this—if ever there was or will be such another! Only believe me, Bunny, when I swear to you that I had not the smallest shadow of a suspicion that *she* was in the house."

And in my heart of hearts I did believe him; but I could not bring myself to say the words.

"You told me yourself that you had written to her in the country," he pursued.

"And that letter!" I rejoined, in a fresh wave of bitterness: "that letter she had written at dead of night, and stolen down to post, it was the one I have been waiting for all these days! I should have got it to-morrow. Now I shall never get it, never hear from her again, nor have another chance in this world or in the next. I don't say it was all your fault. You no more knew that she was there than I did. But you told me a deliberate lie about her people, and that I never shall forgive!"

I spoke as vehemently as I could under my breath. The hansom was waiting at the curb.

"I can say no more than I have said," returned Raffles with a shrug. "Lie or no lie. I didn't tell it to bring you with me, but to get you to give me certain information without feeling a beast about it. But, as a matter of fact, it was no lie about old Hector Carruthers and Lord Lochmaben, and anybody but you would have guessed the truth."

"What is the truth?"

"I as good as told you, Bunny, again and again."

"Then tell me now."

"If you read your paper there would be no need; but if you want to know, old Carruthers headed the list of the Birthday Honors, and Lord Lochmaben is the title of his choice."

And this miserable quibble was not a lie! My lip curled. I turned my back without a word, and drove home to my Mount Street flat in a new fury of savage scorn. Not a lie, indeed! It was the one that is half a truth, the meanest lie of all, and the very last to which I could have dreamed that Raffles would stoop. So far there had been a degree of honor between us, if only of the kind understood to obtain between thief and thief.

Now all that was at an end. Raffles had cheated me. Raffles had completed the ruin of my life. I was done with Raffles, as she who shall not be named was done with me.

And yet, even while I blamed him most bitterly, and utterly abominated his deceitful deed, I could not but admit in my heart that the result was out of all proportion to the intent: he had never dreamed of doing me this injury, or indeed any injury at all. Intrinsically the deceit had been quite venial, the reason for it obviously the reason that Raffles had given me. It was quite true that he had spoken of this Lochmaben peerage as a new creation, and of the heir to it in a fashion only applicable to Alick Carruthers. He had given me hints, which I had been too dense to take, and he had certainly made more than one attempt to deter me from accompanying him on this fatal emprise; had he been more explicit I might have made it my business to deter him. I could not say in my heart that Raffles had failed to satisfy such honor as I might reasonably expect to subsist between us. Yet it seems to me to require a superhuman sanity always and unerringly to separate cause from effect, achievement from intent. And I, for one, was never quite able to do so in this case.

I could not be accused of neglecting my newspaper during the next few wretched days. I read every word that I could find about the attempted jewel-robbery in Palace Gardens, and the reports afforded me my sole comfort. In the first place, it was only an attempted robbery; nothing had been taken, after all. And then—and then—the one member of the household who had come nearest to a personal encounter with either of us was unable to furnish any description of the man—had even expressed a doubt as to any likelihood of identification in the event of an arrest!

I will not say with what mingled feelings I read and dwelt on that announcement. It kept a certain faint glow alive within me until the morning that brought me back the only presents I had ever made her. They were books; jewelry had been frowned on by the authorities. And the books came back without a word, though the parcel was directed in her hand.

I had made up my mind not to go near Raffles again, but in my heart I already regretted my resolve. I had forfeited love. I had sacrificed honor, and now I must deliberately alienate myself from the one being whose society might yet be some recompense for all that I had lost. The situation was aggravated by the state of my exchequer. I expected an ultimatum from my banker by every post. Yet this influence was nothing to the other. It was Raffles I loved. It was not the dark life we led together, still less its base rewards; it was the man himself, his gayety, his humor, his dazzling audacity, his incomparable courage and resource. And a very horror of turning to him again in mere need or greed set the seal on my first angry resolution. But the anger was soon gone out of me, and when at length Raffles bridged the gap by coming to me, I rose to greet him almost with a shout.

He came as though nothing had happened; and, indeed, not very many days had passed, though they might have been months to me. Yet I fancied the gaze that watched me through our smoke a trifle less sunny than it had been before. And it was a relief to me when he came with few preliminaries to the inevitable point. "Did you ever hear from her, Bunny?" he asked.

"In a way," I answered. "We won't talk about it, if you don't mind, Raffles."

"That sort of way!" he exclaimed. He seemed both surprised and disappointed.

"Yes," I said, "that sort of way. It's finished. What did you expect?"

"I don't know," said Raffles. "I only thought that the girl who went so far to get a fellow out of a tight place might go a little further to keep him from getting into another."

"I don't see why she should," said I, honestly enough, yet with the irritation of an unworthy doubt deep down in my inmost consciousness.

"Yet you did hear from her?" he persisted.

"She sent me back my poor presents, without a word," I said, "if you call that hearing."

I could not bring myself to own to Raffles that I had given her only books. He asked if I was sure that she had sent them back herself; and that was his last question. My answer was enough for him. And to this day I can not say whether it was more in relief than in regret that he laid a hand upon my shoulder.

"So you are out of Paradise after all!" said Raffles. "I was not sure, or I should have come round before. Well, Bunny, if they don't want you there, there's a little Inferno in the Albany where you'll be as welcome as ever!"

And still, with all the magic mischief of his smile, there was that touch of sadness which I was yet to read aright.

The Two-Gun Man

Stewart Edward White

The American West and the Silent Men who tamed it had no more steadfast champion than Stewart Edward White. Born in Michigan, whose northern forests provided the background for many of his works, he spent his latter years in California, where he lived long enough to see atomic laboratories spring up in some of the chaparral country where cowboys once rode the range. White, who was born in 1873 and died in 1946, was a prolific novelist and writer of short stories, and after his wife's death believed in, and wrote of, psychic communication with the spirit world.

April 15, 1905

BUCK JOHNSON WAS AMERICAN BORN, BUT with a black beard and a dignity of manner that had earned him the title of Señor. He had drifted into southeastern Arizona in the days of Cochise and Victorio and Geronimo. He had persisted, and so in time had come to control the water—and hence the grazing—of nearly all the Soda Spring Valley. His troubles were many and his difficulties great. There were the ordinary problems of lean and dry years. There were also the extraordinary problems of devastating Apaches, rivals for early and ill-defined range rights—and cattle-rustlers.

Señor Buck Johnson was a man of capacity, courage, directness of method, and perseverance. Especially the latter. Therefore he had survived to see the Apaches subdued, the range right adjusted, his cattle increased to thousands, grazing the area of a principality. Now all the energy and fire of his frontiersman's nature he had turned to wiping out the third uncertainty of an uncertain business. He found it a task of some magnitude.

For Señor Buck Johnson lived just north of that terra incognita filled with the mystery of a double chance of death from man or the flaming desert known as the Mexican border. There by natural gravitation gathered all the desperate characters of three States and two republics. He who rode into it took good care that no one should get behind him, lived warily, slept light, and breathed deep when once he had again sighted the familiar peaks of Cochise's Stronghold.

No one professed knowledge of those who dwelt therein. They moved, mysterious as the desert illusions that compassed them about. As you rode, the ranges of mountains visibly changed form, the monstrous, snaky, sealike growths of the cactus clutched at your stirrup, mock lakes sparkled and dissolved in the middle distance, the sun beat hot and merciless, the powdered dry alkali beat hotly and mercilessly back—and strange grim men, swarthy, bearded, heavily armed, with red-rimmed unshifting eyes, rode silently out of the mists of illusion to look on you steadily and then to ride silently back into the desert haze. They might be only the herders of the gaunt cattle, or again they might belong to the Lost Legion that peopled the country. All you could know was that of the men who entered in but few returned.

Directly north of this unknown land you encountered parallel fences running across the country. They inclosed nothing, but offered a check to the cattle drifting toward the clutch of the renegades and an obstacle to swift dashing forays.

Of cattle-rustling there are various forms. The boldest consists quite simply of running off a bunch of stock, hustling it over the Mexican line, and there selling it to some of the big Sonora ranch owners. Generally this sort means war. Also are there subtler means, grading in skill from the rebranding through a wet blanket, through the crafty refashioning of a brand, to the various methods of separating the cow from her unbranded calf. In the course of his task Señor Buck Johnson would have to do with them all, but at present he existed in a state of warfare, fighting an enemy who stole as the Indians used to steal.

Already he had fought two pitched battles—and had won them both. His cattle increased and he became rich. Nevertheless, he knew that constantly his resources were being drained. Time and again he and his new Texas foreman, Jed Parker, had followed the trail of a stampeded bunch of twenty or thirty, followed them on down through the Soda Springs Valley to the cut-drift fences, there to abandon them. For as yet an armed force would be needed to penetrate the borderland. Once he and his men had experienced the glory of a night pursuit. Then, at the drift fences, he had fought one of his battles. But it was impossible adequately to patrol all parts of a range bigger than some Eastern States.

Buck Johnson did his best, but it was like stopping with sand the innumerable little leaks of a dam. Did his riders watch toward the Chiracahuas, then a score of beef steers disappeared from Grant's Pass, forty miles away. Pursuit here meant leaving cattle unguarded there. It was useless, and the Señor soon perceived that sooner or later he must strike in offence.

For this purpose he began slowly to strengthen the forces of his riders. Men were coming in from Texas. They were good men, addicted to the grass-rope, the double cinch, and the ox-bow stirrup. Señor Johnson wanted men who could shoot, and he got them.

"Jed," said Señor Johnson to his foreman, "the next son of a gun that rustles any of our cows is sure loading himself full of trouble. We'll hit his trail and we'll stay with it, and we'll reach his cattle-rustling conscience with a rope."

So it came about that a little army crossed the drift fences and entered the border country. Two days later it came out, and mighty pleased to be able to do so. The rope had not been used.

The reason for the defeat was quite simple. The thief had run his cattle through the lava beds, where the trail at once became difficult to follow. This delayed the pursuing party; they ran out of water; and as there was among them not one man well enough acquainted with the country to know where to find more, they had to return.

"No use, Buck," said Jed, "we'd any of us come in on a gun play, but we can't buck the desert. We'll have to get some one who knows the country."

"That's all right—but where?" queried Johnson.

"There's Pereza," suggested Parker, "it's the only town down near that country."

"Might get some one there," agreed the Señor.

Next day he rode away in search of a guide.

The third evening he was back again, much discouraged.

"The country's no good," he explained. "The regular inhabitants' a set of Mexican bums and old soaks. The cowmen's all from north and don't know nothing more than we do. I found lots who claimed to know that country, but when I told 'em what I wanted they shied like a colt. I couldn't hire 'em for no money to go down in that country. They ain't got the nerve. I took two days to her, too, and rode out to a ranch where they said a man lived who knew all about it down there. Nary riffle. Man looked all right, but his tail went down like the rest when I told him what we wanted. Seemed plumb scairt to death. Says he lived too close to the gang. Says they'd wipe him out sure if he done it. Seemed plumb *scairt*." Buck Johnson grinned. "I told him so, and he got hosstyle right off. Didn't seem no ways scairt of me. I know what's the matter with that outfit down there. They're plumb terrorized."

That night a bunch of steers was stolen from the very corrals of the home ranch. The home ranch was far north, near Fort Sherman itself, and so had always been considered immune from attack. Consequently these steers were very fine ones.

For the first time Buck Johnson lost his head and his dignity. He ordered the horses.

"I'm going to follow that —— into Sonora," he shouted to Jed Parker. "This thing's got to stop!"

"You can't make her, Buck," objected the foreman. "You'll get held up by the desert; and if that don't finish you, they'll tangle you up in all those little mountains down there, and ambush you and massacree you. You know it damn well."

"I don't give a ——" exploded Señor Johnson, "if they do. No man can slap my face and not get a run for it."

Jed Parker communed with himself.

"Señor," said he at last, "it's no good; you can't do it. You got to have a guide. You wait three days and I'll get you one."

"You can't do it," insisted the Señor, "I tried every man in the district."

"Will you wait three days?" repeated the foreman.

Johnson pulled loose his latigo. His first anger had cooled.

"All right," he agreed, "and you can say for me that I'll pay five thousand dollars in gold and give all the men and horses he needs to the man who has the nerve to get back that bunch of cattle and bring in the man who rustled them. I'll sure make this a test case."

So Jed Parker set out to discover his man with nerve.

At about ten o'clock on the Fourth of July a rider topped the summit of the last swell of land and loped his animal down into the single street of Pereza. The buildings on either side were flat-roofed and coated with plaster. Over the sidewalks extended wooden awnings, beneath which opened very wide doors into the coolness of saloons. Each of these places ran a bar, and also games of roulette, faro, craps, and stud poker. Even this early in the morning every game was patronized.

The day was already hot with the dry, breathless, but exhilarating heat of the desert. A throng of men idling at the edge of the sidewalks, jostling up and down their centre, or eddying into the places of amusement, acknowledged the power of summer by loosening their collars and carrying their coats on their arms. They were as yet busily engaged in recognizing acquaintances. Later they would drink freely and gamble and perhaps fight. Toward all but those they recognized they preserved an attitude of potential suspicion, for here were gathered the "bad men" of the border countries. A certain jealousy or touchy egotism, lest the other man be considered quicker on the trigger, bolder, less aggressive than himself, kept each strung to tension. An occasional shot attracted little notice. Men in the cow countries shoot as casually as we strike matches, and some subtle instinct told them that the reports were harmless.

As the rider entered one street, however, a more definite cause of excitement drew the loose population toward the centre of the road. Immediately their mass blotted out what had interested them. Curiosity attracted the saunterers; they in turn the frequenters of the bars and gambling games. In an incredibly few moments the barkeepers, gamblers, and lookout men alone, held aloof only by the necessities of their calling, of all the population of Pereza were not included in the newly formed ring.

The stranger pushed his horse resolutely to the outer edge of the crowd, where, from his point of vantage, he could easily overlook their heads. He was a quiet-appearing young fellow, rather neatly dressed in the border costume, rode a "centre-fire" or single-cinch saddle, and wore no chaps. He was what is known as a "two-gun man"; that is to say, he wore a heavy Colt's revolver on either hip. The fact that the lower ends of his holsters were tied down in order to facilitate the easy withdrawal of the revolvers seemed to indicate that he expected to use them. He had furthermore a quiet gray eye with the hint of steel that bore out the inference of the tied holsters.

The newcomer dropped his reins on his pony's neck, eased himself to an attitude of attention, and looked down gravely on what was taking place.

He saw over the heads of the bystanders a tall, muscular wild-eyed man, hatless, his hair rumpled into staring confusion, his right sleeve rolled to his shoulder, a wicked-looking nine-inch knife in his hand, and a red bandanna handkerchief hanging by one corner from his teeth.

"What's biting the locoed stranger?" the young man inquired of his neighbor.

The other frowned at him darkly.

"Dares any one to take the other end of that handkerchief in his teeth and fight it out without letting go."

"Nice joyful proposition," commented the young man.

He settled himself to closer attention. The wild-eyed man was talking rapidly. What he said can not be printed here. Mainly was it derogatory of the Southern countries. Shortly it became boastful of the Northern and then boastful of the man who uttered it. He swaggered up and down, becoming always the more insolent as his challenge remained untaken.

"Why don't you take him up?" inquired the young man after a moment.

"Not me!" negatived the other vigorously. "I'll go your little old gunfight to a finish, but I don't want any cold steel in mine. Ugh! it gives me the shivers. It's a reg'lar Mexican trick! With a gun it's down and out; but this knife work is too slow and searchin'."

The newcomer said nothing, but fixed his eye again on the raging man with the knife. "Don't you reckon he's bluffing?" he inquired.

"Not any!" denied the other with emphasis. "He's jest drunk enough to be crazy mad and reckless."

The newcomer shrugged his shoulders and cast his glance searchingly over the fringe of the crowd. It rested on a Mexican.

"Hi, Tony! come here," he called.

The Mexican approached, flashing his white teeth.

"Here," said the stranger, "lend me your knife a minute."

The Mexican, anticipating sport of his own peculiar kind, obeyed with alacrity. "You fellows make me tired," observed the stranger, dismounting. "He's got the whole townful of you bluffed to a standstill. Damn if I don't try his little game."

He hung his coat on his saddle, shouldered his way through the press, which parted for him readily, and picked up the other corner of the handkerchief. "Now, you mangy son of a gun!" said he.

Jed Parker straightened his back, rolled up the bandanna handkerchief and thrust it into his pocket, hit flat with his hand the tousled mass of his hair, and thrust the long hunting knife into its sheath. "You're the man I want," said he.

Instantly the two-gun man had jerked loose his weapons and was covering the foreman.

"Am I!" he snarled.

"Not just that way," explained Parker. "My gun is on my hoss, and you can have this old toadsticker if you want it. I been looking for you and took this way of finding you. Now let's go talk."

The stranger looked him in the eye for nearly a half-minute without lowering his revolvers.

"I go you," said he briefly at last.

But the crowd, missing the purport, and, in fact, the very occurrence of this colloquy, did not understand. It thought the bluff had been called, and naturally, finding harmless what had intimidated it, gave way to an exasperated impulse to get even.

"You —— bluffer!" shouted a voice, "don't you think you can run any such ranikaboo here!"

Jed Parker turned humorously to his companion.

"Do we get that talk?" he inquired gently.

For answer the two-gun man turned and walked steadily in the direction of the man who had shouted. The latter's hand strayed uncertainly toward his own weapon, but the movement paused when the stranger's clear steel eye rested on it.

"This gentleman," pointed out the two-gun man softly, "is an old friend of mine. Don't you get to calling of him names."

His eye swept the bystanders calmly.

"Come on, Jack," said he, addressing Parker.

On the outskirts he encountered the Mexican from whom he had borrowed the knife.

"Here, Tony," said he with a slight laugh, "here's a peso. You'll find your knife back there where I had to drop her."

He entered a saloon, nodded to the proprietor, and led the way through it to a boxlike room containing a board table and two chairs.

"Make good," he commanded briefly.

"I'm looking for a man with nerve," explained Parker with equal succinctness. "You're the man."

"Well?"

"Do you know the country south of here?"

The stranger's eyes narrowed.

"Proceed," said he.

"I'm foreman of the Lazy Y of Soda Springs Valley range," explained Parker. "I'm looking for a man with sand enough and *sabe* of the country enough to lead a posse after cattle-rustlers into the border country."

"I live in this country," admitted the stranger.

"So do plenty of others, but their eyes stick out like two raw oysters when you mention the border country. Will you tackle it?"

"What's the proposition?"

"Come out and see the old man. He'll put it to you." They mounted their horses and rode the rest of the day. The desert compassed them about, marvelously changing shape and color and very character with all the noiselessness of phantasmagoria. At evening the desert stars shone steadily and unwinking, like the flames of candles. By moonrise they came to the home ranch. The buildings and corrals lay dark and silent against the moonlight that made of the plain a sea of mist. The two men unsaddled their horses and turned them loose in the wire-fenced "pasture," the necessary noises of their movements sounding sharp and clear against the velvet hush of the night. After a moment they walked stiffly past the sheds and cook shanty, past the men's bunk houses and the tall windmill silhouetted against the sky, to the main building of the home ranch under its cottonwoods.

There a light still burned, for this was the third day, and Buck Johnson awaited his foreman.

Jed Parker pushed in without ceremony.

"Here's your man, Buck," said he.

The stranger had stepped inside and carefully closed the door behind him. The lamplight threw into relief the bold free lines of his face, the details of his costume powdered thick with alkali, the shiny butts of the two guns in their open holsters tied at the bottom. Equally it defined the resolute countenance of Buck Johnson turned up in inquiry. The two men examined each other—and liked each other at once.

"How are you?" greeted the cattleman.

"Good-evening," responded the stranger.

"Sit down," invited Buck Johnson.

The stranger perched gingerly on the edge of a chair, with an appearance less of embarrassment than of habitual alertness.

"You'll take the job?" inquired the Señor.

"I haven't heard what it is," replied the stranger.

"Parker here—?"

"Said you'd explain."

"Very well," said Buck Johnson; he paused a moment, collecting his thoughts. "There's too much cattle rustling here. I'm going to stop it. I've got good men here ready to take the job, but no one who knows the country south. Three days ago I had a bunch of cattle stolen right here from the home ranch of corrals and by one man, at that. It wasn't much of a bunch—about twenty head—but I'm going to make a starter right here and now. I'm going to get that bunch back and the man who stole them if I have to go to hell to do it. And I'm going to do the same with every case of rustling that comes up from now on. I don't care if it's only one cow, I'm going to get it back—every trip. Now I want to know if you'll lead a posse down into the South country and bring out that last bunch and the man who rustled them."

"I don't know—" hesitated the stranger.

"I offer you five thousand dollars in gold if you'll bring back those cows and the man who stole 'em," repeated Buck Johnson, "and I'll give you all the horses and men you think you need."

"I'll do it," replied the two-gun man promptly.

"Good!" cried Buck Johnson, "and you better start to-morrow."

"I shall start to-night—right now."

"Better yet. How many men do you want, and grub for how long?"

"I'll play her a lone hand."

"Alone!" exclaimed Johnson, his confidence visibly cooling. "Alone! Do you think you can make her?"

"I'll be back with those cattle in not more than ten days."

"And the man," supplemented the Señor.

"And the man," argued the stranger. "What's more, I want that money here when I come in. I don't aim to stay in this country overnight."

A grin overspread Buck Johnson's countenance. He understood.

"Climate not healthy for you?" he hazarded. "I guess you'd be safe enough all right with us. But suit yourself. The money will be here."

"That's agreed?" insisted the two-gun man.

"Sure."

"I want a fresh horse—I'll leave mine—he's a good one. I want a little grub."

"All right. Parker'll fit you out."

"I'll see you in about ten days."

"Good luck," Señor Buck Johnson wished him.

The next morning Buck Johnson took a trip down into the "pasture" of five hundred wire-fenced acres.

"He means business," he confided to Jed Parker on his return. "That cavallo of his is a heap sight better than the Shorty horse we let him take. Jed, you found your man with nerve, all right. How did you do it?"

The two settled down to wait, if not with confidence, at least with interest. Sometimes, remembering the desperate character of the outlaws, their fierce distrust of any intruder, the wildness of the country, Buck Johnson and his foreman inclined to the belief that the stranger had undertaken a task beyond the powers of any one man. Again, remembering the stranger's cool gray eye, the poise of his demeanor, the quickness of his movements, and the two guns with tied holsters to permit of an easy withdrawal, they were almost persuaded that he might win.

"He's one of those long-chance fellows," surmised Jed. "He likes excitement. I could see that by the way he takes up with my knife play. He'd rather leave his hide on the fence than stay in the corral."

"Well, he's all right," replied Señor Buck Johnson, "and if he ever gets back, which same I'm some doubtful of, his dinero'll be here for him."

In pursuance of this he rode in to Willetts, where shortly the overland train brought him from Tucson the five thousand dollars in double eagles.

In the meantime the regular life of the ranch went on. Each morning Sang, the Chinese cook, rang the great bell summoning the men. They ate, and then caught up the saddle horses for the day, turning those not wanted from the corral into the pasture. Shortly they jingled away in different directions, two by two, on the slow Spanish trot of the cowpuncher. All day long thus they would ride, without food or water for man or beast, looking over the range, identifying the stock, branding the young calves, examining generally into the state of affairs, looking always with grave eyes on the magnificent flaming, changing, beautiful, dreadful desert of the Arizona plains. At evening, when the colored atmosphere, catching the last glow, threw across the Chiracahuas its veil of mystery, they jingled in again, two by two, untired, unhasting, the glory of the desert in their deep-set steady eyes.

And all that long day, while they were absent, the cattle, too, made their pilgrimage, straggling in singly, in pairs, in bunches, in long files, leisurely, ruminantly, without haste. There at the long troughs, filled by the windmill or the blindfolded pump-mule, they drank, then filed away again into the mists of the desert. And Señor Buck Johnson, or his foreman Parker, examined them for their condition, noting the increase, remarking the strays from another range. Later, perhaps, they, too, rode abroad. The same thing happened at nine other ranches, from five to ten miles apart, where dwelt other fierce, silent men, all under the authority of Buck Johnson.

And when night fell, and the topaz and violet and saffron and amethyst and mauve and lilac had faded suddenly from the Chiracahuas like a veil that has been rent, and the ramparts had become slate gray and then black, the soft-breathed night wandered here and there over the desert, and the land fell under an enchantment even stranger than the day's.

So the days went by, wonderful, fashioning the ways and the character of men. Seven passed! Buck Johnson and his foreman began to look for the stranger. Eight; they began to speculate. Nine; they doubted. On the tenth they gave him up, and he came.

They knew him first by the soft lowing of cattle. Jed Parker, dazzled by the lamp, peered from the door and made him out dimly, turning the animals into the corral. A moment later his pony's hoofs impacted softly on the baked earth, he dropped from the saddle and entered the room.

"I'm late," said he, briefly glancing at the clock which indicated ten. "But I'm here."

His manner was quick and sharp, almost breathless, as though he had been running.

"Your cattle are in the corral, all of them. Have you the money?"

"I have the money here," replied Buck Johnson, laying his hand against a drawer, "and it's ready for you when you've earned it. I don't care so much for the cattle. What I wanted is the man who stole them. Did you bring him?"

"Yes, I brought him," said the stranger. "Let's see that money."

Buck Johnson threw open the drawer and drew out the heavy canvas sack.

"It's here. Now bring in your prisoner."

The two-gun man seemed suddenly to loom large in the doorway. The muzzles of his revolvers covered the two before him. His speech came short and sharp.

"I told you I'd bring back the cows and the one who rustled them," he snapped, "I've never lied to a man yet. Your stock is in the corral. I'll trouble you for that five thousand. I'm the man who stole your cattle!"

The Patent Medicine Conspiracy Against the Freedom of the Press

Samuel Hopkins Adams

To bring standards of morality to the patent medicine business required legislation, and legislation would only follow an aroused public opinion. One of the outstanding public services of Collier's *was to tackle the nostrum makers, exposing their grip on a large section of the nation's newspapers, and kindling the public opinion that led finally to the enactment of the Pure Food and Drug laws.*

November 4, 1905

WOULD ANY PERSON BELIEVE THAT THERE *is any one subject upon which the newspapers of the United States, acting in concert, by prearrangement, in obedience to wires all drawn by one man, will deny full and free discussion? If such a thing is possible, it is a serious matter, for we rely upon the newspapers as at once the most forbidding preventive and the swiftest and surest corrective of evil. For the haunting possibility of newspaper exposure, men who know not at all the fear of God pause, hesitate, and turn back from contemplated rascality. For fear "it might get into the papers," more men are abstaining from crime and carouse to-night than for fear of arrest. But these are trite things—only, what if the newspapers fail us? Relying so wholly on the press to undo evil, how shall we deal with that evil with which the press itself has been seduced into captivity?*

In the Lower House of the Massachusetts Legislature one day last March there was a debate which lasted one whole afternoon and engaged some twenty speakers, on a bill providing that every bottle of patent medicine sold in the State should bear a label stating the contents of the bottle. More was told concerning patent medicines that afternoon than often comes to light in a single day. The debate at times was dramatic—a member from Salem told of a young woman of his acquaintance now in an institution for inebriates as the end of an incident which began with patent medicine dosing for a harmless ill. There was humor, too, in the debate—Representative Walker held aloft a bottle of Peruna bought by him in a drug store that very day, and passed it around for his fellow-members to taste and decide for themselves whether Dr. Harrington, the Secretary of the State Board of Health, was right when he told the Legislative Committee that it was merely a "cheap cocktail."

In short, the debate was interesting and important—the two qualities which invariably ensure to any event big headlines in the daily newspapers. But that debate was not celebrated by big headlines, nor any headlines at all. Yet Boston is a city, and Massachusetts is a State, where the proceedings of the Legislature figure very large in public interest, and where the newspapers respond to that interest by reporting the sessions with greater fulness and minuteness than in any other State. Had that debate been on prison reform, on Sabbath observance, the early closing saloon law, on any other subject, there would have been, in the next day's papers, overflowing accounts of verbatim report, more columns of editorial comment, and the picturesque features of it would have ensured the attention of the cartoonist.

Now why? Why was this one subject tabooed? Why were the daily accounts of legislative proceedings in the next day's papers abridged to a fraction of their usual ponderous length, and all reference to the afternoon debate on patent medicines omitted? Why was it in vain for the speakers in that patent medicine debate to search for their speeches in the next day's newspapers? Why did the legislative reporters fail to find their work in print? Why were the staff cartoonists forbidden to exercise their talents on that most fallow and tempting opportunity—the members of the Great and General Court of Massachusetts gravely tippling Peruna and passing the bottle around to their encircled neighbors, that practical knowledge should be the basis of legislative action?

I take it if any man should assert that there is one subject upon which the newspapers of the United States, acting in concert and as a unit, will deny full and free discussion, he would be smiled at as an intemperate fanatic. The thing is too incredible. He would be regarded as a man with a delusion. And yet I invite you to search the files of the daily newspapers of Massachusetts for March 16, 1905, for an account of the patent medicine debate that occurred the afternoon of March 15 in the Massachusetts Legislature. In strict accuracy it must be said that there was one exception. Any one familiar with the newspapers of the United States will already have named it—the Springfield "Republican." That paper, on two separate occasions, gave several columns to the record of the proceedings of the Legislature on the patent medicine bill. Why the otherwise universal silence?

The patent medicine business in the United States is one of huge financial proportions. The census of 1900 placed the value of the annual product at $59,611,-355. Allowing for the increase of half a decade of rapid growth, it must be to-day not less than seventy-five millions. That is the wholesale price. The retail price of all the patent medicines sold in the United States in one year may be very conservatively placed at one hundred million dollars. And of this one hundred millions which the people of the United States pay for patent medicines yearly, fully forty millions goes to the newspapers. Have patience! I have more to say than merely to point out the large revenue which newspapers receive from patent medicines, and let inference do the rest. Inference has no place in this story. There are facts a-plenty. But it is essential to point out the intimate financial relation between the newspapers and the patent medicines. I was told by the man who for many years handled the advertising of the Lydia E. Pinkham Company that their expenditure was $100,000 a month, $1,200,000 a year. Dr. Pierce and the Peruna Company both advertise much more extensively than the Pinkham Company. Certainly there are at least five patent medicine concerns in the United States who each pay out to the newspapers more than one million dollars a year. When the Dr. Greene Nervura Company of Boston went into bankruptcy, its debts to newspapers for advertising amounted to $535,000. To the Boston "Herald" alone it owed $5,000, and to so small a paper, comparatively, as the Atlanta "Constitution" is owed $1,500. One obscure quack doctor in New York, who did merely an office business, was raided by the authorities, and among the papers seized there were contracts showing that within a year he had paid to one paper for advertising $5,856.80; to another $20,000. Dr. Humphreys, one of the best known patent medicine makers, has said to his fellow-members of the Patent Medicine Association: "The twenty thousand newspapers of the United States make more money from advertising the proprietary medicines than do the proprietors of the medicines themselves. . . . Of their Receipts, one-third to one-half goes for advertising." More than six years ago, Cheney, the president of the National Association of Patent Medicine Men, estimated the yearly amount paid to the newspapers by the larger patent medicine concerns at twenty million dollars—more than one thousand dollars to each daily, weekly, and monthly periodical in the United States.

Does this throw any light on the silence of the Massachusetts papers? Naturally such large sums paid by the patent medicine men to the newspapers suggest the thought of favor. But silence is too important a part of the patent medicine man's business to be left to the capricious chance of favor. Silence is the most important thing in his business. The ingredients of his medicine—that is nothing. Does the price of golden-seal go up? Substitute whiskey. Does the price of whiskey go up? Buy the refuse wines of the California vineyards. Does the price of opium go too high, or public fear of it make it an inexpedient thing to use? Take it out of the formula and substitute any worthless barnyard weed. But silence is the fixed quantity—silence as to the frauds he practices; silence as to the abominable stewings and brewings that enter into his nostrum; silence as to the deaths and sicknesses he causes; silence as to the drug fiends he makes, the inebriate asylums he fills. Silence he must have. So he makes silence a part of the contract.

Read the significant silence of the Massachusetts newspapers in the light of the following contracts for advertising. They are the regular printed form used by Hood, Ayer, and Munyon in making their advertising contracts with thousands of newspapers throughout the United States.

Consider the contract made by the J. C. Ayer Company, makers of Ayer's Sarsaparilla. At the top is the name of the firm, "The J. C. Ayer Company, Lowell, Mass.," and the date. Then follows a blank for the number of dollars, and then the formal contract: "We hereby agree, for the sum of............Dollars per year, ...to insert in the............, published at............, the advertisement of the J. C. Ayer Company." Then follow the conditions as to space to be used each issue, the page the advertisement is to be on, and the position it is to occupy. Then these two remarkable conditions of the contract: "First—It is agreed in case any law or laws are enacted, either State or national, harmful to the interests of the J. C. Ayer Company, that this contract may be canceled by them from date of such enactment, and the insertions made paid for pro-rata with the contract price."

This clause is remarkable enough. But of it more later. For the present, examine the second clause: "Second—It is agreed that the J. C. Ayer Company may cancel this contract, pro-rata, in case advertisements are published in this paper in which their products are offered, with a view to substitution or other harmful motive, also in case any matter otherwise detrimental to the J. C. Ayer Company's interests is permitted to appear in the reading columns or elsewhere in the paper.

This agreement is signed in duplicate, one copy by the J. C. Ayer Company and the other one by the newspaper.

That is the contract of silence. (Notice the next one to it in identically the same language, bearing the name of the C. I. Hood Company, the other great manufacturer of sarsaparilla; and then the third —again in identically the same words—for Dr. Munyon.) That is the clause which, with forty million dollars, muzzles the press of the country. I wonder if the Standard Oil Company could, for forty million dollars, bind the newspapers of the United States in a contract that "no matter detrimental to the Standard Oil Company's interests be permitted to appear in the reading columns or elsewhere in this paper."

Is it a mere coincidence that in each of these contracts the silence clause is framed in the same words? Is the inference fair that there is an agreement among the patent medicine men and quack doctors each to impose this contract on all the newspapers with which it deals, one reaching the newspapers which the other does not, and all combined reaching all the papers in the United States, and effecting a universal agreement among newspapers to print nothing detrimental to patent medicines? You need not take it as an inference. I shall show it later as a fact.

"In the reading columns or elsewhere in this paper." The paper must not print it itself, nor must it allow any outside party, who might wish to do so, to pay the regular advertising rates and print the truth about patent medicines in the advertising columns. More than a year ago, just after Mr. Bok had printed his first article exposing patent medicines, a business man in St. Louis, a man of great wealth, conceived that it would help his business greatly if he could have Mr. Bok's article printed as an advertisement in every newspaper in the United States. He gave the order to a firm of advertising agents and the firm began in Texas, intending to cover the country to Maine. But that advertisement never got beyond a few obscure country papers in Texas. The contract of silence was effective; and a few weeks later, at their annual meeting, the patent medicine association "Resolved"—I quote the minutes—"That this Association commend the action of the great majority of the publishers of the United States who have consistently refused said false and malicious attacks in the shape of advertisements which in whole or in part libel proprietary medicines."

I have said that the identity of the language of the silence clause in several patent medicine advertising contracts suggest mutual understanding among the nostrum makers, a preconceived plan: and I have several times mentioned the patent medicine association. It seems incongruous, almost humorous, to speak of a national organization of quack doctors and patent medicine makers; but there is one, brought together for mutual support, for co-operation, for—but just what this organization *is* for, I hope to show. No other organization ever demonstrated so clearly the truth that "in union there is strength." Its official name is an innocent-seeming one—"The Proprietary Association of America." There are annual meetings, annual reports, a constitution, by-laws. And I would call special attention to Article II of those by-laws.

"The objects of this association," says this article, "are: to protect the rights of its members to the respective trade-marks that they may own or control; to establish such mutual co-operation as may be required in the various branches of the trade: to reduce all burdens that may be oppressive; to facilitate and foster equitable principles in the purchase and sale of merchandise; to acquire and preserve for the use of its members such business information as may be of value to them; to adjust controversies and promote harmony among its members."

That is as innocuous a statement as ever was penned of the objects of any organization. It might serve for an organization of honest cobblers. Change a few words, without altering the spirit in the least, and a body of ministers might adopt it. In this laboriously complete statement of objects, there is no such word as "lobby" or "lobbying." Indeed, so harmless a word as "legislation" is absent—strenuously absent.

But I prefer to discover the true object of the organization of the "Proprietary Association of America" in another document than Article II of the by-laws. Consider the annual report of the treasurer, say for 1904. The total of money paid out during the year was $8,516.26. Of this, one thousand dollars was for the secretary's salary, leaving $7,516.26 to be accounted for. Then there is an item of postage, one of stationery, one of printing—the little routine expenses of every organization; and finally there is this remarkable item:

"Legislative Committee, total expenses, $6,606.95."

Truly the Proprietary Association of America seems to have several objects, as stated in its by-laws, which cost it very little, and one object—not stated in its by-laws at all—which costs it all its annual revenue aside from the routine expenses of stationery, postage, and secretary. If just a few more words of comment may be permitted upon this point, does it not seem odd that so large an item as $6,606.95, out of a total budget of only $8,516.26, should be put in as a lump sum, "Legislative Committee, total expenses"? And would not the annual report of the treasurer of the Proprietary Association of America be a more entertaining document if these "total expenses" of the Legislative Committee were carefully itemized?

Not that I mean to charge the direct corruption of legislatures. The Proprietary Association of America used to do that. They used to spend, according to the statement of the present president of the organization, Mr. F. J. Cheney, as much as seventy-five thousand dollars a year. But that was before Mr. Cheney himself discovered a better way. *The fighting of public health legislation is the primary object and chief activity, the very* raison d'être, *of the Proprietary Association.* The motive back of bringing the quack doctors and patent medicine manufacturers of the United States into a mutual organization was this: Here are some scores of men, each paying a large sum annually to the newspapers. The aggregate of these sums is forty million dollars. By organization, the full effect of this money can be got and used as a unit in preventing the passage of laws which would compel them to tell the contents of their nostrums, and in suppressing the newspaper publicity which would drive them into oblivion. So it was no mean intellect which devised the scheme whereby every newspaper in America is made an active lobbyist for the patent medicine association. The man who did it is the present president of the organization, its executive head in the work of suppressing public knowledge, stifling public opinion, and warding off public health legislation—the Mr. Cheney already mentioned. He makes a catarrh cure which, according to the Massachusetts State Board of Health, contains fourteen and three-fourths per cent of alcohol. As to his scheme for making the newspapers of America not only maintain silence, but actually lobby in behalf of the patent medicines, I am glad that I am not under the necessity of describing it in my own words. It would be easy to err in the direction that makes for incredulity. Fortunately I need take no responsibility. I have Mr. Cheney's own words, in which he explained his scheme to his fellow-members of the Proprietary Association of America. The quotation marks alone (and the comment within parentheses) are mine. The remainder is the language of Mr. Cheney himself:

"We have had a good deal of difficulty in the last few years with the different legislatures of the different States. . . . I believe I have a plan whereby we will have no difficulty whatever with these people. I have used it in my business for two years, and I know it is a practical thing. . . . I, inside of the last two years, have made contracts with between fifteen and sixteen thousand newspapers, and never had but one man refuse to sign the contract, and by saying to him that I could not sign a contract without this clause in it he readily signed it. My point is merely to shift the responsibility. We to-day have the responsibility of the whole matter upon our shoulders. As you all know, there is hardly a year but we have had a lobbyist in the different State Legislatures—one year in New York, one year in New Jersey, and so on." (Read that frank confession twice—note the bland matter-of-factness of it.) "There has been constant fear that something would come up, so I had this clause in my contract added. This is what I have in every contract I make: 'It is hereby agreed that should your State, or the United States Government, pass any law that would interfere with or restrict the sale of proprietary medicines, this contract shall become void.' . . . In the State of Illinois a few years ago they wanted to assess me three hundred dollars. I thought I had a better plan than this, so I wrote to about forty papers and merely said: 'Please look at your contract with me and take note that if this law passes you and I must stop doing business, and my contracts cease.' The next week every one of them had an article, and Mr. Man had to go. . . . I read this to Dr. Pierce some days ago and he was very much taken up with it. I have carried this through and know it is a success. I know the papers will accept it. Here is a thing that costs us nothing. We are guaranteed against the $75,000 loss for nothing. It throws the responsibility on the newspapers. . . . I have my contracts printed and I have this printed in red type, right square across the contract, so there can be absolutely no mistake, and the newspaper man can not say to me, 'I did not see it.' He did see it and knows what he is doing.

It seems to me it is a point worth every man's attention. . . . I think this is pretty near a sure thing."

I should like to ask the newspaper owners and editors of America what they think of that scheme. I believe that the newspapers, when they signed each individual contract, were not aware that they were being dragooned into an elaborately thought-out scheme to make every newspaper in the United States, from the greatest metropolitan daily to the remotest country weekly, an active, energetic, self-interested lobbyist for the patent medicine association. If the newspapers knew how they were being used as cat's-paws, I believe they would resent it. Certainly the patent medicine association itself feared this, and has kept this plan of Mr. Cheney's a careful secret. In this same meeting of the Proprietary Association of America, just after Mr. Cheney had made the speech quoted above, and while it was being resolved that every other patent medicine man should put the same clause in his contract, the venerable Dr. Humphreys, oldest and wisest of the guild, arose and said: "Will it not be now just as well to act upon this, each and every one for himself, instead of putting this on record? . . . I think the idea is a good one, but really don't think it had better go in our proceedings." And another fellow nostrum-maker, seeing instantly the necessity of secrecy, said: "I am heartily in accord with Dr. Humphreys. The suggestion is a good one, but when we come to put it in our public proceedings, and state that we have adopted such a resolution, I want to say that the Legislators are just as sharp as the newspaper men. . . . As a consequence, this will decrease the weight of the press comments. Some of the papers, also, who would not come in, would publish something about it in the way of getting square. . . ."

This contract is the backbone of the scheme. The further details, the organization of the bureau to carry it into effect—that, too, has been kept carefully concealed from the generally unthinking newspapers, who are all unconsciously mere individual cogs in the patent medicine lobbying machine. At one of the meetings of the Association, Dr. R. V. Pierce of Buffalo arose and said (I quote him verbatim): . . . "I would move you that the report of the Committee on Legislation be made a special order to be taken up immediately . . . that it be considered in executive session, and that every person not a member of the organization be asked to retire, so that it may be read and considered in executive session. There are matters and suggestions in reference to our future action, and measures to be taken which are advised therein, that we would not wish to have published broadcast over the country for very good reasons."

Now what were the "matters and suggestions" which Dr. Pierce "would not wish to have published broadcast over the country for very good reasons?"

Dr. Pierce's son, Dr. V. Mott Pierce, was chairman of the Committee on Legislation. He was the author of the "matters and suggestions" which must be considered in the dark. "Never before," said he, "in the history of the Proprietary Association were there so many bills in different State Legislatures that were vital to our interests. This was due, we think, to an effort on the part of different State Boards of Health, who have of late years held national meetings, to make an organized effort to establish what are known as 'pure food laws.' " Then the younger Pierce stated explicitly the agency responsible for the defeat of this public health legislation: "We must not forget to place the honor where due for our uniform success in defeating class legislation directed against our legitimate pursuits. The American Newspaper Publishers' Association has rendered us valued aid through their secretary's office in New York, and we can hardly overestimate the power brought to bear at Washington by individual newspapers." . . . (On another occasion, Dr. Pierce, speaking of two bills in the Illinois Legislature, said: "Two things operated to bring these bills to the danger line. In the first place, the Chicago papers were almost wholly without influence in the Legislature. . . . Had it not been for the active co-operation of the press of the State outside of Chicago, there is absolute certainty that the bill would have passed. . . . I think that a great many members do not appreciate the power that we can bring to bear upon legislation through the press.") But this power, in young Dr. Pierce's opinion, must be organized and systematized. "If it is not presumptuous on the part of your chairman," he said modestly, "to outline a policy which experience seems to dictate for the future, it would be briefly as follows"—here the younger Pierce explains the "matters and suggestions" which must not be "published broadcast over the country." The first was "the organization of a Legislative Bureau, with its offices in New York or Chicago. Second, a secretary, to be appointed by the chairman of the Committee on Legislation, who will receive a stated salary, sufficiently large to be in keeping with such person's ability, and to compensate him for the giving of all his time to this work." "The benefits of such a working bureau to the Proprietary Association," said Dr. Pierce, "can be foreseen: First, a systematic plan to acquire early knowledge of pending or threatened legislation could be taken up. In the past we have relied too much upon newspaper managers to acquaint us of such bills coming up. . . . Another plan would be to have the regulation formula bill, for instance, introduced by some friendly legislator, and have it referred to his own committee, where he could hold it until all danger to such another bill being introduced were over, and the Legislature had adjourned."

Little wonder Dr. Pierce wanted a secret session to cover up the frank naïveté of his son, which he did not "wish to have published broadcast over the country, for very good reasons."

In discussing this plan for a legislative bureau, another member told what in his estimation was needed. "The trouble," said he—I quote from the minutes—"the trouble we will have in attempting to buy legislation—supposing we should attempt it—is that we will never know what we are buying until we get through. We may have paid the wrong man, and the bill is passed and we are out. It is not a safe proposition, if we considered it legitimate, which we do not."

True, it is not legitimate, but the main point is, it's not safe; that's the thing to be considered.

The patent medicine man continued to elaborate on the plans proposed by Dr. Pierce: "It would not be a safe proposition at all. What this Association should have . . . is a regularly established bureau. . . . We should have all possible information on tap, and we should have a list of the members of the Legislature of every State. We should have a list of the most influential men that control them, or that can influence them. . . . For instance, if in the State of Ohio a bill comes up that is adverse to us, turn to the books, find out who are the members of the Legislature there, who are the publishers of the papers in the State, where they are located, which are the Republican and which the Democratic papers. . . . It will take money, but if the money is rightly spent, it will be the best investment ever made."

That is about as comprehensive, as frankly impudent a scheme of controlling legislation as it is possible to imagine. The plan was put in the form of a resolution, and the resolution was passed. And so the Proprietary Association of America maintains a lawyer in Chicago, and a permanent secretary, office, and staff. In every State capital in the United States it maintains an agent whose business it is to watch during the session of the Legislature each day's batch of new bills, and whenever a bill affecting patent medicines shows its head to telegraph the bill, verbatim, to headquarters. There some scores of printed copies of the bill are made, and a copy is sent to every member of the Association—to the Peruna people, to Dr. Pierce at Buffalo, to Kilmer at Binghamton, to Cheney at Toledo, to the Pinkham people at Lynn, and to all the others. Thereupon each manufacturer looks up the list of papers in the threatened State with which he has the contracts described above. And to each newspaper he sends a peremptory telegram calling the publisher's attention to the obligations of his contract, and commanding him to go to work to defeat the anti-patent-medicine bill. In practice, this organization works with smooth perfection and well-oiled accuracy to defeat the public health legislation which is introduced by Boards of Health in over a score of States every year. To illustrate, let me describe as typical the history of the public health bills which were introduced and defeated in Massachusetts last year. I have already mentioned them as showing how the newspapers, obeying that part of their contract which requires them to print nothing harmful to patent medicines, refused to print any account of the exposures which were made by several members of the Legislature during the debate of the bill. I wish here to describe their obedience to that other clause of the contract, in living up to which they printed scores of bitterly partisan editorials against the public health bill, and against its authors personally: threatened with political death those members of the Legislature who were disposed to vote in favor of it, and even, in the persons of editors and owners, went up to the State House and lobbied personally against the bill. And since I have already told of Mr. Cheney's authorship of the scheme, I will here reproduce, as typical of all the others (all the other large patent medicine concerns sent similar letters and telegrams), the letter which Mr. Cheney himself on the 14th day of February sent to all the newspapers in Massachusetts with which he has his lobbying contracts—practically every newspaper in the State:

"Toledo, Ohio, *Feb.* 14, 1905

"Publishers

——, Mass.

"Gentlemen:

"Should House bills Nos. 829, 30, 607, 724, or Senate bill No. 185 become laws, it will force us to discontinue advertising in your State. Your prompt attention regarding this bill we believe would be of mutual benefit.

"We would respectfully refer you to the contract which we have with you.

Respectfully,

"Cheney Medicine Company."

Now here is the fruit which that letter bore: a strong editorial against the anti-patent-medicine bill, denouncing it and its author in the most vituperative language, a marked copy of which was sent to every member of the Massachusetts Legislature. But this was not all that this one zealous publisher did; he sent telegrams to a number of members, and a personal letter to the representative of his district calling on that member not only to vote, but to use his influence against the bill, on pain of forfeiting the paper's favor.

Now this seems to me a shameful thing—that a Massachusetts newspaper, of apparent dignity and outward high standing, should jump to the cracking of the whip of a nostrum-maker in Ohio; that honest and well-meaning members of the Massachusetts Legislature, whom all the money of Rockefeller could not buy, who obey only the one thing which they look upon as the expression of the public opinion of their constituents, the united voice of the press of their district—that these men should unknowingly cast their votes at the dictate of a nostrum-maker in Ohio, who, if he should deliver his command personally and directly, instead of through a newspaper supine enough to let him control it for a hundred dollars a year, would be scorned and flouted.

Any self-respecting newspaper must be humiliated by the attitude of the patent medicine association. They don't *ask* the newspapers to do it—they *order* it done. Read again Mr. Cheney's account of his plan, note the half-contemptuous attitude toward the newspapers. And read again Mr. Cheney's curt letter to the Massachusetts papers: observe the threat just sufficiently veiled to make it more of a threat; and the formal order, as from a superior to a clerk: "We would respectfully refer you to the contract which we have with you."

And the threat is not an empty one. The newspaper which refuses to aid the patent medicine people is marked. Some time ago Dr. V. Mott Pierce of Buffalo was chairman of what is called the "Committee on Legislation" of the Proprietary Association of America. He was giving his annual report to the Association. "We are happy to say," said he, "that though over a dozen bills were before the different State Legislatures last winter and spring, yet we have succeeded in defeating all the bills which were prejudicial to proprietary interests without the use of money, and through the vigorous co-operation and aid of the publishers. January 23 your committee sent out letters to the principal publications in New York asking their aid against this measure. It is hardly necessary to state that the publishers of New York responded generously against these harmful measures. The only small exception was the 'Evening Star' of Poughkeepsie, New York, the publisher of which, in a very discourteous letter, refused to assist us in any way."

Is it to be doubted that Dr. Pierce reported this exception to his fellow patent medicine men, that they might make note of the offending paper, and bear it in mind when they made their contracts the following year? There are other cases which show what happens to the newspaper which offends the patent medicine men. I am fortunate enough to be able to describe the following incident in the language of the man who wielded the club, as he told the story with much pride to his fellow patent medicine men at their annual meeting:

"Mr. Chairman and Gentlemen of the Proprietary Association," said Mr. Cooper, "I desire to present to you a situation

cessful as with the more elaborately organized newspapers of older and more populous States.

Just now is the North Dakota editor's time of trial. The law went into effect July 1. The patent medicine association, at their annual meeting in May, voted to withdraw all their advertising from all the papers in that State. This loss of revenue, they argued self-righteously, would be a warning to the newspapers of other States. Likewise it would be a lesson to the newspapers of North Dakota. At the next session of the Legislature they will seek to have the label bill repealed, and they count on the newspapers, chastened by a lean year, to help them. For the independence they have shown in the past, and for the courage they will be called upon to show in the future, therefore let the newspapers of North Dakota know that they have the respect and admiration of all decent people.

"What is to be done about it?" is the question that follows exposure of organized rascality. In few cases is the remedy so plain as here. For the past, the newspapers, in spite of these plain contracts of silence, must be acquitted of any very grave complicity. The very existence of the machine that uses and directs them has been a carefully guarded secret. For the future, be it understood that any newspaper which carries a patent medicine advertisement knows what it is doing. The obligations of the contract are now public property. And one thing more, when next a member of a State Legislature arises and states, as I have so often heard: "Gentlemen, this label bill seems right to me, but I can not support it; the united press of my district is opposed to it"—when that happens, let every one understand the wires that have moved "the united press of my district."

Will the "Free" Press Free Itself?

Editorial Bulletin

Early in its campaign against patent medicine "cure-alls" Collier's *found itself forced, in all conscience, to jettison the lucrative patent medicine advertising. Soon its involvement in the anti-saloon fight brought it to the same kind of impasse regarding liquor advertising. It resolved the issue with the following:*

Editorial Bulletin
New York, Saturday, November Fourth, Nineteen Hundred and Five.

WHILE THE PATENT MEDICINE ARTICLE in this number is not a part of "The Great American Fraud" series prepared by Mr. Adams (and therefore not already announced), we have decided that the subjects it treats are of such importance that they are better published now than withheld until the end of Mr. Adams's series. This article shows just how relentless a grip the Patent Medicine claw has upon the newspapers of this country. The nostrum makers can actually forbid the papers from printing news in their news columns. Read the article and become convinced of this. The only solace we find in the situation is that the newspapers can not have realized how enslaved they are. The publication of the facts, however, will deprive them of any further excuse for protecting the Patent Medicine business, and for printing in their columns not only the advertisements of poisonous compounds, but of keeping out of their columns reports of those who die from drinking Peruna, Liquozone, and other "cures"; accounts of the efforts of Health Boards to prevent the sale of these "medicines"; and "any other matter detrimental to" the fakes. Another result of the publication of this article at the present time will be to show our readers how the game is worked behind the scenes, or rather behind the newspapers, by the Patent Medicine makers. Many small newspapers throughout the country are now printing articles in praise of various nostrums and scoring *Collier's* for its "attack" on these highly virtuous products. These poor little fellows publish such stuff (furnished to them by the Patent Medicine makers) because they fear to lose the revenue they derive from that source. But after reading this article our readers will be able to see clearly the motives of any publication which supports or indorses or champions the cause of the Great American Fraud.

We Are Not So "Holy"

Many readers and some of our newspaper friends accuse us of adopting a "holy" attitude toward patent medicines, and charge us with inconsistency because we have printed advertisements of beer and whiskey. Let us remind them that it is not so long since we ourselves published advertisements of some of the worst patent medicines which we are now attacking. We threw them out, not because we wanted to be considered "holy," but because we came to see that we were party to an injury and a fraud, and that the press was at the very basis of the wrong. We have now gone further, but from a different motive. We do not believe that conscience or consistency compels us to reject advertisements of beer or whiskey. Ours is not a total abstinence crusade; it is a crusade against fraud and poison, against alcohol and drugs masquerading in the innocent guise of "tonics" and "headache powders."

We have stated this distinction many times. As it seems impossible to make it clear to thousands of well-intentioned readers, whose help we need in our onslaught on the patent medicine evil, we have decided, not on any "high" moral grounds, but purely to save perpetual explanation and remove all misunderstanding between our readers and ourselves, to drop all advertisements of beer and whiskey from this time forward. We take no credit for the sacrifice of advertising revenue this entails. It will simply save a great deal of useless argument. We have tried to formulate an advertising policy, based on common-sense rather than "holiness," that will protect our readers from being imposed upon. That policy is briefly as follows:

COLLIER's will accept no advertisements of beer, whiskey, or alcoholic liquors; no advertisements of patent medicines; no medical advertisements or advertisements making claims to medicinal effect; no investment advertising promising extraordinary returns, such as stocks in mining, oil, and rubber companies. The editor reserves the right to exclude any advertisement which he considers extravagant in claim, or offensive to good taste.

The Story of an Eye-Witness

Jack London

When the first telegraphic flash of the San Francisco earthquake and fire reached New York, Collier's *wired Jack London to rush down from his home forty miles north of the city and cover it. London did—and filed this eye-witnesser for the next issue of* Collier's. *Then thirty years old, Jack London was already famous as the author of* The Call of the Wolf, Tales of the Fish Patrol, *and other novels;* White Fang *was to come the next year. Will Irwin's story for the* New York Sun, *written at a distance of 3,000 miles, was more imaginative; Robert O'Brien, reconstructing the story for* Collier's *half a century later, was able to provide it greater depth and symmetry. London, watching a spectacle too big for words, wrote what he saw—and wrote it well.*

May 5, 1906

THE EARTHQUAKE SHOOK DOWN IN SAN Francisco hundreds of thousands of dollars' worth of walls and chimneys. But the conflagration that followed burned up hundreds of millions of dollars' worth of property. There is no estimating within hundreds of millions the actual damage wrought. Not in history has a modern imperial city been so completely destroyed. San Francisco is gone. Nothing remains of it but memories and a fringe of dwelling-houses on its outskirts. Its industrial section is wiped out. Its business section is wiped out. Its social and residential section is wiped out. The factories and warehouses, the great stores and newspaper buildings, the hotels and the palaces of the nabobs, are all gone. Remains only the fringe of dwelling-houses on the outskirts of what was once San Francisco.

Within an hour after the earthquake shock the smoke of San Francisco's burning was a lurid tower visible a hundred miles away. And for three days and nights this lurid tower swayed in the sky, reddening the sun, darkening the day, and filling the land with smoke.

On Wednesday morning at a quarter past five came the earthquake. A minute later the flames were leaping upward. In a dozen different quarters south of Market Street, in the working-class ghetto, and in the factories, fires started. There was no opposing the flames. There was no organization, no communication. All the cunning adjustments of a twentieth century city had been smashed by the earthquake. The streets were humped into ridges and depressions, and piled with the débris of fallen walls. The steel rails were twisted into perpendicular and horizontal angles. The telephone and telegraph systems were disrupted. And the great water-mains had burst. All the shrewd contrivances and safeguards of man had been thrown out of gear by thirty seconds' twitching of the earth-crust.

By Wednesday afternoon, inside of twelve hours, half the heart of the city was gone. At that time I watched the vast conflagration from out on the bay. It was dead calm. Not a flicker of wind stirred. Yet from every side wind was pouring in upon the city. East, west, north, and south, strong winds were blowing upon the doomed city. The heated air rising made an enormous suck. Thus did the fire of itself build its own colossal chimney through the atmosphere. Day and night this dead calm continued, and yet, near to the flames, the wind was often half a gale, so mighty was the suck.

Wednesday night saw the destruction of the very heart of the city. Dynamite was lavishly used, and many of San Francisco's proudest structures were crumbled by man himself into ruins, but there was no withstanding the onrush of the flames. Time and again successful stands were made by the firefighters, and every time the flames flanked around on either side, or came up from the rear, and turned to defeat the hard-won victory.

An enumeration of the buildings destroyed would be a directory of San Francisco. An enumeration of the buildings undestroyed would be a line and several addresses. An enumeration of the deeds of heroism would stock a library and bankrupt the Carnegie medal fund. An enumeration of the dead—will never be made. All vestiges of them were destroyed by the flames. The number of the victims of the earthquake will never be known. South of Market Street, where the loss of life was particularly heavy, was the first to catch fire.

Remarkable as it may seem, Wednesday night, while the whole city crashed and roared into ruin, was a quiet night. There were no crowds. There was no shouting and yelling. There was no hysteria, no disorder. I passed Wednesday night in the path of the advancing flames, and in all those terrible hours I saw not one woman who wept, not one man who was excited, not one person who was in the slightest degree panic-stricken.

Before the flames, throughout the night, fled tens of thousands of homeless ones. Some were wrapped in blankets. Others carried bundles of bedding and dear household treasures. Sometimes a whole family was harnessed to a carriage or delivery wagon that was weighted down with their possessions. Baby buggies, toy wagons, and go-carts were used as trucks, while every other person was dragging a trunk. Yet everybody was gracious. The most perfect courtesy obtained. Never, in all San Francisco's history, were her people so kind and courteous as on this night of terror.

All night these tens of thousands fled before the flames. Many of them, the poor people from the labor ghetto, had fled all day as well. They had left their homes burdened with possessions. Now and again they lightened up, flinging out upon the street clothing and treasures they had dragged for miles.

They held on longest to their trunks, and over these trunks many a strong man broke his heart that night. The hills of San Francisco are steep, and up these hills, mile after mile, were the trunks dragged. Everywhere were trunks, with across them lying their exhausted owners, men and women. Before the march of the flames were flung picket lines of soldiers. And a block at a time, as the flames advanced, these pickets retreated. One of their tasks was to keep the trunk-pullers moving. The exhausted creatures, stirred on by the menace of bayonets, would arise and struggle up the steep pavements, pausing from weakness every five or ten feet.

Often, after surmounting a heart-breaking hill, they would find another wall of flame advancing upon them at right angles and be compelled to change anew the line of their retreat. In the end, completely played out, after toiling for a dozen hours like giants thousands of them were compelled to abandon their trunks. Here the shopkeepers and soft members of the middle class were at a disadvantage. But the working-men dug holes in vacant lots and backyards and buried their trunks.

At nine o'clock Wednesday evening I walked down through the very heart of the city. I walked through miles and miles of magnificent buildings and towering skyscrapers. Here was no fire. All was in perfect order. The police patrolled the streets. Every building had its watchman at the door. And yet it was doomed, all of it. There was no water. The dynamite was giving out. And at right angles two different conflagrations were sweeping down upon it.

At one o'clock in the morning I walked down through the same section. Everything still stood intact. There was no fire. And yet there was a change. A rain of ashes was falling. The watchmen at the doors were gone. The police had been withdrawn. There were no firemen, no fire-engines, no men fighting with dynamite. The district had been absolutely abandoned. I stood at the corner of Kearney and Market, in the very innermost heart of San Francisco. Kearney Street was deserted. Half a dozen blocks away it was burning on both sides. The street was a wall of flame. And against this wall of flame, silhouetted sharply, were two United States cavalrymen sitting their horses, calming watching. That was all. Not another person was in sight. In the intact heart of the city two troopers sat their horses and watched.

Surrender was complete. There was no water. The sewers had long since been pumped dry. There was no dynamite. Another fire had broken out further uptown, and now from three sides conflagrations were sweeping down. The fourth side had been burned earlier in the day. In that direction stood the tottering walls of the Examiner building, the burned-out Call building, the smoldering ruins of the Grand Hotel, and the gutted, devastated, dynamited Palace Hotel.

The following will illustrate the sweep of the flames and the inability of men to calculate their spread. At eight o'clock Wednesday evening I passed through Union Square. It was packed with refugees. Thousands of them had gone to bed on the grass. Government tents had been set up, supper was being cooked, and the refugees were lining up for free meals.

At half-past one in the morning three sides of Union Square were in flames. The fourth side, where stood the great St. Francis Hotel, was still holding out. An hour later, ignited from top and sides, the St. Francis was flaming heavenward. Union Square, heaped high with mountains of trunks, was deserted. Troops, refugees, and all had retreated.

It was at Union Square that I saw a man offering a thousand dollars for a team of horses. He was in charge of a truck piled high with trunks from some hotel. It had been hauled here into what was considered safety, and the horses had been taken out. The flames were on three sides of the Square, and there were no horses.

Also, at this time, standing beside the truck, I urged a man to seek safety in flight. He was all but hemmed in by several conflagrations. He was an old man and he was on crutches. Said he: "To-day is my birthday. Last night I was worth thirty thousand dollars. I bought five bottles of wine, some delicate fish, and other things for my birthday dinner. I have had no dinner, and all I own are these crutches."

I convinced him of his danger and started him limping on his way. An hour later, from a distance, I saw the truck-load of trunks burning merrily in the middle of the street.

On Thursday morning, at a quarter past five, just twenty-four hours after the earthquake, I sat on the steps of a small residence on Nob Hill. With me sat Japanese, Italians, Chinese, and negroes—a bit of the cosmopolitan flotsam of the wreck of the city. All about were the palaces of the nabob pioneers of Forty-nine. To the east and south, at right angles, were advancing two mighty walls of flame.

I went inside with the owner of the house on the steps of which I sat. He was cool and cheerful and hospitable. "Yesterday morning," he said, "I was worth six hundred thousand dollars. This morning this house is all I have left. It will go in fifteen minutes." He pointed to a large cabinet. "That is my wife's collection of china. This rug upon which we stand is a present. It cost fifteen hundred dollars. Try that piano. Listen to its tone. There are few like it. There are no horses. The flames will be here in fifteen minutes."

Outside, the old Mark Hopkins residence, a palace, was just catching fire. The troops were falling back and driving the refugees before them. From every side came the roaring of flames, the crashing of walls, and the detonations of dynamite.

I passed out of the house. Day was trying to dawn through the smoke-pall. A sickly light was creeping over the face of things. Once only the sun broke through the smoke-pall, blood-red, and showing quarter its usual size. The smoke-pall itself, viewed from beneath, was a rose color that pulsed and fluttered with lavender shades. Then it turned to mauve and yellow and dun. There was no sun. And so dawned the second day on stricken San Francisco.

An hour later I was creeping past the shattered dome of the City Hall. Than it there was no better exhibit of the destructive force of the earthquake. Most of the stone had been shaken from the great dome, leaving standing the naked framework of steel. Market Street was piled high with the wreckage, and across the wreckage lay the overthrown pillars of the City Hall shattered into short crosswise sections.

This section of the city, with the exception of the Mint and the Post-Office, was already a waste of smoking ruins. Here and there through the smoke, creeping warily under the shadows of tottering walls, emerged occasional men and women. It was like the meeting of the handful of survivors after the day of the end of the world.

On Mission Street lay a dozen steers, in a neat row stretching across the street, just as they had been struck down by the flying ruins of the earthquake. The fire had passed through afterward and roasted them. The human dead had been carried away before the fire came. At another place on Mission Street I saw a milk wagon. A steel telegraph pole had smashed down sheer through the driver's seat and crushed the front wheels. The milk cans lay scattered around.

All day Thursday and all Thursday night, all day Friday and Friday night, the flames still raged.

Friday night saw the flames finally conquered, though not until Russian Hill and Telegraph Hill had been swept and three-quarters of a mile of wharves and docks had been licked up.

The great stand of the fire-fighters was made Thursday night on Van Ness Avenue. Had they failed here, the comparatively few remaining houses of the city would have been swept. Here were the magnificent residences of the second generation of San Francisco nabobs, and these, in a solid zone, were dynamited down across the path of the fire. Here and there the flames leaped the zone, but these fires were beaten out, principally by the use of wet blankets and rugs.

San Francisco, at the present time, is like the crater of a volcano, around which are camped tens of thousands of refugees. At the Presidio alone are at least twenty thousand. All the surrounding cities and towns are jammed with the homeless ones, where they are being cared for by the relief committees. The refugees were carried free by the railroads to any point they wished to go, and it is estimated that over one hundred thousand people have left the peninsula on which San Francisco stood. The Government has the situation in hand, and, thanks to the immediate relief given by the whole United States, there is not the slightest possibility of a famine. The bankers and business men have already set about making preparations to rebuild San Francisco.

Hearst and Hearstism

Frederick Palmer

William Randolph Hearst, with his brash headlines, his roaring vendettas, his "personal" journalism, and his forays into politics, was a prime target of Collier's *attack for many years. Sometimes* Collier's *(itself accused of the "yellow" journalism it accused Hearst of practicing) berated the young publisher at the top of its lungs, sometimes—as in this sketch by Frederick Palmer—it kept a tolerably civil tongue. But it never left doubt as to where it stood on Hearst and Hearstism.*

September 22, 1906

NO OTHER AMERICAN OF EQUAL CELEBRITY is so little known personally as our foremost champion of unrestrained publicity. The character of Hearst himself has been hidden in the shadows behind the searchlight whose rays he has so mercilessly directed against the affairs of other men. It would seem as if his adjutants, by his own connivance, had surrounded him with an air of mystery in order to whet public curiosity.

Long before Hearst was running for office journalistic circles were asking: Is it Hearst or is it Brisbane [Arthur Brisbane, Hearst's principal editor]? as interestedly as the general public was asking after the battle of Santiago: Was it Sampson or was it Schley? From one source you may hear that Hearst is the sole creator of the movement of which he is the head, as the public generally believes; from another you may hear that Hearst is only the name for the millions which a staff of brilliant and daring innovators has used to conjure with.

His movement, at least, has reached a point where the time for scoffing has passed. You may not dismiss him with a breath from the pulpit or a lawyerly quip of satire without flying in the face of our system of government; for the test of political power in the United States is votes. Hearst's poll as an independent candidate in New York's last election for Mayor showed that the propaganda of foot-deep headlines and capitalized editorials was taken seriously by vast masses of people.

Nor was this merely a local and sporadic demonstration. A year later we find him a formidable candidate for Governor of the most populous of our States, with his Independence League in process of organization throughout the Union. He is a strange, new element that presents to us a startling possibility. His is the first one-man party to have gained anything like national headway in the history of our democracy. His party is Hearstism, and his party did not make him, but he made his party. His power has been gained purely by advertising himself and his propaganda in his own daily editions.

In order to make the nature of his power clear, let me mention the fact that only the President of the United States or a candidate for President has the good fortune to have his speeches printed in full in all the newspapers of the country. A Hobson or a Thomas W. Lawson may be the hero of universal public affection, admiration, or curiosity for a few weeks, while other celebrities may hold the attention of some localities for a greater length of time before they drop out of the first-page headlines, victims of the editorial blue pencil responding to the need of new cries and new sensations. But Hearst is his own editor. He may print what he pleases about himself and what he pleases about any one else in his own papers. He is a celebrity who is guaranteed four million readers every day. This is the largest continuous audience that any American public man has ever possessed. It amounts to a trust of publicity.

As his is a one-man power, as it is revolutionary, we ought to know more and not less about his personality than about that of Roosevelt, Taft, and Bryan, who are the representatives of old and tried methods, and subject to the inevitable discipline of party surroundings. It is time that the citizen who regards Hearst as a deliverer, the citizen who regards him as a political buffoon, and the citizen who regards him as a dangerous blackguard should know our man, his morals, his fitness, and his training for the office which he seeks; the sum of the sincerity in his propaganda, and his constructive ability and material for accomplishing the reforms to which he has committed himself with the enthusiasm of the agitator. Therein lies the object of these articles. It is not my purpose to write a character sketch in which I shall seek in Hearst's blue eyes his soul meaning, but rather to align in sequence the pertinent facts of his career and the pertinent features of his public work, and let them speak for themselves.

Yellow journalism was not the product of inheritance or necessity with Hearst, but of choice. His father won a vast fortune by the same methods which the son has spent his life and much of that fortune in attacking. In other words, if a vast personal estate had not been accumulated in a way that our candidate's principles condemn, he would never have had the sinews of his war against capitalism. George R. Hearst, a baron among the California pioneers, made money so easily that it seemed as free as the elements to the only son who was reared without restraint. William was sent to Harvard, which is not proud of him, and yet is loyal to him in the official sense that it will not be a party to his disparagement. From the Dean's office you may learn anything you wish about another eminent Harvard man, Theodore Roosevelt, but nothing about William Randolph Hearst. However, inquiry at Cambridge and of the men of his day has developed all the essential facts of Hearst's university career.

He was known as a good fellow and generally liked. His large allowance was spent generously. His association on account of his wealth was with the wealthy class of students. But he had no chums among them or any other class; he really had no intimate friends. One of his classmates summed up his character as "amiable indolence broken by spasms of energy."

He was not a good student. By that I mean that he did not study regularly or regularly appear in the classroom, while his work, as a whole, indicated dislike of continuous application. Yet he had enormous power of application for a brief period, and he was capable of learning enough of a text-book in a night to pass an examination. This ability would undoubtedly have secured his degree if it had not been that those spasms of energy (which later on were to manifest themselves in a sudden descent upon the "Journal" office at midnight with an avalanche of sensational ideas) took the form of escapades that made dignified professors and college decorum the object of ridicule.

In his second year he was expelled. His old landlady will tell you that while Mr. Hearst was certainly very mischievous, he was very kind to her, and he was blamed for many tricks with which he was not associated. In fact, this was the plea which parental intercession made before President Eliot. The President said that his action was due not only to the "latest" count, but also to an accumulation of evidence against Hearst as a promoter of disorder from the very day that he entered the University. This amiable and indolent student already enjoyed tableaux, and he was creator and leader enough to make other men play the parts he set them. Although he had not studied his lessons diligently, he had read the newspapers diligently. His rooms were always strewn with them, including both the most sensational and the most conservative types. He played a conspicuous part in organizing sentiment in the way of fireworks and torchlight processions at Harvard for Cleveland in the campaign of '84.

When the wayward son came home, the father told him that if he would not go to school he would better go to work and learn how to conserve the great fortune he was to inherit, which is precisely what all millionaires tell their wayward sons. Nobody knew this better than son William, with his keen knowledge of the world and human nature—a kind of knowledge not learned in books or absorbed in curriculums. William was given the choice of beginning his apprenticeship at either one of the Hearst mines or one of the Hearst ranches. He was not interested in either, he said.

Besides his ranches and his mines, the father also owned the San Francisco "Examiner," a broken-down newspaper which he had bought to support his canvass for the Democratic Gubernatorial nomination, and it was even more broken down after the campaign had failed of itself, but had succeeded in becoming a quantity in the political bargain which carried George R. Hearst to the United States Senate. To his mind, newspapers were pawns to be bought and sold and played with like delegates to political conventions. His own newspaper had served its purpose, and he was looking for an opportunity to unload it on some other politically ambitious millionaire.

When William surprised his father by asking for the "Examiner," the Senator was as amazed as if the boy had announced his intention of going on the stage. At least, here was a sign that William had some object in life besides rising at eleven in the morning after having provided a surprise for the university faculty overnight. It would develop some sense of responsibility and application in him, and after he was tired of this plaything he would turn in his maturity to the serious business of life. Besides, the Senator had a great gambler's curiosity to see what Willy would do with the white elephant; and it was not long before he knew.

A young Harvard man with *carte*

blanche, you might say, would inevitably prefer to make a paper of dignity and comprehensive accuracy and intelligence for intelligent people, leaving the scandal and sensation that appeal to the gutters to other promoters who had not wealth and social position. William had no such idea. When he went East to study the field there he did not go to Dana of the "Sun," or Godkin of the "Post," or Medill of the Chicago "Tribune," but to that marvelous oriental genius in the making of ephemeral effects, Joseph Pulitzer, to whom each morning and each evening edition meant a tableau of wonder and surprise.

In the "business of selling newspapers" Pulitzer was as unsurpassed as Disraeli in the art of Parliamentary debate or Belasco in calcium light stage effects. The late member of the select Dicky of Harvard, the fair-haired, blue-eyed son of the Anglo-Saxon pioneer sat at the feet of the effervescing genius who was the scandal-mongering bane of respectable society as admiringly as ever student sat at the feet of a master. Pulitzer never performed a miracle of sensation that he did not advertise it in seven different ways as the "World's" sensation. Other newspapers turned upon him the scorn of rivals who find a new kind of game being played. Dana of the "Sun" emptied upon Pulitzer's head all the vials of his masterly sarcasm. In answer, Pulitzer sold more papers; in answer, Pulitzer erected with his profits the tallest building in New York, and set the map of the world on the globular door-knobs of its hundreds of offices, and circled the dome with rows of electric lights, which were visible from the ferryboats on river and bay. In justification he said that he wanted circulation and the power and influence that go with circulation, and in proof he took strong and determined stands on the enlightened side of many public questions and fought Tammany and Tammany methods.

He won men from other newspapers with offers of higher salaries, and when he had worked out their ideas he hired others to take their places. His average managing editor lasted less than a year. For any idea that would make his paper sell he was willing to pay handsomely. This managerial method was not new. Carnegie broke eggs with much worse ruthlessness to make his steel omelet. Unlike Carnegie, Pulitzer was as unsparing of his own health as of that of his men. When Hearst came to New York as a student of Pulitzerian methods, the "World" was just beginning to publish illustrations, which hitherto had appeared only in the weeklies and the magazines. This was twenty years ago. In that time the modern Sunday edition has come into existence. To-day it is a Coney Island of ink and wood pulp delivered at your door.

Hearst bought new presses; he equipped an art department; he arranged for the Bennett-Herald cable service and sent the bills to his father, who paid them with the same good nature that he would see a raise in a poker game. William was altogether too good a stage manager to make his changes on the "Examiner" gradually. He wanted to awake at eleven and see the sudden effect of his wonder-making on the public as he saw the sudden effect of one of his college pranks on the faculty. So San Francisco arose to a surprise in the newsboy's hand. The "Examiner" had an entirely new dress, the Bennett cable service, and scandal and sensation served under big black headlines according to the Pulitzerian model.

The old Senator made a wry face, but concluded that the boy had at least shown some "gumption" which was a promise of capabilities when youth should have tired of its plaything and turned to the serious business of the mines and ranches. The people whom the Hearsts knew would have classed the present "Examiner" with the "Police Gazette," and they were the class which William frequently made the subject of the sensations. The paradox of a young man who was to inherit one of the luxurious palaces on Nob Hill spending the night over the problem of "featuring" a murder in low life or a divorce in high life under double-column headlines soon passed out of the realm of novelty into that of accepted fact. "Stanford's boy died," said a San Francisco millionaire, "and Hearst's boy went into yellow journalism."

It was Mrs. Hearst who suffered most keenly from her son's venture at the outset of her husband's Senatorial career, when she had a mansion in Washington and a vast income to spend in furthering her ambitions. Both she and the Senator were descended from well-to-do sturdy Scotch-Irish stock, and while his experience and knowledge were limited to the business world in which he struggled and triumphed according to the rough rules of the game of his day, Mrs. Hearst was and is (for she is still living) a woman of culture and fine qualities of heart and mind. With his good looks and charming smile William's destiny seemed to be a marriage with one of the old New York families whose wealth and manners and kindred tastes have made them the (so-called) social aristocracy of the land. This youth had every commonplace which money may purchase, and they bored him. He liked the ballet with its gorgeous colors and he liked colored supplements. His associations were with newspaper men and actresses. All formality was irksome to him. He kept an engagement if it pleased him when the hour came. Society could not punish his dereliction by cutting him when he never sought society.

Those physiologists and social philosophers who are fond of studying heredity may say that the character of Hearst was affected by the yellow of the gold which was the grail of his father's pursuit, the sunsets of the Sierras, the drama of the Overland Trail, the red of the pioneer's shirt, and the wild speculations and exaggerations of mining camps, and that love of color and sound which made us in one stage of our national evolution call trains Cannon-ball Expresses and Imperial Limiteds. The new "Examiner" was blazoned on the bill-boards as the Monarch of the Dailies.

The cost of the new enterprise to the Hearst fortune was enormous the first year, and still heavier the second year, William having conducted it with an extravagance in keeping with his generosity and love of display. But it had gained so large a circulation that putting the balance on the right side of the ledger was only a question of good business management. The "Examiner" became independent of the Hearst fortune in more than name, for the old Senator found that he could not keep sensations about his own political, business, and personal friends out of its columns. News was news, William said.

William's success in making his project pay by no means reconciled the Senator to the style of journalism practised by the Monarch of the Pacific Coast. He still pleaded with his son to give up his folly and turn to the mines and ranches. When he died in '91 he showed his distrust of William by leaving his estate of about

$20,000,000 entirely in the hands of Mrs. Hearst.

The "Examiner's" profits of a quarter of a million a year were insufficient for the further flight which William had in mind. He wanted to carry the war into Pulitzer's own town, into variegated, mercurial, cosmopolitan, electrified New York, which is the true home of yellow journalism. That was possible only with his mother's help.

Hers is the pitiful figure of the Hearst history. She stood between the love of her son and loyalty to the vast fortune which should be his when she died, and which she conserved for his sake alone. She stood between love of her son and the responsibility of making the name of Hearst synonymous with vulgarity in her own world. Love won. The headstrong boy, become headstrong man, had his way. It was in '95, ten years after he had established the "Examiner," at the age of thirty-three, that Hearst turned from the theatre of all Pacific Coast to the theatre of all America.

While Mrs. Hearst spent most of her time abroad, in order to avoid the headlines of her son's papers on every news stand and in every newsboy's hand, she yielded to her son's demands for more and more money, till about ten million dollars, or one-half of the whole estate, had been absorbed. That ten million has not been wasted in a property sense, for the Hearst newspapers, if they do not actually pay it now, can be made at any time to pay a high manufacturer's return on the amount invested. If Hearst be sincere in his political propaganda then the most unwelcome of his adherents ought to be that class who enlist under his flag because he has made a monetary success out of yellow journalism.

Miss Hamilton's Endurance

Gelett Burgess

Gelett Burgess' active literary life spanned nearly the same period as Collier's Magazine, *and good humor was his principal product throughout those prolific years. Only the antique car buff—or a very senior citizen—could follow with complete understanding the technical automotive details concerning the "Cataract" and the "Matchless" models of 1907 that constitute two-fifths of the dramatis personae of "Miss Hamilton's Endurance"—but Miss Hamilton endures admirably in the jet age.*

January 19, 1907

MY CAR IS A "CATARACT" RUNABOUT. That is, it was; I've sold it now, and it makes me sick—I know I'll never have so much fun again even if I should get a 90 H. P. Mercedes. I called her the "Black Bug"—she was painted to order for a doctor, or an undertaker, or somebody who affected black—and, though she didn't have yellow wheels, she was a sporty little model, low and rakish and fast for a 10 H. P. machine. Of course, being a one-cylinder, there was a little vibration when you started up—a horizontal engine has to work, you know, especially when she's climbing—but when you turned her loose and got the proper ratio between spark and throttle, she'd travel as still as a top can spin. She saved gasoline like a miser, but she was a drunkard for oil—that was her one fault. I had her rigged out with all the lamps and meters and brass things you could think of, or that manufacturers could think of for you—everything but one of these "Gabriel's horns"; it was my desire that I didn't have exhaust enough for a three-toned trumpet. But even they are no good when it comes to kids in the road—you simply have to stop or run over them.

The Bug was second-hand when I got her, and if I'm not one of these mythical persons you read about in the catalogues who run a car a whole season and spend only fifty cents for repairs, I attribute the fact to the Bug's first owner. He must have been arrested for speeding once or twice, I imagine, by the way the cones and bushings were worn. Nevertheless, the "Cataract" is the best car of the price on the market. All of which you want to remember when I tell you how I got $1,000 for her, with extras.

I had started out, late one afternoon, for a run from Boston to Arlington. The Bug worked like a gold watch. I just soared over the hills—grade didn't seem to matter at all—and my throttle was never more than half open. I had just put in a new set of batteries, and I was enjoying my confidence in them, the way a bride feels when she has just engaged a thoroughly reliable cook. It was good to be alive and to handle a steering wheel that didn't have more than an eighth of an inch of lost-motion.

Out on Massachusetts Avenue, beyond Cambridge, they were paving the road. There was a steam-roller at work, and the street was fenced off with one of those sawhorse things with a sign on it. So I turned into a little narrow, shady road and stopped by the curb to light my lamps, for the sun had set, and I expected to be out some time. I had my engine slowed down, but still running.

I had just finished when the prettiest girl in the world came up. She was smallish and dark and brown, with what poets call "orbs" that hypnotized me. Soft fluffy hair all around her face gave her that mousey sort of look most men can't resist, but she had a little chin that I was sure meant business—if her delicate, curved mouth didn't prevent. All this I saw at the first glance, and, in the second, I saw that she was in trouble. She was walking slowly and staring rather hard, but not flirting a bit. She wasn't at all that sort of a girl. I smiled back, good-naturedly, and snapped the lamp door. She stopped, looked at me straight in the eyes as if she were doing some quick mind-reading, and I pulled off my cap. That seemed to settle her resolution. Before I knew what was up, she had jumped into the seat beside mine and cried out in a queer, excited voice:

"Won't you please take me away?—anywhere you like, only hurry!"

Well, I had been waiting for a chance like that for so many years that I didn't have to stop and ask questions. I was up beside her before she could change her mind; the throttle was wide open and my foot was on the low-gear pedal at the same moment. We began to move.

Just as I threw the speed-lever forward a big tonneau car swung into the narrow street from the avenue ahead of us, and came tearing down toward us. The girl positively cowered, and turned half round to me.

"Here he comes! He's been following me!" she gasped.

In another moment the big auto had slowed up to us, and the chap driving her yelled out:

"Say! Have you seen—?" and then he stopped just alongside.

"Milly!" he yelled next.

But by this time we were picking up speed. I jammed the spark up notch by notch and let her knock. I didn't need to be told to hurry.

"Can you get away from him?" she asked, in a pretty frightened tone that made me feel like the Squire of Dames. "Oh, he mustn't catch us!"

I gave one quick look back, and there he was, with the nose of his car against the curbstone, preparing to back, turn, and follow us. It was narrow, as I've said twice, and he had a 110-inch wheel-base, at the least. I calculated that I would get about two blocks' handicap before he could head our way.

I didn't slow down at all as we swung into the avenue, and we skated round on two wheels. I suppose I missed the curb by the thickness of the varnish on my mud-guards. I switched back into the straight with a slew that threw the girl fairly into my arms. She grabbed me till I was black and blue. Then we tore up that avenue like a runaway horse. Lord, how we bumped at the crossings! I can almost feel it yet. The girl went right up and down in the air like a rubber ball, holding on with two hands as if she were in a dentist's chair. She was trying to talk, too. All I heard was:

"He's—got bet—ter springs—than you ought—to get—shock absor—bers you ride as—if you were in a—feather—bed—but if you can—beat him I—can stand it!"

I wasn't particularly impressed, for I was rather proud of the way the Bug was lying down to her work. Of course she was light and didn't have "U"-springs, but you can hardly expect a one-ton runabout to soothe you to sleep while you're making thirty miles an hour across cobble-crossings. So I just let her have it for all she was worth, and I guess that girl got as bad a shaking-up as she ever had in her life.

"What is his car, a 'Matchless'?" I asked, after a while.

"Yep—thirty horse-power!"

"And you expect me to save your life with a one-cylinder machine? Thanks for the compliment!" I remarked, grimly.

"I expect you to try!" she said, and then she smiled at me. It was like opening the throttle eight more notches, the way it made me feel.

By this time, the other fellow was about three blocks behind, and his siren was lowing like a fog-horn on a thick night at sea. The girl watched him from over the back of her seat.

"He's gaining on us," she announced quite calmly. "You've got to dodge him, somehow!"

"All right!" I said. The next minute she was piled up in my arms again, and I had shaved a quick corner, diving down into a little cross street. Half-way down the block I turned suddenly to the right, and she nearly fell out of the car. She only said:

"Are you trying to kill me, or what?"

"I thought you wanted to go as fast as possible," I replied, letting the Bug out for a straight run.

"I do, but I prefer to travel on four wheels part of the time. Who are you, anyway? Barney Oldfield?"

"Oh, this is nothing—wait till we get to a good down grade."

"I'll be a quivering mass of pink jelly by that time. You ought to call this thing the 'Corn-Popper.' I'm not afraid to try the 'Loop the Gap' upside down now. Couldn't you try a somersault with your wagon, just to let me see how the 'Dip of Death' feels?"

I switched her up another road, and I didn't do it any too carefully either.

"There's a man behind with a faster machine than mine," I said angrily, "and if you want to change cars now's the time to say so."

She smiled sweetly at me again. "Well, he *has* got pneumatic tubes, anyway," she offered. "I didn't know they used solid rubber tires any more!" She was going up and down as she spoke, but she got the retort off without loss of sarcasm.

I confess that for a minute I was pretty mad. I slowed right down. The girl seized my arm impetuously.

"Oh, *do* go on! Really, I was only joking! It's a beautiful little car, of course! I wouldn't have asked you to take me if I hadn't thought so. Please hurry! See, there he is now!"

He was right on top of us; in fact, only about half a block away. It made me wild to think I had lighted my tail lamp. He couldn't lose us, possibly. And then, that reminded me of something. I dodged back to Massachusetts Avenue. There was a measured half mile there, where the police took time. By the time I had got to the officer on the corner I had slowed down to about twelve miles an hour, and I saw the cop look at his watch and take my number.

"Here's where your friend gets his," I remarked.

"What d'you mean?" she asked.

"If he doesn't know the road, or the policeman, he's going to get into trouble. I've led him into a trap, that's all. He hasn't lighted his lamps yet, and they'll make it hot for him, or I'm mistaken."

"Good!" she cried. "I hope they arrest him! It's our only chance, isn't it?"

I had to laugh. "Talk about looking a gift horse in the teeth," I said. "He might have an accident, I suppose. Shall I pray for a tire to burst? I can't compete with a locomotive, you know."

She was looking back. "He *is* stopped!" she exclaimed. "That policeman is talking to him. But he's awfully rich—he'll give the man a ten-dollar bill and come right along, I'm afraid."

"I hope he'll try that!" said I. "That's the quickest way to jail in this town! If he'd only strip his gears or something, we might succeed in this elopement. But I expect to be held up any minute now."

"His carburetor is working badly today," she said, reflectively.

"Why in Heaven's name didn't you say that before?" I exclaimed. "The nearest hill for us, then. This machine is a regular express elevator!"

So I slipped off the avenue again—the "Matchless" was out of sight before this, and I made for Lexington way. Then, as before, up one street and down another, higgledy-piggledy, I went, in and out, till I thought we were fairly safe. In about half an hour I slowed down and turned to the girl. She had been silent for a good while, and I imagined that she was thinking things over pretty hard.

"Well," I began, "I've saved your life, but I only did my duty. What can I do for you now?"

"You've been awfully kind to me," she began, "not even asking any questions either—"

"I didn't have time for questions before," was my reply. "*Now* I'd like to know what the trouble was?"

"I'd like to go to Arlington," she pursued, "but I'm awfully afraid he'll be on the road."

"He can't remove you from this car by force, you know," I suggested.

"N—no, I suppose not," she said. "But he can make it very disagreeable for me."

"I can make it rather disagreeable for *him*." She didn't seem to be half so grateful now as I had expected she would be.

"Oh, that would be worse!" she exclaimed. "I've had trouble enough already."

"Do you mind telling me just what's the matter?" I asked. "Of course I don't want to appear inquisitive—"

"But you are, you mean?"

"Precisely!"

"Oh, it was only a quarrel."

"I'm sorry for the other chap, if you were as sarcastic as you were with me!"

"Was I? I'm so sorry—really, I don't know how I can ever thank you!"

"I do. Tell me all about it. I'd hate to think I'd gone to all this trouble for nothing."

"Oh! Was it so much—trouble?"

"Not if we've won."

She pulled off her glove and a ruby ring from her forefinger, and touched, thoughtfully, a ruby ring on the fourth finger of her left hand. I thought she was going to take it off, but she didn't.

We were running as slowly as the Bug would go on the high speed. As I was watching her we came to a little rise, and the engine pounded and stopped. I took the crank and got out. The girl looked down at me, her face very near mine. I must confess that I was glad to hear that her engagement was broken. I began to get a little more interested in her on my own account.

"Well, I guess we've beaten him now anyway," I said.

" 'We?' That sounds funny, doesn't it?"

"It sounds all right to me." I threw the wheel over viciously, and the engine began to race. The girl shut down the throttle as if she knew all about it, and I got in beside her. "Well, then—Arlington?" I asked.

"If you would! And, you haven't an extra pair of goggles, have you?"

"Yes, and a veil." I took out my sister's outfit.

"Do you think he recognized me?" she asked.

"I thought he called you 'Milly.' " I replied.

"But he might have been mistaken, you know."

"Sure. You mean it perhaps wasn't you, after all?"

"You know what I mean. I turned my head away, didn't I?"

"Yes. And perhaps Milly isn't your name after all."

"But it is, unfortunately. Milly Hamilton. It's only fair for you to know. He's my fiancé—John Wentworth Forbes. At least, he *was*."

"Harvard '97?"

"Why, yes. D'you know him?"

"Slightly. I don't blame you for breaking it off. He has a nasty temper, I've heard."

"It isn't true at all! That is—well, he does exasperate me sometimes."

"Oh, he's notorious. I don't blame you at all."

"But it was a *little* my fault!"

"It couldn't have been! I don't believe it!"

"But I don't think that he ought to take another girl to dinner twice a week without telling me, do you?"

"Very poor taste—if he could get you."

"I don't mean that at all. Of course, I don't want to be so foolish as to tie him down, but in a public place, you know, while we're engaged—"

"Perhaps it was his country cousin—it usually is, you know."

"No. It was an awfully stunning girl. I don't care a bit, of course, for myself. I want him to have as good a time as he can; but people talk so, and they pity me and hint."

"I'd never forgive it, if I were you."

"Oh, I'd forgive it if he'd only explain. But he's so mysterious about it. He said there was a reason why he couldn't tell me. Wasn't that horrid?"

"It sounds interesting to me. Oh, he's a villain, fast enough. It's a good thing you got rid of him."

"I had hard work doing it. After we'd had it out, and he wouldn't explain, I told him I had a friend living in Cambridge and I'd stop there all night. I'm a little ashamed of it, now I've cooled off some."

"Ashamed of having a friend in Cambridge?"

"No—I didn't have any friend at all! I just pretended to. I refused to drive home with him, I was so angry."

"So you got out?"

"I pointed out a house—the first one I

saw with lights in it. I told him my friend lived there. I got out and went to the door, and a lady came, and I asked her for a drink of water, and she asked me in. He thought I was going to spend the night, of course, or else he would have followed me."

"Brute!"

"Why, what else could a gentleman do? What would you think of him if he let me go walking around the streets alone after dark?"

"But I thought he *wasn't* a gentleman!"

"Oh, he is! But he did treat me badly. You ought to have seen that woman when I came out and the auto was gone! I didn't attempt to explain, and started out alone. Then I happened to run across him, and he followed me till I found you. It was simply maddening."

We had got to the top of a long hill by this time, and, giving her plenty of gas for a start, I coasted down. We sailed along as if we were shooting rapids, faster and faster. There was a big car ahead that we rapidly overhauled, and I had tooted my horn and was preparing to pass when the girl snatched at my arm.

"Wait a minute! Slow up, please!" she commanded. "Oh, I think that's he! Hold back and get your gas lamps on his number."

I slowed down and pointed at the back of the car. The number showed plainly, "13,333."

"Oh, it *is* he! I *thought* I recognized it. Turn around quick and let's get away!"

I didn't stop to look back, and as I turned, a big Limousine car nearly cut us in two. It veered in a great arc, the driver turning back to yell his opinion of us. Miss Hamilton looked around after it.

"Oh, oh, oh!" she exclaimed. "He's stopped, and he's seen us, I'm afraid."

I piled on all the gas she could carry, and started uphill on the jump. In another minute the "Matchless" searchlights lighted us up as if we were posing for a living picture. It was most embarrassing. We had the centre of the stage that time. The girl collapsed into a limp bunch. We began to climb, and the "Matchless" after us. I heard his cut-out working—"*chuf, chuf, chuf!*"—regularly enough for a minute, and then it began to skip—"*chuf, chuf——chuf, chuf, chuf——chuf————chuf, chuf!*"—and I knew that he was in trouble. The skipping grew worse, and we got away fast till he was three blocks behind. We swept over the top of the hill and down the other side. I never touched the throttle, and jammed the spark 'way forward . . . the trees on the side of the road went past in one blurred streak. . . . My left-hand oil lamp began a steady vibration, a sort of steady hum that it always sets up as soon as we get up to thirty miles an hour; as regular as a speedometer it is. We got to the bottom before we knew it, and then flew at the next rise.

And then suddenly the Bug lay down. It was sickening—with the throttle wide open the engine simply ran down and stopped! I had to stop ignominiously enough, jam on the brake, and get out my electric torch to investigate.

"I'm sorry," I said to the girl, "but we've broken down. All I can do for you now is to protect you with my life, or I'm afraid you'll have to change cars. This is as far as we go."

"Never!" she exclaimed. "I'll stay with you. You may have to telephone to the garage. Perhaps he won't know me in this veil and goggles."

"He'd know you if he saw you in a

mummy-case," I said. "You don't happen to be the kind one forgets."

"What d'you think is the matter?" she asked. "Is it the ignition? Turn her over and see if she buzzes all right."

I turned and turned to no avail.

"Where's your switch? This is a funny little car, isn't it!"

I pointed to the switch, looked, and gave a yell like a view-halloo. The switch, for some unheard-of reason had got turned off. No wonder the Bug wouldn't go. I snapped it on and started to crank.

Just then the "Matchless" bore down on us and stopped alongside. I knew that we were in for a scene this time. John Wentworth Forbes had put on his brakes with a jar. I got a good look at him, for we were right under an electric-light pole. He was a clean-cut, gentlemanly sort of chap, smooth-shaven, the big and handsome sort. I had heard of him before—of course my talk to Miss Hamilton was all gammon, and I wasn't sorry of a chance for meeting him, although my own position was equivocal. I liked the way he kept his temper as he leaned over and said:

"Come, Milly, get in, dear!"

"No, thank you, Jack, I can't possibly leave this gentleman; he has been very nice to me."

"I'd like to say a few things to you, Milly," he went on, "and if you won't get in I'll have to say them right out here."

"Say anything you like," she retorted.

"The lady we were speaking of is engaged to my brother," he said.

"Why didn't you tell me that before?" she asked.

"It was to have been kept a secret. He's away, and while she was in Boston he wanted me to be nice to her."

"You might have told me that in the first place."

"Will you get in now?"

"I shall not," she said firmly. "That is, if this gentleman is willing to take me home."

"But I've told you *why* I couldn't explain—"

"Oh, it wasn't that alone—"

"But—"

"I don't care to discuss it here any more, Jack. Won't you be kind enough to go on and leave us alone."

I could see that if I hadn't been there it might have been straightened out in two minutes, and they would have kissed and made up. It seemed time for me to come in as *deus ex machina*. So I went up to Mr. Forbes and said to him:

"May I have two minutes' conversation with you, please?"

Miss Hamilton stared at me, and Forbes stared too, but he got out and walked up the road a few yards with me, and it took me only about two minutes to say what I had to say to him. Then we came back.

"Well," he said, "if you won't come back with me, Milly, I'll have to leave you, I suppose, but I'm sorry that we can't settle it now. It seems foolish to quarrel over so small a thing."

"It may seem small to you—" she replied.

"Good-night, then!" he said, and he waved his hand to us both. The "Matchless" moved off up-hill, skipping badly, but doing well enough to get away. In a minute he was out of ear-shot Miss Hamilton turned on me:

"What did you say to him?" she demanded.

"Why," I replied, "I told him that it wouldn't do to make trouble here on the road, and that I intended to take you home, and that it was useless for him to apologize or anything—that you were mortally offended and that I knew that it was all off."

She swallowed it all. I think she was pretty nearly angry enough to leave me as she had him; but she didn't.

"I'd like to know what right *you* have to interfere," she exclaimed. "It seems to me that you've taken an unconscionable liberty, considering the time you've known me. I think I can arrange my quarrels alone, without your help."

"You didn't think so when you got into my car," I replied, hugely amused.

"I think so *now*. I'm sorry I ever spoke to you."

"Oh, it isn't as bad as that yet, is it? Really, I only did my best to save you from a disagreeable situation. I knew that you had been insulted, and perhaps I was too strong, but—"

"Nonsense, I never *said* I was insulted! John couldn't possibly insult any one—least of all a woman he loved—and besides—didn't he explain it all perfectly?"

"You believe that story, then?" I asked disdainfully.

"Believe it! Of course! Why shouldn't I? He never told me a lie in his life—and I don't believe he'd begin now!"

We had started up, and were climbing the hill.

As we passed the electric lights I did my best to keep my face straight. But I needn't have—she wasn't looking at me now; she was looking off ahead—for a red tail lamp, I suspected, and No. 13,333 in white on a blue sign.

I turned off for Arlington.

"Did he say which way he was going?" she asked after a while.

"No," I replied. "But I doubt if he'll get far unless he stops to fix that carburetor. He's in a bad way."

"Oh—I hope he won't have trouble—I suppose he's rather desperate too, and I'm afraid he'll be reckless. Did he seem to be sorry, do you think?"

"He was pretty badly cut up," I said. "Serves him right."

"Yes," she said curtly.

"Queer looking chap, isn't he?" I remarked, as we turned again.

"I think he's handsome. Or, at least, I used to think so. 'Most everybody does, anyway."

"Rather low of him to chase us about so, though, don't you think?"

"What would you do, I'd like to know, if another man ran away with the girl you were engaged to?"

"But the engagement was broken, wasn't it?"

"Well—I hadn't really told him so."

"Why, hadn't you? Well, he'll know it by tomorrow, I expect."

"I don't know—I want to think it over first. Perhaps we might come to some kind of an understanding, although it seems unlikely. If he couldn't confide in me, then I'm not fit to be his fiancée."

"Oh, I don't trust him myself. He's pretty smooth."

"It isn't that—I trust him implicitly, but he's rude, that's all."

I had been taking it easy, not wanting to get to the corner too soon, for fear Forbes wouldn't be ready for me.

But as she spoke I caught sight of a red light, and speeded up. Miss Hamilton's eyes were sharp ahead.

"There's an auto—it's broken down, I believe. Oh, do you suppose it could be Mr. Forbes?"

"Shall I turn back?" I asked, beginning to curve.

"N—no—let's see if it is—oughtn't we to help him?"

"Just as you say. He's probably trying his spark plugs."

I ran softly down to the big "Matchless" and stopped. There was nobody in sight. Miss Hamilton grew alarmed.

"Why, this *is* his car—where d'you suppose he is?" she asked.

I got out, but took good care not to go in front of his auto.

She followed me and in a moment went ahead a little way.

Then I heard a scream, and I saw her drop to the road. I waited just long enough to touch his quadrant.

The fool had his spark 'way back—just where it ought to be. I moved it up, clear forward, for I expected it would be necessary to supply evidence for so sharp a pair of eyes and so keen an automaniac as Miss Hamilton. Then I joined her.

Mr. John Wentworth Forbes was lying in the dust. His head was resting artistically in Miss Hamilton's lap. Upon his forehead was a very convincing smear of grease, intended to conceal a bruise. She was almost hysterical.

"Get some water, quick!" she cried. "He's been hurt. He must have been hit by the crank—it back-fired on him, and knocked him senseless! Oh, hurry up and do something quick!"

"He'll come to in a minute, I'm sure!" I replied; and as I bent over him I saw his eyes open.

"Where am I?" he gasped. "Is that you, Milly? Kiss me, dear!"

I fled. The next thing I saw he was up, and she was dusting him off. He was talking. I saw him go to the wheel and show her the spark handle and tell what a fool he had been. It *was* lucky I had been there first.

I busied myself with my own car for a while and then I came back. Both of them held out their hands.

"Congratulate us, old chap, we've compromised," said Forbes.

"I knew I'd have to forgive him sooner or later," said Miss Hamilton.

I said nothing, but I never felt more like the proprietor of a marionette show.

"But there's one thing I want to tell *you*," said Forbes, keeping hold of my hand and giving it a grip that I won't soon forget, "and that is that I can't afford to have a car like yours running about after me like this. She's too good a hill-climber. I'd feel safer if I knew it were out of the way. What d'you want for her? Will a thousand do? You could get a pretty good two-cylinder for that."

"I'll take a thousand and your blessing," said I.

"Done!" he cried. "She's won the hardest endurance-test race ever driven!"

Aerial Football: The New Game

George Bernard Shaw

The famous playwright, vegetarian, and Fabian Socialist was about midway in his extraordinarily long career when he submitted this short story to Collier's. Arms and the Man, Candida, Man and Superman, *and* Major Barbara *had already appeared;* Pygmalion, Androcles and the Lion, The Apple Cart, *and innumerable stories, essays, impertinences, and witticisms were yet to come. Even more remarkable than the fact that Shaw lived nearly a full century is the fact that his tremendous talents and energies operated at full blast for nearly all of that time.*

November 23, 1907

"IS SHE DEAD?" SAID THE MOTOR BUS driver, looking very sick as the medical student from the Free Hospital picked up Mrs. Hairns in the Gray's Inn Road.

"She smells frightfully of your petrol," said the student.

The driver sniffed at her. "That's not petrol," he said. "It's methylated spirit. She's been drinking. You'll bear me witness that she smells of drink."

"Don't you know all you've done yet?" said the policeman. "You've killed his lordship."

"What lordship?" said the driver, changing from tallow color to green.

"The back end of the bus swung right into the carriage," panted the footman. "I heard his lordship's neck crack." The footman wept, not because he loved his late employer, but because sudden death affected him that way.

"The Bishop of St. Pancras," said a boy, in explanation.

"Oh, my good Lord!" said the motorman, in great trouble. "How could I help it?" he added, after wiping his brow, appealing to the crowd, which seemed to have been in solution in the air, so suddenly had it precipitated round the accident. "The bus skidded."

"So would any bus skid in this mud, going at that rate," said an indignant bystander.

And immediately the crowd began a dispute as to whether the bus had been going too fast or not, with the motorman passionately maintaining the negative against the affirmative of the whole Gray's Inn Road.

Mrs. Hairns certainly did smell of drink. She had done so more or less for forty years whenever she had twopence to spare. She had never been a nice-looking woman nor a cleanly dressed one; and the passage of the crowded motor bus over her ribs had made surprisingly little difference in her appearance. A little more mud ground into her garments could make them no worse than they were; and the change from being drunk and able to shuffle home and being drunk and incapable was not startling.

As to the bishop, there was not a scratch nor a speck of mud on him. He had not been touched. He had been boyishly proud of being a bishop, and had expressed his pride by holding his neck very stiff. Consequently it broke when the carriage was stopped suddenly by the swinging round of the tail of the bus.

Mrs. Hairns was taken aback when the bus suddenly swooped round at her. That made no difference, because no presence of mind on her part could have saved her. It did not hurt her at all. A single broken rib touching a lung is painful; but when an overwhelming shock annihilates your nerves, and an overwhelming weight makes bone dust of all your ribs, and wraps them up in a squash with your heart and lungs, sympathy becomes ridiculous. The game is up. The remediable has become irremediable: the temporal, eternal. A really flexible mind accepts the situation and thinks a great deal about it before there is time even to die. The suddenest death is a long business compared with the lightning work of imagining an experience of, say, a thousand years.

Mrs. Hairns was squashed clean out of the Gray's Inn Road on to the foot of a hill with a city on the top. It was rather like Orvieto, of which city there was a photograph in the drawing-room of the Vicar of St. Pancras, who employed Mrs. Hairns as a charwoman whenever he attempted to reclaim her, and was beaten every time by her acquired taste for methylated spirits, which enabled her to drink furniture polish with avidity, though you could trust her with untold dozens of mere hock. Beyond getting the photograph focused on her retina occasionally while dusting, Mrs. Hairns knew nothing about Orvieto. A place so unlike Pentonville Hill suggested dread and discomfort to her. She felt sure it must be almost as bad as heaven, which she associated with teetotalism, cleanliness, self-control, being particular, and all sorts of horrors. Now that she found herself actually on the road to it, she looked up at it with the utmost misgiving until a superior voice behind her made her start and attempt a shambling courtesy. It was the bishop.

"Can I obtain a conveyance anywhere here," he said, "to take me up to the gate?"

"I can't say, I'm sure, sir," said Mrs. Hairns: "I'm a stranger here."

The bishop passed on the moment she said "can't say," taking no further interest in her, and resigned himself to walk up.

There was a horse grazing a little way off. As Mrs. Hairns noticed it, a faint ray of heavenly comfort stole into her soul. Though for many years—ever since the passing away of the last rays of her youth at twenty-four or thereabout—she had been interested in nothing but methylated alcohol; she had been born with an unaccountable fancy, not for horses exactly, but, as she put it, for a horse. It was an unintelligent and innocent fancy; but it had won her hand in marriage for the late Alfred Hairns, normally and by economic necessity a carman, but by natural vocation a poacher. This rude fancier of the equine was too poor to afford a horse. But, after all, he was too poor to afford a residence in London, or a double bed, or even a suit of clothes. Yet he always had a London address; he never appeared in the streets naked; and neither he nor Mrs. Hairns slept on the floor. Society had convinced him that the lodging, the bed, and the clothes were indispensable, whether he could afford them or not; accordingly, he had them. The conviction that a horse was equally indispensable was idiosyncratic with him; so he always kept a horse, even when he could by no means afford to keep himself, maintaining that a horse made no difference—that it even paid its way. The same view has been taken of eighty-horse-power motor cars.

Bonavia Banks was attracted by his idiosyncrasy, which was also her own. She easily persuaded him that a wife was as indispensable as a horse, and equally made no difference. She became Mrs. Alfred Hairns, and bore thirteen children, of whom eleven died in infancy owing to the malversation of their parental care by the horse. Finally the horse died; and the heartbroken Hairns was tempted to buy a magnificent thoroughbred for four pounds from the widow of a gentleman who had paid two hundred and thirty for him only three days before. Hairns, while leading his bargain home, was savaged by him so that he died of lockjaw the day after the horse was shot. Thus perished miserably Alfred Hairns, the victim of the bond between man and beast which proclaims that all life is one.

The horse raised its muzzle from the grass, looked at Mrs. Hairns carelessly, switched its tail, moved on a few steps to an uncropped patch of verdure, and was about to continue its repast when, as if some fibre of memory had suddenly vibrated, it erected its ears, raised its neck, and looked more attentively at her. Finally it came to her, stopping only once on the way absent-mindedly to graze, and said: "Don't you remember me?"

"Chipper!" exclaimed Mrs. Hairns. "It can't be."

"It *is*," said Chipper.

Chipper conversed after the manner of Balaam's ass. That is, Mrs. Hairns knew what he was saying too well to notice that he did not actually utter any sound. But for the matter of that neither did she, though she did not notice that also. Conversation in this Orvietan region was wholly telepathic.

"Have I got to walk up that hill, Chipper?" said Mrs. Hairns.

"Yes," said Chipper, "unless I carry you."

"Would you mind?" said Mrs. Hairns shyly.

"Not at all," said Chipper.

"Ain't there a vehicle?" said Mrs. Hairns. "I can't ride barebacked. Not that I can ride anyhow."

"Then you must walk," said Chipper. "Hold on to my mane, and I'll help you up."

They got up somehow and were close to the gate before it occurred to Mrs. Hairns to ask what place it was, and to ask herself why she was going there.

"It's heaven," said Chipper.

"Oh, Lord!" said Mrs. Hairns, stopping dead. "Why didn't you tell me before? I never done anything to get me into heaven."

"True," said Chipper. "Would you rather go to hell?"

"Don't be so silly, Chipper," said Mrs. Hairns. "Ain't there nothin' between hell and heaven? We ain't all saints; but then we ain't all devils neither. Surely to gracious there must be a place for everyday sort of people that don't set up to be too particular."

"This is the only place I know," said Chipper; "and it's certainly heaven."

"Belike there might be some kitchens in it," said Mrs. Hairns. "You won't let on that I used to get a bit overcome once in a way, Chipper, will you?"

Chipper snuffed up a noseful of Mrs. Hairn's aura. "I should keep on the lee side of St. Peter," he said. "That's Peter," he added, jerking his head in the direction of an elderly gentleman with a pair of keys of twelfth century design.

The keys were more for ornament than use, apparently; for the gate stood wide open; and a stone placed against it to keep it from blowing-to was covered with moss, and had evidently not been moved for centuries. This surprised Mrs. Hairns, because it had been strongly impressed on her in her childhood on earth that the gates of heaven were always shut tight, and that it was no end of a business to get them opened.

A group of angels stood in the carriage way. Their wings, purple and gold, heliotrope and silver, amber and black, and all sorts of fine colors, struck Mrs. Hairns as lovely. One of them had a sword with a blade of lambent garnet-colored flame. Another, with one leg naked from the knee down, and a wading boot on the other, had a straight slender trumpet, which seemed long enough to reach to the horizon, and yet was as handy as an umbrella. Through the first-floor window of one of the turrets of the gate Mrs. Hairns saw Matthew, Mark, Luke, and John in bed with their breeches on according to the old rime. Seeing that, she knew this was really the gate of heaven. Nothing else would have quite convinced her.

Chipper addressed himself to Peter. "This woman is drunk," said Chipper.

"So I see," said St. Peter.

"Ow, Chipper!" said Mrs. Hairns reproachfully. "How could you?" They all looked at her, and she began to cry. The angel with the sword of flame drew it across her eyes and dried her tears. The flame did not hurt and was wonderfully reviving.

"I'm afraid she's hopeless," said Chipper. "Her own children will have nothing to do with her."

"Which planet?" said the angel with the trumpet.

"Tellus," answered Chipper.

"What am I to tell them?" said Mrs. Hairns.

The angels laughed. Peter roared. "Come!" said the trumpet angel: "She can make puns. What's wrong with her?"

"She's a liar and a thief," said Chipper.

"All the inhabitants of Tellus are liars and thieves," said the trumpet angel.

"I mean she is what even they call a liar and a thief," said Chipper.

"Oh!" said the sword angel, looking very grave.

"I'm only making it easy for you," said Chipper to Mrs. Hairns; "so that they shan't expect too much." Then, to Peter: "I brought her up because she once got out and walked on a hot Sunday when I was dragging her up a hill with her husband, three of his friends, their wives, eight children, a baby, and three dozen of beer."

"Fancy your remembering!" said Mrs. Hairns. "Did I really?"

"It was so unlike you, if I may say so," said Chipper, "that I have never forgotten it."

"I dessay it *was* silly of me," said Mrs. Hairns apologetically.

Just then the bishop arrived. He had been energetically climbing the hill by the little foot-tracks which cut across the zigzags of the road, and had consequently been overtaken by Chipper, who knew better.

"Is this the gate of heaven?" said the bishop.

"It is," said Peter.

"The *front* gate?" said the bishop suspiciously. "You are sure it is not the tradesmen's entrance?"

"It is everybody's entrance," said Peter.

"An unusual arrangement, and in my opinion an inconvenient one," said the bishop. He turned from Peter to the angels. "Gentlemen," he said, "I am the Bishop of St. Pancras."

"If you come to that," said a youth in a dalmatic, putting his head out of one of the turret windows, "I am St. Pancras himself."

"As your bishop, I am glad to meet you," said the bishop. "I take a personal interest in every member of my flock. But for the moment, I must ask you to excuse me, as I have pressing business at court. By your leave, gentlemen"—and he shouldered his way firmly through the group of angels into heaven and trotted sturdily up the street. He turned only once, for a moment, to say: "Better announce me," and went his way. The angels stared after him quite dumfounded. Then the trumpet angel made a post horn of his trumpet, and first root-a-tooted at the sky, and then swept the trumpet downward like the ray of a searchlight. It reached along the street to the bishop's coat-tails, and the next blast swept him like a dry leaf clean round a corner and out of sight.

The angels smiled a beautifully grave smile. Mrs. Hairns could not help laughing. "Ain't he a tease!" she said to Chipper, indicating the trumpet angel.

"Hadn't you better follow the bishop in?" said Chipper. Mrs. Hairns looked apprehensively at Peter (she was not afraid of the angels), and asked him might she go in.

"Anybody may go in," said Peter. "What do you suppose the gate is for?"

"I didn't understand, sir," said Mrs. Hairns. And she was approaching the threshold timidly when the bishop came back, flushed and indignant.

"I have been through the whole city in a very high wind," said the bishop; "and I can not find it. I question whether this is really heaven at all."

"Find what?" said Peter.

"The Throne, sir," said the bishop severely.

"*This* is the throne," said St. Pancras, who was still looking out of the window, with his cheeks on his palms and his palms propped on his elbows.

"*This!*" said the bishop. "Which?"

"The city," said St. Pancras.

"But—but—where is He?" said the bishop.

"Here, of course," said the sword angel.

"*Here!* Where?" said the bishop hurriedly, lowering his voice and looking apprehensively round from one to the other until he finished with the trumpet angel, who had sat down to take off his wading boot and shake a stone out of it.

"He is the presence in which we live," said the sword angel, speaking very harmoniously.

"That is why they are angels," St. Pancras explained.

"What are you looking about for?" said the trumpet angel, standing up with his boot comfortable again. "Did you expect to see somebody in a shovel hat and apron, with a nose, and a handkerchief to blow it with?"

The bishop reddened. "Sir," he said, "you are profane. You are blasphemous. You are even wanting in good taste. But for the charity my profession imposes on me I should be tempted to question whether you are in the truest sense of the word a gentleman. Good morning." And he shook the dust of heaven from his feet and walked away.

"Ain't he a cure!" said Mrs. Hairns. "But I'm glad there's no throne, nor nobody, nor nothin'. It'll be more like Kings Cross." She looked at them rather desolately; for something in the sword angel's voice had made her feel very humble and even ashamed of being drunk. They all looked back at her gravely; and she would have cried again, only she knew it would be of no use after the sword had touched her eyes; her tears were dried forever. She twisted a corner of her jacket—a deplorable jacket—in her restless fingers; and there was a silence, unbroken until the snoring of Matthew, Mark, Luke, and John became painfully audible, and made her look forlornly up at their common little wooden beds, and at the flyblown illuminated text on the wall above them: "A broken and a contrite heart, O Lord, thou wilt not despise."

"I wonder," she said, "would one of you gentlemen say a prayer for a poor drunken old charwoman that has buried eleven, and nobody's enemy but her own, before I offer to go in."

Suddenly she sat down stunned in the middle of the way; for every angel threw up his hands and wings with an amazing outcry; the sword flamed all over the sky; the trumpet searched the corners of the horizon and filled the universe with ringing notes; and the stars became visible in broad daylight and sent back an echo which affected Mrs. Hairns like an enormous draft of some new and delightful sort of methylated spirit.

"Oh, not sich a fuss about me, gentlemen," she said. "They'll think it's a queen or a lady from Tavistock Square or the like." And she felt shyer than ever about going in. The sword angel smiled, and was going to speak to her when the bishop came back, pegging along more sturdily than ever.

"Gentlemen," he said, "I have been thinking over what you said just now; and while my reason tells me that I was entirely justified in acting and speaking as I did, still your point of view may be a tenable one, and your method of expressing it, however unbecoming, effective for its purpose. I also find myself the victim of an uncontrollable impulse to act in a manner which I can not excuse, though to refrain is unfortunately beyond my powers of self-inhibition."

And with that speech he snatched off his apron, made a ball of it, stuffed it into his shovel hat, and kicked the hat into space. Before it could descend, the sword angel, with a single cut of his wings, sprang into the air whooping with ecstasy, and kicked it a mile higher. St. Pancras, who had no wings, but shot up by mere levitation, was on it in a second and was shooting off with it when the trumpet angel collared him and passed it to the amber and black angel. By that time Matthew, Mark, Luke, and John were out of bed and after Peter into the blue vault above, where a football match was already in full swing between the angels and the saints, with Sirius for one goal and the sun for the other. The bishop looked in amazement for a moment at the flying scrum; then, with a yell, sprang into the air and actually got up nearly fifty feet, but was falling from that dangerous height when the saint he patronized swooped and caught him up into the game. Twenty seconds later his hat was half-way to the moon; and the exultant shouts of the angels had dwindled to mere curlew pipings, while the celestial players looked smaller than swifts circling over Rome in summer.

Now was Mrs. Hairns's opportunity to creep in through the gate unnoticed. As her foot approached the threshold the houses of the heavenly street shone friendly in the sunshine before her, and the mosaics in the pavement glowed like flower-beds of jewels.

"She's dead," said the student from the Free Hospital. "I think there was a spark left when I took hold of her to straighten her out; but it was only a spark. She's dead now all right enough—I mean poor woman!"

The City Saloon and Vicious Politics

Will Irwin

The struggle which culminated with passage of the Eighteenth Amendment was essentially, throughout its long duration, a struggle against saloons. Prohibition, in the minds of the crusaders, was chiefly a means to eliminate this social institution. Collier's *was a tireless leader in the crusade, and through its editorial pages and the dogged reporting of such able newsmen as Will Irwin, it was a major force in the decades-long campaign. This article appeared as the first of a series by Irwin on "The American Saloon."*

February 29, 1908

IN THE PAST TWO YEARS, AND ESPECIALLY *in the year 1907, the country has awakened to realize that we have a "Prohibition Wave." Not until Georgia and Alabama had gone "dry" and prohibition had become the main issue in the tangled politics of Kentucky did the public in general perceive it. Now, at the beginning of the year 1908, nearly one-half the area of the United States is dry; and more than one-third of our people are living under prohibitory laws. The movement has gone further and faster in the South than anywhere else; but it is unfelt only in the Rocky Mountain region and in the Central States of the Atlantic Coast. Georgia is dry; Alabama has passed a prohibitory law; Mississippi has followed just as this article goes to press. In Tennessee one can buy liquor in but three small districts. Kentucky has only four wholly "wet" counties; Florida only a fringe along the seacoasts; Texas is more than half dry; Missouri and Arkansas, community by community, are falling into line; the election of January 14 in Shreveport finished the "manufacture and sale" in all the northern half of Louisiana; it is highly probable that within two years one or both of the Carolinas will vote for State-wide prohibition. Starting from the seaboard at Georgia, one can travel now to the borders of Colorado or New Mexico and cross in passage only one narrow strip of wet territory—the delta counties of Mississippi. Even these will be dry by next January.*

The movement has been only a little less strong in the North. Maine, Kansas, and North Dakota are wholly dry; but they came in on earlier movements. More recently, great areas of Illinois and Indiana have come under prohibitory law. Ohio, which has already gone dry in many spots through ward and township local option, seems on the point of passing a county local-option law. Nearly one-half the area of Chicago is under ward prohibition laws. And even where the movement for ab-

solute prohibition has had no effect, cities and towns are showing a more earnest disposition to enforce the old and half-forgotten laws for regulation of the liquor traffic.

Why is it? What has been working in our people to create this sudden revolution of moral feeling and political opinion? It is the purpose of this series to answer that question—in so far as it is possible to speak with any authority on a problem which goes down, as this one does, to the basic principles of the social structure and to the roots of human nature.

Before we begin, let us brush aside certain considerations which cloud the main issue. This habit of taking a drug which gives a temporary stimulus to all the powers of men and which, being a drug, carries its own form of slavery and degradation, is almost as old as society. The remotest traditions of the world (*vide* Genesis, 9:20), and especially the North European nations, represent men as drinking—and getting drunk. It were better, probably, that alcoholic stimulants had never been discovered; but men, and especially Anglo-Saxon and Celtic men, have taken the drug so long that its use is intertwined with nearly every institution, good and bad, in our modern life. That the elimination of this drug habit by education, by the accommodation of custom, would be for the ultimate good of the human race, is almost a truism. Yet to me it seems impossible that any one should say, in the present state of knowledge on the subject, whether the attempt at sudden and complete suppression of the habit by law would result in good or in evil. Prohibition—even in the face of a fifty-year-old experiment in Maine—is still largely an experiment. So I shall take sides neither for nor against prohibition as a political theory. It is for me only to find the causes of this remarkably strong and steady movement, and to tell the news. The causes first; and before the deeper and final causes, let me take up those reasonable arguments by which prohibition politicians have won their elections. How has it gone in the South?

The North has generally and superficially assumed that the drunken negro has brought about this prohibition wave. Although hardly a main cause, the economic and social corruption of the black people by their Southern saloons has at least been a picturesque and compelling argument. The Southern white still regards the negroes as his subject people; dear if they keep their place; to be chastised if they do not. Economically, the agricultural regions of the South are still mainly dependent upon negro labor. The low negro saloon, which has gone on degenerating year by year, is a great cause of idleness and inefficiency. Ten years ago, when the Committee of Fifty made its admirable study of the saloon in its relation to economics, the results showed pretty clearly that the negroes were everywhere far more temperate than the whites. But corruption has gone fast in this decade. By old custom the negro plantation hands and the small independent farmers on leased lands never work Saturdays. That is "store day," when they pile into the towns to trade—and to drink. The cheap saloons, with inducement in the way of women, gambling, and worse, gather them in, strip them of their tiny earnings, and bring many of them over to Monday morning in the afterstage of a debauch. In those plantation regions where the saloons are running unchecked it is Tuesday or Wednesday before all the hands are settled down to work again. It is even worse for the negro lessees. They spend in these debauches the money that should go for tools, for seeds, for payment on their leases; and this reacts in loss upon the lords of the land. It is highly probable that any body of whites as poor and improvident as these plantation negroes would drink more than they do; but the South is characteristically impatient with any form of negro vice.

Then, too, that crime of the negro which is the sensational feature of the Southern race struggle is encouraged and intensified by liquor and by the drugs which the negro gets in his low boozing-dens. To it the negro dives directly pander. However much to blame the whites were for the Atlanta race riots of 1906, the way of liquor with the negroes had a great deal to do with it. A little of this kind of thing goes a long way in forming Southern opinion.

Then comes a purely economic consideration. Large parts of the South are working to take from the North Atlantic region its old supremacy in manufacturing. It is a vital struggle for industrial rehabilitation after the depression of "reconstruction." Wherever, as in factory towns, there are many laborers, alcohol tends to play havoc with steady industry. The factory owners and business men of any manufacturing community, North or South, are usually against the saloon. At its best a luxury, and the most wasteful of all luxuries, it can most easily be dispensed with in a community which is in the stage of industrial struggle. No point of the prohibition argument seems to be better taken than this. In the South, and under the new prohibition régime, the dry communities have usually grown and prospered after the first strain of adjustment; the others have tended to stand still. I am aware that this has not been the general rule in the older prohibition territory of the North; but it has been true in the South.

The straight moral argument must not be overlooked. The South is the most intensely American part of this country. In blood, feeling, and institutions it is the relic of the old America before the war. It has the old-time American religion—very largely Protestant Evangelical—little touched by later ideals. "The South," said a professor in a Georgia theological seminary—"the South has had many troubles, but, thank God, evolution and the higher criticism are not among them!" The Protestant Evangelical churches all look with unfavoring eyes upon "strong drink," and the less they are touched by the Protestant form of Modernism the less complaisant they are. The Methodist Episcopal Church carries a total-abstinence clause in its discipline book. The Baptists, without stating the thing so formally, usually favor abstinence; the Presbyterians lean decidedly to that opinion. Mississippi, in blood the most American State of the Union, has gone over to prohibition almost from this cause alone. "A new Puritanism in the South," some one has called it. As I shall try to show later, this is not a new Puritanism at all; it is the same old feeling, now turned into a force by a new political system.

Eliminate the question of the drunken negro and the causes at the North are about the same. Probably the moral and religious appeal has had less force in those Middle-Western communities which have gone dry, and the economic argument vastly greater force. Experience has shown that prohibition tends to raise real-estate values in suburban residence communities. Family men, whatever their own practise in the matter, like to bring up their families apart from saloon influences. So it happens that no large city of this country is without its prohibition districts or suburbs. New York has its New Jersey towns, Chicago its Hyde Park district, San Francisco its Palo Alto and Berkeley, Boston its Cambridge and Brookline. Manufacturing districts have gone dry through the belief of employers and business men that the suppression of liquor means increase of output.

Lastly, there is a greater and more remote cause in both North and South which comes nearer the heart of the matter. Everywhere the saloons have disobeyed in the most flagrant fashion all rules made for their government and regulation; and when put under pressure to reform they have fought back through their characteristic American alliance with bad politics. So insolent has been the attitude not only of the saloon-keepers but also of the brewers, distillers, and wholesale liquor men, that many communities have gone dry simply because of the disgust which this attitude has bred in good citizens. Men who do not object to the moderate use of liquor, men who use it themselves, have held the balance of power in these prohibition elections; the result shows how they have voted. South and North, such men returned me the same stereotyped answer. "I do not object to moderate drinking. I drink myself. But I would rather go without it than stand for the saloons as they have been running things in this town."

This brings the question down to that basic cause which is behind the corrupted negro, behind the pernicious effect of the traffic on industry, unconsciously behind much of the purely moral objection. The American saloon, always a peculiarly faulty and vicious system of distribution, has fallen of late into such evil ways that our civilization is sick with it. Socially and politically, it has become a nuisance. In these days of forced reform from within, even the "larger interests" of the liquor traffic partially admit this. When the Model License League, a back-fire reform started by the Kentucky distillers, held its convention in Louisville last January, the speakers talked of little else than the "reform of retail abuses." The brewers of Ohio, of Texas, of Illinois, have admitted that the "low dive" should be eliminated, and are scratching such places from their lists. And one can not study the prohibition communities, North and South, without realizing that this reform is aimed not so much at the consumption of alcohol as at the saloon.

As an institution, the American saloon was born of bad stock. It is the legitimate descendant of the English bar, the most vicious form of distribution in Europe. The drinking places of the Continent existed primarily for sociability, and only secondarily for the consumption of liquor. The English bar, as distinguished from the tavern, existed primarily that men might drink. Further, it did its very worst to spread the use of distilled spirits, the intoxicating essence of those beverages in which men took alcohol until two centuries ago. Our saloon grew up and developed on the old frontier. Although it was a centre for the crime and evil living which marked the limit of our Western advance, it had its uses. With the big vices of the frontier went its big heroisms, and probably it needed some strong form of stimulant to nerve men for those daring ventures of life and fortune by which we conquered a continent. But after the border had passed on, the saloon remained, a survival of frontier disorder after frontier heroism was gone.

It came in time to exist solely that men might drink perpendicularly, might pour down liquor and yet more liquor. Although it had everywhere its virtues on the social side, although the "poor man's club" had its sociological value, the drink was the main thing. In regions untouched by the humanizing influence of later Continental immigrants, the very furnishing of an American saloon proves its purpose. Unless it runs gambling games or is a resort for prostitutes, it has hardly ever any place to sit down. One is expected to buy a drink, standing; to pour it down. If he wants to remain, he is expected to buy another or to have another bought for him on the vicious "treating" system. No better device was ever found for making habitual drunkards out of occasional drinkers. American men came to drink without sense or grace, rime or reason. Every schoolboy knows that we spend more for alcoholic liquors than for bread and meat.

Of course this institution, as it drifted closer to absolute vice, gathered allied vices about it. The American saloon, unless checked by laws steadily backed by vigilance on the part of good citizens, tended always to rapid degeneration.

Out of this condition of affairs came the teetotal movement, aimed at that drinking habit in which Americans have gone so fast and so far; and, just before the Civil War, the first prohibition movement, of which the Maine law is the only relic.

That prohibition wave of the fifties, cut short by the Civil War, crystallized in the American saloon one tendency which did still more to degrade it. In order to beat the regulations made for their curbing, and in order to defeat the attempts at prohibitory laws, the saloon men and the "liquor interests" in general allied themselves with bad municipal politics. There followed that tight union between the powers that rule and the powers that prey which ran nearly every American city before the reform movements of the past ten years.

It is worth while to stop and analyze that alliance. The part of government which comes nearest to the individual citizen, the one which really most concerns him, is the police function. It is usually within police power to enforce or to neglect the enforcement of any law for the regulation of dissipation or of vice. At first the saloons found a way to control the police directly by "inducements." But the system grew; it paid better, it worked better in every way, to control the politicians who had the appointive power over the police. To these politicians the saloon had great inducements to offer. To begin with, it had become, as I have said, in a sense "the poor man's club"; and the working man is the backbone of the primary election system—for it is at the primaries, not at the general election, that the gang usually does its work. The saloon-keeper must be a "good fellow"; he had always a personal following. It was a neighborhood gathering place; a convenient political unit. So the saloon-keeper, for value received in the way of "protection" and favorable legislation, worked to deliver votes, to bring the ward heeler close to his tools. With this gradual degradation of both politics and retail liquor traffic, the saloons went one stage further. They became headquarters for the "repeating" system, for ballot-box stuffing, for all the downright iniquities by which the gang, when pressed to it, maintained its control. Further than this, the saloonkeepers furnished forth, still furnish forth, most of the sinews of war. Not always directly, it is true, although in many towns and cities the collection is made directly before every primary or general election, but by various tricks and devices which run with the complexities of the system. Tammany Hall, for example, maintains its grip in New York, upholds that system of police graft which no Police Commissioner has yet been strong enough to break, and protects the army of small grafters which flourishes in its shadow, by filings from the nickels and dimes and quarters which go over the bars of New York for drinks.

It is probable that this system became, in the end, more of a burden than a help to the saloon-keeper. In many communities it became blackmail. Over the head of the saloon-keeper hung always the fear that the gang, if he refused to come down, would revoke his license. That is the whip to keep the saloon-keeper in line; having the police power, which holds the saloon license privilege in the hollow of its hand, the politicians can and do put out of business any man who squirms.

So the politician is the deep sea on one side of the retail liquor dealer; and driving him on the other side is the devil in the shape of the brewery. This is the paradox of the whole situation; that the branch of liquor manufacture which produces the lighter and less intoxicating form should be the main agent in degrading the business.

The distiller manufactures a concentrated product which bears long keeping. The brewer's goods are bulky and comparatively perishable. In a general way, long hauls are poor business for him. He must work through a limited radius and keep close touch with his customers. With the coming of the Germanic tide of immigration, this business became important and competition became intense. Let us be fair to the brewers; their lighter and less intoxicating product steadily reduced the per capita consumption of the heavy alcoholic beverages. But with increased competition the brewers had to find some way to stimulate production; and not long after the Civil War they began the system of backing saloons—setting them up in business. There is no room here to follow up the system historically; it is enough to say that a saloon man of fair ability and some experience needs no money to start a business nowadays. It is only a matter of getting the license. Some brewery will find him a location, furnish all his bar fixtures, pay an advance on the license money and the rent, get his bondsmen, find him credit with the whiskey dealers. In return for these accommodations, he gives either a mortgage or promissory notes or both, and promises to sell the beer of his backers exclusively. Probably half of the saloons in the United States are now run and owned on this system; perhaps the proportion is greater. In Chicago, a few years ago, when a temporary law required all business establishments to declare their real ownership once a year, five thousand saloon-keepers out of eight thousand called themselves "lessees" of various breweries. At least two-thirds of the saloons in Louisville are controlled by the breweries—and Louisville is the heart of the distilling territory. Well-informed men say that eighty-five per cent of the saloons in Greater New York were opened on this system. It is the very backbone of the saloon business in the United States.

Naturally (they being American business men) the brewers have worked this system for all that they are worth; naturally, they have stuffed every community where they have control to the very limit of returns. And this makes it especially hard for the average retail saloon-keeper to keep ahead of the notes and the mortgages. If he is a man of ingenuity and great personality, he may extend his trade and get enough custom to beat the game by means which may be called legitimate, and which are within the letter of the law. But for the mediocre, with his business always on the verge of failure, there comes ever the temptation to stave off ruin by stretching or breaking the law. He opens rooms for women in the rear of his place; he puts in beds upstairs; he sells himself fully and wholly to the corrupt politicians; he offers inducements to thieves and "peter workers"; with the help of the police he violates closing laws. So he keeps ahead of his notes and mortgages, and the brewery, which holds him to his early promise to sell its beer alone, flourishes wonderfully.

So the brewery also came into politics; and when the reformer, disgusted either with the political control of the saloon in his community or with its persistent violation of regulations, started in to see what he could do about it, he found himself balked by a triple alliance—the saloon-keeper, with his natural following, the small politician with his craft and his knowledge of the game, and the brewery with its money and influence. Further back was often the distiller and the wholesale liquor dealer, keeping their hands off the fight, but furnishing the sinews of war.

The defiant attitude of these allied interests has had its bearing on the question. Until brought face to face with the danger of prohibition, they have usually laughed to scorn all appeals and all efforts to curb them. The vaunted reforms from within the liquor business, of which the country is hearing more or less in these days of peril, followed only upon the greater prohibition movement; such a thing was unheard of before. One must not blame the liquor men unduly; they follow only the law of their kind, the American business men. What rebating railroad but laughed at the law until the courts had closed on it? What municipal service corporation but scorned the reformers? But this particular contempt of control, related as it was to a moral and sentimental issue, was especially irritating. This is the factor which has brought prohibition in community after community of the South.

Let me clinch these generalizations by two or three examples:

Tom Anderson, the "Hon." Tom Anderson, owns a string of highly prosperous saloons in New Orleans. His largest and most profitable establishment is the "Arlington Annex," at Basin and Customhouse Streets—one corner of the restricted district where flourishes that wide-open prostitution peculiar to New Orleans. Down one street from this saloon runs a row of gaudy houses of prostitution; down the other two blocks of those little apartments known in the South and West as "cribs." He who visits the Tenderloin in New Orleans usually begins at the "Arlington Annex." Everything suggests this saloon as the Town Hall in that city of shame, but one activity of Tom Anderson's place suggests it most of all. For twenty-five cents the bartender will sell to any and all comers a pamphlet, called simply the "Blue Book," which is a directory of the prostitutes and houses of prostitution in New Orleans. The directory, plain and formal, runs down the right-hand pages; on the left-hand pages are advertisements. The first twenty-five advertising pages set forth the virtues of Anheuser-Busch Beer, I. W. Harper Rye Whiskey, and other liquors. For the rest of the way the advertisements are formal "write-ups" of certain women in the quarter. In this mute book the saloon and vice proclaim their naked partnership.

Among these, one notices in especial the attention paid to a place called "The Arlington," or "Miss Arlington's," which is honored not only with several "reading notices," but with half-tone photographic views. There appears to be some connection closer than a mere name between the "Arlington Annex" and the "Arlington" brothel. For example, when the brothel was burned out a year or two ago it moved into quarters over the saloon pending repairs.

Tom Anderson overtops the restricted district; he is its law-giver and its king; one of the names for it is "Anderson County." In his shadow flourish the unblushing, street-open shame of Iberville and Bienville and Conti and St. Louis Streets; the saloons with their wide-open poker and crap games; the dives where negroes buy for fifty cents five cents' worth of cocaine. He is, too, the pad between the poor, foolish, awkward law which is written in the books and the people who dwell under his kindlier law. For example, when a woman of "Anderson County" commits robbery, and when the victim complains so loudly that she has to be arrested, Tom Anderson comes down and gets her out. He does not even have to give cash bail; a local law provides that a minor criminal, at the discretion of inspector or judge, may be released on the parole of any responsible prominent citizen.

And the "Hon." Tom Anderson represents in the Louisiana State Legislature a large and important district of New Orleans—has represented it for two terms—was nominated at the primaries last month for a third term, and will, by every probability, be elected in April. He is a member of the Ways and Means Committee and the Committee on the Affairs of the City of New Orleans—two of the most important in the Legislature. Mr. Anderson belongs to the liberal wing of the State Legislature; he does not believe in sumptuary laws; he thinks that it degrades the citizen to take away from him the privilege of choosing for himself between right and wrong.

Briefly, here is the reason for Tom Anderson: With a little break here and there, New Orleans has been in the grip of a ring. No large city in the United States gets such poor returns for the public money expended as New Orleans. It is ill-paved, ill-policed, behind in municipal improvements; the public money is needed for a thousand and one sinecure jobs. By the same token, no other city of the country runs vice of every kind so wide open. Tom Anderson has been a great help. Highly prosperous himself, he has not failed to divide up with the power which enabled him to be prosperous; and he has helped to make the saloon-keepers, the gamblers, and the brothel-keepers generous. It was his whim to go to the Legislature; and a grateful people, recognizing his services, rewarded him.

Just consider him a moment as a phenomenon in modern American life. Because he represents the lowest, he is honored among you; because he is a convenient go-between, attending to your necessary relations with vice, you have clothed him in garments of power; because he has spent his life in a business which fosters vice, harbors crime, weakens your coming generation, you assign to him the public duty of levying taxes, regulating corporations, protecting the weak from the strong, leading the commonwealth in all good causes. And if he were the only example of his kind!

Consider also Tom Lee in New York. I am referring now not to the famous Chinese of that name, but to a mysterious white man calling himself Tom Lee, who is understood to be the proprietor of the saloons at Nos. 9 and 28 Bowery. These places are not held in his name; two dummy names figure on the records for both lease-holders and license-holders. But the Bowery and Tammany know these as Tom Lee's places, and he assumes all the airs of proprietorship. His place at 28 Bowery is one of the headquarters for the "yeggmen" on their visits to New York. These men—thieves of the road, crackers of country safes, mostly desperate criminals—resort to his saloon to "blow" the profits of their industry. So from the proceeds of burglary the Tom Lee saloons make their money.

The Hon. Timothy D. Sullivan known as "Big Tim," is the law above the leader in Tammany Hall; and therefore the law above the law in New York. It were better that a millstone were about the neck of a police patrolman or captain than that he should try to curb the criminal activities of that place. For Tom Lee helps to keep the district in-line for Tammany; he is able to furnish "gorillas" to the number of 500 for the straight ticket, obtaining them through his and other neighboring hotels and lodging houses. Does Tom Lee "give up" a proportion of his gains to Tammany? He does, or he would not be there. And from Tammany the money dribbles out through several foul lines of conveyance. It keeps in office those small grafters who bleed public utilities; it helps elect judges, aldermen, State legislators, and Congressmen. The trails are wide open to-day—police, saloon-dealer, crooks, and the local political organization.

Tom Anderson and Tom Lee are not exceptions; it only happens that they are better known than a thousand others; that their operations are more easily traced. But let us now take up a general situation, and study the late history of the "saloon influence" in Louisville.

For time out of mind, Louisville had been ruled by a Democratic gang closely allied with the saloons. The politicians in this gang sought no more remote aim than keeping the saloons open and protected and happy in their activities; there was no special dalliance with large graft. They got their pickings from fat public offices and from blackmailing vice. That is, they had not risen to the second degree of their order, wherein the gang politician begins to tap the corporations.

In 1903 there came a reform movement of considerable strength, which focused on the election of a criminal judge. The "gang" won. The reformers proved that the voting places in sixteen precincts had been "moved." That is, the polling place would be set by law and advertised for one place; but when the election officers arrived they would take all the paraphernalia secretly to another place and hold the election there—or pretend to hold it. The sixteen "moved" precincts gave an average majority of 250 for the gang candidate. The corruption of this election brought a general reform movement. The "Evening Post," for years the hope of reform in Louisville, printed in December, 1904, an account of the illegal proceedings at Patrick J. Sharkey's saloon. Sharkey, alleging libel, sued Richard W. Knott, editor of the "Post," both criminally and civilly. By a decision which in face of the evidence bewilders a layman, Sharkey won a verdict, with a fine of $500, in the criminal case. A week after, the reformers proved in court that Sharkey was running an illegal gambling game. Simultaneously, Sharkey applied through the regular channels for a renewal of his license. His prayer was granted at once.

This incident, following the election, stirred up all Louisville. The reform movement came to a focus in the general municipal election of 1905. The City Club nominated for Mayor J. T. O'Neill, a Democrat. The Republicans gave him their endorsement. Paul C. Barth was nominated by the gang on the "straight Democratic ticket." Behind him were the gang, all the saloon-keepers, and especially (note this) the powerful brewery combine.

That election, on the face of it, was a Democratic and gang victory by majorities of from three thousand to five thousand. Trouble began at the primaries, when the regular police knocked down and beat up reform workers who were insisting that the law be observed. One of the victims was the venerable and respected General Basil Duke. The regular election was the finest farce on democracy which has been played in this country for many years.

The reformers contested the election in court. They lost in the lower court by another inexplicable decision; but the Court of Appeals, five to one Democratic, returned a unanimous opinion declaring the election void.

Let me summarize the points of this decision which bear on our question. *About 4,500 fraudulent registrations were proved. Of the voters so registered, about 4,000 "resided" in the upper rooms of saloons. The saloons implicated averaged 26 fraudulent registrations apiece! On election day 83 bartenders and 16 saloon-keepers qualified as election officers—at least one man of this element was on guard in every precinct which figured in the decision. Of ten precincts "moved," nine ended up in the rear room of some saloon.* When the Court of Appeals inspected the ballots and books of these ten precincts it found a peculiar state of affairs. So well had order, Heaven's first law, been observed that the registered voters cast their ballots in alphabetical order from A to Z. Mr. Austin had voted before Mr. Baker, and Mr. Zusatz last of all. The Bergman Street precinct is in the heaviest Republican district of Louisville—its normal majority is about 180. Just as the Republican election officers were ready to count, six men carrying revolvers raided the place and carried off the ballot-boxes to the saloon of a man named Hendricks—the cousin of a police captain and the holder of a long "pull." In Hendricks's place they burned the ballots, disenfranchising the whole precinct. Dozens of reform election watchers were thrown out of the polling-places, clubbed, beaten. In almost every case a policeman in uniform did this work. Under a newer and better administration thirty policemen were broken in one day for their participation in that election.

There you have it—mostly proved in court. A brewery combine, furnishing money and brains for the protection of "large interests"; the whole body of retail saloon-keepers furnishing the machinery of corruption; the gang furnishing direction; all fighting together with criminal weapons that they might win the privilege of breaking and disregarding the law. And this case of the city of Louisville is not the exception any more than the cases of Tom Anderson and Tom Lee; it is only an extreme example.

An Indignant Letter

George Bernard Shaw

The extraordinary short story, "Aerial Football: The New Game" (P. 134), was submitted to Collier's *by George Bernard Shaw in 1907. It was published in the Thanksgiving issue, and later won for Shaw a one thousand dollar prize as the best story received by* Collier's *during the final quarter of 1907. In the issue of April 25, 1908,* Collier's *published the following letter from Shaw, along with the attached editorial comment:*

"10 Adelphi Terrace, W. C.
"14th March, 1908.

"Editor Collier's:

"Dear Sir.—What do you mean by this unspeakable outrage? You send me a cheque for a thousand dollars, and inform me that it is a bonus offered by Messrs. P. F. Collier & Son for the best story received during the quarter in which my contribution appeared. May I ask what Messrs. P. F. Collier & Son expected my story to be? If it were not the best they could get for the price they were prepared to pay, they had no right to insert it at all. If it was the best, what right have they to stamp their other contributors publicly as inferior when they have taken steps to secure the result beforehand by paying a special price to a special writer? And what right have they to assume that I want to be paid twice over for my work, or that I am in the habit of accepting bonuses and competing for prizes?

"Waiving all these questions for a moment, I have another one to put to you. How do Messrs. P. F. Collier & Son know that my story was the best they received during the quarter? Are they posterity? Are they the Verdict of History? Have they even the very doubtful qualification of being professional critics?

"I had better break this letter off lest I should be betrayed into expressing myself as strongly as I feel.

"I return the cheque. If you should see fit to use it for the purpose of erecting a tombstone to Messrs. P. F. Collier & Son, I shall be happy to contribute the epitaph, in which I shall do my best to do justice to their monstrous presumption.

"Yours faithfully,
"(Signed) G. BERNARD SHAW"

Happy Mr. Shaw, at one stroke thus to disburthen your mind of its Olympian scorn and your purse of our unwelcome thousand. To what noble uses shall that now historic check be put? Shall it go toward the erection of a Shaw-Shakespeare Memorial at Stratford? Or for the foundation of the Shaw Chair of Advertising at Oxford? Or shall we lay it by against the day when our impatient readers clamor for more *Shaw and we are compelled (with a reluctance only known to publishers)* again *to pay "a special price to a special writer"? However, you must be right about "Aerial Football—The New Game." The awarding of that offensive thousand to your story was a mistake. It will not occur again. The responsible "readers" for that quarter were out of town, and the verdict lay with the Sporting Editor, who happens to be a devotee of Football, a Vegetarian, a Socialist, a Misanthrope, a Misogynist, in short, a true disciple of the incomparable G. B. S. You will be glad to know that the young man has been discharged, and that a portion of that contemned "bonus" will be devoted to the support of his family and his own education in a correspondence school of advertising.*

The New World

Richard Harding Davis

Had he been born two generations later, Richard Harding Davis would doubtless have been first in line to report the sensations of flying to the moon—an adventure only a little more hazardous than the flight he reports here with barnstormer Frank Coffyn a few years after the Wright Brothers conquered gravity at Kitty Hawk. Darling of what was yet to be called Cafe Society, Davis was born in 1865, wrote plays, novels, and short stories, and had covered four wars and part of a fifth when he died in 1916—the most romantic journalist of an era of memorable by-lines.

September 16, 1911

THE AIKEN POLO TEAM HAD JUST DEfeated the New Orleans team for the Southern championship and the spectators had started down the Whisky Road for Aiken, when the airman in his Wright biplane came sailing over them, spanking through the air from Augusta, and dropped into the polo field. The spectators, with such old-fashioned means of locomotion as motor cars, buggies, mule teams, and polo ponies, raced after him, and gave the stranger from the skies a welcome. He liked his welcome; built a nest for his birdship in a turn of the race-track, and for a month made Aiken his home. Frank T. Coffyn was his name, and in the morning he was the chanticleer that woke us from slumber. And in the evening, after the polo games, we would wait to watch his biplane spin on its bicycle wheels over the field, rough with pony tracks, and then, scorning the earth, sweep up and over the pine trees and disappear like a great black buzzard into the crimson sunset. At first when the beat of the engines was lost in the silence we were apprehensive until again we heard them ticking steadily over the cotton fields. But in a week we decided Mr. Coffyn was quite able to take care of himself. We were less concerned about the young man in the skies than whether his devil wagon would frighten the particular pony upon which we happened to be perilously balancing.

Mr. Coffyn held the key to the new world. He, and only he, before our final carrying off could transport us to the skies, could lift us from the earth upon which in humdrum satisfaction we had crawled for numberless years. As a result he was much sought after, much cajoled, much flattered. He moved to an accompaniment of clicking cameras. Strong men bent their backs wheeling his aerial chariot, small boys stood in his way, hoping he might fall over them, and when he sank into the cotton fields, beautiful ladies galloped their ponies at the encroaching "gallery," and for so brief a time as he remained on earth, acted as his traffic policeman. But, though when he was on his feet he could see us all very plainly, as soon as he was seated in his biplane we became invisible. As passengers, unless we were small boys or young women, who should have been frightened, but who were not, he could not see us at all. He would not look at the men, and then invitingly at the empty seat beside him. Instead he looked toward the tree-tops, or toward the ground, or pumped his oil valve. Then he would pull down his goggles, and shout "Leggo!" and with a wave of his hand sweep across the field, leaving us looking hungrily at the empty seat. At least some of us looked hungrily. Others only pretended they were hungry. The really honest and the really brave announced in loud tones: "I wouldn't go up in that thing, not for a hundred thousand dollars, not—if he asked me!"

But there was no occasion for alarm, he did not ask us. We had to ask him. I asked him, not because I wanted to "go up," but because when you see children in baby carriages watching their mother hurtling through space at sixty miles an hour, it requires more nerve to stay on the side lines with the children than to take a dare from their mother. So regularly every evening, trembling and with shaking knees, I asked to be taken up, and was as regularly refused, and as regularly gave secret thanks that I had not been taken up in any sense of the word. But as the small boys continued to shame me, I telegraphed the manager of the Wright brothers for permission. He said no. I telegraphed the Wright brothers. They said no. I telegraphed officers of the Aero Club in New York to use their influence. Their answer was encouraging: "Best friends here," they wired, "hope you will break your neck. Are using every influence to that end." Their influence was effective. At midnight I got a telephone from Coffyn saying I was to "go up" at daybreak.

I know now how the man feels who the following morning is to ride the favorite in the Lincolnshire Handicap, who at sunrise is to fight his first duel, who the next evening has to speak a speech to a first-night audience. I know now how the condemned murderer spends his last hours on earth with the prison chaplain and the death watch.

"He rose at six, washed and shaved with his usual care, and breakfasted sparingly on ham and eggs. The warden offered him a second helping of coffee, but he had no appetite." When I got to the polo field two friends were waiting to see me go up or, more probably, to see me come down. Their exact motives I have not yet determined. But I think they had hopes, for one of them snapped many photographs; entirely too many photographs. I could see no reason for so many photographs. The other asked tactfully if there was anything I would like him to "hold." I bequeathed him a roll of bills, and, probably to reimburse himself for rising at such an hour, or to pay him for his disappointment, he forgot to return them.

I crawled between a crisscross of wires to a seat as small as a racing saddle, and with my right hand choked the life out of a wooden upright. Unless I clung to Coffyn's right arm, there was nothing I could hold on to with my left but the edge of the racing saddle.

My toes rested on a thin steel cross-bar. It was like balancing in a child's swing hung from a tree. Had I placed myself in such a seat on a hotel porch, I would have considered my position most unsafe; to occupy such a seat a thousand feet in mid-air while moving at fifty miles an hour struck me as ridiculous.

"What's to keep me from falling out?" I demanded.

Coffyn laughed unfeelingly.

"You won't fall out!" he said.

I began to hate Coffyn and the Wright brothers. I began to regret I had not been brought up a family man so that, like the other men of family at Aiken, I could explain I could not go aloft, because I had children to support. I was willing to support any number of children. *Anybody's* children. I regretted too late that, except for a paltry mug or two, even to my godchildren, I had not done my duty. I wanted to get down at once, and hear my godchildren say their catechism.

Behind us the propeller was thrashing the air like a mowing machine, and Coffyn had disguised himself in his goggles. To me the act suggested only the judge putting on his black cap before he delivers the death sentence. The moment had come. I tried to smile at my two faithful friends, but one was excitedly dancing around taking a farewell snapshot, and the other already was calmly counting *my* money.

On the bicycle wheels we ran swiftly forward across the polo field. There was no swaying, no vibration, no jar. We might have been speeding over asphalt in a soft-cushioned automobile. We reached the boundary of the polo field.

"You are in the air!" said Coffyn. I did not believe him, and I looked down to see, and found the earth was two feet below us. We were moving through space on as even a keel as though we still were touching the level turf.

And then a wonderful thing happened. The polo field and the high board fence around it, and a tangle of telegraph wires, and the tops of the highest pine trees suddenly sank beneath us. We seemed to stand quite still while they dropped and tumbled. They fell so swiftly that in a moment the Whisky Road became a yellow ribbon, and the Iselin house and gardens a white ball on a green billiard cloth. We wheeled evenly in a sharp curve, and beyond us for miles saw the cotton fields like a great chessboard. Houses and barns and clumps of trees were chess men. Coffyn tried to tell me something of, I believe, a reassuring nature; but the thrashing of the engines and the steady roar of the propellers drowned his voice. I did not particularly care to hear. Already I had a confidence in Coffyn that no assurance of his could strengthen, and I had got into another world, one which to him, through long association, was no longer a miracle.

It was a topsy-turvy world. Instead of gazing up into the lower branches of trees, we saw them as one sees violets in the grass. It was not like looking down from a skyscraper, because on a tall building you have beneath you the solid floors. Nor was it like looking down from the window of an express train as one rushes over a high trestle, because even then there is still beneath you the cushioned seat and the floor of the railroad car. But from the biplane there was swinging between you and the old world only your two feet. You saw the toes of your boots dangling, and then emptiness, much emptiness, and then tiny toy houses flattened against the soil, trees as small as rose bushes, and like ants, mules, and black men crawling across a checkerboard. The long lines on the checkerboard were plowed furrows. They were ruled in with delicate pencil strokes.

These Noah's Ark houses, cattle, men, swept beneath our eyes as swiftly as do the figures on a tape-measure when you set free the spring. A man would raise his arm from the plow to wave his hat, and already you were looking down the chimney of his cabin. The speed was so great, the elevation so great, that you saw the objects blurred and wavering as at night from an express train you see the many lights of a station drawn out into one long flame. When you saw anything you had passed it.

Since we rose from the polo field I had not breathed. I was confident that if I were to move I would spill out, or, worse, that I would upset the marvelous balance of the airship and that Coffyn also would spill out. But in time, cautiously, and clinging to the wooden upright as a drowning man clings to a rope, I moved my head, stiffly, and looked about. My idea was that we were moving on as level a keel as when on wheels we had crossed the polo field. But when I looked above and behind me, I found that the airship was tilting like a pair of scales, and that on either side the great planes dipped and rocked. When from the ground I had watched these same gyrations I had believed that each moment the airship was about to turn turtle. Now that I was seated in it I felt no motion at all and complete confidence. Some one who understands psychology and aeroplanes can explain. I know only that when I was on the ground I was scared, and when I was in the air I was not. And that when I thought I was moving on a dead level, and that the wings were as perfectly balanced as those of the eagle on a St. Gauden's gold piece, we were careening like a catboat in a heavy sea.

Coffyn had his own sense of humor. Perhaps first with a glance he assured himself that my feet were wrapped around the steel bar and my fingers clutching the wooden upright, perhaps he did not. In any event, when we were a thousand feet in the air, about as high as a twelve-story building, he pulled a lever and the airship *dived!* An instant before I had been taking a bird's-eye view of South Carolina. It was as unsubstantial-looking and purely pictorial as a map flung upon a table. The next instant a perfectly solid red clay road was rising to hit me in the face. It was coming at me at fifty miles an hour. Now not even my feet obstructed my view. There was *nothing* between me and the red clay road. We were tilted so far forward that I knew my face and knees would hit it at the same moment. I knew the end had come. But all my past life did not unroll before me. Instead, I had time only to think what had been Coffyn and what had been me would make a terrible mess in the red clay road. And then when it was so near that I shut my eyes, Coffyn pulled another lever, and, like a rocket, the airship shot into the skies. Probably many times you dream you are falling from a great height, and wake to find yourself in bed. Pile all the agony of all those nightmares into one, and that was how I felt.

When I looked at Coffyn he was laughing. My only desire was to punch him, just once on the tip of his square jaw. The only reason I did not was because I was afraid to let go of the wooden upright.

Having demonstrated that he could handle his airship as a boy twists a bicycle, Coffyn proceeded to make it show off. He forced it to climb imaginary hills, he sent it like a toboggan shooting down long aerial lanes, he jumped it like a qualified hunter, up and down over unseen hurdles.

When black folks waved to us from the porch of a cabin, he would swoop upon them, dipping and courtesying, and by only a few feet pass above them, so that they screamed and ran, as chickens scatter before the downward rush of a hawk. I began to feel a contempt for these clumsy children of the old world who could not leave it, who moved about only on the two stumps they called legs. High above them we bucked and buffeted the rising wind, or at fifty miles an hour ran free before it straight into the rising sun. I began to understand why young men with apparently everything to make them happy on earth persist in leaving it by means of aeroplanes, with a chance of leaving it forever. What lures them is the call of the new world waiting to be conquered, the sense of power, of detachment from everything humdrum, or even human; the thrill that makes all the other sensations stale and vapid, the exhilaration that for the moment makes each one of them a king.

We dropped into the same spot on the polo field from which we had set forth as lightly as a rubber ball.

"We went six miles," said Coffyn.

But we had gone much farther than that. And how much farther we still will go no man can tell.

Disentangling Old Duggie

P. G. Wodehouse

The man who invented Jeeves, the Butler; Psmith, the man-about-town, and Bertie Wooster, was a rather frequent contributor to Collier's*—and rightly so. Almost fifty years after Reggie Pepper set about to disentangle old Duggie Craye, the process and results, as related by Pelham Grenville Wodehouse, remain as sprightly under the author's expert touch as they undoubtedly seemed in the tenure of William Howard Taft.*

March 3, 1912

DOESN'T SOME POET OR PHILOSOPHER FELlow say that it's when our intentions are best that we always make the worst breaks? I can't put my hand on the passage, but you'll find it in Shakespeare or somewhere, I'm pretty certain.

At any rate, it's always that way with me. And the affair of Douglas Craye is a case in point.

I had dined with Duggie (a dear old pal of mine) one night at his club, and as he was seeing me out he said: "Reggie, old top"—my name's Reggie Pepper—"Reggie, old top, I'm rather worried."

"Are you, Duggie, old pal?" I said.

"Yes, Reggie, old fellow," he said, "I am. It's like this. The Booles have asked me down to their place for the week-end, and I don't know whether to go or not. You see, they have early breakfast, and besides that there's a frightful risk of music after dinner. On the other hand, young Roderick Boole thinks he can play piquet."

"I should go," I said.

"But I'm not sure Roderick's going to be there this time."

It was a problem, and I didn't wonder poor old Dug had looked pale and tired at dinner.

Then I had the idea which really started all the trouble.

"Why don't you consult a palmist?" I said.

"That sounds a good idea," said Duggie.

"Go and see Dorothea in Forty-second Street. She's a wonder. She'll settle it for you in a second. She'll see from your lines that you are thinking of making a journey, and she'll either tell you to get a move on, which will mean that Roderick will be there, or else to keep away because she sees disaster."

"You seem to be next to the game all right."

"I've been to a good many of them. You'll like Dorothea."

"What did you say her name was—Dorothea? What do I do? Do I just walk in? Shan't I feel a fearful chump? How much do I give her?"

"Five bucks. You'd better write and make a date."

"All right," said Duggie. "But I know I shall look a frightful fool."

About a week later I ran into him between the acts at the Knickerbocker. The old boy was beaming.

"Reggie," he said, "you did me the best turn anyone's ever done me, sending me to Mrs. Darrell."

"Mrs. Darrell?"

"You know. Dorothea. Her real name's Darrell. She's a widow. Her husband was in some regiment, and left her without a penny. It's a frightfully pathetic story. Haven't time to tell you now. My boy, she's a marvel. She had hardly looked at my hand, when she said: 'You will prosper in any venture you undertake.' And next day, by George, I went down to the Booles and separated young Roderick from seventy dollars. She's a wonderful woman. Did you ever see just that shade of hair?"

"I didn't notice her hair."

He gaped at me in a sort of petrified astonishment.

"You—didn't—notice—her—hair!" he gasped.

I can't fix the dates exactly, but it must have been about three weeks after this that I got a telegram: "Call Madison Avenue immediately—Florence Craye."

She needn't have signed her name. I should have known who it was from by the wording. Ever since I was a kid, Duggie's sister Florence has oppressed me to the most fearful extent. Not that I'm the only one. Her brothers live in terror of her, I know. Especially Edwin. He's never been able to get away from her and it's absolutely broken his spirit. He's a mild, hopeless sort of chump who spends all his time at home—they live near Philadelphia—and has never been known to come to New York. He's writing a history of the family, or something, I believe.

You see, events have conspired, so to speak, to let Florence do pretty much as she likes with them. Originally there was old man Craye, Duggie's father, who made a fortune out of the Soup Trust; Duggie's elder brother Edwin; Florence; and Duggie. Mrs. Craye has been dead some years. Then came the smash. It happened through the old man. Most people, if you ask them, will tell you that he ought to be in Bloomingdale; and I'm not sure they're not right. At any rate, one morning he came down to breakfast, lifted the first cover on the sideboard, said in a sort of despairing way, "Eggs! Eggs! Eggs! Curse all eggs!" and walked out of the room. Nobody thought much of it till about an hour afterward, when they found that he had packed a grip, left the house, and caught the train to New York. Next day they got a letter from him, saying that he was off to Europe, never to return, and that all communications were to be addressed to his lawyers. And from that day none of them had seen him. He wrote occasionally, generally from Paris; and that was all.

Well, directly news of this got about, down swooped a series of aunts to grab the helm. They didn't stay long. Florence had them out, one after the other, in no time. If any lingering doubt remained in their minds, don't you know, as to who was going to be boss at home, it wasn't her fault. Since then she has run the show.

I went to Madison Avenue. It was one of the aunts' houses. There was no sign of the aunt when I called—she had probably climbed a tree and pulled it up after her—but Florence was there.

She is a tall woman with what, I believe, is called "a presence." Her eyes are bright and black, and have a way of getting right inside you, don't you know, and running up and down your spine. She has a deep voice. She is about ten years older than Duggie's brother Edwin, who is six years older than Duggie.

"Good afternoon," she said. "Sit down."

I poured myself into a chair.

"Reginald," she said, "what is this I hear about Douglas?"

I said I didn't know.

"He says that you introduced him."

"Eh?"

"To this woman—this Mrs. Darrell."

"Mrs. Darrell?"

My memory's pretty rocky, and the name conveyed nothing to me.

She pulled out a letter.

"Yes," she said, "Mrs. Dorothy Darrell."

"Great Scott! Dorothea!"

Her eyes resumed their spine drill.

"Who is she?"

"Only a palmist."

"Only a palmist!" Her voice absolutely boomed. "Well, my brother Douglas is engaged to be married to her."

"Many happy returns of the day," I said.

I don't know why I said it. It wasn't what I meant to say. I'm not sure I meant to say anything.

She glared at me. By this time I was pure jelly. I simply flowed about the chair.

"You are facetious, Reginald," she said.

"No, no, no," I shouted. "It slipped out. I wouldn't be facetious for worlds."

"I am glad. It is no laughing matter. Have you any suggestions?"

"Suggestions?"

"You don't imagine it can be allowed to go on? The engagement must be broken, of course. But how?"

"Why don't you tell him he mustn't?"

"I shall naturally express my strong disapproval, but it may not be effective. When out of the reach of my personal influence, my wretched brother is self-willed to a degree."

I saw what she meant. Good old Duggie wasn't going to have those eyes patrolling his spine if he knew it. He meant to keep away and conduct this business by letter. There was going to be no personal interview with sister, if he had to dodge about America like a snipe.

We sat for a long time without speaking. Then I became rather subtle. I had a brain-wave and saw my way to making things right for Dug and at the same time squaring myself with Florence. After all, I thought, the old boy couldn't keep away from home for the rest of his life. He would have to go there sooner or later. And my scheme made it pleasant and easy for him.

"I'll tell you what I should do if I were you," I said. "I'm not sure I didn't read some book or see some play somewhere or other where they tried it on, and it worked all right. Fellow got engaged to a girl, and the family didn't like it, but, instead of kicking, they pretended to be tickled to pieces, and had the fellow and the girl down to visit them. And then, after the fellow had seen the girl with the home circle as a background, don't you know, he came to the conclusion that it wouldn't do, and broke off the engagement."

It seemed to strike her.

"I hardly expected so sensible a suggestion from you, Reginald," she said. "It is a very good plan. It shows that you really have a definite substratum of intelligence; and it is all the more deplorable that you should idle your way through the world as you do, when you might be performing some really useful work."

That was Florence all over. Even when she patted you on the head, she had to do it with her knuckles.

"I will invite them down next week," she went on. "You had better come, too."

"It's awfully kind of you, but the fact is—"

"Next Wednesday. Take the three-forty-seven."

I met Duggie next day. He was looking happy, but puzzled, like a man who has found a dime on the street and is wondering if there's a string tied to it. I congratulated him on his engagement.

"Reggie," he said, "a queer thing has happened. I feel as if I'd trodden on the last step when it wasn't there. I've just had a letter from my sister Florence asking me to bring Dorothy home on Wednesday. Florence doesn't seem to object to the idea of the engagement at all; and I'd expected that I'd have to call out the police reserves when she heard of it. I believe there's a catch somewhere."

I tapped him on the breastbone.

"There is, Dug," I said, "and I'll tell you what it is. I saw her yesterday, and I can put you next to the game. She thinks that if you see Mrs. Darrell mingling with the home circle, you'll see flaws in her which you don't see when you don't see her mingling with the home circle, don't you see? Do you see now?"

He laughed—heroically, don't you know.

"I'm afraid she'll be disappointed. Love like mine is not dependent on environment."

Which wasn't bad, I thought, if it was his own.

I said good-by to him, and toddled along rather pleased with myself. It seemed to me that I had handled his affairs in a pretty masterly manner for a chap who's supposed to be one of the biggest chumps in New York.

Well, of course, the thing was an absolute fliver, as I ought to have guessed it would be. Whatever could have induced me to think that a fellow like poor old Dug stood a dog's chance against a determined female like his sister Florence, I can't imagine. It was like expecting a rabbit to put up a show with a python. From the very start there was only one possible end to the thing. To a woman like Florence, who had trained herself as tough as whalebone by years of scrapping with her father and occasional by-battles with aunts, it was as easy as killing rats with a stick.

I was sorry for Mrs. Darrell. She was a really good sort and, as a matter of fact, just the kind of wife who would have done old Duggie a bit of good. And on her own ground I shouldn't wonder if she might not have made a fight for it. But now she hadn't a chance. Poor old Duggie was just like so much putty in Florence's hands when he couldn't get away from her. You could see the sawdust trickling out of Love's Young Dream in a steady flow.

I took Mrs. Darrell for a walk one afternoon, to see if I couldn't cheer her up a bit, but it wasn't much good. She hardly spoke a word till we were on our way home. Then she said with a sort of jerk: "I'm going back to New York to-morrow, Mr. Pepper."

I suppose I ought to have pretended to be surprised, but I couldn't work it.

"I'm afraid you've had a bad time," I said. "I'm very sorry."

She laughed.

"Thank you," she said. "It's nice of you

to be sympathetic instead of tactful. You're rather a dear, Mr. Pepper."

I hadn't any remarks to make. I whacked at a nettle with my stick.

"I shall break off my engagement after dinner, so that Douglas can have a good night's rest. I'm afraid he has been brooding on the future a good deal. It will be a great relief to him."

"Oh, no," I said.

"Oh, yes. I know exactly how he feels. He thought he could carry me off, but he finds he overestimated his powers. He has remembered that he is a Craye. I imagine that the fact has been pointed out to him."

"If you ask my opinion," I said—I was feeling pretty sore about it—"that woman Florence is an absolute cat."

"My dear Mr. Pepper, I wouldn't have dreamed of asking your opinion on such a delicate subject. But I'm glad to have it. Thank you very much. Do I strike you as a vindictive woman, Mr. Pepper?"

"I don't think you do," I said.

"By nature I don't think I am. But I'm feeling a little vindictive just at present."

She stopped suddenly.

"I don't know why I'm boring you like this, Mr. Pepper," she said. "For goodness' sake let's be cheerful. Say something bright."

I was going to take a whirl at it, but she started in to talk, and talked all the rest of the way. She seemed to have cheered up a whole lot.

She left next day. I gather she fired Duggie as per schedule, for the old boy looked distinctly brighter, and Florence wore an off-duty expression and was quite decently civil. Mrs. Darrell bore up all right. She avoided Duggie, of course, and put in most of the time talking to Edwin. He evidently appreciated it, for I had never seen him look so nearly happy before.

I went back to New York directly afterward, and I hadn't been there much more than a week when a most remarkably queer thing happened. Turning in at Hammerstein's for half an hour one evening, whom should I meet but brother Edwin, quite fairly festive, with a fat cigar in his mouth. "Hello, Reggie," he said.

"What are you doing here?" I said.

"I had to come up to New York to look up a life of Hilary de Craye at the library. I believe Mister Man was a sort of ancestor."

"This isn't the library."

"I was beginning to guess as much. The difference is subtle but well marked."

It struck me that there was another difference that was subtle but well marked, and that was the difference between the Edwin I'd left messing about over his family history a week before and the jovial rounder who was blowing smoke in my face now.

"As a matter of fact," he said, "the library would be all the better for a little of this sort of thing. It's too conservative. That's what's the trouble with the library. What's the matter with having a cross-talk team and a few performing dogs there? It would brighten the place up and attract custom. Reggie, you're looking fatigued. I've heard there's a place somewhere in this city, if you can only find it, expressly designed for supplying first-aid to the fatigued. Let's go and look for it."

I'm not given to thinking much as a rule, but I couldn't help pondering over this meeting with Edwin. It's hard to make you see the remarkableness of the whole thing, for, of course, if you look at it, in one way, there's nothing so record-breaking in smoking a cigar and drinking a highball. But then you have never seen Edwin. There are degrees in everything, don't you know. For Edwin to behave as he did with me that night was simply nothing more nor less than a frightful outburst, and it disturbed me. Not that I cared what Edwin did, as a rule, but I couldn't help feeling a sort of what d'you-call it—a presentiment, that somehow, in some way I didn't understand, I was mixed up in it, or was soon going to be. I think the whole fearful family had got on my nerves to such an extent that the mere sight of any of them made me jumpy.

And, by George, I was perfectly right, don't you know. In a day or two along came the usual telegram from Florence, telling me to come to Madison Avenue.

The mere idea of Madison Avenue was beginning to give me that tired feeling, and I made up my mind I wouldn't go near the place. But of course I did. When it came to the point, I simply hadn't the common manly courage to keep away.

Florence was there as before.

"Reginald," she said, "I think I shall go raving mad."

This struck me as a mighty happy solution of everybody's troubles, but I felt it was too good to be true.

"Over a week ago," she went on, "my brother Edwin came up to New York to consult a book at the library. I anticipated that this would occupy perhaps an afternoon, and was expecting him back by an early train next day. He did not arrive. He sent an incoherent telegram. But even then I suspected nothing." She paused. "Yesterday morning," she said, "I had a letter from my aunt Augusta."

She paused again. She seemed to think I ought to be impressed.

Her eyes tied a bowknot in my spine.

"Let me read you her letter. No, I will tell you its contents. Aunt Augusta had seen Edwin lunching at the Waldorf with a creature."

"A what?"

"My aunt described her. Her hair was of a curious dull bronze tint."

"Your aunt's?"

"The woman's. It was then that I began to suspect. How many women with dull bronze hair does Edwin know?"

"Great Scott! Why ask me?"

I had got used to being treated as a sort of "Hey, Bill!" by Florence, but I was darned if I was going to be expected to be an encyclopedia as well.

"One," she said. "That appalling Darrell woman."

She drew a deep breath.

"Yesterday evening," she said, "I saw them together in a taximeter cab. They were obviously on their way to some theatre."

She fixed me with her eye.

"Reginald," she said, "you must go and see her the first thing to-morrow."

"What!" I cried. "Me? Why? Why me?"

"Because you are responsible for the whole affair. You introduced Douglas to her. You suggested that he should bring her home. Go to her to-morrow and ascertain her intentions."

"But—"

"The very first thing."

"But wouldn't it be better to have a talk with Edwin?"

"I have made every endeavor to see Edwin, but he deliberately avoids me. His answers to my telegrams are willfully evasive."

There was no doubt that Edwin had effected a thorough bolt. He was having quite a pleasant little vacation: Two Weeks in Sunny New York. And from what I'd seen of him, he seemed to be thriving on it. I didn't wonder Florence had got rather anxious. She'd have been more anxious if she had seen him when I did. He'd got a sort of "New-York-is-so-bracing" look about him, which meant a whole heap of trouble before he trotted back to the fold.

Well, I started off to interview Mrs. Darrell, and, believe me, I didn't like the prospect. I think they ought to train A. D. T. messengers to do this sort of thing. I found her alone. The rush hour of clients hadn't begun.

"How do you do, Mr. Pepper?" she said. "How nice of you to call."

Very friendly, and all that. It made the situation darned difficult for a fellow, if you see what I mean.

"Say," I said. "What about it, don't you know?"

"I certainly don't," she said. "What ought I to know about what?"

"Well, about Edwin—Edwin Craye," I said.

She smiled.

"Oh! So you're an ambassador, Mr. Pepper?"

"Well, as a matter of fact, I did come to see if I could find out how things were running. What's going to happen?"

"Are you consulting me professionally? If so, you must show me your hand. Or perhaps you would rather I showed you mine?"

It was subtle, but I got on to it after a bit.

"Yes," I said, "I wish you would."

"Very well. Do you remember a conversation we had, Mr. Pepper, my last afternoon at the Crayes'? We came to the conclusion that I was rather a vindictive woman."

"By George! You're stringing old Edwin so as to put one over on Florence?"

She flushed a little.

"How very direct you are, Mr. Pepper! How do you know I'm not very fond of Mr. Craye? At any rate, I'm very sorry for him."

"He's such a chump."

"But he's improving every day. Have you seen him? You must notice the difference?"

"There is a difference."

"He only wanted taking out of himself. I think he found his sister Florence's influence a little oppressive sometimes."

"No, but see here," I said, "are you going to marry him?"

"I'm only a palmist. I don't pretend to be a clairvoyant. A marriage may be indicated in Mr. Craye's hand, but I couldn't say without looking at it."

"But I shall have to tell her something definite, or she won't give me a moment's peace."

"Tell her her brother is of age. Surely that's definite enough?"

And I couldn't get any more out of her. I went back to Florence and reported. She got pretty excited about it.

"Oh, if I were a man!" she said.

I didn't see how that would have helped. I said so.

"I'd go straight to Edwin and *drag* him away. He is staying at his club. If I were a man I could go in and find him—"

"Not if you weren't a member," I said.

"—And tell him what I thought of his conduct. As I'm only a woman, I have to wait in the hall while a deceitful small boy pretends to go and look for him."

It had never struck me before what a splendid institution a club was. Only a few days back I'd been thinking that the subscription to mine was a bit steep. But now I saw that the place earned every cent of the money.

"Have you no influence with him, Reginald?"

I said I didn't think I had. She called me something. Invertebrate, or something. I didn't catch it.

"Then there's only one thing to do. You must find my father and tell him all. Perhaps you may rouse him to a sense of what is right. You may make him remember that he has duties as a parent."

I thought it far more likely that I should make him remember that he had a foot. I hadn't a very vivid recollection of old man Craye. I was quite a kid when he made his great speech on the Egg Question and beat it for Europe—but what I did recollect didn't encourage me to go and chat with him about the duties of a parent. As I remember him, he was a rather large man with elephantiasis of the temper. I distinctly recalled one occasion when I was spending a school vacation at his home, and he found me trying to shave old Duggie, then a kid of fourteen, with his razor.

"I shouldn't be able to find him," I said.

"You can get his address from his lawyers."

"He may be at the North Pole."

"Then you must go to the North Pole."

"But say—!"

"Reginald!"

"Oh, all right."

I knew just what would happen. Parbury and Stevens, the lawyers, simply looked at me as if I had been caught snatching bags. At least, Stevens did. And Parbury would have done it, too, only he had been dead a good time. Finally, after drinking me in for about a quarter of an hour, Stevens said that if I desired to address a communication to his client, care of this office, it would be duly forwarded. Good morning. Good morning. Anything further? No, thanks. Good morning, *Good* morning.

I handed the glad news on to Florence and left her to do what she liked about it. She went down and interviewed Stevens. I suppose he'd had experience of her. At any rate, he didn't argue. He yielded up the address in level time. Old man Craye was living in Paris, but was to arrive in New York that night, and would doubtless be at his club.

It was the same club where Edwin was hiding from Florence. I pointed this out to her.

"There's no need for me to butt in after all," I said. "He'll meet Edwin there, and they can fight it out in the smoking room. You've only to drop him a line explaining the facts."

"I shall certainly communicate with him in writing, but, nevertheless, you must see him. I cannot explain everything in a letter."

"But doesn't it strike you that he may think it pretty bad gall-impertinence, don't you know, for a comparative stranger like me to be tackling a delicate family affair like this?"

"You will explain that you are acting for me."

"It wouldn't be better if old Duggie went along instead?"

"I *wish* you to go, Reginald."

Well, of course, it was all right, don't you know, but I was losing several pounds a day over the business. I was getting so light that I felt that, when the old man kicked me, I should just soar up to the ceiling like an air balloon.

The club was one of those large clubs

that look like prisons. I used to go there to lunch with my uncle, the one who left me his money, and I always hated the place. It was one of those clubs that are all red leather and hushed whispers.

I'm bound to say, though, there wasn't much hushed whispering when I started my interview with old man Craye. His voice was one of my childhood's recollections.

He was most extraordinarily like Florence. He had just the same eyes. I felt boneless from the start.

"Good morning," I said.

"What?" he said. "Speak up. Don't mumble."

I hadn't known he was deaf. The last time we'd had any conversation—on the subject of razors—he had done all the talking. This seemed to me to put the lid on it.

"I only said 'Good morning,'" I shouted.

"Good what? Speak up. I believe you're sucking candy. Oh, good morning? I remember you now. You're the boy who spoiled my razor."

I didn't half like this reopening of old wounds. I hurried on.

"I came about Edwin," I said.

"Who?"

"Edwin. Your son."

"What about him?"

"Florence told me to see you."

"Who?"

"Florence. Your daughter."

"What about her?"

All this vaudeville team business, mind you, as if we were bellowing at each other across the street. All round the room you could see old gentlemen shooting out of their chairs like rockets and dashing off at a gallop to write to the governing board about it. Thousands of waiters had appeared from nowhere, and were hanging about, dusting table legs. If ever a business wanted to be discussed privately, this seemed to me to be it. And it was just about as private as a conversation through megaphones in Longacre Square.

"Didn't she write to you?"

"I got a letter from her. I tore it up. I didn't read it."

Pleasant, was it not? It was not. I began to understand what a shipwrecked sailor must feel when he finds there's something gone wrong with the life belt.

I thought I might as well get to the point and get it over.

"Edwin's going to marry a palmist," I said.

"Who the devil's Harry?"

"Not Harry. Marry. He's going to marry a palmist."

About four hundred waiters noticed a speck of dust on an ash tray at the table next to ours, and swooped down on it.

"Edwin is going to marry a palmist?"

"Yes."

"She must be mad. Hasn't she seen Edwin?"

And just then who should stroll in but Edwin himself. I sighted him and gave him a hail.

He curveted up to us. It was amazing the way the fellow had altered. He looked like a two-year-old. Flower in his buttonhole and a six-inch grin, and all that. The old man seemed surprised, too. I didn't wonder. The Edwin he remembered was a pretty different kind of a fellow.

"Hullo, dad," he said. "Fancy meeting you here. Have a cigarette?"

He shoved out his case. Old man Craye helped himself in a sort of dazed way.

"You *are* Edwin?" he said slowly.

I began to sidle out. They didn't notice me. They had moved to a settee, and Edwin seemed to be telling his father a funny story.

At least, he was talking and grinning, and the old man was making a noise like distant thunder, which I supposed was his way of chuckling. I slid out and left them.

Some days later Duggie called on me. The old boy was looking scared.

"Reggie," he said, "what do doctors call it when you think you see things when you don't? Hal-something. I've got it, whatever it is. It's sometimes caused by overwork. But it can't be that with me, because I've not been doing any work. You don't think my brain's going or anything like that, do you?"

"What do you mean? What's been happening?"

"It's like being haunted. I read a story somewhere of a fellow who kept thinking he saw a battleship bearing down on him. I've got it, too. Four times in the last three days I could have sworn I saw my father and Edwin. I saw them as plainly as I see you. And, of course, Edwin's at home and father's in Europe somewhere. Do you think it's some sort of a warning? Do you think I'm going to die?"

"It's all right, old top," I said. "As a matter of fact, they are both in New York just now."

"You don't mean that? Great Scott, what a relief! But, Reggie, old fox, it couldn't have been them really. The last time was at Louis Martin's, and the fellow I mistook for Edwin was dancing all by himself in the middle of the floor."

I admitted it was pretty queer.

I was away for a few days after that in the country. When I got back I found a pile of telegrams waiting for me. They were all from Florence, and they all wanted me to go to Madison Avenue. The last of the batch, which had arrived that morning, was so peremptory that I felt as if something had bitten me when I read it.

For a moment I admit I hung back. Then I rallied. There are times in a man's life when he has got to show a flash of the old bulldog pluck, don't you know, if he wants to preserve his self-respect. I did then. My grip was still unpacked. I told my man to put it on a cab. And in about two ticks I was bowling off to the club. I left for England next day by the *Lusitania.*

About three weeks later I fetched up at Nice. You can't walk far at Nice without bumping into a casino. The one I hit my first evening was the Casino Municipale in the Place Masséna. It looked more or less of a Home From Home, so I strolled in.

There was quite a crowd round the boule tables, and I squashed in. And when I'd worked through into the front rank I happened to look down the table, and there was Edwin, with a green Tyrolese hat hanging over one ear, clutching out for a lot of five-franc pieces which the croupier was steering toward him at the end of a rake.

I was feeling lonesome, for I knew no one in the place, so I edged round in his direction.

Halfway there I heard my name called, and there was Mrs. Darrell.

I saw the whole thing in a flash. Old man Craye hadn't done a thing to prevent it—apart from being eccentric, he was probably glad that Edwin had had the sense to pick out anybody half as good a sort—and the marriage had taken place. And here they were on their honeymoon.

I wondered what Florence was thinking of it.

"Well, well, well, here we all are," I

said. "I've just seen Edwin. He seems to be winning."

"Dear boy!" she said. "He does enjoy it so. I think he gets so much more out of life than he used to, don't you?"

"Sure thing. May I wish you happiness? Why didn't you let me know and collect the silver fish-slice?"

"Thank you so much, Mr. Pepper. I did write to you, but I suppose you never got the letter."

"Mr. Craye didn't make any objections, then?"

"On the contrary. He was more in favor of the marriage than anyone."

"And I'll tell you why," I said. "I'm rather a chump, you know, but I observe things. I bet he was most frightfully grateful to you for taking Edwin in hand and making him human."

"Why, you're wonderful, Mr. Pepper. That is exactly what he said himself. It was that that first made us friends."

"And—er—Florence?"

She sighed.

"I'm afraid Florence has taken the thing a little badly. But I hope to win her over in time. I want all my children to love me."

"All your what?"

"I think of them as my children, you see, Mr. Pepper. I adopted them as my own when I married their father. Did you think I had married Edwin? What a funny mistake. I am very fond of Edwin, but not in that way. No, I married Mr. Craye. We left him at our villa to-night, as he had some letters to get off. You must come and see us, Mr. Pepper. I always feel that it was you who brought us together, you know. I wonder if you will be seeing Florence when you get back? Will you give her my very best love?"

Sealed Orders

Helen Churchill Candee

The White Star liner Titanic, *greatest ship of her time, struck an iceberg in Mid-Atlantic on April 15, 1912, and sank within two hours, carrying to their death 1,517 of the 2,223 persons on board—including many of the most famous personages of the day. Helen Churchill Candee, one of those rescued, wrote the story for* Collier's*—not as a news report, but as one woman's impression of a tremendous human drama.*

May 4, 1912

When all the lands were thrilling with the blossoming month of shower and sun, three widely differing craft crept out upon the sea.

One sailed from the New World's city of towers, plowing east.

Another coquetted with three near ports of Europe and then sailed west.

The third slipped down unnoticed from the glacial north.

The first was a little ship, and modestly, decorously glided down the bay and took her place on the ocean highway.

But across, on the other side of the world, the triumph of shipbuilding was starting her maiden trip—challenging the sea, men said; but a challenge is given by those who have rivals. The mammoth had none. She was the largest ship man had ever made; in her construction and in her finish, from keel to topmast, she was the ultimate note of talent and skill and invention. Triumphant was the word that best told her imperial progress.

And the third, the sinister craft, set out from the north with an insolent indifference that transcended even the magnificence of the greatest ship afloat.

And to all three of these craft the power that is greater than man gave sealed orders. All three, though they knew it not, were bound for the same unmarkable spot on the shifting surface of the deep.

The titan's departure was the one man noticed, for power and riches cannot be obscure.

Three days out the ship knew she was Queen of the Seas. Not only was she the largest, the most beautiful, but she was hour by hour discovering herself a possible fleetest. And that way came destruction.

There had been delays in detaching from the shore; at one port a too close touch with another ship, a stop of hours at another for heavy bags of mail. But when free of the land, at last on the high sea, day followed day with the weather in which ships make time. When the run went on the board it astonished, and there was a light laugh of pleasure from smoking room, deck, and lounge. Each man felt it a credit to himself. The ship was to make the record trial run. The oldest captain of the fleet had had the crowning and final honor of his sea life in his assignment. The head man of the line was on board. From stokehole to bridge the men had been picked with care from among their fellows on lesser boats, that the crew might be worthy of their trust.

It almost seemed that passengers had been picked too. The richest man was there, and he who by striving had nearly reached him. About the decks strolled the artist of renown and the great writer, the man of theatrical success, the giant in the world of trade, the aid of a nation's President, the prettiest woman, the woman who represented social prominence, the indispensable American girl, presidents of railways, aristocrats of Europe—all these to add to the glory of the first sea-crossing of the biggest ship.

Two days to try her wings, to prove her powers, and she was off for the saving of time. And the passenger for whom the keel had been laid and the magic wrought looked over the side at the flying water and laughed as a child.

A blond woman on the steerage deck stands like a viking's daughter, facing the wind. Her hair is golden bright in the sun, her long lines of grace show bold where the wind presses hard their draping. Around her is her little brood shouting and leaping in the wild free air. All have their faces set to the new Land of Possibility, whither the ship is taking them smooth and fleet, day and night. Over the child asleep in her arms the woman's wide eyes are directed forward with the look of the emigrant, the look of courage which has conquered fate since the days of Columbus and the colonies.

"Let us wander over the ship and see it all," said she of the suite de luxe to him of the bachelor's cabin. So they mounted to the hurricane deck and gazed across to the other world of the second class and wondered at its luxury, and further across to the waves and wondered at their clemency.

A door along the starboard side was open, clicking sounds within and a cheery English voice. "Come in, come right in, and try your strength," cried the exhibitor of this particular booth in Donnybrook Fair. "Have a race with me on the wheel, sir, while the lady takes a trot in the saddle. Or, here is a camel for you, sir—good for the liver." His own could not have needed it, so rubicund and clean of tint was he, this powerful five-feet-five of white flannels. He bounded about the place, pulling weights with a smooth finish, slipping into a sliding seat and begging him of the Two to take the other boat and beat him with a Cambridge stroke. He was up again like a cat and gave a hard hand to the lady's foot to mount her into the saddle and to turn on the appliance for the trot.

And so they played an hour with the toys in this wonderful retreat, never thinking of the sweet blue waters that lay so far away.

"I expect you'll be having a plunge in the pool after all this exercise, sir," said the white flannels. "But I'll see you both in the morning for another go with the wheel and the oars."

It was getting cold, biting cold, the cold that makes you glad to be alive, with air and water clear and clean as young blue eyes. The acres of decks were cleared of loungers, even of those whose chairs were placed well behind the plateglass weather screen. It was a time for activity, and a scattered parade was on.

"You are flirting with the prettiest girl," she accused, laughing.

"Man is omnivorous," he admitted, laughing back. "One of the women I most admire is this one," he signified an elderly figure, soberly dressed, walking arm in arm with her husband. With no parleying you knew they were people who had gained and accepted the sweets of success without intoxication. Sobriety and modesty were theirs; strength and calm showed on their faces.

"They, too, have been using one of the ship's appliances. They have just finished a Marconi talk with their son, whose east-bound ship is talking with ours."

"I see the glow on their faces—the same parent glow of the woman on the steerage deck. And there it is again—that handsome woman over there—see, it is for her son who is beside her with the adorable young wife. I have noticed them all the way over."

Then they went inside to escape the cold sparkling in the water and snapping in the air. And snugly in a green bay of the saloon, a bay made of velvet and wood in furniture shapes, they settled down before a glowing grate as one settles down before the home fire after a frosty afternoon ride over the fields. And servants brought tea and toast, and a general feeling of well-being brought content. The old couple came in and settled near by; the lady with the fine son drifted in and showed her pride to the world, her loving care to him. The quiet hour was on, the hour when the sun grows sleepy.

At dinner, two hours later, the scene might have been in London or New York, with the men in evening dress, the women shining in pale satins and clinging gauze. The prettiest girl even wore a glittering frock of dancing length, with silver fringe around her dainty white satin feet.

And after dinner there was coffee served to all at little tables around the great general lounging place, for here the orchestra played.

Some said it was poor on its Wagner work; others said the violin was weak. But that was for conversation's sake, for nothing on board was more popular than the orchestra. You could see that by the way everyone refused to leave it. And everyone asked of it some favorite bit. The prettiest girl asked for dance music, and clicked her satin heels and swayed her adolescent arms to the rhythm.

He of the Two who had walked the deck asked for Dvorak, while she asked for Puccini, and both got their liking, for the orchestra was adroit and willing.

At eleven, folk drifted off to their big cabins, with happy see-you-in-the-mornings, until a group formed itself alone, and the only sounds the musicians made were those of instruments being shut in their velvet beds.

The Two had all their friends about them. It was early yet. There was the restaurant above, a more cozy place for a little crowd—and things to drink were there on the end of a word of order.

So they all strayed easily up the regal stairway—refusing this time the lift—and arrived at the littlest place where one might eat, and took a table large enough for the seven. The only other table was made gay by the party of a President's aid.

"But how cold it is, how arctic!" and she of the Two drew close her scarf.

"Something hot, then," said he to the waiter, and the steam savored of Scotch and lemons.

How gay they were, these seven. The

talkative man told stories, the sensitive man glowed and laughed, the two modest Irishmen forgot to be suppressed, the facile Norsemen cracked American jokes, the cosmopolitan Englishman expanded, and the lady felt divinely flattered to be in such company.

Half-past eleven came. Even the last parties were breaking up, and only a handful of men strayed ladyless into the smoking room and fell to cards or reminiscence. Except for these and the night watch, the ship's company had settled down for another night of motionless repose.

Silence and emptiness were all the illumination shone on in the great public room and corridors of the great vessel. And in this soft silence the titan was flying like an arrow on the trackless sea whither the sealed orders were sending her.

But she was not the first to arrive at the tryst.

Down from the silent north that other sinister craft had slipped into her destined place. No wireless equipment, no port and starboard lights, no lines of cabins showing bright, no compass, no captain. But the power that is greater than man has no need of man's methods.

The white craft stretched its low, uneven length over miles of smoothest sea, shooting up peaks of dazzling white in lieu of sails, and her escort was the sleek, black seal and the white-winged gull.

With implacable patience the white craft awaited the coming of the greatest ship in the world, the virgin cleanly running to the unknown bridal across the starlit sea.

It was nearly midnight when she shuddered with horror in the embrace of the northern ice. Twice, from bow to stern she shook with mighty endeavor to crush beneath her the assailant.

And it seemed she had succeeded. A great calm at once fell upon the ship, such a calm as falls in port, and solitude reigned along the corridors and the wide halls. A head or two were thrust from cabin doors, but seeing nothing went back to bed. Stewards were reassuring, gay, and idle. In the smoking room men went on bidding for the trump.

But the Two went for a walk about in the keen cold air of the decks, "because I was startled," she apologized.

They mounted to the hurricane deck and stood by the closed door of the gymnast's chamber. They looked up at the stream, violently roaring, of steam escaping by the mammoth funnels.

"It is all right," he said; "that is always a precaution when machinery stops."

"But why are not the other engines doing the same?" He could not answer; he did not know the bottom had been torn from the ship beneath him. They walked aft and looked down where the mother and children of the steerage had been playing, and where the prosperous second-class passengers had reveled in their comforts. Solitude, desertion. Not a human being in sight.

"There is a list to starboard," said she.

He was grimly silent. They went forward to make sure. There the list was worse. The forward deck below them leaned as a man leans with a sword in his living side. On the deck below they found the same desertion as everywhere, the deck where all the chairs were spread, where folk displayed themselves and criticized others. The Two seemed all the people in the world, and because of the cold and because each had hard sorrow, although they walked about for warmth of body, they cracked jokes for warmth of heart.

"If I had had a wireless—if I knew that

my child was no longer living"—she left him to imagine the rest.

"I don't mind going either," he said, grim for a moment.

"Nevertheless," she laughed, "I'd fight death to the last if it came. I'd be Mrs. Lecks and put on black stockings to scare sharks. Why are we so calm?"

"We are Anglo-Saxons," said he.

The cold drove them into the big, green velvet room with its glowing grate, empty in its blaze of light.

A young man—he of the adoring mother and adorable wife—sprang gayly across the wide floor holding cuplike hands together. "Ice!" he laughed. "Have some iceberg. Take a piece! That's what happened. We struck an iceberg. This is what she left on the deck."

He flew away as gay as a boy. She took the bit, wondering in awe, and he dashed it from her and chafed the cold small hand until it glowed again, nor released it then, but turned the chafing to a caress, nor ever let the hand go. And in that minute they looked into each other's faces, acknowledged the presence of death, and accepted it. But neither spoke a word.

After that people began to come about, some dressed, some not, none alarmed, all quiet and curious to learn the cause of the disturbance. They took the seats about the companionway and talked low.

Women still in sweeping dinner gowns drew wraps about them as the deck door opened. People talked quietly in conventional groups, and all waited, waited, nor knew for what they delayed. The Two went again outside. The list had terribly increased as they viewed it from the deserted deck.

"Listen!" said she, holding his arm. "That noise over our heads—it is the sound of lifeboats being put out."

His answer was to force her to the scene above.

Scarce a passenger, but the port side filled with a growing crowd of wiry men, black alike in face and dress, in order crowded about the strong, quiet figure of the captain.

The firemen had been ordered up from the engine rooms and the black crew huddled together awaiting the order to man the lifeboats, the order that would put life again into their hands, for they knew, these hard-faced toilers, that only those little boats would save from death. She smiled on them as she walked through the iron crew, and they looked, startled, at the smile, thinking it lack of wit, not excess of courage.

But he was uneasy, and again took her downstairs and within, in search of less grim scenes.

Different, but was it less grim? Up the sweep of the regal stairway was advancing a solid procession of all the ship's passengers, wordless, orderly, quiet, and only the dress told of the tragedy. On every man and every woman's body was tied the sinister emblem of death at sea, and each one walked with his life-clutching pack to await the coming horrors. It was a fancy-dress ball in Dante's Hell.

Another glance between the Two. He caught her by the arm and forced her to a cabin, threw over her shoulders the white and bulky pack, saw that she was warmly wrapped, seized a rug, and said briefly: "Come."

They passed those who huddled within the ship and mounted again to the topmost deck. A line of boats swung on davits at deck level. The black cloud of firemen still waited in order the command to jump in, faces set. The order came on the clear, cold air. "Down below, men. Every one of you, down below!"

And without a sound they wittingly turned from life and went to death, no protest, no murmur, no resistance, a band of unknown heroes.

And then it was that the captain ordered: "Put the women in the boats. No men are to go." He spoke hard words in a quiet voice, but none might disobey.

Now for tragedy; all the horrors of separation had begun.

"See, captain, my arm is broken. My husband must go with me or I am helpless."

"No men allowed in the boats, madam," and the couple turned away.

"I am not young, and need my son; may he not come?"

"Only women."

And the young man in gay courage gave his mother and wife to the care of the swinging boat.

Others got in; the captain, who knew he was living his last hour, stopped a number, then augmented it, then ordered the little craft lowered, and twenty-five silent women descended nearly a hundred feet, filled with hope, sure that those on board were better off than they, sure that all would be reunited in an hour either on the big ship they had just left, or on that other vessel whose far white light just showed over the port quarter.

The Marconi man was hard at work, the second biggest ship was in near waters, and hope was high.

Terrible was the artillery of the rockets. The great ship seemed shrieking in despair. Before that was a dignity of self-confidence, but in that wild cry to heaven went up all the horror of death.

Then it was the women already in the lifeboats agonized over what love had coerced them into doing. What was life but love, and what was life without loved ones? The horrors of the discovery can never be told. Women of courage had been tricked by noble heroes into saving their own lives. It was an easy ruse—get into the boats, obey because it helps me; we will soon be together again. Do it for my sake, or the children's. By these sophistries of love were the women put into the boats at a time and in a place where theirs seemed the harder part to do.

But when by endless lowering each boat reached the water the women knew. They saw the salt flow sloping over the lighted ports of the third deck, and knew the vessel was already sunken thirty or forty feet into oblivion.

"Keep all the boats together and pull away from the vessel," the captain has said in a strong, low voice. Why pull away? Because presently the great palace of light would be following the lead of her diving bow, and in the final plunge would draw everything after her.

On the ship the bravely competent still loaded boats with protesting women and wailing children.

"Take her from me; take her!" cried the men from whom wives refused to part, and it was done.

In a corner against the cabin stood the aged couple, arm in arm, calmly resolute. "Come into this boat," the rescuers said to her. "I stay with my husband," she said simply. It was not the frantic protest of the younger women, but the firm will of the seasoned soul. And in death these two were not divided.

What can one whose profession is to amuse do in time of tragedy? They, too, have a part in the great play of courage. Over the crowds, quiet, inactive, anguished, there flowed a flood of music, such music as never before was heard—a gay march, a two-step, light operatic airs, all freighted with a burden of love, that love which lays down its life for a friend.

The ship orchestra was sending out courage from man to man in its peculiar expression, cheering others while itself faced death.

Men of courage and resource who had been loading and lowering boats from the very first came at last to a stop. The last boat was ready for the launching. Two who had held together in the work went a deck below to see if any stray women were there unrescued. All was brilliant desolation.

The lights were beginning to burn low, water—soft, noiseless water—was creeping up the slanting deck so fast that in another minute they would have been imprisoned under the deck's roof. They leaped to the railing and mounted it.

At that moment the last boat was floating just before them, three yards away, with vacant room in the bow. Surely they had the right! They looked in each other's faces to ask the question, and each nodded to the other yes. They leaped the space and caught the sides of the boat, the last to leave the ship by boat, almost the only rescuers who were saved.

The hundreds that were left drew closer. the beaten bow was hidden under water, the only uncovered space of deck sloped high toward the stern, and on this diminished point huddled this close pack and waited death with the transcendent courage and order and quiet that had been theirs for the horrible two hours.

And over them trembled the last strains of the orchestra's message: "Autumn" first, and then "Nearer, my God, to Thee."

Down on the sea the little lifeboats were following the captain's orders to pull away from the ship in water as calm, as full of reflected stars as the pool in a Moorish garden. All waited the end, transfixed with horror. Window after window of the ship became dark as the water covered it in the sloping, slow descent; less and less became the stern space where the hushed crowd waited.

At the last, the end of the world. A smooth, slow chute. Life went out on the big ship.

The death call of sixteen hundred units of divine selflessness spread its volume over the waters as a single cry to God. There was no shriek nor wail nor frantic shout. Instead, a heavy moan as of one being from whom final agony forces a single sound.

And with this human protest against stifling arctic waters was a muffled sound from within, the groan of the dying ship, as if she, too, were sensate and joined her agony with man's.

The mass in the dark waters was thrown hither and thither, and one or two caught rafts and boats. In the human instinct to preserve life, one man had drawn himself upon a raft.

He was white-haired, but short and strong, and had much to live for. At last the raft had rescued so many she endangered all, and then began the horrid task of fighting off the swimmers.

Those who looked for the gray beard on the raft saw him no more. Seeing the press, he had ceded his place and slipped silently into the sea.

"Don't get on, you'll swamp us."

"All right; God keep you all. Good-by," and the waters closed over him. It was the little gymnast.

After that, silence, silence on the surface of the deep, and awe on the faces of the stricken freight in the scattered lifeboats. Where had been the glowing lights from the luxurious cabins of the mammoth ship was now a soft, impersonal sheen of silver starlight, the implacability of nature.

And how futile were the little boats. Where were they going? Why were they there?

The distant light that some had followed from the first scudded away into the aurora as fast as the first breath of breeze rippled over the glassy waters.

Why live now to die miserably of cold and starvation and drenching? And always with the horror of that death groan sounding in ears and soul. It was then that those in the boats who had been picked up from the water gave up the spirit.

It was then the mother of the fine son began to call for him in the unmeaning repetition of the mind which has snapped. It was then that the emigrant woman of the many babes sent screams for them ringing to the stars in maniac baby-talk. It was then the ghostly gulls swung and cried in the icy air.

Three hours before the Marconi man had been at his post on the ship. Out over the oily waters, out on the clear, crisp air, as far as the twinkling canopy of stars, had trembled the soundless cry from the magic wires:

"Ship is sinking fast!"

Full sixty miles away a faithful wire had trembled in response.

And thus the third craft that went a-sailing on an April day learned of her sealed orders and their import, and turned flying to the trysting place.

All night she was preparing to help the proud big ship, happy to serve so great a supplicant.

She would be but small and shabby beside the greater vessel, but would humbly do her best, and so she pounded the engines and kicked the waters and strained the boilers.

The latitude and longitude given by the cry for succor were attained, yet the keenest glass could find no lights other than the stars. Darkness brooded on the face of the waters, and horror was in the faces of the relief.

Dawn showed the vast, vast reaches of the sea empty of big craft, but, floating near, a swaying tangle of deck chairs and cushions, and a pale white babe rocked in the cradle of that fashioning.

The sun lingered in coming on such a scene. The rescue boat lay still and watched it.

The aurora in the north was paled by the rosy chiffon scarfs that waved over the sun's east. Close down in the warm glow nestled an impertinent crescent moon.

Toward the sun rose sinister points dark against the light, the peaks of ice.

Away from the sun, struck by its light, were wondrous glistening sails of frozen white and pearly pink, ice mountains glorified into celestial beauty, and as far as the eye could see, the limitless level of the ice pack, purer and whiter than man's imagining.

The sound of the woman calling her babes because they were not, the moan of the woman calling her son—these were almost the only sounds from the scattered fleet of rowboats that showed like shells on the waters, the limping, chilled, and sorrowing fleet to whom the rescue ship brought salvation.

But a few hours more and the modest ship of gentle aim was turning back to port, heavy with the hundreds saved, and the flag at half-mast. But the burden of sorrow in the widows' hearts was to be read in the dark, dark shadows of their eyes.

The wail of mothers was heard in the closed chamber of the sick.

For every life on board three other braver ones had surrendered theirs in God-like selflessness.

The ice pack lay for miles, dazzling in the sun, peaks rising proudly here and there.

Seals black and shiny showed in the waters, gulls flew and cried, active white against the silent white.

Superb, thrilling, dominant, the ice pack held the region with nature's implacable strength. The power that is greater than man's had prevailed, the crushing insensate power against which there is no defense, from whom is no pity and no sparing.

But the power that is greater than all dominated even that, a power that is of God, which is the divinity of noble men.

Those who love them call them gone, but they live with a virility immortal.

The courage and tenderness of sixteen hundred souls who quietly gave their lives for others floods an entire world and makes it humbly eager to give tribute by living nobler lives.

And as long as man lives the tale will be told to the uplifting of men, for showing them the divinity which is man's and his kinship to God.

The Zayat Kiss

Sax Rohmer

Fu-Manchu, since become the very symbol of Oriental malevolence, first greeted Collier's *readers nearly a half-century ago. His creator, Arthur Sarsfield Ward, has since chilled the blood of two generations of Americans under the pen name, Sax Rohmer.*

February 15, 1913

"A GENTLEMAN TO SEE YOU, DOCTOR." From across the common a clock sounded the half hour.

"Ten-thirty!" I said. "A late visitor. Show him up, if you please."

I pushed my writing aside and tilted the lamp shade as footsteps sounded on the landing. The next moment I had jumped to my feet, for a tall, lean man, with his square-cut, clean-shaven face sun baked to the hue of coffee, entered and extended both hands with a cry:

"Good old Petrie! Didn't expect me, I'll swear!"

It was Nayland Smith, whom I had thought to be in Burma!

"Smith," I said, and gripped his hands hard, "this is a delightful surprise! Whatever—however—"

"Excuse me, Petrie!" he broke in. "Don't put it down to the sun!" And he put out the lamp, plunging the room into darkness.

I was too surprised to speak.

"No doubt you will think me mad," he continued, and dimly I could see him at the window, peering out into the road, "but before you are many hours older you will know that I have good reason to be cautious. Ah, nothing suspicious! Perhaps I am first this time." And stepping back to the writing table, he relighted the lamp.

"Mysterious enough for you?" he laughed, and glanced at my unfinished MS. "A story, eh? From which I gather that the district is beastly healthy—what, Petrie? Well, I can put some material in your way that, if sheer uncanny mystery is a marketable commodity, ought to make you independent of influenza and broken legs and shattered nerves and all the rest."

I surveyed him doubtfully, but there was nothing in his appearance to justify me in supposing him to suffer from delusions. His eyes were too bright, certainly, and a hardness now had crept over his face. I got out the whisky and siphon, saying:

"You have taken your leave early?"

"I am not on leave," he replied, and slowly filled his pipe. "I am on duty."

"On duty!" I exclaimed. "What, are you moved to London, or something?"

"I have got a roving commission, Petrie, and it doesn't rest with me where I am to-day, nor where I shall be to-morrow."

There was something ominous in the words, and putting down my glass, I faced round and looked him squarely in the eyes.

"Out with it!" I said. "What is it all about?"

Smith suddenly stood up and stripped off his coat. Rolling back his left shirt sleeve he revealed a wicked-looking wound in the fleshy part of the forearm. It was quite healed, but curiously striated for an inch or so around.

"Ever seen one like it?" he asked.

"Not exactly," I confessed. "It appears to have been deeply cauterized."

"Right! Very deeply! A barb steeped in the venom of a hamadryad went in there!"

A shudder I could not repress ran through me at mention of that most deadly of all the reptiles of the East.

"There's only one treatment," he continued, rolling his sleeve down again, "and that's with a sharp knife, a match, and a broken cartridge. I lay on my back raving for three days afterward in a forest that stank with malaria, but I should have been lying there now if I had hesitated. Here's the point. It was not an accident!"

"What do you mean?"

"I mean that it was a deliberate attempt on my life, and I am hard upon the tracks of the man who extracted that venom—patiently, drop by drop—from the poison glands of the snake, who prepared the arrow, and who caused it to be shot at me."

"What fiend is this?"

"A fiend who, unless my calculations are at fault, is now in London, and who regularly wars with pleasant weapons of that kind. Petrie, I have traveled from Burma not in the interest of the British Government merely, but in the interests of the entire white race, and I honestly believe—though I pray I may be wrong—that its survival depends largely upon the success of my mission."

To say that I was perplexed conveys no idea of the mental chaos created by these extraordinary statements, for into my humdrum suburban life Nayland Smith had brought fantasy of the wildest. I did not know what to think, what to believe.

"I am wasting precious time!" he rapped decisively, and, draining his glass, he stood up. "I came straight to you because you are the only man I dare to trust. Except the big chief at headquarters, you are the only person in England, I hope, who knows that Nayland Smith has quitted Burma. I must have some one with me, Petrie, all the time—it's imperative! Can you put me up here, and spare a few days to the strangest business, I promise you, that ever was recorded in fact or fiction?"

I agreed readily enough, for, unfortunately, my professional duties were not onerous.

"Good man!" he cried, wringing my hand in his impetuous way. "We start now."

"What, to-night?"

"To-night! I had thought of turning in, I must admit. I have not dared to sleep for forty-eight hours, except in fifteen-minute stretches. But there is one move that must be made to-night and immediately. I must warn Sir Crichton Davey."

"Sir Crichton Davey—of the India—"

"Petrie, he is a doomed man! Unless he follows my instructions without question, without hesitation—before Heaven, nothing can save him! I do not know when the blow will fall, how it will fall, nor from whence, but I know that my first duty is to warn him. Let us walk down to the corner of the common and get a taxi."

"What's this?" muttered my friend hoarsely.

Constables were moving on a little crowd of curious idlers who pressed about the steps of Sir Crichton Davey's house and sought to peer in at the open door. Without waiting for the cab to draw up to the curb, Nayland Smith recklessly leaped out, and I followed closely at his heels.

"What has happened?" he demanded breathlessly of a constable.

The latter glanced at him doubtfully, but something in his voice and bearing commanded respect.

"Sir Crichton Davey has been killed, sir."

Smith lurched back as though he had received a physical blow, and clutched my shoulder convulsively. Beneath the heavy tan his face had blanched, and his eyes were set in a stare of horror.

"My God!" he whispered. "Just too late!"

With clenched fists he turned and, pressing through the group of loungers, bounded up the steps. In the hall a man who unmistakably was a Scotland Yard official stood talking to a footman. Other members of the household were moving about, more or less aimlessly, and the chilly hand of King Fear had touched one and all, for, as they came and went, they glanced ever over their shoulders, as if each shadow cloaked a menace, and listened, as it seemed, for some sound which they dreaded to hear.

Smith strode up to the detective and showed him a card, upon glancing at which the Scotland Yard man said something in a low voice, and, nodding, touched his hat to Smith in a respectful manner.

A few brief questions and answers, and, in gloomy silence, we followed the detective up the heavily carpeted stair, along a corridor lined with pictures and busts, and into a large library. A group of people were in this room, and one, in whom I recognized Chalmers Cleeve of Harley Street, was bending over a motionless form stretched upon a couch. Another door communicated with a small study, and through the opening I could see a man on all fours examining the carpet. The uncomfortable sense of hush, the group about the physician, the bizarre figure crawling, beetlelike, across the inner room, and the grim hub, around which all this ominous activity turned, made up a scene that etched itself indelibly on my mind.

As we entered, Dr. Cleeve straightened himself, frowning thoughtfully.

"Frankly, I do not care to venture any opinion at present regarding the immediate cause of death," he said. "Sir Crichton was addicted to cocaine, but there are indications which are not in accordance with cocaine poisoning. I fear that only a post-mortem can establish the facts—if," he added, "we ever arrive at them. A most mysterious case!"

Smith stepping forward and engaging the famous pathologist in conversation, I seized the opportunity to examine Sir Crichton's body.

The dead man was in evening dress, but wore an old smoking jacket. He had been of spare but hardy build, with thin, aquiline features, which now were oddly puffy, as were his clenched hands. I pushed back his sleeve and saw the marks of the hypodermic syringe upon his left arm. Quite mechanically I turned my attention to the right arm. It was unscarred, but on the back of the hand was a faint red mark, not unlike the imprint of painted lips. I examined it closely, and even tried to rub it off, but it evidently was caused by some morbid process of local inflammation if it were not a birthmark.

Turning to a pale young man whom I had understood to be Sir Crichton's private secretary, I drew his attention to this mark and inquired if it were constitutional.

"It is not, sir," answered Dr. Cleeve, overhearing my question. "I have already made that inquiry. Does it suggest anything to your mind? I must confess that it afforded me no assistance."

"Nothing," I replied. "It is most curious."

"Excuse me, Mr. Burboyne," said Smith, now turning to the secretary, "but Inspector Weymouth will tell you that I act with authority. I understand that Sir Crichton was—seized with illness in his study?"

"Yes, at half-past ten. I was working here in the library and he inside, as was our custom."

"The communicating door was kept closed?"

"Yes, always. It was open for a minute or less about ten-twenty-five, when a message came for Sir Crichton. I took it in to him, and he then seemed in his usual health."

"What was the message?"

"I could not say. It was brought by a district messenger, and he placed it beside him on the table. It is there now, no doubt."

"And at half-past ten?"

"Sir Crichton suddenly burst open the door and threw himself, with a scream, into the library. I ran to him, but he waved me back. His eyes were glaring horribly. I had just reached his side when he fell, writhing, upon the floor. He seemed past speech, but as I raised him and laid him upon the couch he gasped something that sounded like 'The red hand!' Before I could get to the bell or telephone he was dead!"

Mr. Burboyne's voice shook as he spoke the words, and Smith seemed to find this evidence confusing.

"You do not think he referred to the mark on his hand?"

"I think not. From the direction of his last glance I feel sure he referred to something in the study."

"What did you do?"

"Having summoned the servants, I ran into the study. But there was nothing unusual to be seen. The windows were closed and fastened. He worked with closed windows in the hottest weather. There is no other door, for the study occupies the end of a narrow wing, so that no one could possibly have gained access to it while I was in the library unseen by me. Had some one concealed himself in the study earlier in the evening—and I am convinced that it offers no hiding place—he could only have come out again by passing through here."

Nayland Smith tugged at the lobe of his left ear, as was his habit when meditating.

"You had been at work here in this way for some time?"

"Yes. Sir Crichton was preparing an important book."

"Had anything unusual occurred prior to this evening?"

"Yes," said Mr. Burboyne with evident perplexity, "though I attached no importance to it at the time. Three nights ago Sir Crichton came out to me and appeared very nervous; but at times his nerves—you know? Well, on this occasion he asked me to search the study. He had an idea that something was concealed there."

"Some*thing* or some one?"

" 'Something' was the word he used. I searched, but fruitlessly, and he seemed quite satisfied and returned to his work."

"Thank you, Mr. Burboyne. My friend and I would like a few minutes' private investigation in the study."

Sir Crichton Davey's study was a small one, and a glance sufficed to show that, as the secretary had said, it offered no hiding place. It was heavily carpeted, and overfull of Burmese and Chinese ornaments and curios, and upon the mantelpiece stood several framed photographs which showed this to be the sanctum of a wealthy bachelor who was no misogynist. A map of the Indian Empire occupied the larger part of one wall. The grate was empty, for the weather was extremely warm, and a green-shaded lamp on the littered writing table afforded the only light. The air was stale, for both windows were closed and fastened.

Smith immediately pounced upon a large, square envelope that lay beside the blotting pad. Sir Crichton had not even troubled to open it, but my friend did so. It contained a blank sheet of paper!

"Smell!" he directed, handing the letter to me.

I raised it to my nostrils. It was scented with some pungent perfume.

"What is it?" I asked.

"It is a rather rare essential oil," was the reply, "which I have met with before, though never in Europe. I begin to understand, Petrie."

He tilted the lamp shade and made a close examination of the scraps of paper, matches, and other débris that lay in the grate and on the hearth. I took up a copper vase from the mantelpiece, and was examining it curiously when he turned, a strange expression on his face.

"Put that back, old man," he said quietly.

Much surprised, I did as he directed.

"Don't touch anything in the room. It may be dangerous."

Something in the tone of his voice chilled me, and I hastily replaced the vase and stood by the door of the study, watching him search methodically every inch of the room—behind the books, in all the ornaments, in table drawers, in cupboards, on shelves.

"That will do," he said at last. "There is nothing here and I have no time to search further."

We returned to the library.

"Inspector Weymouth," said my friend, "I have a particular reason for asking that Sir Crichton's body be removed from this room at once and the library locked. Let no one be admitted on any pretense whatever until you hear from me."

It spoke volumes for the mysterious credentials borne by my friend that the man from Scotland Yard accepted his orders without demur, and, after a brief chat with Mr. Burboyne, Smith passed briskly downstairs. In the hall a man who looked like a groom out of livery was waiting.

"Are you Wills?" asked Smith.

"Yes, sir."

"It was you who heard a cry of some kind at the rear of the house about the time of Sir Crichton's death?"

"Yes, sir. I was locking the garage door, and, happening to look up at the window of Sir Crichton's study, I saw him jump out of his chair. Where he used to sit at his writing, sir, you could see his shadow on the blind. Next minute I heard a call out in the lane."

"What kind of call?"

The man whom the uncanny happening

clearly had frightened seemed puzzled for a suitable description.

"A sort of wail, sir," he said at last. "I never heard anything like it before and don't want to again."

"Like this?" inquired Smith, and he uttered a low, wailing cry, impossible to describe.

"The same, sir, I think," Wills said, "but much louder."

"That will do," said Smith, and I thought I detected a note of triumph in his voice. "But stay! Take us through to the back of the house."

The man bowed and led the way, so that shortly we found ourselves in a small, paved courtyard. It was a perfect summer's night, and the deep blue vault above was jeweled with myriads of starry points.

"Up yonder are the study windows, sir. Over that wall on your left is the back lane from which the cry came, and beyond is Regent's Park."

"Are the study windows visible from there?"

"Oh, yes, sir."

"Who occupies the adjoining house?"

"Major General Platt-Houston, sir, but the family is out of town."

"Those iron stairs are a means of communication between the domestic offices and the servants' quarters, I take it?"

"Yes, sir."

"Then send some one to make my business known to the Major General's housekeeper; I want to examine those stairs."

Singular though my friend's proceedings appeared to me, I had ceased to wonder at anything. Since Nayland Smith's arrival at my rooms I seemed to have been moving through the fitful phases of a nightmare. My friend's account of how he came by the wound in his arm; the scene on our arrival at the house of Sir Crichton Davey; the secretary's story of the dying man's cry. "The red hand!"; the hidden perils of the study; the wail in the lane—all were fitter incidents of delirium than of sane reality. So, when a white-faced butler made us known to a nervous old lady who proved to be the housekeeper of the next-door residence, I was not surprised at Smith's saying:

"Lounge up and down outside, Petrie. Everyone has cleared off now. It is getting late. Keep your eyes open and be on your guard. I thought I had the start, but *he* is here before me, and, what is worse, he probably knows by now that I am here, too."

With which he entered the house and left me out in the square, with leisure to think, to try to understand.

The crowd which usually haunts the scene of a sensational crime had been cleared away, and it had been circulated that Sir Crichton had died from natural causes. The intense heat having driven most of the residents out of town, practically I had the square to myself, and I gave myself up to a brief consideration of the mystery in which I so suddenly had found myself involved.

By what agency had Sir Crichton met his death? Did Nayland Smith know? I rather suspected that he did. What was the hidden significance of the perfumed envelope? Who was that mysterious personage whom Smith so evidently dreaded, who had attempted his life, who presumably had murdered Sir Crichton? Sir Crichton Davey, during the time that he had held office in India and during his long term of service at home, had earned the good will of all, British and native alike. Who was his secret enemy?

Something touched me lightly on the shoulder.

I turned, with my heart fluttering like a child's. This night's work had imposed a severe strain even upon my callous nerves.

A girl wrapped in a hooded opera cloak stood at my elbow, and, as she glanced up at me, I thought that I never had seen a face so seductively lovely nor of so unusual a type. With the skin of a perfect blonde, she had eyes and lashes as black as a Creole's, which, together with her full red lips, told me that this beautiful stranger, whose touch had so startled me, was not a child of our northern shores.

"Forgive me," she said, speaking with an odd, pretty accent, and laying a slim hand with jeweled fingers confidingly upon my arm, "if I startled you. But—is it true that Sir Crichton Davey has been murdered?"

I looked into her big, questioning eyes, a harsh suspicion laboring in my mind, but could read nothing in their mysterious depths—only I wondered anew at my questioner's beauty. The grotesque idea momentarily possessed me that, were the bloom of her red lips due to art and not to nature, their kiss would leave—though not indelibly—just such a mark as I had seen upon the dead man's hand. But I dismissed the fantastic notion as bred of the night's horrors, and worthy only of a medieval legend. No doubt she was some friend or acquaintance of Sir Crichton's who lived close by.

"I cannot say that he has been murdered," I replied, acting upon the latter supposition and seeking to tell her what she asked as gently as possible. "But he is—"

"Dead?"

I nodded.

She closed her eyes and uttered a low, moaning sound, swaying dizzily. Thinking she was about to swoon, I threw my arm round her shoulders to support her, but she smiled sadly and pushed me gently away.

"I am quite well, thank you," she said.

"You are certain? Let me walk with you until you feel quite sure of yourself."

She shook her head, flashed a rapid glance at me with her beautiful eyes, and looked away in a sort of sorrowful embarrassment, for which I was entirely at a loss to account. Suddenly she resumed:

"I cannot let my name be mentioned in this dreadful matter, but—I think I have some information—for the police. Will you give this to—whomever you think proper?"

She handed me a sealed envelope, again met my eyes with one of her dazzling glances, and hurried away. She had gone no more than ten or twelve yards, and I still was standing bewildered, watching her graceful, retreating figure, when she turned abruptly and came back. Without looking directly at me, but alternately glancing toward a distant corner of the square and toward the house of Major General Platt-Houston, she made the following extraordinary request:

"If you would do me a very great service, for which I always would be grateful"—she glanced at me with passionate intentness—"when you have given my message to the proper person, leave him and do not go near him any more to-night!"

Before I could find words to reply she gathered up her cloak and ran. Before I could determine whether or not to follow her (for her words had aroused anew all my worst suspicions) she had disappeared! I heard the whirr of a restarted motor at no great distance, and in the instant that Nayland Smith came running down the steps I knew that I had nodded at my post.

"Smith!" I cried as he joined me, "tell me what we must do!"

And rapidly I acquainted him with the incident.

My friend looked very grave; then a grim smile crept round his lips.

"She was a big card to play," he said; "but he did not know that I held one to beat it."

"What! You know this girl? Who is she?"

"She is one of the finest weapons in the enemy's armory, Petrie. But a woman is a two-edged sword, and treacherous. To our great good fortune, she has formed a sudden predilection, characteristically Oriental, for yourself. Oh, you may smile, but it is evident. She was employed to get this letter placed in my hands. Give it to me."

I did so.

"She has succeeded. Smell."

He held the envelope under my nose, and, with a sudden sense of nausea, I recognized the strange perfume.

"You know what this presaged in Sir Crichton's case? Can you doubt any longer? She did not want you to share my fate, Petrie."

"Smith," I said unsteadily, "I have followed your lead blindly in this horrible business and have not pressed for an explanation, but I must insist before I go one step farther upon knowing what it all means."

"Just a few steps farther," he rejoined. "As far as a cab. We are hardly safe here. Oh, you need not fear shot or knives. The man whose servants are watching us now scorns to employ such clumsy, telltale weapons."

"Pull up the window on your side, Petrie, and look out behind. Good! We've started."

The cab moved off with a metallic jerk, and I turned and looked back through the little window in the rear.

"Some one has got into another cab. It is following ours, I think."

Nayland Smith lay back and laughed unmirthfully.

"Petrie," he said, "if I escape alive from this business I shall know that I bear a charmed life."

I made no reply as he pulled out the dilapidated pouch and filled his pipe.

"You have asked me to explain matters," he continued, "and I will do so to the best of my ability. You no doubt wonder why a servant of the British Government, lately stationed in Burma, suddenly appears in London in the character of a detective. I am here, Petrie—and I bear credentials from the very highest sources—because, quite by accident, I came upon a clue. Following it up in the ordinary course of routine, I obtained evidence of the existence and malignant activity of a certain man. At the present stage of the case I should not be justified in terming him the emissary of an Eastern power, but I may say that representations are shortly to be made to that power's ambassador in London."

He paused and glanced back toward the pursuing cab.

"There is little to fear until we arrive home," he said calmly. "Afterward there is much. To continue: This man, whether a fanatic or a duly appointed agent, is, unquestionably, the most malign and formidable personality existing in the known world to-day. He is a linguist who speaks with almost equal facility in any of the civilized languages and in most of the barbaric. He is an adept in all the arts and sciences which a great university could teach him. He also is an adept in certain obscure arts and sciences which no university of to-day can teach. He has the brains of any three men of genius. Petrie, he is a mental giant."

"You amaze me!" I said.

"As to his mission among men. Why did M. Jules Furneaux fall dead in a Paris opera house? Because of heart failure? No! Because his last speech had shown that he held the key to the secret of Tongking. What became of the Grand Duke Stanislaus? Elopement? Suicide? Nothing of the kind. He alone was fully alive to Russia's growing peril. He alone knew the truth about Mongolia. Why was Sir Crichton Davey murdered? Because had the work he was engaged upon ever seen the light, it would have shown him to be the only living Englishman who understood the importance of the Tibetan frontiers. Is there a man who would arouse the West to a sense of the awakening of the East, that the millions only await their leader? He will die. And this is only one phase of the devilish campaign. The others I can merely surmise."

"But, Smith, this is almost incredible! What perverted genius controls this awful secret movement?"

"Imagine a person, tall, lean, and feline, high shouldered, with a brow like Shakespeare and a face like Satan, a close-shaven skull, and long, magnetic eyes of the true cat green. Invest him with all the cruel cunning of an entire Eastern race, accumulated in one giant intellect, with all the resources of science past and present. Imagine that awful being and you have a mental picture of Dr. Fu-Manchu, the yellow peril incarnate in one man."

I sank into an armchair in my rooms and gulped down a strong peg of brandy.

"We have been followed here," I said. "Why did you make no attempt to throw the pursuers off the track, to have them intercepted?"

Smith laughed.

"Useless, in the first place. Wherever we went *he* would find us. And of what use to arrest his creatures? We could prove nothing against them. Further, it is evident that an attempt is to be made upon my life to-night—and by the same means that proved so successful in the case of poor Sir Crichton."

His square jaw grew truculently prominent, and he leaped stormily to his feet, shaking his clenched fists toward the window.

"The villain!" he cried. "The fiendishly clever villain! I suspected that Sir Crichton was next, and I was right. But I came too late, Petrie! That hits me hard, old man. To think that I knew and yet failed to save him!"

He resumed his seat, smoking hard.

"Fu-Manchu has made the blunder common to all men of unusual genius," he said. "He has underrated his adversary. He has not given me credit for perceiving the meaning of the scented messages. He has thrown away one powerful weapon—to get such a message into my hands—and he thinks that, once safe within doors, I shall sleep, unsuspecting, and die as Sir Crichton died. But without the indiscretion of your charming friend I should have known what to expect when I received her 'information,' which, by the way, consists of a blank sheet of paper."

"Smith," I broke in, "who is she?"

"She is either Fu-Manchu's daughter, his wife, or his slave. I am inclined to believe the latter, for she has no will but his will, except"—with a quizzical glance—"in a certain instance."

"How can you jest with some awful thing—Heaven knows what—hanging over your head? What is the meaning of these perfumed envelopes? How did Sir Crichton die?"

"He died of the Zayat Kiss. Ask me what that is and I reply 'I do not know.' The zayats are the Burmese caravansaries, or rest houses. Along a certain route—upon which I set eyes for the first and only time upon Dr. Fu-Manchu—travelers who use them sometimes die as Sir Crichton died, with nothing to show the cause of death but a little mark upon the neck, face, or limb, which has earned in those parts the title of the 'Zayat Kiss.' The rest houses along that route are shunned now. I have my theory, and I hope to prove it to-night if I live. This was my principal reason for not enlightening Dr. Cleeve. Even walls have ears where Fu-Manchu is concerned. I wanted an opportunity to study the Zayat Kiss in operation, and I shall have one."

"But the scented envelopes?"

"In the swampy forests of the district I have referred to a rare species of orchid, almost green and with a peculiar scent, is sometimes met with. I recognized the heavy perfume at once. I take it that the thing which kills the travelers is attracted by this orchid. You will notice that the perfume clings to whatever it touches. I doubt if it can be washed off in the ordinary way. After at least one unsuccessful attempt to kill Sir Crichton—you recall that he thought there was something concealed in his study on a previous occasion?—Fu-Manchu hit upon the perfumed envelopes. He may have a supply of these green orchids in his possession—possibly to feed the creature."

"What creature? How could any creature have got into Sir Crichton's room to-night?"

"You no doubt observed that I examined the grate of the study. I found a fair quantity of fallen soot. I at once assumed, since it appeared to be the only means of entrance, that something had been dropped down; and I took it for granted that the thing, whatever it was, must still be concealed either in the study or in the library. But when I had obtained the evidence of the groom, Wills, I perceived that the cry from the lane or from the park was a signal. I noted that the movements of anyone seated at the study table were visible, in shadow, on the blind, and that the study occupied the corner of a two-storied wing and, therefore, had a short chimney. What did the signal mean? That Sir Crichton had leaped up from his chair and either had received the Zayat Kiss or had seen the thing which some one on the roof had lowered down the straight chimney. It was the signal to withdraw that deadly thing. By means of the iron stairway at the rear of Major General Platt-Houston's I quite easily gained access to the roof above Sir Crichton's study—and I found this."

Out from his pocket Nayland Smith drew a tangled piece of silk, mixed up with which were a brass ring and a number of unusually large-sized split shot, nipped on in the manner usual on a fishing line.

"My theory proven," he resumed. "Not anticipating a search on the roof, they had been careless. This was to weight the line and to prevent the creature's clinging to the walls of the chimney. Directly it had dropped in the grate, however, by means of this ring I assume that the weighted line was withdrawn, and the thing was only held by a slender thread, which sufficed, though, to draw it back again when it had done its work. It might have got tangled, of course, but they reckoned on its making straight up the carved leg of the writing table for the prepared envelope. From there to the hand of Sir Crichton—which, from having touched the envelope, would also be scented with the perfume—was a certain move."

"My God! How horrible!" I exclaimed, and glanced apprehensively into the dusky shadows of the room. "What is your theory respecting this creature—what shape, what color?"

"It is something that moves rapidly and silently. I have observed that the rear of this house is ivy covered right up to and above your bedroom. Let us make ostentatious preparations to retire, and I think we may rely upon Fu-Manchu's servants to attempt my removal, at any rate—if not yours."

"But, my dear fellow, it is a climb of thirty-five feet at the very least!"

"You remember the cry in the back lane? It suggested something to me, and I tested my idea—successfully. It was the cry of a dacoit. Oh, dacoity, though quiescent, is by no means extinct. Fu-Manchu has dacoits in his train, and probably it is one who operates the Zayat Kiss, since it was a dacoit who watched the window of the study this evening. To such a man an ivy-covered wall is a grand staircase."

The clock across the common struck two.

Having removed all traces of the scent of the orchid from our hands with a solution of ammonia, Smith and I had followed the program laid down. It was an easy matter to reach the rear of the house, by simply climbing a fence, and we did not doubt that, seeing the light go out in the front, our unseen watcher would proceed to the back.

The room was a large one, and we had made up my camp bed at one end, stuffing odds and ends under the clothes to lend the appearance of a sleeper, which device we also had adopted in the case of the larger bed. The perfumed envelope lay upon a little coffee table in the center of the floor, and Smith, with an electric pocket lamp, a revolver, and a brassy beside him, sat on cushions in the shadow of the wardrobe. I occupied a post between the windows.

The distant clock struck a quarter-past two. A slight breeze stirred the ivy.

Something rose, inch by inch, above the sill of the westerly window. I could see only its shadow, but a sharp, sibilant breath from Smith told me that he, from his post, could see the cause of the shadow.

Every nerve in my body seemed to be strung tensely. I was icily cold, expectant, and prepared for whatever horror was upon us.

The shadow became stationary. The dacoit was studying the interior of the room.

Then it suddenly lengthened, and, craning my neck to the left, I saw a lithe, black-clad form, surmounted by a yellow face, sketchy in the moonlight, pressed against the window panes!

One thin, brown hand appeared over the edge of the lowered sash, which it grasped, and then another. The man made absolutely no sound whatever. The second hand disappeared—and reappeared. It held a small square box.

There was a very faint *click*.

The dacoit swung himself below the window with the agility of an ape as, with a dull, sickening thud, *something* dropped upon the carpet!

"Stand still, for your life!" came Smith's voice, high pitched.

A beam of white light leaped out across the room and played fully upon the coffee table in the center.

Prepared as I was for something horrible, I know that I paled at sight of the thing that was running round the edge of the envelope.

It was an insect, full six inches long, and of a vivid, venomous red color! It had something of the appearance of a great ant, with its long, quivering antennæ and its febrile, horrible vitality; but it was proportionately longer of body and smaller of head, and had numberless rapidly moving legs. In short, it was a giant centipede, apparently of the Scolopendra group, but of a form quite new to me. These things I realized in one breathless instant; in the next—Smith had dashed the thing's poisonous life out with one straight, true blow of the golf club!

I leaped to the window and threw it widely open, feeling a silk thread brush my hand as I did so. A black shape was dropping with incredible agility from branch to branch of the ivy, and without once offering a mark for a revolver shot, it merged into the shadows beneath the trees of the garden.

As I turned and switched on the light Nayland Smith dropped limply into a chair, leaning his head upon his hands. Even that grim courage had been tried sorely.

"Never mind the dacoit, Petrie," he said. "Nemesis will know where to find him. We know now what causes the mark of the Zayat Kiss. Therefore science is richer for our first brush with the enemy, and the enemy is poorer—unless he has any more unclassified centipedes. I understand now something that has been puzzling me since I heard of it—Sir Crichton's stifled cry. When we remember that he was almost past speech, it is reasonable to suppose that his cry was not 'The red hand!' but 'The red *ant!'* Petrie, to think that I failed by less than an hour to save him from such an end!"

"The body of a lascar, dressed in the manner usual on the P. & O. boats, was recovered from the Thames off Tilbury by the river police at 6 a. m. this morning. It is supposed that the man met with an accident in leaving his ship."

Nayland Smith passed me the evening paper and pointed to the above paragraph.

"For 'lascar' read 'dacoit,'" he said. "Our last night's visitor, fortunately for us, failed to follow his instructions. Also, he lost the centipede and left a clue behind him. Dr. Fu-Manchu does not overlook such lapses."

What Is an American?

Charles W. Eliot

Best known to the public as editor of the "Harvard Classics"—the famous "Five-Foot Shelf" of books—Charles William Eliot was one of the architects of the American education system. As its president from 1869 to 1909 he helped build Harvard University into a great national institution. A professor of mathematics and chemistry, he championed a balanced education embracing both science and the humanities. And as evident in this article, written ten years before his death in 1926, he held a deep and reasoned faith in the principles of American democracy.

August 12, 1916

IN THE FIRST PLACE, THE AMERICAN IS THE product of certain moral inheritances. He is usually the descendant of an immigrant or an immigrant himself. That immigrant, in many cases, was escaping from some sort of religious, political, social, or economic oppression. He was some kind of non-conformist; and he was dissatisfied with his surroundings and wished to better them. Therefore he must have had an unusual amount of imagination, ambition, and venturesomeness. This is as true of the late comers to America as of the earlier comers. The English Pilgrims and Puritans, the French Huguenots, the Scotch Covenanters, the Moravians, the Quakers, the Russian Jews, the Armenians, and the Syrian Christians all fled from religious hostilities or restrictions, and meant to secure, or expected to find, in the New World freedom to worship God each in his own way. They found that liberty, and ultimately established in the United States a régime of absolute religious toleration. After 1848 a large German immigration took refuge here from political oppression. Millions of European and Near-Eastern people have crossed the Atlantic and taken the serious risk of attempting to secure a foothold in fresh and free America, because they hoped to escape from economic pressure and chronic poverty. They have exiled themselves from home and friends in search of some better opportunity for a successful and happy life than the native land offered. The migrations of the Irish and the Scotch Highlanders have been strong cases of escape from harassing economic and social conditions. The early comers took the risks of the wilderness, the Indians, the untried climate, and the unknown diseases. The late comers have dared the perils of congested cities, of novel industries, and of insecure employment. Hence, by heredity, the white Americans of to-day—of whatever race or stock—have a fair chance to be by nature independent, bold, and enterprising.

In the second place, the environment of the immigrants into North America during the past three centuries has exerted a common influence on them all, which has tended to produce in the successive generations certain advantageous qualities. All the American generations thus far may fairly be said to have done pioneering work, and all the earlier generations lived a life of conflict with the hostilities of adverse Nature and with hostile human beings, both savage and civilized. Such pioneering and such conflict all across a continent supply men and women alike with a strenuous training.

The American colonies were engaged most of the time in some kind of warfare. From the beginning the American settlers carried arms, and were often called upon to defend their homes and their communities. The Massachusetts Puritan farmer carried his flintlock with him to the meeting house, and the frontier settler has always had firearms in his cabin and has taught his boys how to use them.

In the nineteenth century the United States was involved four times in costly war. No American generation has escaped the discipline of war. Among the most recent immigrants from southern Europe and the Near East there have been many thousands of young men who, before they had really established themselves in the New World, returned home to bear their part in the present agonies of the Old. An American, therefore, is likely to be a man of individualistic quality, who nevertheless possesses a strong community sense and is ready to fight in defense of his family and his community. His environment has trained him to energetic industry, sharp conflict with natural obstacles, and the use of protective force. Nevertheless his inheritance and his environment alike predispose him to condemn military establishments, a military class, and militarism in general. He is and means to be a freeman.

A genuine American regards his Government as his servant and not as his master, and will have no chief executive in city, State, or nation except an elected executive. He recognizes that men are not equal as regards native capacity or acquired power, but desires that all men shall be equal before the law and that every individual human being—child or adult—shall have his just opportunity to do his best for the common good. He believes in universal education, and is always desiring the improvement of the free schools. In respect to this desire for education, however, many of the most recent Americans outdo some of the earlier ones—particularly in the zeal and assiduity of their children in school.

As a result of his own experience in public affairs and of his ancestors' experience, a true American always acquiesces in the decision of a majority of the legitimate participants in an election or other public contest. This is an American trait of high political value. It makes American political and social progress, as a rule, a peaceful evolution. People who have long been helpless under political or ecclesiastical oppression, and have had no practice in self-government, have difficulty in acquiring this trait.

The characteristic American believes, first, in justice as the foundation of civilized government and society, and next in freedom for the individual, so far as that freedom is possible without interference with the equal rights of others. He conceives that both justice and freedom are to be secured through popular respect for the laws enacted by the elected representatives of the people and through the faithful observance of those laws, and because of his confidence in law as the enactment of justice and the security for freedom, he utterly condemns all lawless practices by public servants, private citizens, or groups of citizens. For him lawless violence is the worst offense which can be committed by either the governors or the governed. Hence he distrusts legislation which is not faithfully executed, and believes that unsuccessful legislation should not lapse, but be repealed or replaced. It should be observed, however, that American justice in general keeps in view the present common good of the vast majority, and the restoration rather than the punishment of the exceptional malignant or defective individual. Indeed, the American conception of justice is very different from that of traditional Christian theology, or of feudal institutions, or of any of the despotic governments. It is essentially democratic; and especially it finds sufferings inflicted on the innocent unintelligible and abhorrent.

The American believes that if men are left free in the planning and conduct of their lives they will win more success in the professions, the trades, and the industries than they will if their lives are regulated for them by some superior power, even if that power be more intelligent and better informed than they. Blind obedience and implicit submission to the will of another do not commend themselves to characteristic Americans. The discipline in which they believe is the voluntary cooperation of several or many persons in the orderly and effective pursuit of common ends. Yet Americans are capable of intense collective action when they see that such action is necessary to efficiency or to the security of the community as a whole. Thus they submit willingly to any restrictions on individual liberty which can be shown to be necessary to the preservation of the public health, and they are capable of the most effective cooperation at need in business, sports, and war.

Such are the common ideals, hopes, and aims of the heterogeneous peoples assembled on the territory of the United States. Whoever accepts them and governs his life by them is an American, whatever his origin, race, or station. No other assimilation of different national stocks is needed—or is even desirable—than this acceptance of the common American ideals; but with this acceptance should go, and ordinarily does go, an ardent love of the new country and its liberal institutions, a love not inconsistent with an affectionate regard for the old country from which the original immigrant into America took his resolute departure.

A Reporter's Diary

Ring W. Lardner

Ringgold Wilmer Lardner was first and foremost a great reporter, and while he is best remembered by the public at large for his short stories ("Haircut," "You Know Me, Al," and the rest) his fellow-newspapermen remember him as one who could make a news story sing without sacrificing the facts. In his Collier's *series, "A Reporter's Diary," he left statistics and grand strategy to his colleagues, and devoted himself to Ring Lardner's personal war.*

October 13, 1917

FRIDAY, AUGUST 17. (A FRENCH PORT)

IN OBEDIENCE TO THE CAPTAIN'S ORDERS we remained on deck last night, fully dressed, till our ship was past the danger zone and in harbor. There was a rule against smoking or lighting matches, but none against conversation.

The Gentleman from Louisiana and a young American Field Service candidate had the floor. The former's best was a report of what he saw once while riding along beside the Columbia River. An enormous salmon jumped out of the water and raced six miles with the train before being worn out. Whether the piscatorial athlete flew or rode a motorcycle, we were unable to learn.

The Gentleman from Louisiana yielded to his younger and stronger countryman. Some one had spoken of the lack of a convoy. "Don't you think we haven't a convoy," the kid remarked.

I scanned the sea in all directions and saw nothing but the dark waters. "Where is it?" I inquired.

"There's one on each side of us," said Young America. "They're about twenty miles from the ship."

"I should think," said somebody, "that a very slender submarine might slip in between our side kicks and us and do its regular job."

"No chance," the youth replied. "The convoy boats are used as decoys. The sub would see them first and spend all its ammunition."

A little later he confided in me that the new American warships were 245,000 horsepower. I had no idea there were that many horses left to measure by.

We spotted a shooting star. "That was a big one," I said.

"Big! Do you know the actual size of those things? I got it straight from a professor of astronomy. They're as small as a grain of sand."

"Why do they look so big?"

"Because they're so far away and they travel so fast."

Round ten o'clock, beckoning lights ashore told us we were close to safety. But the French gunners remained at their posts two hours longer. The captain's shouted order, relieving them from duty, was music to our ears.

After midnight, however, we turned a complete circle, and at once the deck was alive with rumors. We had been hit, we were going to be hit, we were afraid we would be hit, and so on. The fact was that our pilot from ashore was behind time and we circled round rather than stand still and be an easy target while awaiting him. We were in harbor and anchored at three. Many of us stayed up to see the sun rise over France. It was well worth the sleep it cost.

They told us we would not dock until six to-night. Before retiring to my cabin for a nap, I heard we had run over a submarine and also that we had not. The latter story lacked heart interest, but had the merit, probably, of truth. Submarines have little regard for traffic laws, but are careful not to stall their engines in the middle of a boulevard.

I was peacefully asleep when the French officers came aboard to give us and our passports the Double O. They had to send to my cabin for me. I was ordered to appear at once in the salon de conversation. A barber hater addressed me through his beard and his interpreter: "What is Monsieur Laudanum's business in France?"

I told him I was a correspondent.

"For who?"

"Collier's Weekly."

"Have you credentials from them?"

"No, sir."

"Your passport says you are going to Belgium. Do you know there are no trains to Belgium?"

"I know nothing about it."

"Well, there are no trains. How will you go there?"

"I'll try to get a taxi," I said.

"Are you going from here to Paris?"

"Yes."

"And where are you going from Paris?"

"I don't know."

"Please explain that answer."

"I will go wherever the authorities permit me to go."

"That is not a satisfactory answer."

"I'm sorry."

"What is your real business in France?"

"To write."

"I'm afraid we'll have to keep your passport. You will appear to-morrow morning at nine o'clock at this address."

And they handed me a scary-looking card.

On the deck I met our congressman and told him my troubles.

"I know these fellows very well," he said. "If you like, I can fix it for you."

"No," I replied proudly. "I'd rather do my own fixing."

At the dock I got into a taxi and asked to be taken to the —— Hotel. Not to my dying day will I forget that first ride in a French taxi. Part of the time we were on the right side of the street, part of the time on the left, and never once were we traveling under a hundred and fifty miles an hour. We turned twenty corners and always on one ear. We grazed dozens of frightened pedestrians, many of them men crippled in the war, or by taxis, and women too old to dodge quickly. We aimed at a score of rickety horse-drawn vehicles, but our control was bad and we bumped only one. In front of the hostelry we stopped with a jerk.

"Comme beaucoup?" I asked the assassin.

"Un franc cinquante," he said.

Only thirty cents, and I thought I knew why. When they get through a trip without killing anyone, they feel they have not done themselves justice nor given you a square deal.

I found myself a seat at a sidewalk table and ordered sustenance. The vial they brought it in was labeled "Bière Ritten," but I suspect the adjective was misspelled.

Till darkness fell I watched the passing show—street cars with lady motormen and conductors; hundreds of old carts driven by old women, each cart acting as a traveling roof for an old dog; wounded soldiers walking or hobbling along, some of them accompanied by sad-faced girls; an appalling number of women in black; a lesser number of gayly garbed and extremely cordial ones, and whole flocks of mad taxis, seeking whom they might devour.

By using great caution at the street crossings, I succeeded in reaching the telegraph office where I wrote a message informing Paris friends of my arrival. I presented it to the lady in the cage, who handed it back with the advice that it must be rewritten in French. I turned away discouraged and was starting out again into the gloom when I beheld at a desk the songbird of the ship. Would she be kind enough to do my translating? She would.

The clerk approved the new document, and asked for my passport. I told her it had been taken away. She was deeply grieved, then, but without it monsieur could send no message. Bonne nuit!

Back at the hotel I encountered the Yankee vice consul, a gentleman from Bedford, Ind. I told him my sad plight, and he said if matters got too serious his office would undertake to help.

With his assurances to comfort me, I have retired to my room to write, to my room as big as Texas and furnished with all the modern inconveniences.

Saturday, August 18. (Paris)

It is Saturday night and they have hot water, but before I take advantage of it I must recount the thrilling experiences of the day.

After a sidewalk breakfast of "oofs" and so-called café in Bordeaux, I went to keep my engagement at court. It was apparent that I was not the only suspect. The walk outside and the room within were crowded with shipmates, most of them from the second cabin, all looking scared to death.

I stood in line till I realized that I must make it snappy if I wanted to catch the 11.05 for Paris; then I butted my way into the august presence of Him of the Beard.

He recognized me at once and told me with his hands to go upstairs. In a room above I found the English-speaking cross-examiner, with the accent on the cross.

He motioned me to a chair and began his offensive.

"Monsieur Laudanum," he said, "when I asked you yesterday how you expected to get to Belgium, you said something about a taxi. That answer was not satisfactory. You have not explained anything to us. I do not believe we can allow you to leave Bordeaux."

"All right, sir." I arose.

"Sit down!" he barked. "Now tell me if you have any explanations to make."

"Nothing beyond what I said yesterday. I have come here to write. I want to go to Paris, and when I arrive there

I will find out where else I will be permitted to go."

"It seems strange that you have no papers."

"Yes, sir."

"Have you any?"

I searched my pockets and produced a used-up check book on a Chicago bank. The ogre read every little stub and I felt flattered by his absorbed interest. When he had spent some five minutes on the last one, which recorded a certain painful transaction between me and a man-eating garage, he returned my book and said: "You don't satisfy me at all. You will have to stay here."

"Suppose," said I, "that the American consul vouches for me."

"That will make no difference. You do not seem to realize that we are at war."

"Not with America."

"I don't know your nationality."

"I thought," said I, "that my passport hinted at it."

"You will have to stay in Bordeaux," was his pertinent reply.

"Thank you, sir," I said, and arose again.

"Sit down," said he, "and wait a minute."

He was out of the room five years.

"If he ever does come back," I thought, "it will be in the company of five or six large gendarmes."

But when he came back he came alone.

"Here," he said abruptly, "is your passport. You will be permitted to go to Paris. We will keep track of you there." And he bowed me out of the joint.

The crowd downstairs seemed as great as ever, and as scared. I picked my way through it with my head held high, a free man.

I decided on a fiacre for my trip from hotel to station. It would be safer, I thought. But I learned, on our interminable way, that defensive fighting in the streets of Bordeaux is far more terrifying, far more dangerous than the aggressive taxi kind. We were run into twice and just missed more times than I could count, and besides my conveyance was always on the verge of a nervous breakdown. 'Spite all the talk of periscopes and subs, the journey across the ocean was parlor croquet compared to my fiacre ride in Bordeaux.

While awaiting my turn at the ticket window I observed at the gate a French soldier wearing a large businesslike bayonet. "Probably to punch tickets with," I thought, but was mistaken. Another gentleman attended to that duty, and the soldier did not give me so much as the honor of a glance.

Outside on the platform were a few of the Red Cross and Y.M.C.A. men of our ship, and I learned from them that one of their number had suffered a sadder fate than I. He had tried to get by on a Holland passport, viséed at the French consulate in New York, and been quietly but firmly persuaded to take the next boat back home.

I shared a compartment on the train with a native of the Bronx, and a French lady who just couldn't make her eyes behave, and two bored-looking French gentlemen of past middle age, not to mention in detail much more baggage than there was room for. The lady and the two gentlemen wore gloves, which made the Bronxite and me feel very bourgeois.

Our train crew, with the possible exception of the engineer and fireman whom I didn't see, was female, and, thinking I might some time require the services of the porter, I looked in my dictionary for the feminine of George.

To try out my knowledge of français, I had purchased at the station a copy of

"Le Cri de Paris." I found that I could read it very easily by consulting the dictionary every time I came to a word.

But the scenery and the people were more interesting than "Le Cri," the former especially. Perfect automobile roads, lined with trees; fields, and truck gardens in which aged men and women, young girls and little boys were at work; green hills and valleys; winding rivers and brooks, and an occasional château or a town of fascinating architecture—these helped to make us forget the heat and dust of the trip and the ear-splitting shrieks of our engine. No wonder the boche coveted his neighbor's house.

We stopped for some time at one particularly beautiful town and went out for air. I wondered audibly concerning the name of the place. An American companion looked at the signs round the station.

"It's Sortie," he said.

But it wasn't. It was Angoulême, and I wouldn't mind moving thither. My American friend was probably from Exit, Michigan.

The discovery was made and reported that one might go into the dining car and smoke as much as one liked without asking permission from the maiden with the dreamy eyes. This car was filled with French soldiers and officers going back to the front after their holiday. There seemed to be as many different uniforms as there were men, and the scenery indoors was almost as brilliant as that outside.

It was about eight-thirty in the evening when we reached Paris. The sophisticated soldiers engaged their "redcaps" before they left the train, calling to them through the open windows. The demand was much greater than the supply, and I was among the unfortunates who had to carry his own baggage. I staggered to a street where a whole flotilla of taxis was anchored, but when I asked for one the person in charge said "No, no, no, no, no," meaning "No," and pointed round the corner. I followed his directions and landed on a boulevard along which there was a steady procession of machines, but it was fully twenty minutes before one came that was going slow enough to stop.

Our city is not all lit up like a church these nights, and it was impossible to see much of what we passed on the way to the hotel.

At the desk an English clerk, dressed for a noon wedding, gave me a blank to fill out. All the blank wanted to know was my family history. It is to be sent, said the clerk, to the prefect of police. I had no idea he was interested in me.

Sunday, August 19.
(Paris)

When I get back to Chicago I shall insist that my favorite restaurant place tables out on the walk. It is more hygienic and much more interesting.

But Chicago, I'm afraid, can't provide half as much sidewalk entertainment as Paris. As I remember the metropolis of Illinois, there is a sad lack there of demonstrative affection on the streets. In fact, I fear that a lady and gentleman who kissed each other repeatedly at the corner of Madison and Dearborn would be given a free ride to Central Station and a few days in which to cool off. Such an osculatory duel on Paris's Grand Boulevard—also known by a dozen other names—goes practically unnoticed except by us Illinois hicks.

An American officer and I—at the former's expense—lunched sur curb to-day. The food was nothing to boast about, but we got an eyeful of scenery. Soldiers—French, British, and American—strolled by constantly, accompanied by more or less beautiful brunettes, and only a few were thoughtless enough not to stop and kiss a few times in full view of our table. We also observed the inmates of passing taxis. No matter how wide the back seat, the lady occupant invariably sat on her escort's lap. A five-passenger car in America is a ten-passenger car in Paris, provided the chauffeur has a girl of his own.

When the American officer was tired of buying, I left him and sought out the Chicago "Tribune" office, conveniently located above Maxim's. The editor was there, but he was also broke, so I went back to the Ritz and got ready for bed.

The express office will be open tomorrow and I will be a rich man.

LUNDI, 20 AOUT (PARIS)

Went down to the express office and cashed a large part of my order. Friends were with me, and they immediately relieved me of most of the burden. I was hungry for lunch, having had no breakfast. Meat was what I wanted, and meat was what I couldn't get. Which led me to inquire into the Rules de la vie of Paris.

1. Monday and Tuesday are meatless days.

2. All except Saturday and Sunday are heatless days. Hot baths are impossible on Mondays, Tuesdays, Wednesdays, Thursdays, and Fridays.

3. Strong drink is procurable between noon and 2 p. m. and 7.30 and 9.30 at night. At other times ye toper must be content with light wines.

4. All public places except the theatres must close and douse lights at 9.30 in the evening.

5. There is no speed limit for taxis or privately owned cars. A pedestrian run over and killed is liable to imprisonment. The driver is not only innocent, but free to hurl as many French curses as he likes at his victim. If the pedestrian is not killed, he must explain why not to the judge.

6. It is not only permissible but compulsory to speak to any girl who speaks to you, and a girl who won't speak to you should be reported to the police.

7. No watch or clock is wrong. Whatever time you have is right and you may act accordingly.

8. Matches never ignite. A smoker must purchase a cigar or cigarette lighter and keep it filled with essence, the français term for gas. Sometimes the lighters work.

9. American cigarettes are not procurable. Bum ones may be bought at any tabac store or café for only five times what they are worth.

10. Water must never be used as a thirst quencher, and seldom for any other purpose. It's worse than bourgeois; it's unheard-of.

The lack of water, hot or cold, drove me to a barber shop this morning. The barber first made me put on a shroud, and I was afraid he was either going to cut me to pieces or talk me to death. But his operation was absolutely painless and his incessant conversation harmless because I couldn't understand a word of it.

From the barber shop I went to the information department of American Army Headquarters. That's where you get permits to visit our camps. But of course, if you've run over here from America, you have lots of spare time on your hands, so they're doing you a favor if they hold you up a few days. What is a week or so when a man's here for a whole month?

They have queer ideas at the Maison de

la Presse, which is the French equivalent for our publicity bureau. They receive you cordially there and treat you just as if you were not dregs.

I jumped thither after a futile visit to our own headquarters. I said I would like to go to the French front.

"Certainly," replied the man in charge. "Whenever it's convenient for you, we'll see that you get a trip."

So I told him when it would be convenient and he's going to see me through. I hear that the British are similarly peculiar. They are polite even to newspaper men and magazine writers. They might even speak to a cartoonist.

Returning to our side of the Seine, I bumped into some Australians, here on leave. One had been in Germany before the war and could speak and understand the "schoenste language."

"They use me as an interpreter," he said. "When they bring in a bloody boche prisoner, I talk to him. First we give him a real meal, maybe bacon and eggs and coffee, something he hasn't seen for months. Then I ask him where he came from and how he got here. Most of them are glad to tell me the truth. Those that do, I mark them down as 'Very intelligent.' Those that volunteer information I record as 'Extremely intelligent.' Those that say 'Nicht verstehe' go down in the record as 'Not intelligent.' But the majority are so bloody well glad to be out of the war that they talk freely.

"I asked one Heinie if he was going to try to escape. 'Not me,' he said, 'I'm tickled to be here.' They're all fed up on the war. You'd be too with three years of it."

This young man admitted that he was one of the best football players in Australia. "Maybe I've forgotten how now," he said. "I've been over here three years. Just think of it—I traveled twelve thousand miles, or maybe it's kilos, to mix up in this."

Baseball, he told me, had taken a strong hold on Australia.

"I don't hit well," he said, "but I can catch what you call flies! I can catch the widest flies that are knocked."

Which gift would probably be useless in America, where most of the flies knocked are bloody narrow.

Before I left him I learned also that Les Darcy was all right at heart, but that the professional "sports" spoiled him, and that he could have "knocked Jack Johnson, Stanley Ketchel, Billy Papke, or Jess Willard clean out of the ring."

He is going back to the trenches tonight, and I hope there are plenty of extremely intelligent Heinies there to keep him busy interpreting till his next leave. Interpreting, I should think, would be much pleasanter than going over the top.

Tuesday, August 21

This time it was an American of the French Ambulance Service.

"Say, listen," he said. "I can give you some mighty good stories. Real stuff, do you get me? Listen: One night there was a boche wounded out there and I brought him in. He had one leg all shot to pieces and we had to operate. I was going to give him the ether when he turned over and looked me in the face. 'Why, Dan,' he said, 'aren't you going to speak to me?' It was a chap I'd gone to school with in America. I could give you lots of stuff like that; do you get me? I used to be in New York, and Rube Goldberg used to call me up out of bed at six in the morning. 'Dan,' he'd say to me, 'I'm up against it for an idea. Will you give me an idea?' Do you get me? And there's a dramatic critic in New York—I won't tell you his name—but he used to tag round me after a first night and ask me what I thought of the show. Do you get me? I can give you a lot of good stuff."

I told him I was afraid that if he gave it to me all at once I wouldn't remember any of it. So he is coming to my hotel every day during his leave, to give me a little at a time—if he can find me.

Last night a good-hearted American officer took me to dinner at La Tour d'Argent, which is said to be the oldest restaurant in Paris and which, they say, is the place the Kaiser was going to have his banquet on a certain night three years ago if Gott hadn't gone back on him at the last moment.

We ordered duck, the restaurant's specialty. They cook it in your presence, slice off whatever is sliceable, and then put the bird in a press and give you the result as gravy. After the meal they hand you a post card on which is inscribed *le numéro de votre canard.* I looked up "canard" in my dictionary and found that it meant a drake, or false news, or a worthless newspaper. I have heard lots of false news, but I know no one took the trouble to count the items. Also I know that my newspaper is neither worthless nor numbered. So canard in this case must mean drake. The number of mine was 41654. If he had happened to disagree with me, I could have taken his number and traced him to the source. It's a very good idea and might be used in America on eggs or drinks.

I made another trip to the office which is supposed to be in charge of American correspondents and accommodations for them. I will go there again to-morrow and again the next day. I will bother them to death. Meantime I have applied to a person in London for permission to go to the British front, and have been assured a visit to the French lines late next week. I have wonderful vision and can see things twelve miles away.

P.S. It was revealed to me to-night that my detention and trial in Bordeaux was a frame-up, conceived by loving friends aboard ship and carried out by that English-speaking cross-examiner, who, believe me, is a convincing actor.

Thanks, gents. It was good for about two thousand words.

The Yanks Go Through

William Slavens McNutt

The first World War had reached its roaring climax. Veteran magazine writer William Slavens McNutt, covering the Western Front for Collier's, *had the luck and the reporter's instinct to reach the right place at the right time to watch and record a chapter that was a complete drama in itself.*

October 5, 1918

I HAVE SEEN THE GAME OF WAR PLAYED in the open fields under a clear sky as a writer or painter might order it for his own purpose; seen it played in a sunlit gold and green valley of France by men of my own land as a moving-picture director might have arranged it for the eye of his camera. I have sat on an open hillside under a screaming roof of loaded steel and watched our farthest thin brown line of fighting infantry smash irresistibly into the worst the German has to offer, flank and rush frantically chattering machine guns, dodge far-flung blows of barrage fire as a boxer dodges a fist: dodge and rush and strike—and win!

I have seen all that as one might sit in the bleachers and watch a football game played out on the field below; seen it as the occupant of a choice seat in a huge, natural amphitheatre, watching what will be important history carved out in action before my eyes.

It was during the German retreat from the Marne, out of the Soissons-Rheims salient, and it had been in progress for a number of days. The Germans were getting back as best they might, leaving behind them quantities of munitions and equipment, fighting chiefly rear-guard actions with machine guns. And always at their heels, twenty-four hours of each victorious day, were the French and Americans, slugging them back with whining tons of high explosive, showering them with the death that the buzzing shrapnel bears, stinging them to greater speed by the high-whistling little metal words with which a machine gun argues, stabbing and smashing them out of town and wood with bayonet and gun butt.

So swift was the advance that as dignified and complex an institution as a division headquarters might move several times in one day, and the front line was as hard to locate as an address in Brooklyn! And behind that ever-moving thin brown line of fighting infantry to a depth of thirty miles there was spread out a magnitude of movement that stunned the imagination; a bewildering military panorama that attacked the eye with vast picture after vast picture until at last one watched unseeing, wrung dry of the capacity for further impression.

I first came upon this grumbling sea of mighty movement while riding toward the front in a correspondent's car. It was near Belleau Wood, the scene of the first signal American success on the Marne. The machine sped up to the crest of a hill, and there, just ahead of us, blotting out the white of the French road with a moving stain of brown, was a long column of American artillery stretching ahead as far as the eye could reach. Shortly we overtook and rode beside it. They had been on the way for days. Grimy, dust-powdered men were sprawled out fast asleep on the jolting caissons. Weary officers were nodding in their saddles as they rode. The heads of the horses were all adroop as they plodded on. The soldiers afoot were walking bent forward, slowly, wearily, mechanically slogging on through the dust like automatons driven by a mechanism that had almost run down but would never, never quite stop and so moved them irresistibly onward, slow, thumping step after slow, thumping step, wearily on and on over the flinty road through the choking, gritty haze of dust.

For the space of half an hour we whirled by this monotonous, slow-moving but ever forward-slogging line of weary, dust-smothered life, and groaning, creaking mechanism of wheel and spring, of gun and wagon body.

Beyond the column of artillery we passed a long line of machine gunners, men riding humped up on funny little dwarf one-horse carts no bigger than a baby carriage (they reminded me at first of circus clowns in a parade and then of burlesque charioteers); beyond the machine gunners motor lorries, huge brown vehicles, swaying, groaning, growling sullenly along on their way to the distant front, some packed with weary, lolling soldiers, some piled high with supplies. Then big guns jouncing slowly along in tow of clanking, grinding tractors. Then more troops and artillery and more and more. Seemingly there was no end to this slow-moving, brown line of energy crawling up toward the battle field. And it was all American. In one day I rode probably seventy-five miles, every yard of the way past this grumbling, dust-befogged procession. For other days I rode through this staggering immensity of action, going from correspondents' headquarters to the front and back again. And then my hour of luck arrived!

The Germans were making a desperate stand on the Ourcq on the line running to the right from Fère-en-Tardenois. I arrived near noon in the shell-wrecked town where was located the headquarters of the American division that was then thunderously, savagely slugging the boche with its every power of man and gun to stun him loose from his desperate grip on the far slope of the Ourcq. Together with two friends I visited the division intelligence officer and for the twentieth time inquired as to a point of vantage from which we might really see some of the infantry action. The town was semicircled with American heavy artillery, and it was necessary to talk in quick bursts of speech between the obliterating attacks of sound that roared forth at rapid intervals from the hot mouths of the fighting metal monsters.

"Our infantry's going over this afternoon about here," he said, indicating on the map a spot on the far side of the Ourcq to the right of Fère-en-Tardenois. "If you could get up to the Château-Forêt, you might see a little of the work."

"How about Hill 212?" I asked. I had heard about that hill from an officer friend, and I wanted to get there. The intelligence officer smiled and shook his head.

"Not a chance. Great observation if you could get there—which you couldn't—and if you did the betting's all against your getting back. Better try Château-Forêt. The view's not as good from there, but you'll probably live longer to tell about what little you do see."

Speaking in the short intervals between gunfire, he gave us our directions, and our car crawled slowly through a village to the fork in the road at the foot of a hill; then we took the road up the hill to the right. I had thought there was a certain degree of noise in the valley below where the heavy guns were located and where quivering nerves were beaten to numbness! I was mistaken! Until I reached the plateau at the top of that hill I had no conception of noise. For that plateau, stretching out before us for some two thousand yards to a wood ahead, was sown thick with rapid-firing seventy-fives. From copse and gun pit and open field all about us they were spitting flame and steel.

And it was a different world up there on that flame-spouting plateau. The traffic was less, and it moved faster. The men were more alert. The plateau was clean! We had come through thirty miles of a world that was dirty, dust-choked, greasy, slow-moving; a world that was stupid with monotony and fatigue, a sluggish, low grumbling world of hard, mean service. And on this plateau was the beginning of the clean, swift, deadly world of action for which that hard, slow-grinding service was rendered. There was a soul tonic in the spiritual atmosphere of that clean world.

We whirled across the plateau and into the wood beyond. None of the soldiers we met knew anything about Château-Forêt, so we kept on going. We arrived at last at a crossroad where a sweating M. P. halted us. "Château-Forêt?" he bawled in my ear. "Don't know nothin' about it. Mebbe find out down at brigade headquarters. Take this road to the left through the woods an' leave your car at the first-aid dressin' station. They'll tell you how to reach brigade."

Three hundred yards down the road to the left and we reached the first-aid dressing station, a mere hut in the woods. The newly wounded were there, lying on stretchers on the ground awaiting transportation to the rear. And immediately about that rude dressing station, in the midst of all that cannon fire, among those newly wounded there was a curious illusion of peace. On the faces of all the wounded there was a common expression of ecstatic tranquillity, of exalted content. They had done the ultimate thing well; for them at that moment nothing mattered; and from them radiated an aura of peace, so that one had the feeling of being remote from the war; of being safe in a spiritual shelter.

"Brigade headquarters is right ahead along that path through the woods there," an orderly directed us. "Château-Forêt? Never heard of it."

We went on along the little path through the thick wood, a path walled by a dense growth of underbrush, past quantities of German ammunition and equipment, past infantrymen curled up in the scanty shelter of individual pits, past men sleeping sprawled out in the underbrush, men in whom fatigue had conquered caution. We came then upon a lieutenant who discouraged us.

"Château-Forêt?" he exclaimed. "Why, that's away over to your left, and you couldn't get into the observation post there anyway. The general's up there now and a lot of others. It's full up. No, I don't know of a place from where you could see the infantry go over. You can go on up to the edge of the woods, but you couldn't see much of anything from there. I'd advise you to go back."

"Well, we'll go up to the edge of the woods anyway."

"You can do that. I'll tell you what: I'll take you up to brigade, and we'll see what they can do for you."

A hundred yards farther along the path we stopped. There was a narrow trench there perhaps ten feet long and partly roofed with sheet iron.

"This," said the lieutenant, pointing at the partly roofed trench at our feet, "is brigade headquarters. Wait for me a minute."

He squirmed in at one end of the trench, and almost immediately a major popped out at the other.

"Hello!" said the major. "Do you know Floyd Gibbons? Where is he now?"

I told him. He asked after other correspondents I knew. A colonel crawled up out of the trench and joined us, and for five minutes we left the battle flat on its back and stood there gossiping eagerly about mutual acquaintances. (I know of nothing more strange than the usual conversations in which one indulges at the front in the heat of battle. Recently I was racing down a road to get out from under heavy shell fire, falling on my face every five or ten yards as a whistling scream announced a fresh arrival. A panting lieutenant caught step with me. "Do you know So-and-So?" he gasped. "Yes," I replied as a shell whirred down out of the sky and we both fell flat on our faces. "Where is he now?" he continued as the sound of the explosion died away and we rose, running together. "I think he's in Paris," I answered, and even as I spoke rolled flat with him in a muddy ditch as another shell screamed down and broke near by. And thus we continued our way for several hundred yards, discussing our friend and his characteristics between dives into the mud.) After a little our lieutenant guide appeared, followed by Captain X., an artillery officer. Captain X. was heavy of chest and slightly bowed as to underpinning. "I can take you where you can see something," he assured us. "I won't guarantee to bring you back. It's not healthy out where I'm going, but the view's fine. All right? Come ahead."

We said good-by to the major and the colonel and trailed on after the captain through the woods. After a walk of perhaps a hundred and fifty yards we came to the edge of the forest and stepped suddenly out into the open field. There was no gradual thinning of the trees to warn us that we were about to reach the clear. The edge of that forest was as definite as though it had been carved with a blade. One step took us from the thick wood into the open. I took that one step and stopped, gasping, my heart pounding against my ribs.

For there, spread out before me, was War, War as I had not hoped to be able to see it, War in the open over a sunlit visible line of seven or eight miles, War spread out in a great semicircle at my very feet. Around the foot of the bare hill upon which we had so suddenly emerged curved the River Ourcq. At the left end of the visible semicircle spread out below was the city of Fère-en-Tardenois, but newly captured by the French. It was that day under heavy bombardment by the Germans. As I looked it seemed to me that the city in the valley below me was seething, boiling; that underlying it there must be volcanic action, a fire and pressure that was melting the town and breaking through the gradually liquefying crust of the place in huge upsquirting geysers of smoke and flying houses. To the immediate right of Fère-en-Tardenois, across open grain fields on the far side of the Ourcq, was the village of Seringes, then doubtfully held by our troops. Still farther to the right, across yet other open fields, was Sergy, destined for a place in American history. On the previous day American troops from a farming State of the Middle West had there met the Prussian Guard. Four times the Americans took that town with bayonet and gun butt, and four times they were driven out by the best that the Prussian army boasts. So they took it again, those American farm boys, took it and held it, and the proud Prussian Guard retired, licked to a frazzle in its first humiliating encounter with the "Idiotic Yankees." Farther yet to the right lay Cierges, still partially held by the boche.

From Fère-en-Tardenois along the opposite bank of the Ourcq, as far to the right as I could see, the German shells were breaking. That long line of shell explosions was approximately the line of our infantry. As I saw it first it was a grotesque, billowing river of smoke and flame and uptossing earth winding through the open fields along the gentle slope on the opposite bank of the Ourcq. And all along above this crooked river of smoke and flame and dancing earth there floated slowly in the still air what first impressed me as being questing vultures. They were the compact, feathery puffs of jet-black smoke that marked the bursting shrapnel.

Beyond that first river of smoke, farther up the slope, for the most part skirting the edge of the woods on the heights, was its counterpart, a twin stream of flame and rolling smoke with the black, searching shrapnel puffs floating above. It marked the boche line upon which the American artillery was playing. Twin rivers of death they were, flowing tumultuously along the opposite bank of the Ourcq below us there, roughly parallel. At some places they were from five to six hundred yards apart: at others not more than two hundred.

At that time I could not distinguish the individual fighting men down there in the line. I was to see them later. At first the lines were clearly marked for my eyes, only by those two winding rivers of smoke and flame and flying earth.

I cannot express how naked I felt as I followed Captain X. out into that open field in plain view of the boche lines. I felt like a scraped new skeleton hung high in the sunlit sky for the assembled world to gaze at! We were out beyond our foremost artillery, between our last guns and the line below us where the shells were breaking. In comparison to the churning sea of sound through which we had passed it seemed weirdly quiet out there in that open field.

There was the dull, hollow-sounding gro-o-o-mp of the breaking shells on the line ahead—the muffled groan and boom of the flow of those two parallel rivers of death. Behind us there was the consolidated but now somewhat distant roar of our own gun reports, and above the constant, brassy swish of flying steel with which the field was roofed. But it seemed quiet there, and in comparison it was. Conversation in an ordinary tone was possible.

"Just what position is this, Captain X.?" I inquired.

"This," he said casually, "is Hill 212!"

Hill 212! The place I couldn't reach! Misunderstanding of directions, and dumb, blind luck had brought me to the spot of spots that I wanted to reach at that particular time. The day was clear, the sun was at our backs, and the attack up that bare slope below us was due!

The top of that bare hill upon which we stood was speckled with small shell holes until it looked like a huge slab of Swiss cheese. They were dug by shells with instantaneous fuses which explode immediately on contact and do their biting in whatever unfortunate substance happens to be above ground rather than gouging large craters in the earth.

We walked across the top of the hill and down the slope toward the Ourcq for perhaps three or four hundred yards. There, squatted comfortably on the edge of what then seemed to me to be a fairly large shell hole, we came upon two American observers. One held a field telephone between his knees; about the neck of the other dangled a pair of observation glasses. One was industriously chewing tobacco while the other was smoking a cigarette. Both seemed bored. Squatting there on the edge of that shell hole, on that open battle field, leaning forward, elbows on knees, they reminded me of nothing so much as two life-weary small-town loafers hopelessly fishing away an afternoon from the bank of a small creek. They greeted us without surprise or enthusiasm. One allowed guardedly that it was tolerably hot down below there; the other wearily gave his opinion that everything seemed to be about the same! The captain and I knelt on the grass at the foot of a small tree some thirty feet from the shell hole and adjusted our glasses.

"See what looks like a kind of a white line down there in that open field on the other side of the river?" the captain asked, pointing. "Well, that's our infantry. They're dug in there in individual positions waiting the order to go over."

I looked and saw. There they lay, down there in that open field, beneath the flow of the river of death that the boche artillery had loosed upon them, each man curled up in a small, hastily scooped-out hollow in the earth—waiting!

As I looked I saw a man rise from one of these small pits and, bolt upright, walk slowly along the line for perhaps twenty yards through the tossing current of that dread river, kneel down by another soldier—evidently speaking to him—and then rise and stroll back to his own scant shelter. As he walked back toward his own small pit a new sound was added to the swish of flying steel, the boom of the guns and the hollow, disgruntled gro-o-o-mp of the shells breaking on the lines.

It was the angry, simianlike staccato chattering of a machine gun: Ruppity-pup-pup! Ruppity-pup-pup-pup-pup!

"They're after him with the machine guns," the captain shouted. "Watch!"

I found watching difficult. I was so shaken with excitement that I could not hold my glasses steady at my eyes.

Why didn't that lone man walking upright down there drop flat? Why didn't he run? I suddenly found myself yelling at him to run, to hurry; foolishly shouting aloud across that stretch of battle field that they were after him, motioning for him to lie down! Seen through the powerful glasses, he seemed so near that it did not occur to me that he could not hear my voice nor see my frantic signaling.

It was only the space of a few seconds before he reached his place in the line and lay down, but it seemed to me that for hours that lone American figure was walking there in the open through that swirling dread flow under the lead hail from that savagely chattering machine gun. When he finally lay down in his place my muscles were as sore from tension as though some one had beaten me with a club!

"There they go," the captain bawled. "Off to the right there. Look!"

I looked. A little to the right there was a break in the line of recumbent figures and just in advance of that break the sunlit yellow of the open, sloping wheat field was dotted with moving brown stains. They were off!

I found myself on my feet, shaking in every limb. I remember that I was crying as I think I have never cried before, crying with excitement and an ecstatic, reverent admiration for the example of high courage that I was witnessing.

There they went, toiling along in the open up that bare slope toward a small clump of trees some three or four hundred yards ahead. And from that clump of trees there came to our ears a frantic, rattling chorus of machine-gun fire that I think more perfectly expressed fear than anything I have ever heard. The boche was in that little clump of trees with his machine guns, fighting madly to force back that menacing, upward seepage of brown that was moving over the clear yellow of the open wheat field.

On they went! I don't see how a man lived out there, and yet while I watched I did not see a man fall! We could see the glint of their bayonets in the sun. There was one man four or five yards in advance of the rest—a lieutenant, I think—and we could see him turn every few steps and wave his men on with a gesture of his right arm.

As they approached the wood they spread out into a thin line. I saw one whole half of the line drop, and thought they had been mowed down by the fire. The other half of the line moved forward faster and suddenly dropped flat. Even as they disappeared in the wheat I saw the men on the other end of the line rise and rush. Then they dropped and those to their left rose and rushed. And so it went. They were closing in gradually on the machine guns in those woods. They were advancing now by twos, by threes, by squads in short rushes. They were outguessing the gunners. When the fire swept to the left the men on the right rushed forward, and when the fire swept back to the right the men on the left rose and rushed.

They were in the woods! The trees hid them. We waited. It may be only imagination—probably is—but it seemed to me that at that moment I heard faintly a wild, wild exultant yell.

And then in the wheat field on the opposite side of the wood from which the Americans had entered it I saw movement again. I saw it first with the naked eye and thought it was made by our men advancing yet farther to the big wood beyond. But when I used my glasses I saw that the moving stain on the wheat field there was not brown but greenish-gray. Those moving dots were boches, and they were running. They were the ones who had been serving the guns in that little bit of wood as our men moved up the hillside and rushed the position. And they were indeed going some across that wheat field for the big wood beyond! I saw some of them go down. I saw others stop in their flight and turn, with hands high lifted in the air, turn and walk slowly back and vanish from my sight in the wood from which they had been driven—prisoners! When I looked at the field again where the others had been running I saw no movement. And I understood the fear I had sensed in the frantic savage chattering of those machine guns in the wood as they battled to stop that upward rush of the Americans across that open field!

By this time scores of machine guns in the big wood on the crest of the slope that was held by the boches were rattling away. All that bare slope was being swept and reswept by boche machine guns in the big wood. And then I saw the most painfully dramatic thing I have witnessed in all this war.

Out from the little strip of wood that the Americans had just captured, walking slowly out into that open, bullet-swept field over which the charge had passed, I saw two men with the brassard of the Red Cross on their arms, bearing a wounded man on a litter. They had perhaps three hundred yards to go back across that open field before the curve of the hill would shelter them from the machine-gun fire from the hill above. And they could not run, they could not duck, they could not take cover. They must walk upright on their work of mercy, walk upright in that storm of lead, and walk slowly for the burden they bore!

"There goes two dead men," the captain said solemnly. "They haven't got a chance in that field. The machine guns'll get 'em sure! Watch!"

I watched. I have never watched anything so intently in my life. And with all the fervency of reverence and belief that there was in me I prayed for those two men of mercy over there who could not fight back; those men who had made the charge up the hill with their comrades of the gun and bayonet and must now march back bearing a wounded fighting man to safety, back through that storm of lead that was sweeping the field from the big wood—march back standing straight and walking slow. So slow!

They had made perhaps a hundred yards when one of them slipped to his knees and rolled over.

"I told you," the captain exclaimed. "They've got 'em!"

"Only one," I said. "The other fellow's not hit."

"They'll get him," the captain prophesied gloomily.

I saw the unwounded man kneel by his stricken comrade. For the space of a minute he knelt there, I suppose applying first aid. Then he stood erect. And then the man who had been hit, the stretcher bearer on the ground, rose slowly—oh, so very slowly—till he was propped up on one elbow. Then to his knees. Slow! Then very, very slowly he got to his feet. Once up, he leaned over—and, from where I was, through my glasses I could see by the movement the pain it cost—leaned over, grasped the handles of the litter, and straightened up again. He had been hit, but he was going on! On they went. I have no power to describe how slowly they seemed to be moving across that deadly open field. A hundred yards! Another hundred would mean comparative safety under the slope of the hill. Fifty of that accomplished! Twenty-five more! And then, slowly yet, they vanished from sight under the protecting slope. They had made it!

I think I shouted. I know I tried to,

and I know that my knees were suddenly too weak to hold me up and that I abruptly knelt and grasped the slim bole of the little lone tree near by to steady myself.

"There goes another bunch," the captain cried. "Off to the left there."

I saw them. They were marching up the slope to the left of the little clump of trees that had just been captured, a thin brown skirmish line, and even as I looked the boche barrage descended on them, a great thundering fist of smoke and steel and flame driving down out of the sky.

"They're caught!" the captain groaned.

But even as that great fist crashed down, that thin line of men developed an action more swift than any I had yet seen. With one accord they turned to the left, running. I could see them leaping along through the explosions, and within the space of a minute they were out of the area upon which the barrage was descending, out of it and marching along again up the hill toward the big wood. Behind them the huge artillery fist was pounding, pounding, pounding away at an empty field.

"There goes another bunch over," the captain shouted again. "Look at 'em go! Oh, boys! Go on! Get 'em!"

They were going over everywhere all along the line. From this moment on I was in the position of a one-eyed boy trying to see everything in a three-ring circus. Wherever I looked, along that line on the far side of the Ourcq, I saw men on their way forward. The attack was on in force!

I had just steadied myself to make a systematic attempt to analyze the movement, so that I might later describe it intelligently, when I heard a wild yell from the captain.

"Beat it," he shouted. "Beat it! Beat it!"

I did! I beat it both in the slang and literal sense. Otherwise I would not be writing this. I knew what the disturbance was without asking the captain for particulars. Even my comparatively untrained ears had caught the threat of a new note in the chorus of flying steel that was passing above. It was the note made by a shell that was not flying over our heads but at them.

I think it was about thirty feet from where I was kneeling to the shell hole which was in use as an observation post. I have no recollection of getting there—but I got there! The shell and I lit at the same time. I lit in the bottom of the old shell hole, and the new shell lit precisely where the captain and I had been kneeling. It was right where we had been, but about thirty feet short of where we were.

I have a very confused recollection of the next few minutes. There were six of us tangled up in that shell hole—and what a tiny hole it was! It was one of the puniest excuses for a shell hole that I have seen on any battle field! Really, it seemed to me that it was not a hole at all, but an eminence. The bottom of that hole felt to me like Pikes Peak on a clear day! I lay there among arms and legs, rolled into as small a lump as possible and trying to stuff all my anatomy under my tin hat. After two minutes came another shell that lit perhaps thirty feet beyond us. The first one had been short of the shell hole; the second was long!

"Boys," the captain said seriously, "we're in for it! They've got us bracketed, and we're going to get hell. Keep down as low as you can, and if any of you know any little prayers you think'll do any good, go right ahead and say 'em! Look out! Here she comes!"

She came, all right! The third was nearer than either of the first two! The fourth was nearer yet. It showered us with dirt.

"They're gettin' better all the time, aren't they?" the captain observed dryly.

They were! They just naturally sewed a ring around that shell hole. I had been shelled before, but it was the first time I had had the experience of realizing that I was a known and visible mark for a gunner to snipe at with a cannon!

We were a reasonably serious lot in that shell hole. We joked a little to show that we weren't scared—which, of course, we were—and did a little weak laughing. But it was no joke and nothing legitimate to laugh about except in retrospect. I think it was the ninth or tenth shell that for the fraction of an instant fully convinced me that I was through. The explosion turned me quite over where I lay flat there, all huddled up, and stung us all plentifully with clods. The captain told me it had exploded about ten feet away. That was close enough!

They gave us twenty shells in all at intervals of about two minutes. At the end of about forty-five or fifty minutes the captain decided that the direct salvo was over and that we might duck, one at a time. One by one we rolled out over the edge of that shell hole and went scuttling away on all fours for the nearest protection that offered, an old wall a hundred yards away. I don't know what the all-fours record for a hundred yards is, but I think I hold it. Streaking it across the field a few minutes later on the way to the road, I stopped long enough to look back and search the opposite slope where I had last seen the action. There were no moving figures to be seen in the open field, but I noted that the rivers of smoke and flame were flowing along the edge of the big wood on the crest of the slope, where before they had wound through the open fields below.

Two days later I rode over that battle field on the far side of the Ourcq in a limousine, rode over it and for miles beyond up toward the Vesle. Those moving brown figures in the open, yellow grain fields had done their work! They had ripped the boche loose from his desperate grip on the heights beyond the Ourcq, and his next stopping place was miles away —in the general direction of Berlin.

Why I Hate to Walk

Babe Ruth

In 1920 Collier's *offered a suggestion that the "deliberate pass" be outlawed from baseball—and asked the greatest slugger of them all, George Herman "Babe" Ruth, what he thought of the idea. The "Babe," quite logically, didn't think it would work, because he couldn't see how the rule could be enforced. However,* Collier's *got a bonus in the article, for the "Babe," warming to the subject nearest his heart, wrote eloquently of the incomparable "home run feeling."*

July 10, 1920

THERE I STOOD IN THE NINTH INNING OF our last game in the Washington series, crowding the plate and waggling my pick handle with the ball game on the bases and the Senators ahead, seven to six. Get that situation: Ninth inning, two men out, two men on base, and the Yankees just one run behind, fighting to win their eleventh straight game.

It was my best home-run day. I got two in the morning game, our tenth straight win, and a third in the earlier innings of the afternoon game.

I felt good for another, but Bill Snyder served me four consecutive wide ones that I couldn't have reached with a boat hook. They were not pitchouts, really, because the catcher did not step out of his box to receive them until they had been thrown. But Snyder wasn't giving me a chance to hit and I had to walk. I might as well have been standing there with a fathom of garden hose; my old bat was about as useful as a breeches buoy on the Erie Canal.

We lost the ball game.

Of course I was pretty sore at the time, but I cooled off under the shower and realized that Bill Snyder was only taking all the advantage the rules allow in order to win his game. But I used to be a pitcher myself and I never gave an intentional pass in my life. Any batter who could hit better than I could pitch was welcome to blast the skin off the ball.

Collier's may suggest half a dozen rules to prevent the intentional pass, but after all the umpire is in the position of a jury, and unless it is perfectly plain that the pitcher is trying to prevent the batter from getting a bite at the ball, he has to give the pitcher the benefit of the doubt. Suppose they should adopt a rule permitting the batter to take another turn at bat when he is passed intentionally and permitting the manager of the batting side to name some other man, preferably a weak hitter, to take the base. If you could be sure that the pitcher was not just plain wild, such a rule would make him pitch to all hands alike. But the umpire cannot be sure, and that is why the present rule can be evaded.

Imagine standing there at the plate, feeling a home run turned in the wood of your bat, with the ball game riding on the sacks waiting for a blow to send home the winning runs—and being passed!

There is nothing quite like the home-run feeling. You come up with your eye on the ball; you watch it streak up the lane toward you, following the "break" with your eye, if it is a curve. You swing from way back; you feel the solid, satisfying smack as the bat gets it square. You follow through with a long, curving sweep; your shoulders swing around, carrying the blow. If it's a real over-the-fencer, you're going to know it by the feel without watching where the ball goes.

Hitting a home run is about the finest sensation that I know of in sport, unless it be the wonderful feel of a long, low drive straight from the tee in golf. They're somewhat alike. If your baseball days are behind you and you want to have that old home-run thrill again, take a wide swing with your driver, follow it all the way through, shut your eyes, and imagine you are back on the sand lots. If the blow is "right," you'll know you've put it over the fence onto the railroad tracks, and sent the runners home ahead of you.

Batting and golfing run parallel on other points too. For instance (you're batting now), if you happen to chip the ball just below the center, the feel of the blow in the bat is just a hope, not a certainty. You know it's a high one without much distance and you tear away for first, hoping some one drops it. Or suppose your swing is downward instead of straight, or you clip the ball on top—you know in that instance that it is going to hit the ground, probably in the infield, and that if the other side is fielding a good game, you're through. The same situations happen in golf; you know when you've sliced before your eye catches the course of the ball.

There has been some talk about this year's baseball being a kangaroo ball, furnished with springs or something like that to make the hitting livelier, but I don't like to believe it. I am sure of breaking my old home-run record this year, unless I break a leg first, and I wouldn't like to think that it was due to assistance from the fellows who make the balls. Last year I sacrificed some long drives learning to place my hits. This season I have the knack pretty well accomplished; at least I am satisfied with the way they go over that right-field wall at the Polo Grounds.

There has been a great deal of heavy hitting this year. We have four .300 hitters on the Yankees—Meusel, Bodie, Peckinpaugh, and myself—and some of the other fellows have home runs to their credit. Hap Felsch of the White Sox has started after a home-run record, and there is Rogers Hornsby of the Cardinals.

Some of these homers may be due to new restrictions on the pitchers, and, if that is the case, the restrictions are good for the game, because the fans like hitting. I know, however, that a number of these homers at the Polo Grounds would have been fouls if they hadn't gone on top of the stand. If they cross the fence on the fair side of the white line, they are homers, but some of them strike on the foul side after they've crossed. One of my own homers did that. So I know.

After all, the pitcher ought to depend on what he has in his head and his arm to win ball games. If the leagues did not draw the line somewhere, there's no telling what tricks would come into play to prevent the batters from hitting. As it is, a pitcher with speed, curves, and a head on his shoulders can fool the batters more times than they can solve him. Look at the percentage columns for proof of this. Why are .300 hitters exceptional? Because the pitcher usually has a seven to three chance of retiring the batter without a hit.

Sometimes I come up to the plate ready to murder the ball. I watch it sailing up the path and lay all the way back to take a long swing. I keep my eye on the ball and let go hard enough to knock it out of the park. But instead of feeling the feel of a home run, I nearly upset myself splitting three cracks in the atmosphere and then wonder how the dickens I missed it.

The fans are going to keep the ball game straight. They are learning what there is to be known of inside baseball; they can tell when a pitcher is giving an intentional pass, and they will not stand for a pitcher who makes a practice of it because they like to see a hitter strike out or fly out or hit. They pay for action and we will have to keep our bargain with them.

Hitters needn't worry so long as the fans are on the job with that humiliating weapon of torture—the razzberry.

Come Out of the Cave

Walter Camp

Walter Camp, often called the "father of American football," and best remembered for creating the original All-America teams, was one of the most influential men in the history of American sports. His association with Collier's *was long and close; the magazine sponsored the All-America team from 1899 to 1956—thirty-one years after Camp's death. But Walter Camp's interest was not confined to football. He was widely respected as an advocate of sound health practice, and "Come Out of the Cave" has a message of timeless wisdom on the subject. Published with the article is the famous "Daily Dozen" exercise manual—Walter Camp's most memorable contribution to the art of keeping fit.*

January 1, 1921

IT WASN'T EASY TO THINK OF IT IN SUCH a way at the time, but the series of snowstorms that crippled New York so severely last winter was a blessing, no matter how greatly it was disguised. If you happen to live in that city, or if you had to go there, during that time, on business, you need no reminder of what happened. The snow clogged the trolley slots; almost from the first the street cars stopped running. For several days even the Fifth Avenue busses were out of commission; you could see them, and street cars as well, standing where their crews had abandoned them.

Taxicabs were scarce, and inordinately dear. Their drivers made no pretense at all of charging what the meter called for; they made their own rates, based on the eternal laws of supply and demand and the public necessity. And so a great part of New York walked unaccustomed miles —which was good for it, body and soul, heart and brain, lungs and nerves!

I used to go over to New York from New Haven, and the men I went to see would talk of nothing but the scandalous condition of the streets. They couldn't take out their own cars; they were afraid the springs would be broken. And the streets were so rough that the jolting made riding uncomfortable, anyway. They had to walk. They had to get up early. If they went out to lunch, except in the immediate neighborhood of their offices, they had to walk. Going to the theatre, going out to play cards in the evening—anything a man wanted to do—involved walking. Terrible!

Well, they either thought I was unsympathetic, or a provincial unused to the ordinary comforts of life in a great city,

I suppose. Because I wasn't properly impressed with their sufferings. I wasn't—and the reason was that I knew that some of those men were going to live through the winter just because of the hardships they were bewailing, and that I was going to be spared, for a time at least, from seeing the name of some friend, taken off in comparative youth, staring at me from the obituary column in my morning paper.

Have you noticed—but of course you have—that it is in the winter, in the main, that so many men who are still young, or, rather, who ought to be still young, die untimely deaths? They go under when influenza assails them, or pneumonia. And why? Because their hearts cannot stand the extra strain those diseases impose. Pneumonia, which takes so terrible a toll of the lives of such men, won't, as a rule, kill the man who is in good condition. It may, and usually will, give him a bad time; it will demand the putting forth of all his reserve power. But, if he is properly equipped, if his heart is strong, and hasn't been required to do extra work right along, he can get through even a severe attack of double pneumonia.

But your ordinary office man, who doesn't give himself a chance, who has let himself become soft and flabby, who has subjected his heart regularly to an unfair strain, has a much smaller chance of recovery. It sounds brutal to say so, I know, but the plain truth is that a great many of the men who die in the early years of middle life, in the decade from forty to fifty, are only committing suicide more slowly than the poor devils who shoot themselves or slip into the water to drown.

Not intentionally—of course not. They simply don't know; they don't see the truth for themselves, and they often don't see doctors with the good sense and the courage to tell them what they ought to hear.

It is not winter itself that is to blame. No season of the year is inherently unhealthy. And if any season has a balance in its favor it is winter, probably. What is wrong is the adjustment of life to the season of cold weather and to the cessation of vacations and outdoor sport.

People call me an alarmist sometimes. They say I am trying to frighten them. I admit it. Too many men need to be scared into a realization that they are not being fair to themselves and to those who love them and need them. It isn't pleasant to sit down, when you have come to the middle years, and think of the friends of your youth who have already died. It is the sort of thing no man wants to do—partly because it is a painful thought, and partly because he can scarcely help wondering whether, perhaps, he may not follow those friends.

Precisely! He may. But the decision is much more largely in his own hands than he thinks.

It is, of course, the great group of sedentary workers of whom I write, principally. No matter how varied their pursuits, how different their positions, the same things are true of most men who work in offices or shops—generally speaking, at desks. Clerks, bookkeepers, executives—their routine is essentially and fundamentally similar. They run the same risks, and they have open to them, equally, regardless of earnings, the same simple and effective means of insuring their health.

Now, consider this past summer. How did you spend it? You had a vacation, unquestionably. You may have had two weeks at seashore or in the mountains;

you may have spent two or three months in the open. But it is routine that affects your health, principally, and your condition. Now, naturally, in the summer, you are out of doors more. If you go in for games at all, you have played some golf or tennis. The chances are that you have done at least a little swimming. You may live in the suburbs, and have a garden. That, too, will have kept you out of doors.

But now the critical time is coming: everything has been covered and made ready for the winter's sleep.

Certain animals, of course, meet a somewhat similar situation in a manner especially designed by nature to fit their case. They hibernate. Your brown bear stuffs himself all summer and fall, until he is hog-fat, and then retires into a cave or a hollow tree and goes to sleep. He lives on his own fat, and in the spring he yawns and stretches and comes out, lean, hungry, and as fit as a fiddle.

Man, however, doesn't hibernate—completely. In a certain sense he does do just about that. He takes little more exercise than the sleeping bear. But he goes on eating, and there isn't the bear's complete suspension of activity.

The winter routine of the office man, in altogether too many cases, is dangerously softening. He gets up late, and rides to his office—in a street car, or a subway, or a limousine. He works at his desk all morning, goes around the corner for lunch, and works for as much of the afternoon as remains after he has emerged from the period of drowsiness induced by eating his lunch. After dinner he either sits around or goes to some place of amusement.

That sort of living produces, inevitably, certain results. There is too much breathing of vitiated air—meaning more work for the heart. There is a softening of the big body muscles that ought to be hard and supple, like a corset of muscle about the waist. There is a slackening of the intestines, and an increasing difficulty for them in doing their work, because they no longer get the help they ought to have from well-conditioned muscles.

The whole man grows soft, and he finds himself increasingly annoyed by slight colds, headaches, drowsiness, when he wants to be keen and alert. Instinctively, of course, when you become aware of these symptoms, you guess the cause.

And, in too many cases, the next step is an altogether mistaken one. Men who realize that they are in need of exercise rush from one extreme to another. Friends see that they aren't fit.

"Look here, old man," one will say, "you want to get busy, or you'll be doing business with the doctor. Now I'm working out every night at half past five at the Y gym. Come along."

He goes along—to the Y. M. C. A., or an athletic club, or the gymnasium of some specialist in physical culture—all excellent places in their proper use. He finds Indian clubs, dumb-bells, chest weights, the medicine ball, a handball court—and I don't know how many other forms of sugar coating for the pill of exercise. Again, these are all excellent things—properly used, by the man in condition to use them.

But if you've done no exercise for two or three months, don't try to work chest weights for ten minutes, play with a medicine ball ten more, go through a set of calisthenics, and wind up with four or five games of handball and, as a chaser, a plunge in the pool. You can't do it without paying the penalty. You must put yourself in condition for indulgence in violent exercise; you must approach peaks of effort gradually.

Now, the effect, upon a man of forty-five, of sudden and abrupt indulgence in such an orgy of violent exercise as I suggested is very much what the effect of unprepared participation in a four-mile rowing race would be upon a healthy but untrained youngster of twenty-one. The chances are, indeed, that the boy would come out of the ordeal better than the man.

If you tax yourself too heavily when first you try to make up for your autumn of lassitude, you will be lucky if you escape with stiff, sore muscles. But even those will have bad effects. They will make it impossible for you to take any real exercise at all for some time, and they will leave you disinclined to do so for a much longer period. And it is entirely possible, and, indeed, probable, that you will not escape with a mere stiffness and soreness of joints and muscles; you may suffer from an actual strain, which is always painful and often disabling.

Moreover, as you grow older, unless you have kept your muscles loose and supple—not flabby, of course; hard, but pliable—your recovery from lameness and from strains is bound to be slow.

Here, of course, is the very real and terrible danger that is attendant upon ill-advised muscular effort. It would surprise you to know how often men drop dead after exercise of this sort. They play handball, or take some such exercise. Then they feel like a swim. Sometimes a man will have his swim, feel a little tired, and start to pull himself up to the edge of the pool—only to fall back.

That last extra exertion has been too much for his overworked heart. There may have been no lesion; nothing to warn him. Had he but been moderate, he would have achieved his object.

Enough of warning! The case isn't hopeless, by any means. The office man can condition himself; fit himself for moderate, agreeable indulgence in handball or any other winter sport. He can do it easily, without undue effort, without boredom. Let him go through the exercises of the Daily Dozen, which are fully described in this article, every morning and every night. Let him do some, at least, of the exercises occasionally during the day, when he feels the need of them to ward off drowsiness, or a headache, or when he wants to sharpen his wits.

Those exercises, simple as they are, easy as they are to do, run through the whole scale of the body. They will keep fit muscles fit; given time, they will restore flabby ones to their proper state. They will, faithfully pursued, do more to defeat constipation, that arch-enemy of middle age, that advance guard of so many diseases, than all the medicines ever brewed.

I am asked, very often, about various forms of diet. People want to know how to regulate their food so as to lose weight. One thing ought to be said at once concerning this—no one should attempt radical modifications of diet, with a view to reducing weight, without previous consultation with his physician. There is a system of diet, based upon a reduction of—almost the elimination of—fats, starches, and carbohydrates from the diet, and a very high protein content, which has proved highly effective in a number of cases known to me. But that diet is poison to anyone with a rheumatic tendency, and harmful to certain people. Do not let the brilliant success achieved by some friend persuade you into following his

The Daily Dozen

The first three positions, "Hands," "Hips," and "Head," for use only by groups with a leader, are omitted here. The nine exercises that follow are for personal use, morning and night, and whenever needed for refreshment during the day

4. GRIND: Arms outstretched straight from shoulders — called the "cross" position. Turn palms upward; make six-inch circles with hands, five times forward, five backward; keep arms stiff.

5. GRATE: Arms at "cross" position; palms down. Lift arms very slowly to angle of about forty-five degrees, inhaling; bring them down slowly to shoulder position, exhaling. Repeat ten times.

6. GRASP: Let fingers of both hands meet at back of neck. Bend neck back. Bend body forward very slowly from waist, keeping head up, neck bent back; eyes fixed on object height of man's eyes. Come back slowly to first position; then bend backward. Repeat ten times.

7. CRAWL: Stand at "cross" position. Raise right arm; let left drop at side. Then let left crawl slowly down toward the knee, at same time curving right arm over head until fingers touch left side of neck. Return to "cross" position and let right hand crawl and left curl over head. Five times with each hand.

8. CURL: Stand at "cross" position. Clench fists. Begin to inhale deeply while lowering arms and bringing them slowly forward, bent at elbow; curl arms around until fists come under armpits. Bend head and shoulders backward as inhalation is completed. Loosen hands and push straight forward, beginning to exhale. Bend forward from waist, exhaling, and letting hands come back across hips; continue movement until, as you remain bent, the arms are raised behind you. Begin to inhale again as you return to "cross" position, ready to repeat. Ten times.

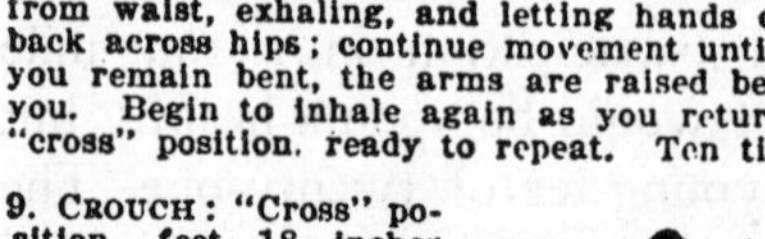

9. CROUCH: "Cross" position, feet 18 inches apart. Raise on toes; keep arms out. Squat slowly down as far as you can, inhaling. Come up slowly, exhaling, and letting heels touch floor as you rise. Five times.

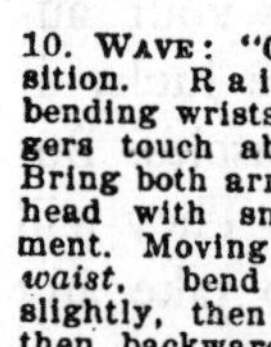

10. WAVE: "Cross" position. Raise arms, bending wrists until fingers touch above head. Bring both arms against head with snap movement. Moving *only from waist*, bend forward slightly, then to right, then backward, then to left, and continue until you are making a circle with your clasped hands extended above head. Repeat five times in each direction, reversing circle after first five.

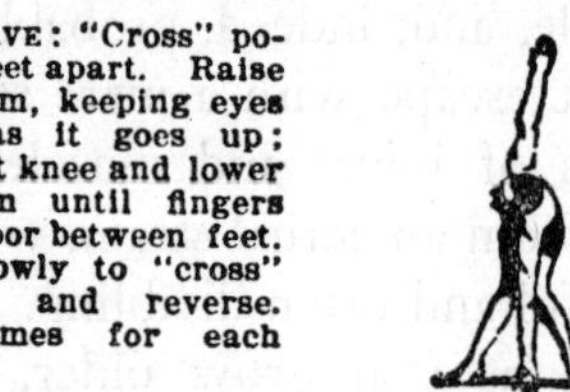

11. WEAVE: "Cross" position, feet apart. Raise right arm, keeping eyes on it as it goes up; bend left knee and lower left arm until fingers touch floor between feet. Back slowly to "cross" position and reverse. Five times for each hand.

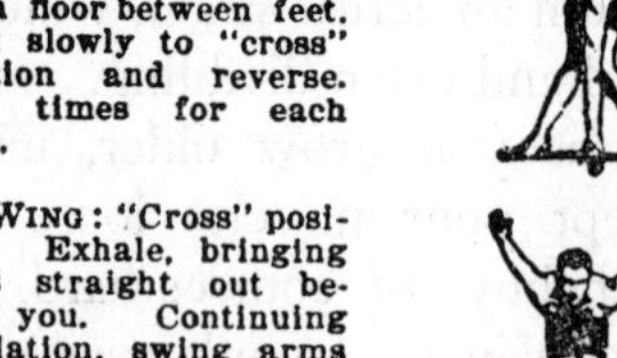

12. WING: "Cross" position. Exhale, bringing arms straight out before you. Continuing exhalation, swing arms down and back, bending forward slowly from waist. Continue bending forward, pushing arms back and letting breath out as movement is completed. Keep head up and eyes forward. Now inhale as you go back slowly to "cross" position. Repeat ten times.

diet until you make sure that it is suited to your particular physical condition.

Generally speaking, in this matter of diet, I like to lay stress on two main points. One is that meals should be eaten with regularity; the other is that overindulgence should be avoided. Otherwise a man, by the time he is mature, must know pretty well what agrees with him, and what foods his system rejects. So many individual idiosyncrasies have to be considered in this matter that it is very hard to lay down general rules. Still, it is pretty safe to say that we need less meat as we grow older, and, for that matter, less food of any kind.

A growing boy is physically very active, as a rule, and has more waste tissue to replace than a grown man. He can do things in the way of eating that would send his father to a hospital. As we do less and less actual physical work, we can profitably cut down the amount of food we eat.

You may have found that you feel better if you do not eat your heavy meal at night—at the conventional dinner hour. Very well—even though, for social reasons, it may be difficult—apply your discovery.

I always think it a good sign when a man is hungry for his breakfast. If you have much mental work to do in the afternoon, I should say that a luncheon of crackers and milk, or something equally light, would be an excellent thing, two or three times a week, anyway. Certainly no one ever suffered who rose from the table feeling that he could still eat something more.

Here, however, are points about which it seems to me impossible to be too emphatic. Don't eat when you are worn out—mentally or physically. Get some rest first. And don't eat when you are angry or worried—especially when you are angry. Your food will do you no good; it is more likely to do you positive harm.

Of course, a certain reasonable length of time should be allowed to pass between finishing any violent exercise and sitting down to a meal. That warning enforces itself in most cases, however; few men can eat, for excellent physiological reasons, just after heavy exercise. They simply don't feel hungry until bodily relaxation has set in. Equally, don't eat heavily just before exercise. That doesn't mean, however, that you ought to lie down after a meal, and that you ought not to walk back to your office after lunch. Far from it. A short walk, at a moderate pace, is an aid to digestion and the proper assimilation of what you have eaten.

Perhaps this is not quite in order. But I have been asked, too, to describe a treatment of mine for colds, which has very seldom failed to break up even a rather obstinate cold within forty-eight hours. It is rather heroic, extremely unpleasant, but distinctly effective.

As soon as you get up in the morning drink two or three cupfuls of water as hot as can be taken comfortably with a teaspoon. Then spread a blanket on the floor, and lie down, flat on your back. Raise the arms slowly and carry them back so that they are over your head—stretched out on the floor behind you, that is. Inhale deeply as you carry them back; exhale, slowly, as you return them to your side. Do this ten or a dozen times. If you have been doing the Daily Dozen, you will recognize this as the "Wing," modified by the recumbent position.

This clears out the air passages. There will be a good deal of coughing and expectoration—that is unpleasant but necessary. Repeat the hot water and the exercise once in the morning, once during the afternoon, and just before you go to bed. Eat as little as possible—go without food altogether for a day, if you can. And go through the exercises of the Daily Dozen three times a day. Few colds resist this.

I have tried to point out the danger of winter to the sedentary man—especially the man of middle age. But many a young man needs such advice, too—for if the middle-aged man grows old too soon, many a youngster passes into middle age years before he should. Especially is this true of the athlete who is condemned to labor at a desk, and forced to give up, all at once, the sports which have kept him fit.

If the remedy were not given with the warning, the latter would be pointless. But it is so easy to keep fit, mentally and physically, and the results of neglect to do so are so tragically wasteful that no man, it seems to me, has any real excuse for letting himself grow soft, no matter what his age.

One Reel of Autobiography

Douglas Fairbanks

An editor's note that accompanied "One Reel of Autobiography," described Douglas Fairbanks as "one of the two best-known men in the world." Those whose memories go back that far will hardly disagree—and any who knew his dazzling smile and dashing manner in "The Black Pirate," "The Three Musketeers," "The Thief of Bagdad," and the rest, will be able to summon up a vivid recollection to this day. It is precisely these famous Fairbanks trademarks—the smile and the swashbuckling—that he discusses in this article—with a wit and depth of perception that add another dimension to the foremost star of the silent screen.

June 18, 1921

Sometimes I wonder whether, if you could sneak up on one of the men who are held up before the eyes of the world as successful business men, scientists, artists, or what not, you would not discover that beneath the outward mask of success he wears a surprisingly disgruntled and twisted look; whether he might not be found dreaming disconsolately, like anyone else, of what might have been, painfully exhuming old aspirations which he had one by one sentenced to death, wondering if there is any market where one may barter fame for a good digestion and turn bank balances into a recipe for happiness.

This is no doubt a melancholy thought, and it should be, for it is the preface to a melancholy story. There are times, I may as well confess, when I have thought of myself as a success. It is a bit of egotism for which an actor with any kind of a following may be pardoned, for he is particularly responsive to what the public thinks and readily falls into the habit of taking himself at their valuation. When millions of people insist that you are great stuff as an actor, it is sometimes difficult not to add one more to the circle of your admirers and include yourself. I know of no subject on which a man stands so ready to be convinced as this—on which he receives arguments with such an open mind and such a disposition to admit that, after all, they may be right.

But just as I have almost convinced myself and decided to accept the flattering verdict of my friends, the sinister truth breaks in and spoils the picture—the truth that, measured by even the most generous standards of success, I must be classed as a terrific and unquestionable failure, if this is a source of any satisfaction to the reader.

And I am sure it is, for if the reader will indulge himself in a moment's honesty, as I am trying to do, he will be forced to admit that nothing gives him quite the same acute, if secret, sense of satisfaction as to hear of the adversity and misfortune of some one else. It gives him very little pleasure indeed to read that Mr. So-and-So was a bank president at the tender age of thirty, with an income beyond all the dreams of avarice, or that Mr. What's-His-Name rose brilliantly to the peak of his profession while fumbling with his first mustache. When he considers that at the same age he is lucky if he can look the landlord in the face and buy his wife a spring hat, he feels like going down to the river brink and ending it all then and there. What he wants to read about is some one who is worse off and harder up than he is, whose life is an unbroken chain of disappointments and failures. As he regards this poor wretch stumbling blindly and unsuccessfully through life, his pulses begin to quicken, something like a glow of satisfaction steals over him, and he decides that the world, after all, is not such an overrated place to live in. If I were a magazine editor, and wanted to gain the real interest and approval of my readers, I would publish nothing but stories of failure.

But this is not an explanation of why I am writing about my own failure. It is the sheer novelty of telling the truth about myself that has appealed to me.

Perhaps the reader can stand about one reel of concentrated autobiography in which I explain myself. I will promise not to take him back to early life on an Ohio farm or struggling youth in a dingy boarding house on the East Side of New York. The dismal drama begins, as a matter of fact, on a sunny June day in a New York club some years ago. If I hadn't made the colossal blunder of eating lunch at that club, there would be—as the fiction writers say—no story.

It so happened that I had lunch on that fatal day with a fellow actor who had a great reputation as a wit. He had just heard a new one which, as he told it, struck me as tremendously funny. It was not one of those stories which cause one brief explosion of laughter and are promptly forgotten when some one else says: "That reminds me—" It was the kind of story that keeps coming back to you with some lingering phrase long after you have dismissed it and, with a kind of cumulative force, seems funnier every time you think of it.

I went to the midweek matinée performance of "All for a Girl"—one of the first plays in which I had been starred—chuckling over this story. I ought to explain that I had reached a point in my career when it seemed that my ambitions might soon be realized. My training had all been in classic and serious rôles. My father was a Shakespearian scholar of some note, and to our home in Denver there came at one time or another almost all the great actors of the period—Mansfield, Booth, Barrett, Robson, and many others. It was under the influence of these men and my early Shakespearian schooling that my ambitions took a definite direction. My first engagement was with Frederick Warde's company of Shakespearian players. Since that time I had been diverted to comedy rôles, but I felt that this diversion was only temporary, and I was merely waiting for an opportunity to resume more serious parts.

As I say, I strolled over to the theatre on this bright June afternoon, never dreaming that this silly story which caused me so much amusement was to wreck all these fine plans and completely ruin me. They say that in everyone's life there comes one important turning point. Well, this was the turning point in mine.

Somewhere along in the second act the one really serious and dramatic moment in this play occurs, and I was naturally expected to maintain a grave demeanor. There was absolutely nothing to laugh at. But at precisely this moment that accursed story, which I thought I had successfully banished, leaped back into my mind with sudden perversity and seemed twice as funny as it had before. My face broke out into a broad grin—not a stage smile at all, not a mere mechanical registry of mirth, but a genuine convulsion which spread itself wantonly over my whole face. I felt terribly about it, but I couldn't help it. The more I tried to control myself the worse I got. I was sure that I had ruined the play. It had been going badly enough, anyway, playing to smaller and smaller houses, and so close to the margin of complete failure that only a little shove was necessary to send it over. I knew I had given it this shove. When I walked off the stage at the end of the performance I was all ready to be told what several people thought of me. I braced myself for the ordeal, but it didn't come.

You can believe it or not, but I was received with open arms and congratulated. "Great stuff!" everybody told me. "It's marvelous how you did it!" When I came to I discovered that I had broken all amateur and professional records for smiling. Mr. William Brady, who was producing the show, was just as bad as the others. He wanted to know why I had been holding back on him and concealing this marvelous smile until it was too late to do the drooping fortunes of the play any good. Advertisements were promptly prepared counseling the public to *Come and See the Famous Fairbanks Smile*. I now think that the public response to this appeal represented correctly the proper valuation of the smile. It brought in box-office receipts of thirty-seven dollars and fifty cents, and shortly after this the play failed and was withdrawn.

But the harm was already done. Up to the time of this unfortunate matinée performance I had conceived myself to be a fairly serious-minded person and had never once fancied myself particularly as a smiler. I had never supposed that my smile was any different from anybody else's. But a conspiracy in which the public maliciously took part was organized to ruin me. Friends told me my smile was immense. Dramatic critics spoke of it warmly and analyzed it carefully as if smiling were an art which I had personally invented.

Now, I was at that time young and impressionable, and this furor which I had caused by a purely inadvertent and accidental smile was too much for me. The smile, if I may so describe it, went to my head. I began to take myself seriously as a smiler. I began practicing it before a mirror to see if my face was all that it was cracked up to be. I enlarged it and perfected it until I could have got a job anywhere as an advertisement of a tooth paste. I admitted freely that when it came to the matter of smiling I could give anyone else a couple of teeth and win, going away. I smiled with Tom Wise in "The Gentleman from Mississippi," in "The Cub," and half a dozen other plays and through twenty-one screen productions before the terrible truth burst upon me.

I had gone too far! I could not stop

smiling! This constant misuse of the facial muscles had grown beyond all control. No effort of the will could restore my face to its natural expression—it was practically frozen into a permanent grin. I was sentenced to go through life, for all I could see, grinning like a madman, and nothing could stop it. The most melancholy thoughts, the most serious situations were without the slightest effect.

I can never forget an afternoon on Broadway when my affliction was in its most acute stage. I met a fellow actor coming up the street with a mourning band on his arm and a generally grief-stricken look on his face—a man who up to that moment had been one of my best friends. In answer to my query he told me sadly that he had just lost a member of his family. I went through a moment of terrible anguish, for I knew what was coming. I made a superhuman effort to control myself, but I knew in my heart it was hopeless. I felt a premonitory twitching of the overworked muscles around my mouth and knew that I was lost—that nothing in this world or the next could prevent the fatal convulsion.

"Ha-ha!" I shouted, fairly bursting with laughter. "You don't say so." I still remember most painfully the shocked and bewildered look in his eyes as he turned away and crossed me forever off the tablet of his friendship, although I think it dawned upon him that something was wrong with me and that I was more to be pitied than censured.

There were countless other like instances which the reader must really excuse me from relating.

Some time I hope to meet one of those cheerful idiots who write songs and poems about driving away care with a smile—and when I do I won't answer for the consequences. One of us will be carried away on a litter. I have no doubt that a beaming smile is all right on occasion, that it may even add to the gayety of the party and take rank with some of the other social graces, but when it comes to being perpetually harnessed to one of them, to going around with a warped face, showing your teeth at other people's troubles and laughing at grief—it is an unspeakable affliction. Imagine, if you can, going through life without any serious relief whatever.

Still, I have only hinted at the real tragedy. I believe that if I had taken some heroic remedy during this early phase of the illness I might have been cured. During the first years it might have been possible to restore my face to normalcy.

But no one would permit this for a moment. When I came to the full realization of what this smile had done to me—how it had wrecked the serious career which I had planned and played havoc with all my real ambitions—when I wanted to attempt a different sort of part, which would give my face a rest and give me an opportunity to be serious again, friends, producers, and associates laughed at me. I might not be much of an actor, they as much as hinted, but as a smiler I was a knockout. The public, I was told, wanted to see me go on smiling, and I must do it however gloomy it made me feel. I do not know that I can seriously blame the public for their unconscious cruelty, for it was something I had started myself. So the ghastly thing went on. I kept on smiling. Measured by film length, I have smiled over twenty miles. And I feel as if I had smiled twenty thousand.

Some deep thinker has said that troubles never come singly. I am quite ready to indorse this discovery as genuine. If anything further was needed to complete my alienation from the career which I had planned, to send all my early hopes and dreams of a serious success scurrying into the offing, it was another innocent diversion which I introduced in my pictures without any suspicion of the consequences. It was not unpremeditated and accidental, like the smile, but contained a serious and sound idea back of it. I am speaking of my "athletic" stunts. When I first started these I had not the slightest ambition to win fame as an acrobat.

I thought I was using a rather obvious, perhaps crude, form of symbolism, but apparently I had a complete monopoly of this idea—no one else guessed it. In my efforts to portray the type of American boy about town, I was trying to catch the real spirit of youth as I conceived it to be; the spirit that takes short cuts and dashes impetuously at what it wants, that doesn't take the time to walk around obstacles, but hurdles them—the fine, restless, impatient, conquering spirit of youth that scales whatever hazards are in its way, and rejoices in the fight.

To represent this on the screen I had to rely mostly upon a physical method. I had to indicate as well as I could a mental attitude by a physical one. I did not mean for a minute to develop the idea that all my heroes were professional gymnasts who spent the greater part of their time dangling from chandeliers and jumping from roof tops. It was not bodily agility, but litheness and exuberance of spirit that I wanted to indicate. It was not always easy to show them jumping over mental obstacles, but it was comparatively simple to show them surmounting physical ones.

But I am afraid that this pretty philosophy miscarried somewhere. It is probably too great a jump from philosophy to acrobatics. If I were suspected of having a real idea back of all this gymnastic exercise and boisterous behavior, it was that I wanted to show off, or needed exercise, or something of the sort. The fact was that none cared why I was doing those stunts, but they liked to see them done. If I leaped upstairs via the balcony instead of going up the usual way, the least worry anyone had was why I was doing it. What people wanted was to see me jump up to a higher balcony.

Again I weakened. I found that I had once more started something I couldn't stop. If the public wanted acrobatics, I decided that I would give them what they wanted. I would show them what I really could do if I tried. I quite forgot, myself, why I had started all these tricks. They began to possess me, almost as completely as the smile. No one thought of presenting a play to me that did not contain new and varied opportunities for me to be "athletic." I am only a fair athlete, but I am carefully trained and have some specialties that I can probably do as well as anyone. I did them and invented new ones. I romped, jumped and skylarked through one play after another.

Perhaps the reader can begin to perceive the tragedy in all this. It really is not pleasant to realize that you have jumped and smiled yourself out of a serious career, that you began with serious intentions of becoming an actor and that some perverse fate has turned you into a smiler and an acrobat. It is not a thought which exactly leads one to review his life with complacency and approval.

I probably could not speak of this matter as calmly as I do were it not that I am now almost confident that this gruesome chapter of my life is finished. The smile has at least partially relaxed its merciless grip, and there is a fair prospect that I can now go through life in just as mournful a fashion as I like. The gymnastic spell has left me too, and I am free. I hesitate to recount how it happened, for fear that the reader will think I am fooling. But it is too serious a matter to fool about.

Anyone who has seen "The Mollycoddle" or "The Nut" must have noticed that something strange has happened. In "The Mollycoddle" the smiles are only occasional and sustained for but a brief period of time, and in "The Nut" they have disappeared almost altogether, like the last few flickers of a lamp that is going out. In the play which I am now producing, "The Three Musketeers," there is hardly a smile. D'Artagnan—thank Heaven—is not a smiling person. He takes himself and the world seriously. When he does smile, it is not a polite and affable expansion of the features, but a snarling, warriorlike affair—like the smile on the face of a prize fighter who has just knocked out his opponent.

This, briefly and without any decoration of the facts, is how it happened: Not long ago I engaged a very solemn-looking director who, judging from all appearances, had never smiled in his life. His face was positively cavernous in its gloom. It was a great pleasure for me to look upon this solemn man, although the pleasure was not unmixed with envy. I felt that I would have given almost anything I possessed to change expressions with him.

During the long months which it takes to prepare a picture it was this man's duty to watch me faithfully, study my expression, and guide me to the best of his ability. He had to look at me, poor fellow, for at least four or five hours every day. But I could see that after a few weeks his work was beginning to tell on him. Some subtle change was taking place. His face lost by degrees a little of its grimness, and even a ghost of a smile now and then flickered across it. He didn't seem to be smiling at anything in particular, but in a forced and distracted way, as if it pained and distressed him. Once I caught him smiling broadly when an overhead light crashed to the floor, just missing one of the cast by a few inches.

It was not, however, until the last days of the production, when he came to work with his face set in a fixed and terrible grin and chuckling to himself like a madman, that I realized what had happened. He had actually caught my smile. Looking at me constantly for months had been too much for him. Unhappy man that he was, he had entirely absorbed my expression. I could not at this time extend to him quite the sympathy he deserved, for I had been too busy studying an adverse phenomenon that had happened to me. I had lately been able to go whole hours without smiling. My face was straightening out day by day, and permanent relief seemed in sight. What I didn't realize at first was that not only had he caught my expression, but I had caught his!

The last time I saw this miserable man he was jumping over tables and chairs and trying without much success to walk up a perpendicular wall, grinning all the time to himself as if he enjoyed it.

As I have gone on with this pitiful story the conviction has grown on me that I have not been writing what I was expected to write. I was expected, I am sure, to tell youthful aspirants how they might become successful movie actors by a few well-spent hours every night by the light of the kitchen lamp, and from my own experience to deduce certain principles of success which could be applied equally well by the artist, the writer, the salesman, and the drug clerk. Now it can readily be seen from what I have already said that I am not at all equipped to pose as a guide in the pursuit of success. Moreover, I don't understand how anyone can seriously set out to prescribe his own rules of conduct for the rest of humanity. It would be just as sensible to prescribe a suit of Arbuckle's clothes for the citizen of average stature. There are some people no doubt who find it stimulating to rise at six-thirty and take a glass of hot milk as a preparation for the strain of a long day's work; but I am sure that there are others who could do better to sleep until eight.

But if I *were* permitted the privilege of advising the world how to live and achieve, I know what I would say. I would suggest that we all stop listening to advice and paying attention to rules. We are all soaked and groggy with advice. We are so full of information on how to do things that we are inclined to overlook the fact that the principal thing is to do them.

I know hundreds of potential playwrights and authors and actors who go around positively bristling with fine inspirations and ideas. But there is just one little detail in the program of achievement that they overlook. They forget to write their plays, or they never take the plunge and start learning to act.

There is only one law of achievement which I know anything about, and that is that there should be some balance between intake and output; that there is no real achievement in the simple process of absorption, in filling up with high-minded ideas and intentions; that the more important part of the process lies in giving them some kind of useful outlet. Imprisoned and ingrowing ideas and inspirations are of very little service either to ourselves or to the world. Even a half-baked idea which is expressed and set in motion is better than half a dozen better ones stored away like useless furniture in the mind. I would add that success is not a result of rules or other people's advice. It is a matter of enthusiasm and strong desire. If you have these, you will discover all the rules that are necessary without asking some one to tell you about them. It is an old one, I know, but it still holds good that any reasonable desire, if it is strong enough, will be realized.

These things—I hope it is distinctly understood—are in the nature of what I might have said if I had felt in a position to mount the platform and admonish the world how to amble along in the general direction of achievement and success.

My Bootlegger

Samuel Hopkins Adams

Collier's was one of the most outspoken critics of the liquor trade and its attendant evils—and a factor in bringing Prohibition. A year and a half after the Volstead Act went into effect, the article reprinted here, "My Bootlegger," exposed precisely what was wrong with Prohibition and why, and illuminated the causes of the coming gangster era. Hopkins, whose versatile mind produced novels, biographies and successful movies ("It Happened One Night"; "The Harvey Girls") died in 1958, at the age of eighty-seven.

September 17, 1921

"MY BOOTLEGGER USED TO BE A GOOD citizen. So did I. He respected and obeyed the law. As I did. Before the Volstead enactment he would never have considered taking part in any furtive or forbidden trade; not any more than I would. But he needed the money, and when he saw his opportunity of making it at the expense of a law which he believed unfair and oppressive, he took it. I wanted liquor to which I had always been accustomed and which I had never abused, and when he offered me opportunity of supplying myself at the expense of a law which I believe unfair and oppressive, I took it. Thus he became an illicit seller and I became an illicit buyer. Together we are successfully defeating and overthrowing the law of the land. Doubtless there are thousands of teams like us all over the country. We represent, I suppose, an abnormal condition of the body politic. My bootlegger is the symptom of it. I, I suspect, am the disease."

So writes to me a friend of many years' standing, a man who has attained success and prominence in his chosen profession, honored, thoughtful, fair-minded, courageous enough to look at himself in relation to the problem under discussion with candor, tenacious of his own rights, respectful of the rights of others, an instinctive believer in law and order, a typical "best citizen." Yet the phrase "my bootlegger" comes naturally from his pen. A profoundly significant phrase. Back of it lies the implication that the hired violator of law, the criminal who makes his profit out of systematized defiance of the will of the people duly enacted, has become an established institution, partnership in which need not be occasion for shame on the part of a self-respecting citizen. The man who asserts his right or privilege to live on the same basis as in ante-Volstead days now has his bootlegger as he has always had his physician, his lawyer, his tobacconist.

So far have we progressed along the road into which prohibition has led us! And here at the turn of the road stands "my bootlegger" pointing the way to contempt of the law, to anarchism, limited to one selected phase, it is true, but essentially corruptive of respect for all law. How widespread and important an institution "my bootlegger" has become may be estimated from any week's file of the larger newspapers. Everywhere the drink question is to the fore. Properly and logically it should be a dead issue, since for nearly two years we have theoretically banned booze; yet it still holds the center of the stage.

As a nation, if the newspapers correctly reflect what most interests us, we sit in rapt contemplation of ourselves in the act of discrediting a law which we enacted only after the maturest and most careful consideration; and if many of us greet the anomalous performance with hisses, millions of others contribute laughter and applause. A stranger, ignorant of our peculiar national psychology, might justifiably suspect a deliberate conspiracy to overthrow the law of the land, with "our leading citizens" and "my bootlegger" as chief conspirators.

There is, of course, no such conspiracy. If there were, the situation would be far simpler. Conspiracy is positive action. It can be dealt with positively. The present revulsion is mainly negative. It is an unformulated, almost instinctive campaign of obstructon and nullification; a sullen, contemptuous, resentful determination not to be bound by a restriction upon personal tastes, even though every dictate of patriotism and good citizenship calls for submission. It therefore follows with inevitable logic (does it not?) that the revolt is made up of the lawless and disreputable classes; criminals, wastrels, the vicious, the outcast, the dregs of society?

Nothing could be farther from the fact. The people who are in more or less active rebellion against prohibition (that is to say, the law) comprise pillars of the social structure—as well, of course, as many of the other kind—props of church and state, leaders in the professions, the industrial world, and society, men such as the friend from whose letter I quote above; the type which exults in terming itself 100 per cent American. A strange and saddening phenomenon, the solubility of 100 per cent Americanism when it encounters the one-half of 1 per cent alcoholic limit.

Taking laws in general, it is practicable to classify as respectable citizens those who obey them and as dubious citizens those who do not. Not so with this National Prohibition Law; there is no such line of cleavage. In fact, there is no clear line of cleavage whatsoever, social, sectional, political, economic, or religious, other than the elementary difference between those who want to take a drink and those who are determined—though most ineffectually thus far—that they shall not take it.

The trail of the bootlegger is over us all. From the Mexican border come reports of a reliable supply pouring into States, some of which were dry before the nation voted that way, and are decidedly less dry now. A southern California acquaintance tells me:

"I can go or send across the border to Tia Juana or other places, put in an order, and have the stuff delivered to me, safe and not too expensive, at whichever one of half a dozen spots is most convenient."

The officials on the border estimate that not more than 3 per cent of the contraband is confiscated.

San Francisco is well supplied both by land and by water. The "Barbary Coast" resorts are wide open except when warned of occasional spasmodic reactions of official virtue, and "Dago red" flows plentifully at many restaurants.

On the Eastern coast the "booze ships," despite an occasional capture, do a steady traffic. The moonshiner continues to supply the South as he has always done, except that his trade area has broadened to take in the cities as well as the country districts. Along the northern border there is a constant stream of Canadian booze flowing in through systematized channels: from original seller to Canadian representative of bootlegger, thence to boat for transfer across the water, from boat to temporary storage in boathouse on the American side, finally by motor car or van to bootleg headquarters in the city whence it is distributed. There was a time when as high as 3,000 cases a week were coming into Buffalo, mainly by moving van, from the banks of the Niagara River. That the profit is worth the risk is evinced by figures furnished me by one of the inner circle of bootleggers:

Original cost, per case, $20; boat transportation, per case, $5; car transportation, per case, $1; "grease" for officials, per case, average, $10; total, $36.

"As I can get from $65 to $90 a case for the stuff," says my informant, "the going is pretty good. Once in a while one of us gets pinched and loses a car and has a fine to pay. But the cars are mostly cheap stuff, and the fines aren't very stiff, and generally we get tipped off when there's any stir going on. We're lying quiet now on a tip. Figuring it all in, the proposition will show close to 100 per cent profit."

The Niagara River district, by the way, may be regarded as an interesting index to the Federal Government's attitude toward violations of the law. The influx into Buffalo via water probably averages 500 cases a week. Yet when I was recently there the local government office had available just two agents for field work! A regiment might successfully have guarded the river frontage, though I am inclined to think that the regiment would have needed a fleet to reenforce it.

However, such matters do not, I infer, seriously affect the peace of mind of those members of Congress who voted (many of them with baited breath) for the Volstead Bill. They are apparently content with having satisfied their well-organized dry constituents by the mere process of enactment, as if a law enforced itself. Meantime the bootleggers are making a sieve of this particular law.

If there were no other testimony to the absurdity to which the law has been reduced, the figures of the Department of Commerce for the fiscal year would be enough, showing that $5,000,000 worth of intoxicants were imported into the United States (not including, of course, that brought in by border runners), as against one-tenth of that total in the previous year. One item which may be commended to the thoughtful and law-abiding is 195,000 gallons of whisky, brought in from overseas. All this *may* be for non-beverage, medical, sacramental, or manufacturing purposes, but as the reported shipments for 1920 were but 32,000 gallons, the inference is that Europe is acting the part of "my bootlegger" on an increasing international scale.

It is impossible to study the effects of prohibition over a large area and escape the conviction that never before has there been enacted a law which has bred such widespread corruption, official and unofficial. To hold the law itself responsible is, of course, the shallowest casuistry. The blame must be imputed first to our national spirit of insubordination which bids us refuse allegiance to the will of the majority unless our own private conscience jump with it; second, to the attitude, supine or worse, of those who, having promulgated the law, now cripple their own enactment by negligence of the means to enforce it, as if a man should build and launch a ship and then leave it, masterless, to the disposal of wind and wave.

Prohibition enforced would be at least an honest and worthy experiment. Prohibition half enforced or unenforced is merely an incitement to trickery, lawlessness, blackmail, and extortion. It has hatched a precious brood of lawbreakers ministering to the unashamed demand for stimulants of a public which would blush at the thought of a tacit conspiracy to nullify any other law; many of these enterprises being adjuncts to otherwise reputable trades.

Then there are the minor financiers who find the capital to back the "rum runners" in their larger operations, stand the risk of the cars, pay the fines if the operator gets caught, and take a 30 or 40 or 50 per cent profit on their investment when all goes well.

One such backer of whom I know is a builder and contractor, at present "tied up" by the deadlock in his trade. Another is a wholesale grocer of unimpeached character; a third, a minor but "strong" politician; a fourth, a gambler who considers this the best sure-thing game he has yet discovered; and still another, the son of a banker and himself a promoter in a small way of business.

All this bootlegging fraternity finds its immediately practical or more remote moral support in "easy" officials; jurymen who, despite their oath, refuse to convict; lenient judges and a public opinion potently influenced by the private attitude of those who are officially responsible for the execution or administration of the law; administrative officials who are known to disregard the law in their own private actions; judicial officers whose formal dicta are not borne out by their informal acts, and that class of congressmen and State legislators who have made themselves notorious in Washington and other capitals by voting one way and drinking another.

It is a matter of common report that the legal department of a large Eastern city, almost swamped under the flood of liquor cases imposed upon it, gathered its forces together for a final clean-up and spent a large part of several nights previous to the special term in working out the cases under the stimulus of strong coffee and Scotch whisky.

In another city a banquet given in honor of a high judicial officer of the State was so "wet" that the newspapers commented freely upon the quantity of booze consumed.

In the realm of legitimate business "my bootlegger" has become a recognized agency and stimulus of trade. "Don't mention this particular line," says the manufacturer of a certain article of apparel, "because there are plenty of other lines doing the same thing, though I believe we started it. In the old days, when the buyers from Western territory which was already dry came to town, we took 'em out and blew 'em to a good dinner and a show, with drinks all the way along the line. The blowing isn't as good now as it used to be; you can't buy drinks at the Waldorf or the Ritz, and we don't care to take our trade to the cheap hooch joints; so the out-of-town buyer can't have quite the time he used to. But after he's given us a good, fat order and gone back home he gets a letter from us advising him of a special shipment to him personally, and a few days later along comes a neat little wooden box without any trade label and with a fake shipper's address in the corner, all stenciled and businesslike. He opens it, and there are half a dozen quarts of hooch under the good old labels that used to gladden the eye. Maybe that man's trade doesn't come our way next time he takes his buying trip to New York! We're buying customers booze in quantity right now. So are our competitors. We've even thought of getting together with some firms in other lines and starting our own manufacturing—on the quiet, of course, and under cover. It'll get so by and by that a manufacturer with dry principles can't do business."

With new demands, such as these, the supply of alcohol seems to increase and the ranks of the bootleggers to swell. Notwithstanding the earlier prophecies and the present claims of the dry advocates that there would be a steady decrease in supply, my observations indicate that there is more booze on sale and more readily obtainable to-day than six months ago, and much more than a year ago. Furthermore, this is borne out by the prices which, allowing for temporary fluctuations arising usually from sporadic official activity, tend downward rather than upward; and, if there is less of the genuinely branded Scotch, rye, and Bourbon whiskies, there is more of the fake stuff and the fabricated type of gin, masquerading under false labels, it is true, but nevertheless answering sufficiently to the purpose for which it is bought and sold. There is a prevalent rumor, by the way, which I have been unable to trace to an actual market, that empty Gordon, Booth, or Barnett gin bottles with the labels intact command a price of 50 cents each—for refilling, of course.

Upholders of the law may find an indirect encouragement in the fact that the personnel of the bootlegging industry seems to be deteriorating. "My bootlegger," in New England and the Middle States, at least, is less likely to be of the type cited in the letter which introduces this article, more likely to come from the shadier classes of society. A friend of mine who is a district attorney in central New York and who, while personally unsympathetic to the dry law, is conscientiously endeavoring to enforce it, believes that the character of the men into whose hands the clandestine trade has fallen will eventually prove its ruin.

"Most of our local bootleggers to-day are of the criminal or semicriminal class," he says. "They tend to organize into gangs, and the gangs fight each other through the agencies not only of knife and gun, but of informer and spy as well. Therefore we have the aid of insiders in cleaning up the situation. Booze-running murders have been committed here and in neighboring districts; and that tends to open the eyes of decent citizens to what the whole rotten business means in the way of general lawlessness. Men whom no considerations of their own private responsibility to the prohibition law would dissuade from buying bootleg stock will sheer off from dealing with thugs of the type that murdered one of our best officers lately. There is coming to be too much of a smell of blood and crime about the traffic for decent people to take even the passive purchaser's part in it indefinitely.

And without the patronage of decent people the industry will collapse."

From the Middle West comes another voice of optimism, a letter written by an intelligent, keen-visioned woman in a small Indiana city, who tells a tale of two bootleggers, one of whom, bragging that he was exempt from the law, was caught, fined, resumed his rum running, was caught again, jailed, lost his car and his home and is out of the game; the other "ran" genuine whisky at big prices until his home was paid for and he had a good car and $5,000 in the bank, when he wisely quit.

"There used to be a dozen [runners], more or less, as the weather ran, stopping here every week. That was in the spring. Now one is a curiosity. . . . Among the young folks of our class a drinker now would be worse than 'scandalous,' where before prohibition they were common. I think," she adds pertinently, "before writing any more on these subjects you would do well to investigate the poorer but more law-abiding class of people's viewpoints and habits."

It is, of course, just that class of clear-sighted, straight-thinking, upright "common people" that forms the bulwark of our laws in general. Where they are in a majority or even in an effective minority, drinking will be a stigma merely because it is contrary to law. But this class is influential for good mainly in the smaller communities. In the cities of considerable size it is the leading citizens, through their prominence and natural leadership, and the laboring class, through its numerical strength, which constitute public opinion. And it is these classes which have not yet orientated themselves to the new and restrictive law and show no signs of so doing. In my former article I endeavored to indicate the attitude of "our best citizens" toward the problem. Here is an incident throwing light upon the reaction of the lower tenth to "my bootlegger" and what he represents:

A Buffalo matron who employs a man and his wife as window cleaners noticed one morning that they were doing their work listlessly and asked them what was wrong.

"The old woman and I," explained the man, "were out on a party last night."

"Where did you go?" asked their employer.

He named several low-class popular resorts in East Buffalo, known to sell drinks more or less openly.

"And I suppose you had beer at all of them."

"Beer, nothin'!" put in the wife. "Highballs; that's what we had. The real stuff. Seventy-five cents a throw."

Knowing that their combined earnings were $1.30 an hour, the matron remonstrated with them for their extravagance, but without effect.

"All your swell folks are gettin' theirs, ain't they?" demanded the working woman, and when an affirmative reply was returned the man said obstinately: "There ain't no law goin' to stop me from gettin' it when other folks can get it."

In ante-Volstead days the window-cleansing celebrants would doubtless have "tanked up" on their party, but it would have been with beer, not hard liquor. Why have they changed? For the same reason, I suppose, as has operated upon the minds and habits of thousands of others: under restriction people want the strongest drink obtainable. Quick results!

No plea of the prohibitionists has more force than their argument that our future citizens, not having before them the constant temptation of the saloon, will grow up with little or no incentive to drink. But "my bootlegger" has a word to say to that. He has a shrewd eye on the rising generation.

"Some of my best customers," an old and skilled practitioner tells me, "are the kids back from school. They're wise to where the stuff can be got, and they borrow the old man's car and come right to headquarters for it."

Manicure shops and hairdressing parlors, he further states, are the sources for young girls who feel the need of a "bracer" as well as for older women who are not supposed, by their families, to indulge. And, in a dozen cities that I know of, there are certain doctors—the same ilk that can be "confidentially consulted in private troubles"—who make a specialty of the prescription trade for women. Apropos of the supposed freedom from temptation which the younger generation enjoys, let me adduce as testimony a conversation between two débutantes of last year, reported to me in jocular vein by one of them, the speaker of the first part:

"Cissie, why do you give so many dances to the older men?"

"Oh, I've got my reasons."

"Do you like 'em better than the boys of our bunch?"

"In the middle of the evening I do."

"Tell *me*. I'm waiting."

"Well, along about midnight at a dance you begin to lose your zip, don't you?"

"Yes, you do, a little."

"The old boys usually have something on the hip to cure that tired feeling."

"So do our own crowd, some of 'em."

"But they hang to it tighter. They don't loosen up so easy. But when you sit out with one of the older bunch and begin to look a little droopy, it's 'Cissie, how would a little drink go, about now?' And there you are, all pepped up for a couple of hours more."

Which goes to show that the wise virgin of to-day knows how to keep her lamp supplied with the social oil. It is merely a matter of locating and marking down her own private bootlegger or bootleggers for the evening's entertainment. A seasoned old stager of New York society is credited with the saying that "Drinking is no longer a social amusement; it is a social achievement." Status and popularity are to some extent measured by one's capabilities of entertainment in that line; by what one "carries on the hip"; and the private flask, with its concentrated essence of bootleg, has taken the place of the comparatively mild and innocuous communal punch bowl of earlier festivities. A youngster with whom I played golf at a Cleveland club confided to me that he was giving up the weekly dances as a matter of economy.

"It takes ten to fifteen dollars' worth of Scotch to see me through an evening properly," he declared. "Pretty much all the young married women expect a highball if you sit out a dance with 'em, and a lot of the kids take a shot on the side, and at the present price of booze it isn't worth it. The funny part of it is that before prohibition nobody thought of that kind of thing; at least, not in these parts." He paused and added thoughtfully: "But now, if you don't come through with the stuff, you're in for a dull evening."

Nor is the bottle less of an asset at the lower end of the social scale. To a young, progressive, observant, and philosophic bootlegger who does business in and about Rochester, I am indebted for reflections upon the matter as he views it. He was formerly a race-track tout, but, having ambitions for self-improvement, quit that occupation because it involved his constant association with a class whom he regards as "cheap skates." So he went into the booze trade.

"Now I'm doing business with some of the swellest guys in town," he declared proudly. "Some of 'em belong to the big clubs. It's a classy trade. Then, of course, I've got my one-bottle line. They're more sporty."

"One bottle?" I echoed. "I should think there would be a small profit in that."

"That's where the big profit is," he corrected. "I get as high as twelve or even fifteen a quart, while the case guys are sellin' at seventy-five per dozen. Is that a swell profit or ain't it?"

Admitting that it was, I inquired as to the precise nature of the one-bottle traffic.

"It's the boat trade," explained the expert.

"Boat trade? On the lake?"

"Nah! Boat. Automobile. Do you get me?"

I was obliged to confess that I did not fully.

"It's this way," he explained, patient to enlighten my ignorance. "One of my customers has got a girl dated up for the evening. Let's say she's all right. When the town was wide open, what'd be the evening's program? Why, they'd have dinner some place with a couple of drinks and go to a dancing place afterward and have a couple more, and good night. No harm done. Well, it ain't that way now. The dancing joints are mostly closed. So what do they do now? Why, Bill he gets out his car, and he stops for his girl and he comes here to my stand and picks up a little package from me; maybe it's newspapers and maybe it ain't, but the odds are on the ain't. They snuggle the package into the restaurant with 'em and take the top off it for dinner, and that's the start. They're startin' on real hard stuff, see? Not on beer or a bottle of Dago red like they used to. And a couple of hours later, if you followed that car, you'd find it drawn up beside a country road somewhere within a few miles of town. You may have noticed cars like that if you motor at night."

I had noticed them, though without any special thought regarding the social phenomenon portended.

"There's a bottle in most of 'em," continued my mentor. "Ten to one, it stays there empty when the car moves on. Now it's one thing for a nineteen-year-old kid to be in a dance place where folks'll notice if she takes one drink too many more than is good for her. And it's another thing for her to be soakin' it up in a parked car where it's so dark that she can't see how little's left in the bottom of the bottle. . . . Well," he observed reflectively, "she ain't *my* sister."

My curiosity was aroused. "Have you got a sister?" I inquired.

"Sure, I have. And I'm givin' her a good convent-school education on what I'm makin'," he averred proudly. His expression altered to a grim ferocity as his mind followed the direction indicated in my query. "If ever I catch her startin' a boat trip with a guy and a bottle," he growled, "I'll smash her between the eyes."

Decidedly different, this view, though possibly not less expert than the view of an enthusiastic prohibition orator whom I once heard publicly exulting over the achievement of prohibition in wiping out the night life of the dance halls, all of which he lumped in one category as recruiting stations for hell.

"Praise God, we have extinguished the white lights of the Broadways of America!" he declared.

True, to a great extent. But I should like to take that reverend gentleman along some of the near-city roads which I have observed since my illuminating conversation with the youthful bootlegger, and then have him state frankly and honestly whether his hell—which is, I take it, substantially the same as the young bootlegger's or his customers' or mine—is likely to receive more recruits from the white lights of the dance halls or from the black darkness of the roadside automobiles.

Wherever we turn to examine the workings of prohibition, there looms "my bootlegger," clear or dim in outline, working quite openly his immediate territory, as in the border cities and industrial centers, or projecting his supply across long distances, as into the prairie communities; but in one way or another contriving to make the supply answer to the demand. What are we going to do about him? Arrest and punish; that is the obvious, the superficial solution. But even where punishment follows arrest, which is not always nor even commonly the case in many localities, how radically effective is it?

Either "my bootlegger" reverts to his well-rewarded trade and continues to supply me, or, if he become discouraged and quit, another comes forward to take his place, his risks, and his profits.

Broadly speaking, the profits more than justify the risk. There is at least presumptive evidence in the centers, where popular opinion is adverse to the law, that the enforcement officials make only enough arrests to keep the policy of extortion in force and the price of immunity high. Punitive measures have not thus far worked satisfactorily. Alone they give no promise of leading the way out of the morass of lawlessness to the high and dry lands of acceptance and obedience.

For they are directed against "my bootlegger" alone. And "my bootlegger" is not the parent, but the offspring of liquor lawlessness. As my correspondent first quoted puts it: "He is the symptom; I am the disease." For every seller-bootlegger there are a hundred buyer-bootleggers who hold themselves and are held by the opinion of their peers privileged to disregard and deride the objectionable enactment without incurring criticism or censure.

I know many people of all classes—drinkers, some of them—who would not knowingly welcome to their houses or their clubs a professional seller-bootlegger. I know no man who does or would establish any social barrier between himself and the buyer-bootlegger—who may very well be his next-door neighbor, his fellow church member, his physician, or the mayor of his city! Yet the buyer is the center and core of the problem. He is the true corrupter of the law.

Here it is that the professional prohibitionists, whose militant political and social strategy before the Volstead enactment were of so high and amazingly effective an order, seem to me to have failed dismally. Speaking frankly, they have shirked the job in its final and most important phase, so that now it is a grave question whether, for better or worse, much of what the new dispensation was meant to accomplish will not remain permanently undone. The prohibition leaders most skillfully stimulated public opinion to pass the law. They have not inspired it to respect the law. They ceased effective work just when their missionary endeavors were most needed. For—let me repeat it again—new and restrictive laws do not enforce themselves.

Hence "my bootlegger." So long as the prohibition enactment remains, in the minds of a large, determinedly rebellious, otherwise law-abiding and self-respecting minority, as "your law" or "Volstead's law" or "blue law," it will continue in its present slow-poisoning process of dry rot. But if ever, by a repetition of the endeavors which enacted it, it can be made to be regarded in any wide sense as "my law," to be rigorously respected and jealously upheld, then good-by to "my bootlegger" and all that he implies.

A Big Catch on Rum Row

William G. Shepherd

By 1925 rum-running—importation of foreign-made liquor into the United States—had settled into a systematic, large-scale business. So had the fight against rum-runners. Here is reporter William G. Shepherd's story of one engagement: "the story of the greatest single-handed capture ever made in the sea fight against rum runners," Collier's *declared.*

June 6, 1925

PRETZELS—THAT'S WHAT WE EAT IN OFF hours on Coast Guard Rum Chaser 115. By off hours I mean the hours when regular meals were not under way. In the little kitchen-diningroom—down at the foot of the steel ladder in the rear of the boat—the cook is always working, washing the dishes of the last meal or peeling potatoes or chopping celery or making other preparations for the next. He has seven men to feed. They are mostly young men under thirty, who have passed stringent physical tests. Their stomachs are as sound as their teeth, and their teeth must be perfect. They live outdoors on the sea. Their appetites seem to give them no peace. One of them, in the midst of a conversation with you, will suddenly look worried and distrait—he may, to a stranger, appear seasick; he will excuse himself, climb down the steel ladder to the "galley," as they say at sea, and climb back to the deck with a handful of something to eat. Then he's ready for more talk. The cook may go to his bunk to sleep, but the kitchen runs along, during the night watches, just the same.

The men are allowed $1 a day, each, for food; they pool their funds, and the cook or the man in charge of the boat does the buying. Therefore each of the twenty-four 75-foot needle boats in the New Jersey sector of the Battle of Jugland has its own culinary individuality. For instance, on Chaser 117, rye bread and ham was the off-hour food. On Chaser 160, when you climbed down the ladder to get something to nibble on, it was crackers and a hearty, biting cheese that made your palate tingle. The coffeepot, tied to the stove, is always hot. Every man in the crew, including the two engineers of the two powerful gasoline engines, knows where the coffee is kept, as well as where the cheese or crackers or ham may be found. It seems to be the duty of the man, who during the cook's off hours finds the coffee getting weak, to toss into the pot a dozen tablespoonfuls of new coffee. "Wash your cup at the sink and hang it back on its hook," is the cook's only order to the crew. On every chaser several men took the greatest pains to tell me where to find off-hour eating material.

The two captains on Chaser 115 ate pretzels together and separately and got along very well with each other. It was Captain John O'Brien's boat, but I had requested that Captain John Reeder be allowed to go out "on the Row" with me. His boat was laid up with a twisted propeller shaft and he was pining away on shore.

"Go out with Shepherd and keep him company," Commander Kinnaly, in charge of operations, had said to Reeder after I made my request.

Reeder, I knew, was one of the most daring of the young Coast Guard commanders at Section Base No. 2.

That simple and impulsive request of mine for Reeder's company cost some unknown dealer in "wines, liquors and cigars"—and one-thousand-dollar bills—just about half a million dollars.

It provided one of the most spectacular single-handed captures in Rum Row history.

The lazy spring Saturday afternoon on the lazily pulsing sea, thirty miles out from shore, had been uneventful. Our chaser had ambled around slowly from one rum schooner to another, four and five mile trips between boats, and had found only one rum runner, which it had shot at, chased and lost.

That afternoon I had my first view of tracer bullets, invented and used during only the latter months of the war. Someone took down the 40-pound Lewis machine gun from its shelf in the rear of the pilot house and found that it had jammed; its trigger would not snap. It was an hour's work to clean and oil it. And then it had to be tried. The tracer bullets were new and the boys used those. In the brilliant sunshine O'Brien fired a "panful" of tracers. The effect was astonishing. Everyone who has ever watered a lawn with a hose knows how easy it is to hit a certain mark with the stream of water. Well, this Lewis machine gun sent out over the sea a thin line of smoke that waved up and down or from side to side as O'Brien pleased; he could direct it where he wanted it to go, and in that two-mile string of smoke there was a core of drilling death. I'd hate to be a rum runner and have that Lewis smoke hose turned on me.

At night the sight of the tracer bullets was even more amazing. I saw it at the entrance to the Ambrose Channel in the moonlight of the early evening. The boat had run in toward the New York shore to hunt for rum runners that might be heading out toward the Row. They're something like hunters, these Coast Guard men; they have their places where they lie in wait.

At a certain spot on the sea the captain had shut off the engines and put out all lights; the boat lay rolling gently and drifting. There was a distant roar of engines. There was a rum runner about. On the deck there was a scampering for rifles and one-pounder shells for the big gun. The man in charge of the Lewis gun took it out on deck. The roar grew louder, but the youngest, finest eyes on our boat could see no lights on the water. The rum runner was running without lights, running toward us. He didn't see us and we couldn't see him. There was a chance for a smash. Fate had it that, like a flash, he should miss us by about 200 feet. He passed in front of us, in the path of the moon. Twenty things happened all at once on our boat. Bells rang. The engines started full speed. We jumped forward. Someone pulled the siren as a signal for the runner to stop. He didn't. Someone pulled the lanyard of the one-pounder gun and sent a shot across his bow as a further signal to stop. He didn't. His boat swerved straight into the moonlight. Someone turned the searchlight on the place where the boat had been a moment before.

"Get him!" came the order. Here was human game! Do men feel wicked when they shoot to kill? I've never thought so. That part of them with which men feel wicked isn't working at the time.

Suddenly a stream of fire as thick as my wrist shot out from our deck over the sea—the Lewis gun with its tracer bullets. The daytime thread of smoke had become a hawser of fire. Two rifles sent out the same blazes. An automatic spat four times. That rum runner had only to stop and the shooting would have ended instantly. What could he have been more afraid of than this stream of tracer bullets, these one-pounder shells and the rest of the killing missiles? He chose to run away, and he succeeded—if he didn't go to the bottom. He knew what he was doing; he dashed back and forth across the path of the moon. His white spray in the moonlight, the dull grayness of his boat, the glitter on the water, made him almost invisible. The searchlight could not find him.

And right here, I may remark, he had something to get away in. I asked a rum-runner prisoner on our boat, later in the evening, what sort of boat this shot-defying runner probably had and the description he gave me—I'll repeat it later on—indicated that it was perhaps one of the fastest boats on the coast, amazingly equipped for speed.

I have never, in revolution or war, among machine-gun men in Mexico or among revolutionists in Russia or at various fronts in Europe, seen such desperateness and such willingness to gamble with life as that rum runner, under a tracer-bullet fire from a machine gun, displayed that night. Suddenly there was nothing to shoot at; nothing toward which to steer our boat. We couldn't even hear the thunder of the engines. The rum runner was gone. Flesh and blood had done the almost incredible thing of defying that stream of killing fire.

I have said he might have gone to the bottom. No one on our boat could say he hadn't. And I found out from the rum-runner prisoner, later in the evening, that often his associates never come back to shore—they "stay" at sea.

The rum-runner prisoner mentioned above, whom we did succeed in catching that evening, had started out with a companion, and one of their engines had gone wrong. When 115 signaled them they rounded to and started toward us. The Coast Guard boat came to a stop and waited for them. Their boat was a Seabright dory; in form and type a great, glorified rowboat. It was open, like a rowboat. There were no seats in it, but running from side to side, in the middle of it, was a box to house the engines.

Two men stood leaning against this box as the dory came up to us; one had a hand on a rudder lever behind him; the familiar shape of their seagoing dory made them appear, in size, like dolls. But they were grim dolls. They were covered from head to foot in black oilskins. Their faces peered out through hoods that ran down over their chests. They might have been dressed for moving pictures; instead they were dressed for a night in a fast open boat on the high seas. A wind had come up with the evening, and the sea was choppy. Their boat came up alongside 115 with a bang. Reeder, with revolver and ammunition strapped to his waist, jumped across into her.

"Where are you going?" he asked.

"Oh, we're just hunting for a skiff we lost," answered the taller of the two.

"Where are your papers?" asked Reeder.

"Papers" are issued by the federal government, and it is against the law to operate without them.

"Papers?" repeated the tall man. "I left 'em ashore. I didn't expect to come out this far."

"Fellow," said Reeder quietly, "I'll have to take you in."

"Throw out a towrope, please," he said to Captain O'Brien.

He stood on the engine box, above and behind the two sinister, monkish-looking figures as the dory trailed along behind us. The 115 headed for the port of New York and for the Barge Office at Battery Park, the sea end of Manhattan Island, where the jails and the cells and the patrol wagons are. We had a thirty-mile run ahead of us.

Pretty soon we lost the moon behind clouds, and it was difficult to see the boat behind. Reeder shouted to stop, and the dory ran alongside us again.

"It's too rough to be towed," he explained. "I'm going to put one of these prisoners aboard you. Please give me a seaman, a pocket flashlight, and an oilskin coat. You get up there," Reeder ordered one of the two prisoners.

One of the black, monk-dolls made a grab at the railing of our boat, just as we gave a lurch. He barely grasped the rail, his booted feet slipped and he dangled over the side. Three of us grabbed him and pulled him up.

He stamped on the deck as if his feet were cold; he shook his body in his oilskins. Then I heard a very pleasant voice issue from the face circle in the hood:

"Let him have my oilskins."

"Fine!" said Reeder, "I'll take them."

The rum runner's fingers were cold; he could not unbutton his tightly buttoned cuffs.

"If you'll help me off with these—" he suggested. I unbuttoned his cuffs and helped him to pull his great rubber hood off over his head. I'd like to read a Conrad or a McFee story or see a good moving picture about the kind of fellow he looked to me as his face came out of that hood. It was not a bad face; it was used to smiling; it had a chin that could set square when necessary; there were sound, white teeth in it and clear whites in the eyes. It was a young face, but it had weather wrinkles about the temples. The hair was short and crisply curly, with a touch of gray. The tan of sunshine, wind and sea was on him. If a moving-picture camera had caught us, out in that black night, the unhooding of that curly-headed rum runner would have made a picture that would thrill thousands of audiences and queer prohibition for the evening, in any theatre.

They threw the oilskins to Reeder and someone handed him a pocket flashlight.

"Jacobsen, you go with Captain Reeder," ordered Captain O'Brien.

Big Jacobsen, a seaman, in a short blue overcoat and a tightly knitted cap of the sailor type, jumped down into the dory. He didn't stop to get his revolver or ammunition.

"Please watch for my light signals," said Reeder. "See you at the Barge Office, Mr. Shepherd," he added. "Cast off."

The little boat fell behind us in the darkness. Ten minutes later, far behind, we saw a little white light flashing in code. Reeder was telling us that everything was O. K.

But consider what had happened. We had had two captains on 115; now we had only one. Out there, on the black sea, Reeder, at the end of the day, had a boat of his own, even if it was operated by a rubber-hooded prisoner. A crew's a crew, so long as it obeys. And Reeder had his revolver and the unarmed but huge Jacobsen.

The place to put the prisoner was down in the kitchen. He climbed down the seven-stepped steel ladder into the glare of the kitchen lights. He wore corduroy trousers, stuck into hip-length rubber boots, and a brown shirt. He was a clean man, with the cleanliness that costs money; probably a little vain of his "working clothes"—not a man who would wear them after they were much soiled.

It was inordinately hot down there in the kitchen, with the coal stove and the boat's heating plant going full blast, but, after he had turned down the uppers of his boots, he backed up against the stove and shivered.

The cook was sympathetic. There is something maternal about a good cook.

"He's shivering," said the cook. "I know where I can get you a nip," he said to the man. He had in mind my little flask of seasickness medicine. I suppose. Now, in a fiction story, this rum runner would have refused a drink: he would have said, quietly, "Thanks, I don't drink."

The fact is that that's just about what he did say. Only he put it this way, to the amazement of myself, the cook and the seaman who had brought him down:

"No, thanks. I don't touch the stuff."

"All right. Better take a cup of Java, then," said the cook, raising the coffeepot from the stove.

"Yes, sir, I'll have coffee," said the man, his face lighting for the first time. He drank three cups of hot coffee, sitting on a bench beside the white oilcloth-covered table.

I went up on deck. The lights were out on our halyards: we were running dark. O'Brien wanted to make another catch, if he could, on the way in. Those schooners on Rum Row must get food and water from shore or the crews will suffer, and Rum Row be routed. This was the hour when the fast boats that run out to the Row with victuals and supplies might be expected to be abroad. O'Brien had stationed a man on the rear deck to watch for Reeder's signals, which came in tiny, pure-white flashes from time to time.

"Meet you at the Barge Office," he flashed one time. But always he flashed the code message "O. K."

When I went down below to the kitchen half an hour later the rum runner was another man; he was talking to one of the two engineers. Gasoline engines was their theme. They were both experts. The rum runner made no bones about it; he had run many a high-powered boat that had outsped the Coast Patrol. The conversation became three-sided, what with the questions that a curious correspondent had to ask; and, finally, when a ringing of bells took the engineer up the ladder and back to his engine, I found myself alone, except for the cook, with the man in the rubber boots.

"I'm not a Coast Patrol man," I explained to him. "I'm a Collier's correspondent."

"Yes, I know," he answered. "The cook told me who you were."

So we buckled down to an hour's talk.

"Say," he said, "have you ever been on one of these patrol boats when they're shooting?" he asked.

I told him I had been in at least ten chases.

"Why don't you fellows stop?" I asked. He didn't answer my question.

"Does it look to you as if they were shooting to hit us?"

"I never saw more careful aiming in the whole war," I answered.

"That's it," he said earnestly. "I've been telling the boys back at Atlantic Highlands and Keansburg that these men are really trying to kill us. They wouldn't believe it. But I know! You'd think we were a lot of birds, a bunch of wild ducks, the way these fellows shoot.

"What do they fire at us?" he asked later. "Ain't they using some kind of a shell that explodes after it hits?"

"Yes, sir," I said. "It's a one-pounder shell that bursts."

"That's what we've heard," he answered. "They could bust your boat to pieces. More than one of the Jersey runners has never come to shore again. And the boats come in with bullet holes in them pretty often these days."

"Have you ever had any tracer bullets fired at you?" I asked.

"What kind are they?" he asked.

I explained the trail of smoke by day and the two-mile-long string of fire by night.

"No," he answered. "I've never seen any of them, and I don't want to."

And then I did the fair thing. I told him what was on my mind about the daring of his kind. I had to tell him that I had never seen greater daring even among the fatalistic Mexicans.

"I don't see how a man can sit in one of those little boats out on the high seas and let these fellows pop away at him."

He didn't take my remarks as a compliment to bravery. Instead he earnestly tried to explain it to me.

"You see," he said, "a runner has got a faster boat than theirs; he knows that. He knows that he'll be in range only a minute or two and then he'll outspeed 'em. All that shooting on the deck makes a lot of noise when you're near the cannon and the guns, but you must remember that we don't hear the shooting. Our engines are making so much noise at high speed that we can't hear ourselves think. All we can see is little splashes in the water around us. Pretty soon the splashes are behind us, and then we know we're all right. But lately I've been hearing kind of an explosion when the shells hit the water, and I suspected they were explosive."

"Isn't it a kind of tough game?" I asked.

"Well, you see for yourself," he answered. "It's the toughest game I was ever in. It was pretty soft two years ago, when the Row was only three miles from shore and the only place they chased you was on land. But now we have to go out on the high seas in all kinds of weather, with these fellows shooting at you as if you were a flock of wild ducks!"

The cook got up from the bench and brought back three cups of coffee. It isn't often you can hold a kaffee-klatsch with a rum runner.

"It doesn't even pay the way it used to," he went on.

At this point I must stop a moment to comment in advance on what this man, straight off Rum Row, had to volunteer about the direction that drinking is taking to-day in America. I have said, in previous articles, that white-collar drinking, the drinking of pure, unadulterated stuff, is dying out because the pure stuff is disappearing; I have said that most of what we are drinking in America to-day is raw industrial alcohol, jiggered around in different disguises. A tour of the country, as shown in a recent article in Collier's, proved this point, but I had not expected to find any connection between raw industrial alcohol and this open-sea, widely scattered Rum Row.

"It doesn't even pay the way it used to," he continued. "People don't seem to be willing to pay the prices for real stuff any more. You can buy that stuff they call 'Scotch mash' out there on the boats. It's real name is 'iolene.' It comes in barrels, and I think it costs about $10 a gallon, but I've never bought any of it. You take that to shore and mix it with industrial alcohol and water and you can make any kind of Scotch you want. Just label your bottles as you please. One fellow I know, who didn't know much about whisky, got a lot of queer-shaped bottles called 'pinch bottles' that only a certain brand of whisky comes in and he filled 'em with 'iolene' whisky. The only labels he could get were 'Old Smuggler' labels, so he glued these on to the bottles. It was a great joke—'Old Smuggler' whisky in pinch bottles. But he sold 'em all right.

"People think prices of whisky are going down. Good whisky isn't going down. But there's so much fake whisky, even out on Rum Row, that it doesn't pay to try to handle real good whisky unless you have special customers.

"I like real liquor," he continued, "but I take home beer and wine. I won't touch the other stuff any more. It's green. You see, in England they must age whisky for three years before they can sell it. But lately they've been exporting green Scotch to France or Belgium or Germany and then reshipping it to the Row. That's what we're getting mostly now. They're cheating over at the other end of the line."

I asked him about how fast the rum runners' boats really were and how they were engined.

"I know some boats that have three Liberty engines in them," he said. "The engines cost $5,000 apiece, installed. That's $15,000 for the three. They are 450 horsepower each. That makes 1,350 horsepower in one small boat." We figured out, on the table, that, if it were possible, the Mauretania, powered at the same rate, would have nearly fourteen million horsepower in her engines instead of 70,000.

"Some of the boats are good for forty-five land miles an hour, empty. Put a hundred cases on them and the engines are so powerful that you don't cut down the speed more than five miles an hour. That leaves you forty miles an hour to get away with."

"How did you get caught to-night?" I asked.

"Only one of our engines was working right. We saw you two miles away and tried to quiet our engines, but we couldn't. We'd have been all right, at that, if we hadn't left our papers home. That means a $350 fine, I hear."

Up on deck they had been receiving Reeder's flashing O. K.'s from time to time, but when I went up on deck, after the talk, I found Captain O'Brien and the crew worried. We were nearing New York. The lights of Coney Island and Staten Island were visible, and here and there around us were the lights and the dark hulls of ships that had passed through the Narrows and were heading out to sea, or were finding their ways toward the

Narrows and New York Harbor. The flashing buoy lights of Ambrose Channel added to the liveliness. But among all these lights no tiny white flashes appeared. Reeder had stopped signaling.

O'Brien became worried after a quarter of an hour. He decided to light up his boat so that Reeder could see it. Still no white flashes came. He turned the boat around, facing the sea. He began to signal with his red and green lights, high up on the halyards. No one on the sea could miss those signals. But there was no answer.

There was only one gun in Reeder's boat that we knew of; he carried it in its holster. Jacobsen was unarmed. What kind of gun did the tall man in the black clothes carry?

I went down into the kitchen again. "They're worried because they can't signal your boat," I said to the prisoner. "Did your partner have a gun?"

"Lord, no!" he said. "We never carry guns out here. You can't fight back with these fellows. You can shoot back at the hijackers on shore, but you'd better not be caught with a gun out here. But I wish I'd stayed on the boat," he said. "It's pretty hard for one man to handle it alone, and the sea's pretty rough. You could get three drowned men out of this mix-up, if that boat swamped."

There was only one thing for O'Brien to do after vainly trying to get news of Reeder, and that was to hurry into base headquarters at Staten Island and report that Reeder was lost.

He put on full speed, and within half an hour we were at the pier—with the prisoner guarded by an armed seaman, down in the kitchen—and O'Brien was telling his story to the base commander.

But Reeder's little boat wasn't swamped.

I saw him twelve hours later on the deck of the big ex-cable ship Robert C. Clowry, named for the late president of the Western Union Telegraph Company. The newspaper reporters and photographers had just finished besieging him; overnight he had become a Coast Guard hero. The big ship was moored at the Barge Office pier—his prisoner.

"I stopped signaling you fellows," he said, "because I was busy."

"What happened?" I asked. Reeder doesn't tell a story very well; his kind never does.

"Well, we were running along in the little boat, and I was keeping my eye on 115 for signals when I suddenly smelt booze. We were near a big boat, and I headed over toward her. Of course they never suspected me, because I was in a rum runner's boat." He laughed. "As soon as I got near I could hear singing and talking—drunken men. I ran up alongside, and I could see cases of whisky and champagne. Well, all I did was to flash my light to the captain to stop. He was way up in the pilot house, but he saw my uniform and he stopped. I tied up to the boat and told Jacobsen to take our prisoner aboard. Then I went to the upper decks, climbed up into the pilot house, and told the captain to steer for the Barge Office. Then I signaled shore to be ready to receive prisoners at the pier.

"Most of the crew were drunk, and I told the captain he'd be responsible for any disorder among the men."

" 'We'd better let them keep on drinking, then,' said the captain. I told him that would be the best thing to do."

So the Robert C. Clowry headed into the harbor, while the crew of twenty-three men, most of them drunk after a sea voyage, with home in sight, sang their way toward the patrol wagons that were waiting, surrounded by Saturday night crowds, at the Battery pier.

That's all there was to the big capture. Just a grim young fellow, singlehanded, with a gun in a pilot-house.

There were 4,000 cases of genuine stuff from Europe on that 8,000-ton ship. The government seized it all and the ship as well. This is written so shortly after the seizure that no trial, as yet, has been held. Someone is "out" over $400,000, but the owner of the stuff has not, up to this writing, yet appeared. It was a record singlehanded seizure. Reeder, between leaving shore and setting foot on it again, had been in three boats.

Catching a big ship by using a rum runner's boat was a new stunt in the Coast Guard.

Within a few days orders were issued in Washington that Coast Guard men would be permitted to use captured rum runners' boats in the Rum Row war.

There are other Reeders in the Coast Guard. I didn't pick him out to heroize him; it just happened that I saw him at work. The Coast Guard—older than our navy, devoted to saving lives and property at sea, ready to answer S O S calls anywhere in the wildest storms, guardian against icebergs in the steamer lanes, protector of our coasts against smugglers of all kinds, part of the navy itself during war—is no part of the Prohibition Unit.

The Anti-Saloon League has nothing to do with its doings. Those who hate the league and prohibition make a mistake when they blame and criticize the Coast Guard for its activities along Rum Row.

"We have been ordered to stop the smuggling of liquor," says Admiral Billard, commander of the Coast Guard, "and we're going to do it."

Of course the drys will cheer the Coast Guard. But I cannot see that the Coast Guard wants any dry cheers. The wets are criticizing the Coast Guard, especially the wet newspapers. Do they expect a man, serving under the American flag, with the ancient tradition of the Coast Guard behind him, to disobey orders? That's too much to ask, with the old flag right over your head, all the time. You can't ask our school children to salute the flag every day and expect a Coast Guard man to turn against it for a few cases of booze.

The Coast Guard is neither wet nor dry; it's just Coast Guard.

If You Know What I Mean

Don Marquis

A cockroach named archy, usually found in company of his friend mehitabel, a cat, philosophized in the pages of Collier's *for several years. Their master, Donald Perry Marquis, was best known in his day for his columns, "The Sun Dial," in the* New York Sun, *and "The Lantern," in the* Herald Tribune. *He was also the author of several books, one of which,* The Old Soak, *became a play and a motion picture. In the column presented here, Marquis explains something about archy, and archy psychoanalyzes William Shakespeare.*

November 14, 1925

How is it that so many people are always wishing that they had gone into some other business, trade or profession? Archy the Cockroach has a word to say on this subject. Archy, you know (or maybe you don't know), was once a free-verse poet; the free-verse poet died, and its soul went into the body of a cockroach. Archy has many acquaintances among insects, human beings, birds, mice and ghosts, and one of his newest friends is peter the parrot, who claims that he is between three and four centuries old and was taken to England from Central America by Drake. He came to America right after the Revolutionary War, and has hung in a cage in an old chop house downtown in New York ever since. But let archy tell the story; he butts the typewriter keys with his head and can't manage capital letters nor punctuation marks:

pete says he used
to belong to the fellow
that ran the mermaid tavern
in london then i said
you must have known
shakespeare know him said pete
poor mutt i knew him well
he called me pete and i called him
bill but why do you say poor mutt
well said pete bill was a
disappointed man and was always
boring his friends about what
he might have been and done
if he had only had a fair break
two or three pints of sack
and sherris and the tears
would trickle down into his
beard and his beard would get
soppy and wilt his collar
i remember one night when
bill and ben johnson and

frankie beaumont
were sopping it up
here i am ben says bill
nothing but a lousy playwright
and with anything like luck
in the breaks i might have been
a fairly decent sonnet writer
i might have been a poet
if i had kept away from the theatre
yes says ben i ve often
thought of that bill
but one consolation is
you are making pretty good money
out of the theatre
money money says bill what the hell
is money what i want is to be
a poet not a business man
these damned cheap shows
i turn out to keep the
theatre running break my heart
slap stick comedies and
blood and thunder tragedies
and melodramas say i wonder
if that boy heard you order
another bottle frankie
the only compensation is that i get
a chance now and then
to stick in a little poetry
when nobody is looking
but hells bells that isn t
what i want to do
i want to write sonnets and
song and spenserian stanzas
and i might have done it too
if i hadn t got
into this frightful show game
business business business
grind grind grind
what a life for a man
that might have been a poet
well says frankie beaumont
why don t you cut it bill
i can t says bill
i need the money i ve got
a family to support down in
the country well says frankie
anyhow you write pretty good
plays bill any mutt can write
plays for this london public
says bill if he puts enough
murder in them what they want
is kings talking like kings
never had sense enough to talk
and stabbings and stranglings
and fat men making love
and clowns basting each
other with clubs and cheap puns
and off color allusions to all
the smut of the day oh i know
what the low brows want
and i give it to them
well says ben johnson
don t blubber into the drink
brace up like a man
and quit the rotten business
i can t i can t says bill
i ve been at it too long i ve got to
the place
now where i can t write anything else
but this cheap stuff
i m shamed to look an honest
young sonneteer in the face
i live a hell of a life i do
the manager hands me some mouldy old
manuscript
and says bill here s a plot for
you this is the third of the month
by the tenth i want a good
script out of this that we
can start rehearsals on
not too big a cast
and not too much of your
damned poetry either
you know your old
familiar line of hokum
they eat up that falstaff stuff
of yours ring him in again
and give them a good ghost

or two and remember we gotta
have something dick burbage can get
his teeth into and be sure
and stick in a speech
somewhere the queen will take
for a personal compliment and if
you get in a line or two somewhere
about the honest english yeoman
it s always good stuff
and it s a pretty good stunt
bill to have the heavy villain
a moor or a dago or a jew
or something like that and say
i want another comic welshman in this
but i don t need to tell
you bill you know this game
just some of your ordinary
hokum and maybe you could
kill a little kid or two a prince
or something they like
a little pathos along with
the dirt now you better see burbage
tonight and see what he wants
in that part oh says bill
to think i am
debasing my talents with junk
like that oh god what i wanted
was to be a poet
and write sonnet serials
like a gentleman should
well says i pete
bill s plays are highly
esteemed to this day
is that so says pete
poor mutt little he would
care what poor bill wanted
was to be a poet

archy

The Wedding Dress

Louis Bromfield

The author of The Green Bay Tree *wove this brief, memorable story around two moments in the life of a woman—two moments separated by a span of eighty years.*

October 31, 1925

ZENOBIA WHITE IS DEAD! THIS MORNING as I came down to breakfast I saw through the tall window that overlooks the meadows the figure of Jabez Torrence, who lives on the river farm, coming up the lane from the highroad. He was running, and when he saw me he cried out in a loud voice, "Zenobia White is dead!"

And then he fell silent, embarrassed, speechless, as if he understood at once how silly it was to be excited over the death of a queer old maid who had lived long past her time—an old woman who had lived for almost a century.

"Zenobia White is dead!"

Something had gone out of our world . . . the world of Jabez and me and all the county. Who could say what it was?

She had been dead for three days, said Jabez. No one would have found her in her little house among the bushes if her dogs had not set up a mournful unbroken howling. Jabez' father had walked in through the thicket surrounding her house. "Even the birds," said Jabez, "were still." He walked through the chickens and dogs and cats up to the door, and knocked. But there was only silence, as there had been only silence on one lonely night more than seventy years before. Inside on her bed Zenobia White lay dead. She was dressed in a wedding gown of white silk, with the veil of a bride covering her immensely old and wrinkled face. The stuff of the dress was so old that it had turned yellow. It must have been made eighty years ago.

So something had gone out of our world, and Jabez in his bewilderment knew it as well as I. We should never see Zenobia White again, walking down the highroad with the long train of her yellow taffeta dress trailing in the white dust, a basket over one arm, her lace mitts adjusted neatly, the plumes in her big hat waving in the breeze. . . . Zenobia White, walking down the white highroad, very tall and straight and proud for such an immensely old woman, her black eyes flashing proudly beneath the little veil of black lace that hung from her queer bedraggled bonnet . . . Zenobia White, immensely fierce and old, dressed always in yellow taffeta like Sarah Bernhardt in the picture by Carolus Duran . . . Zenobia

White, followed by a whole procession of cats.

Far down the valley beyond the figure of Jabez I could see the little house surrounded by bushes. I could even see for a moment a glimpse of the old white horse which Zenobia had raised from a colt and which had never known harness or saddle . . . the old white horse which lived inside her garden and attacked any intruder with bared teeth and unshod hoofs . . . the old white horse which this morning had *not* attacked Jabez' father. This morning, when Zenobia White lay dead in her wedding dress, he stood sadly, waiting. . . . The garden was full of birds, orioles and wrens and cardinals and a great number of dogs—queer, yellow mongrel dogs, unwanted by anyone, which had come to live with old Zenobia. And cats too, scores of them, which prowled in peace beside the dogs.

Zenobia White, with a thousand stories clinging to her memory! The story of the night when robbers evaded the old white horse and tortured Zenobia by baking her feet in her own oven! But she had not told them where her money was. They had gone away when she fainted, defeated. And after that Zenobia's proud walk carried the hint of a limp. . . .

But she belonged to my grandfather's day—a tall, handsome girl of twenty who sat a horse like an Amazon and was courted by half the men of the county. But even in those days she had lived alone in the cottage. The mother of Zenobia White had been an Indian woman, an Iroquois princess, who died soon after she was born. At twenty she was an orphan.

Zenobia White at twenty, living alone in the days when prowlers and renegade Indians infested the county. But Zenobia, young and beautiful, had stayed in the little house by the river, alone, armed with her father's pistols.

"But Zenobia," my grandfather used to say, "could look out for herself." He knew, perhaps, because he was one of those who admired her.

But Zenobia loved, with all the fierceness in her black eyes, young McDougal, red-haired and fiery-tempered, the fastest runner in all the county. And she was to marry him. They went in the long, still summer evenings to ride the tangled trails of the wild countryside. And they quarreled, for they were both of high tempers. And one night, two days before they were to be married, my grandfather, returning from the mill, saw them come home. They had quarreled, and Zenobia rode a little ahead of her lover, flushed and angry and handsome. And when they reached the cottage she turned in alone, without a word. . . . My grandfather says she was a beautiful woman.

And then (my grandfather said) Zenobia had gone into the house, and after bolting the doors and windows of the lonely house against intruders sat down to read her Bible and pray that her fierce spirit might be subdued. She sat reading thus until long after midnight . . . in a tiny house set in a clearing pressed upon by the great trees of the forest. And presently, as Zenobia read, the sound of footsteps stole in upon her consciousness—faint and confused in the rustling of the lilacs—the sound of footsteps—the footsteps of one or perhaps of many men.

Zenobia put out the flame of the single mutton tallow candle and sat listening, listening to the sounds in the garden, the sound of the owls and of the wind rising over the river. And slowly, when the sounds persisted, she took her father's pistol and, raising it, fired through the door, to frighten the ghostly intruders. The sound of a shot and then a silence while Zenobia stood there in the darkness with the smoking pistol in her hand, waiting—waiting!

There was only silence. They had gone away. There was nothing but the sighing wind and the hooting of the owls. . . .

And in the morning (my grandfather said) Zenobia was awakened by the brilliant spring sun streaming in at the window and by the happy clamor of the thrushes and cardinals in the garden. The sunlight fell upon the wedding dress that lay spread out over the chair at her side. And when she had dressed and gone downstairs (she was singing, she told my grandfather) she unbolted the doors and windows one by one until she came to the last which opened into the garden. And there, full in the path, face downward, his red hair flaming in the sunlight, lay Jock McDougal—dead—with a bullet through his heart.

I looked up and saw the figure of Jabez, sitting under a tree in the lane, still puzzling. We shall never again see Zenobia White with the procession of cats at her heels, her yellow taffeta trailing the white dust. Zenobia White is dead. She is being buried tomorrow in her wedding dress.

Journey's End

Octavus Roy Cohen

Is crime ever justified? The author, renowned for his stories of humor and heart-tug, answers the question before it is raised.

January 2, 1926

"You are not too late," said the grave and kindly physician, "but you understand, of course, that there is no hope. She may live half an hour. Perhaps two hours. No longer."

The young man was haggard. His clothes were travel-stained. "I have crossed the country—just to be with her," he explained. "Isn't there any chance? Has every possible effort been made?"

"Yes. . . . Even your presence will only mean that she will die happy. She is conscious: her brain is crystal clear. You—you would be happy to know how she has called for you—from the first."

The light in the sickroom was mercifully dim.

The young man entered softly and stood framed in the doorway. As though at a signal, the white-clad nurse nodded and padded from the room. The air was oppressive with the odor of liniments—tinctured somewhat by a profusion of flowers.

It had been a ghastly thing—this automobile smash-up which was ending the life of a beautiful young woman before it was well started.

Her voice—bright and glad and without a quiver—came to his ears: "Edward!"

He was on his knees by the bed, his arms about her frail form, his head pillowed on her breast. If his embrace gave her pain, she did not show it, for it was a pain glorified by love: it was a moment of supreme happiness of which she had abandoned hope. There had been a time—three years before—when he had gone bravely west . . . promising to return and marry her. Three spans of eternity. "Oh, Cicely," he cried brokenly, "I came as soon as I heard. I came—"

"To bid me good-by, sweetheart."

"No! Not that!"

"Yes, dear. In an hour—or two—or three. But, if you will, you can sit here with your hand in mine—or with your head—where it is. I never knew, dear, until recently how I have loved you: how I shall always love you—even afterward. You shall remain with me and your kiss of Godspeed will make my journey's end a happy one."

Her flowerlike face twitched with pain.

"It is so different, my boy, from what we planned. You were coming back to marry me—"

His stricken eyes stared into hers. "I have come back to marry you. Please . . . Right here! Now!"

Even in the half light of the curtained room he could see the expression of ineffable contentment which crossed her weary face. "You would really do that?"

"If you will let me."

"Oh, my darling! Only to know—even for a moment—that I am your wife."

He stepped from the sickroom and spoke hurriedly with the physician. Then he sat quietly by the bedside until the minister arrived with prayer book and license.

They did not speak—and if the eyes of the young man were misted with tears, those of the girl were starry.

And there, on the threshold of the hereafter, they were united in marriage.

Then they were alone—the bridegroom whose life lay glittering ahead; the bride who was about to die.

She would not let him explain why he had never before returned. The hourglass of her life had nearly run its course, and she refused to mar her last precious moments by thought of anything save the perfect present.

It was as his wife that she was dying, and if there was an agony of regret that she had been denied the reality of wifehood . . . the knowledge that he was here, even for so brief a time, robbed her of all pain.

It was as though the gates of heaven had been opened to her even before the Angel of Death touched her with his kindly, relieving wand.

Her voice dropped to a whisper as she bade him bend closer. Their lips clung for a moment, and then she took his head in her two hands and rested it on her breast. He could feel the fluttering of her heart—faint . . . fainter . . . then it was still and his sobs signaled those in the adjoining room that the end had come.

The minister dropped his arm across the shoulders of the young man and walked with him into another room.

"This is a house of death, my son—and of happiness."

"Yes. . . ." The young man was choked with tears. He turned pleadingly toward the minister who had performed the marriage ceremony. "Tell me," he questioned, "do you believe that there is ever an excuse for crime?"

"For crime, my son?"

"Yes. I have committed a crime. You see—" He nodded toward the room where lay the body of his wife. "She didn't ask me why I never returned. It was sufficient that I was here. And I couldn't tell her—"

The minister questioned gently.

"What is this crime you have committed?"

And the young man answered:

"Bigamy."

The Odor of Sanctity

Stephen Vincent Benét

Poet, novelist, short story writer, Stephen Vincent Benét ranks among the finest literary craftsmen America has produced. "The Odor of Sanctity," barely longer than a short-short story, is a compact example of form and dramatic impact achieved by the author without raising his voice above a whisper. Benét died in 1943, at the age of forty-five.

January 23, 1926

JOHN SIMEON WAS DYING AS HE HAD ALways meant to die—decently, respectably, in the odor of sanctity—and yet he was afraid. He had not expected to be afraid when he died, and the fact that he was afraid perplexed and annoyed him greatly.

From his lifelong friend, the silver-haired bishop who had been with him not half an hour ago, to the great-grandchild who had been brought in yesterday in his nurse's arms—so that he might say when he grew up that he had once received his famous great-grandfather's blessing—there was not one of them who would be ready to believe that he, John Simeon, could feel an unreasonable fear in the last hour of the flesh. Other and more heedless men might be afraid to die with their work undone, their affairs disordered, their sins unreconciled, but not John Simeon.

He was not being wrenched out of life with brutal abruptness in the strength of youth. He was dying full of years and honors—the account of his work was closed, and, when he thought of it, he knew that it had been good. He left no widow to mourn him—the shock of that parting had been borne by himself years ago. His sons and daughters were men and women: they and their families were well provided for.

As for sins and hidden tragedies—he almost smiled. He had had his share of grief and pain no doubt, but on the whole his life had been a singularly happy and fortunate one, and when the obituaries came out in the newspapers they would speak of a man who had justly deserved such fortune—a man who in an age not greatly distinguished for probity had practiced every one of the old-fashioned virtues without pomp or pretense.

He sighed a little, thinking of so much virtue for one pair of shoulders to bear.

The formless and potent fear that lay on his breast had nothing to do with a shadowy judgment hereafter—that, at least, he knew. If such a judgment existed it must be a just one, and he was ready to face it. On the other hand, if the end were mere obliteration—and though his faith, for the most part, was as simple and direct as a child's, he was too intelligent not to have considered this other possibility—surely there was nothing to fear. One sank into sleep, no more, and sleep was good after toil. There was nothing to fear—nothing; and yet he was afraid—afraid, and growing more pitifully afraid each moment. Afraid of what?

Wearily he rehearsed before him for the dozenth time the rich and varied pageant of that honorable life now past, trying to find some reason for his fear. Scenes he had thought forever forgotten rose in front of him—little, tiny, glowing pictures, brief and poignant as a flash of landscape seen from a railway train. He examined them, one by one, probing and prying, and still the reason eluded him like a ghost.

It had never been hard for him to avoid temptation. He had not coveted his neighbor's wife, nor his ox or his ass. He had not killed or thieved. Adultery would have been as foreign to his nature as any physical untidiness. He had honored God; he had tried to love his neighbor; he had been, by any ascertainable human standard, a good husband, a wise father, a devoted son. Surely, therefore, he should be able to be at peace now, at the end—and yet the rehearsal of what he had been and done brought with it neither peace nor solace. It was true enough, but true like something written in a book—it did not help an atom.

The sweat began to start on his face as he finished the count. He could not die afraid, he, John Simeon. It would be a negation of everything he had lived—something worse, appallingly worse, than any obliteration, than any painted hell—and yet even as he shivered at the thought he knew the cords that still bound him to existence were loosening and the minutes still left him slipping away like sand.

Desperately he tried to think of other deathbeds he had known. This man had died suddenly in his prime, that one had wasted away through years of distress, yet both faces afterward had had a peace on them, a promise almost. There had been others of course, but he wished to think of those who had seemed to die secure. What had they had that he had not, and where had they found their security? Margaret, his wife, had always been a saint, but what of that bitter acquaintance of his youth, George Hammer. He was no saint, but a sinner, and a weak and fumbling sinner at that. He had believed in nothing, made fun of all belief—a drunkard, a profligate, a blasphemer: the harsh, stately Biblical epithets rolled on John Simeon's tongue like grains of iron. The man had worked of course—at least there were his books—but a dip into the books had been enough for John Simeon. The things he found there, while well enough phrased, repelled him as much by their sensual beauty as by their carelessness of sin. And yet George Hammer had died almost exultantly, and his features in repose had had the look of an imprisoned ecstatic who has come to deliverance at last.

What was it George had said to him, when they used to talk together, years ago? "You'll go to heaven of course, John, I suppose—and yet, somehow, I can't imagine anyone's going there without one saving sin." The remembered sentence sank into his mind and pierced it—an arrow of lead. He had thought little of it at the time, but now his fear made him clutch at straws, and it seemed an omen. Could it be there was something in it, after all? Could it be that even his own God, his, John Simeon's, did not desire His creatures to be inexorably flawless all the days of their life? Had he lost the color and richness of life itself in cleaving too closely to the odor of sanctity?

He remembered other phrases now—the joy over the one sinner that repenteth; the parable of the sheep. The sinner that repenteth, yes. But what of the unhappy sinner who had nothing to repent? Would even oblivion receive to its kindly darkness the luckless being who had never fallen from grace, because he had never had a true temptation to withstand?

Again, but a little frantically now, he ransacked every nook and corner of memory, seeking for that saving sin. In boyhood, surely, all boys did sinful things. But he had always been the model boy of the neighborhood. He had never even lied to escape a punishment—it would have been too unpleasant to lie. His work—his business life—there perhaps— But there, from the first, he had found the maxim that honesty was the best policy very profitable and, finding it so, had never tried another. Margaret—one could not have been dishonest with that pure flame. His children— But no. He had always been fond of children; they had never irked him, really—never given him a chance to be really unjust to them.

There was nothing—nothing—not one place in his whole long life where he could definitely say, "Here I, John Simeon, sinned. It was only a little sin, but I sinned it." He could have groaned aloud.

He lay back on his pillows, exhausted. The fear was very close now—very cold around his heart. Then, somehow, slowly, on the shaken screen of his mind, a picture took shape.

Linda Verrill. He had not thought of Linda Verrill in thirty years.

The apple tree, old and gnarled, its trunk black with age, was in its first frail flowering of the year. There was a smell of apple blossom in the air—a smell of wet grass. The grass beneath the apple tree was new and green—it was late afternoon, fifty years ago—and he and Linda Verrill were standing beneath the apple tree, locked in each other's arms.

He remembered the smell of the apple bloom and the smell of her hair. He remembered the streaks of wet on his shoes from the wet grass, and his kisses and Linda Verrill's, and how they said they loved each other, in what fierce and broken words.

They had met only a few times. It had come to nothing—meant nothing. He had always known he was going to marry Margaret. Later Linda had married—happily too—and lived and had children and died. Even then they both must have known it was all impossible, and yet they had taken the moment for what it was and found it sweet. And that was wrong of course, wrong as could be. Even while he was kissing Linda he had known, somewhere in his mind, that he was going to marry Margaret—and Linda was half promised to Stephen Cray at the time. They had deceived their families—and Margaret and Stephen and each other—willfully, perversely, for the sake of a few kisses that came to nothing. And yet, when he thought of it, he could not repent it; he could only know that, if it were to happen again, he would let it happen again. . . .

The apple tree, old and black . . . the smell of the wet grass . . . Linda's mouth on his, warm and kind . . . he must not think of these things . . . he was dying

. . . old and honored . . . in the odor of sanctity . . . he must think of sacred things . . . apple blossom in the air. . . .

He was smiling. Why was he smiling? Then suddenly he realized, with a shock, that he was smiling because he had forgotten to be afraid. It was only a tiny shock—but sometimes tiny shocks are enough to stop a heart.

"Very peacefully," said the nurse professionally a little later. "No, he wasn't asleep, but I'm sure he was thinking of a prayer, or something just at the end—you can see. . . ."

Beyond the room a creature released took up the burdens of a new journey, with one small redeeming sin clutched tight to its breast like a single petal fallen on the gnarled and blackened trunk of a virtuous apple tree.

The Table

John V. A. Weaver

Poet, novelist, playwright, and scenarist, John Van Alstyn Weaver wrote this touching little story about a yellow oak dining-room table—and the family it served.

March 6, 1926

NO, IT ISN'T MUCH OF A TABLE TO LOOK at. Just an old yellow oak thing, I suppose you'd call it. It isn't that we couldn't have had mahogany or walnut, of course. Only—well, thirty-eight years sort of turns anything into a treasure.

It was Sam's father's wedding present to us. It and the six chairs—four plain-bottomed, two with leather seats.

I recollect as well as yesterday the first supper we ate at it. We came back from our honeymoon in Canada on a Monday afternoon. Sam had made the lease for the little five-room house on Locust Street the week before we got married.

All the month we were up there lazying around and fishing and getting used to each other I was worried about what we were going to do for furnishing the dining-room. I had a good deal of furniture from Mother's house, and Sam had some from his flat, but neither of us had a dining-room table. We had talked a lot about it. But that trouble was settled the minute we went into the room and saw the yellow oak, bright and shiny, with a note from Father Graham on it.

I scrambled around and got some sort of a meal together. What it was doesn't matter.

Pretty soon we were sitting in the chairs opposite each other, so close we could touch hands.

Sam didn't pay much attention to the food.

He kept looking at me. You know the way newlyweds will go on. After a while Sam didn't say anything for most a minute. Then he looked and looked at me, and said, "I guess you're about the prettiest girl anywhere, Mary. I'm glad this table is so short. It lets me see you all the better."

I had to laugh. "Why, silly," I answered, "it opens in the middle. There's extra leaves in the china closet. We can make it as long as we want!"

He looked a little sheepish, and glanced around at the four other chairs. Then he grinned.

"Well," he said, "we'll have use for those leaves before we get through, I reckon."

I couldn't half eat for laughing. Yes, and blushing too.

See that whole row of round dents up next to my place? That's what Sallie did with her spoon. She was the only one that always hammered. She was the first.

Over there, right by the opening—that's where Sam Jr. tried to carve his initials one time when he was about five. Sam caught him just as he was finishing the "S." It was a warm night for one young man, I can tell you.

Of course we'd put in one of the extra leaves a good many times before Ben came. The children were forever having friends over. Ben made the extra leaf permanent.

Then we commenced adding the second leaf. More friends, you see. Sam kept moving farther and farther away from me, I used to tell him. He'd always answer the same thing. "My eyesight's all right," he'd say. "I can see just as well how pretty you are." And he said it as if he meant it.

So the children grew up and the table came to its longest. Sallie married Tom Thorpe when she was nineteen, and they both lived with us for three years.

The boys were in high school then, and I tell you we made a big family. All three extra leaves hardly did. Sam at one end and me at the other, Ben and Sam Jr. and Sallie and Tom—and my first granddaughter, Irene, in her high chair.

But she had her place too. By that time we were in the big house on Maple, and the noise—and the life—and the happiness! The table was certainly getting battle-scarred. Look at that brown burnt place. That's where Senator Berkeley put down his cigar the night he stopped with us.

Well, then, Sam Jr. went off to college, and a little while after that Tom and Sallie set up housekeeping in their own home up on the Heights. So one of the leaves came out for good, and we didn't have so much use for the second, except for company once in a while. Except vacations, of course.

It was quite a shock when Sam Jr. left college at the end of his third year, and went out west to California. He didn't run off, you understand. We said he could go, although we were very disappointed he didn't stay and finish his education. But he was right. He's made a heap of money in real estate out there.

He comes back once a year for a week or so with Myra, that's his wife, and their two youngsters. Then the old table gets swollen back to its biggest. It seems mighty quiet when they go.

Ben came back and stayed with us two years after he graduated. We hoped he'd be content to settle down in town here for good, he was doing so well in life insurance. But that was just the trouble. The New York office wanted him, at twice the money, so he went. And the last leaf went out of the table with him.

That's been a year now. Sometimes I think of taking a roomer. Not just any ragtag and bobtail; some nice young fellow who needs a good home. It's so quiet—

I said so to Sam the other night. "My goodness," I said, "the table's so little again. Why, you're right on top of me. You can see all my wrinkles."

Sam laughed, and then he put his hand out and squeezed mine. "My eyes have grown dim to correspond," he answered. "You look as beautiful to me as ever. I guess you're about the prettiest girl anywhere."

But, still . . .

When the Air Raiders Come

William Mitchell

The year before this article appeared, Brigadier General William "Billy" Mitchell was tried by court martial on charges of insubordination and sentenced to five years' suspension from the U.S. Army. His "crime": advocating a strong air arm, a view that found disfavor in the eyes of tradition-bound generals and admirals. Mitchell resigned, dedicated himself to pleading his cause, and died in 1936—before Congress got around to vindicating him by rescinding his court martial sentence, and before his dream of a separate air force finally came true.

May 1, 1926

WHAT WOULD WE DO IF THE UNITED States were attacked and New York menaced? It is a muggy, listless afternoon. Lights glimmer in the countless offices of that daytime-crowded stretch of New York between City Hall and the Battery. At their desks tens of thousands of workers who have dragged themselves wearily back from luncheon, through the fog, sit and pray for five o'clock.

A deafening roar—another and another. Trembling of the mighty skyscrapers! The district jumps to activity, not slowly, like a giant drowsily bestirring himself, but instantly, electrically.

Another "Red" attempt to blow up the Morgan offices? The destruction of a great chemical plant—perhaps across the river in Jersey? A rush to the windows. But the streets below hold no answer: only a mass of curious upturned faces of pedestrians halted, turning to one another. Surface cars crawling along Broadway.

There is another blast—and the rush to the streets begins. Now, during office hours, the population of downtown New York is vast. There are, for instance, nineteen buildings on lower Broadway, not including the capacious Equitable structure, which have a business population of 90,000 persons. And so when these buildings begin to pour their tenants out into the streets it is an unlovely scene.

Elevators drop them down in loads; stairways are jammed. From the subway kiosks there begin to emerge frightened, panic-stricken men and women. The streets are tightly filled before a third of the office workers have poured out. Tardy ones claw and clutch and scramble, clambering on top of those who have fallen. Before long there is a yelling, bloody, fighting mass of humanity.

The explosions are coming more frequently now, but many thousands will survive to learn their cause. The fortunate ones are they who die under the heels of their fellows.

They will never know that the awful thing, threatened so long, has come to pass.

They will never know that a hostile air fleet has at last attacked New York and found it easy prey because the United States has no adequate air defense force.

They will never know how the raiders bombed the entire Island of Manhattan, how crowds hurrying across bridges to the mainland were slain by thousands as bridges were hit and shattered. Nor of how the attacking planes, leaving New York a heap of dead and smoldering ashes, had proceeded safely to other strategic points where they duplicated their bloody triumph.

There is nothing wrong with the picture that I have painted above. Of all the large cities of the world, New York offers the ideal target for aërial attack.

In case of an air war the action will be direct against the vital centers, and the outcome will be determined in a comparatively short time. One side or the other will be completely victorious.

To begin with, it is on a narrow peninsula between the Hudson and East rivers. Night or day it is easily picked up and identified by aircraft flying at any altitude. There are instruments which, aided by radiotelegraphy, will guide an airplane over a target the size of New York City, whether the place is visible or not. The character of the target offered by New York is especially favorable to air attack. While it has many fireproof buildings, the majority are only of fire-retarding construction, and a great many are of very inflammable material. Fire starting anywhere in New York, sweeping either up or down the island, would cause a loss of life that would be appalling, because the inhabitants could not be removed with sufficient rapidity. The limited means of transportation available, in the form of subways, ferries and bridges, could not possibly accommodate the population.

The use of gases by aircraft, even tear gases which are nonpoisonous, and the gases produced by a conflagration in a city such as New York, would fill the subways and all places below ground in short order. The mere threat of an air attack against such a city would in all probability cause its evacuation, which would place a severe strain on the resources of that entire section of the country.

Such a thing would be impossible of accomplishment if this country had a well-developed air force. Any hostile ship coming within at least two hundred miles of our coast could be sunk with dispatch, and the only vessels which could offer us harm would be submarines. They might mine the entrances to our harbors, attack our merchantmen with torpedoes and gunfire, or even launch airplanes especially adapted for this kind of work. However, they could do us no really vital harm had we an air force.

But the United States has no air force and still adheres to practically the same system of defense in effect during the Revolutionary and Civil wars. That system consists of:

(1) A battleship fleet, supposed to go out and find the hostile fleet, destroy it and thereby gain sea control.

(2) Coast-defense vessels, operating close inshore, and charged with opposing any hostile vessels attempting to force a landing on our coasts.

(3) The coast artillery, designed to protect harbors, river mouths and all places where foreign troops might de-

bark or foreign vessels find anchorage.

(4) The mobile army, which may be concentrated at any place to resist a hostile landing force.

Notice particularly in this organization that no place is given to an air force. It is not regarded as of sufficient importance to merit a specific assignment in the nation's defense scheme. It is split up between the army and navy, the Marine Corps and the Post Office Department, merely as auxiliaries to these services. It has no unified training, no well-established airways, no meteorological or weather service attached to it and no real scheme of operation as an air force.

As far as local defense against aircraft of such cities as New York is concerned, no such thing exists.

Let us turn to England and consider her system of defense. She has a navy and army and an air force. The navy is concentrated in what might be termed a high-seas operating force, in the form of battleships, submarines and swift cruisers. It is in no way tied to the coasts. In fact, it is supposed to operate at the greatest possible distance from the home country.

The air force—the first line of defense—is definitely charged with the defense of the coast against air or sea attack and with the complete protection of the air. At the beginning of a Continental attack the air commander will automatically take control of the air force, the army and the navy.

The British learned this system was necessary by hard experience during the World War.

Third in the British scheme of defense is the army, only to be used when all other means have failed.

The modern conception of war is entirely different from that which governed before and even during the World War. We consider it necessary to pierce the line of a hostile navy. On landing, a series of clashes must ensue with the army, in order to break through to the vital centers and force the enemy to capitulate.

Chief among the nerve centers of a country are the great populous cities.

New York City is one of the world's most striking examples of this kind of center. It is said to contain over two thirds of the cash and securities in the United States, and it is the financial capital of the world. While its destruction would not necessarily mean the defeat of the United States, it would be a very serious loss.

Other points particularly susceptible to such attack would be the Pittsburgh mining district, the automotive industries in Detroit, the canals connecting the Great Lakes, which carry the wheat and iron of the West to the mills and foundries of the East. The great cities on our Pacific Coast would invite attack in proportion to their importance.

Even agricultural districts would not be immune.

Strangely enough, our National Capital is not a particularly vital nerve center like Paris or London.

The more compact and concentrated a country is, the easier it is to destroy it from the air. Formerly, with good generalship, a small country could theoretically always mass a superior ground force at any point where an attack was expected.

British air power has now made an attack by vessels across the English Channel an absolute impossibility, but, on the other hand, an air attack directed against England has a greater chance of success than an attack by sea or land. Undoubtedly this is how she will be attacked. She is more vulnerable than ever before.

Great Britain is taken as an example of

a concentrated target for air operations. Japan is another, and to an even greater extent. Only a certain proportion of the Japanese islands are suitable for human habitation. Japanese cities are built along the streams and rivers, and on account of earthquakes the houses are of the flimsiest material.

The United States is extremely fortunate in this respect, as the vast extent of its territory obviates the necessity of such overcrowding and concentration of its important centers. However, should the triangle, Chicago-Chesapeake Bay-Bangor, Maine, be laid waste by an attacking air force, and complete mastery of the air obtained by a foe, for the United States to continue any resistance would be futile and well-nigh impossible.

It is fortunate that we are not at this time in peril of attack by any of the world powers, because they would first assail us with their entire aërial strength. As we have no air force and no scheme for creating one at this time, we would be a choice morsel.

Two oversea routes are perfectly feasible. One is over the Atlantic by way of Iceland and Greenland to Canada, and the other is over the Pacific, by way of Siberia, Alaska and the islands along the Pacific Coast. Aircraft would be supplied, protected and aided by submarines and surface vessels. While surface seacraft are entirely unable to operate wherever air power can menace them, still if a nation entirely controls the air it can operate its seacraft with comparative ease.

So it is evident that we must evolve a different scheme from the one we now possess to handle possible incursions of this nature. Invasions will first come through the air, projected from island to island, on which air bases will be established and defended while control of the air is contended for in great air battles. If the invader is defeated, he will be driven back and will lose the war; if he is the victor in the air, everything lies spread before him.

Compared with the power of making war in the air today, what little air fighting we did in Europe was almost as crude as were the firearms used at the battle of Crécy compared with modern weapons. While the operation of those first primitive air fighting machines cannot be taken as a criterion of what may be expected today, the performance of the ground armies in Europe is a perfect indication of what they will do in the future. The defensive power of modern firearms is such that no army can advance or drive the other from a prepared position. A war on the ground will therefore become nothing but an orgy of killing, continuing over a period of years and ending in utter exhaustion. It will decide nothing.

It is hardly worth while estimating what would happen to our armed forces were we attacked by a first-class power such as, for instance, England. While this is highly improbable, still, if we have any national defense at all, it should be designed to protect us from the country most capable of carrying out an oversea expedition. Great Britain would come, with her united air force and the navy operating with it, supporting it and pushing it forward—all under one command. If our navy attempted to engage hers, our ships would be sunk forthwith, as they would be outnumbered in their aircraft about ten to one. These having been disposed of, the army air service, scattered about the United States among various infantry commands, without united training and without a real theory of conducting an air war, would merely be chaff before the wind.

If by any chance the army and navy air forces acted together, they would find themselves quite unable to coördinate activities. The naval air forces have really no combat training whatever. Their directing officers have had no actual experience in war, and they have had no combined training with the army air service. Their system of work and chain of command are entirely different. Worse than anything else, the naval air forces are tied up to the navy on the water and the army air forces are tied up to the army on the land—neither is made to think that its main mission is in the air and that it must keep itself free from encumbrances on land or sea.

As far as local air defense is concerned for great cities like New York, there is no such thing provided, and our army officers charged with this duty are completely ignorant of the rudiments of a modern defense against air attack.

What, then, it may be asked, is the answer to such a condition of affairs?

Unquestionably it is the organization of an air force just as independent of the army as the navy is of the army, and just as independent of the navy as the army is of the navy. Each of these arms, the air force, the army and the navy, should be placed under a single department of national defense, because national defense is one concrete problem for the United States. All military power proceeds from and is prescribed by the people. We think of this as exemplified by armies and navies; but neither of these can win a war alone without the support of the population and industries of the country. The dictates of ordinary common sense point directly to concentrating our overhead and not having two or three organizations detailed to do the same thing, and to fixing the responsibility on each branch of the service for the work it is supposed to do.

The navy should be given the specific job of protecting all water areas beginning two hundred miles away from the coast and beyond that. The modern trend of naval development certainly points to the ever-increasing use of the submarine, as the surface ship, menaced from above by the airplane and from underneath by the submarine, has not long to exist.

The air force should be specifically charged with the protection of all air areas over the country, the coast defense up to two hundred miles offshore, which is easy operating distance for aircraft, and the local defense of the great cities such as New York.

Suppose, for instance, an air attack did come by way of Iceland, Greenland and Canada, and we were organized as I have indicated above—the whole air force of the United States, acting under one command, would immediately concentrate in the northeastern part of our country, and would meet and fight the enemy aircraft as far away from our frontiers as possible. The object is always to keep hostile planes from flying over any part of our country, or a hostile foot from touching our shores; and the air force is more capable of doing this than any other service.

For our great cities, we should have local defense air forces to afford protection against any hostile planes or airships which might elude the vigilance of our large fighting units.

This local defense system should also be provided with a network of observation and reporting stations radiating out for a distance of 200 miles, because that distance is necessary to report the approach of hostile planes in sufficient time to allow our craft to rise and engage them. As airplanes can be made completely noiseless they will not be heard as they were in the last war, so other methods of detecting their presence will have to be resorted to.

The French employ lighted areas—not searchlights, but comparatively dimly lighted places, several miles in extent. Above these are kept a constant patrol of airplanes. If any hostile aircraft are observed, they are reported by radio and the watching planes swoop down and attack them. We must be prepared to fight in the air at night as well as in the daytime. All the reporting posts of this aircraft defense system must have their own special wires and radio so that instantaneous communication can be transmitted to the commander of the defense. Aircraft move so fast that a delay of a few minutes may mean destruction.

Besides our reporting posts and communicating lines, antiaircraft cannon and machine guns are used. These have comparatively little effect, except as a means of following and indicating where hostile aircraft may be. With noiseless airplanes, the effect will be even less. Possibly they will have some value in strengthening the morale of the people by making them feel that they are being protected, but on the other hand fragments of their shells falling back on the cities often do much harm to their own people.

Searchlights in the past have been used in conjunction with the antiaircraft guns and may be necessary in the future. They must be placed well away from the towns themselves because their beams are a sure indication of their location. They have to be moved frequently for this reason, otherwise the enemy will be guided by them and know exactly where to go. I remember a disastrous and at the same time amusing example of this during the war. At the airdrome of Ochey, a few miles back of Toul, the British had two squadrons of the then giant Handley Page airplanes and numerous others of a smaller kind—FE 2-b's, they were called. They indicated the position of the airdrome at night by the vertical beam of a searchlight, flashed intermittently, at some distance from the airdrome itself. When friendly planes came near, they gave a certain signal with fireworks, previously agreed upon, and the lights of the airdrome were turned on so that night landings could be made. One night the Germans watched this proceeding and on the following night a single German plane destroyed twenty-four ships in a couple of minutes.

The greatest precaution and wariness must be exercised in night attack. Feint upon feint is made by the enemy. The antiaircraft crews are worn out firing at invisible targets. Their eyes are blinded from the constant flashes of the guns and they become disheartened and tired out from not hitting anything. Often when my force in Europe had to make night attacks against localities where we wished to avoid any possible loss, we would begin soon after dark by sending over feint attacks against these points, keeping this up hour after hour until the enemy searchlight and gun crews were completely exhausted; then we would send the main attack over at two or three o'clock in the morning and invariably succeed. In those days we had great big lumbering machines of a speed of about sixty miles an hour, that could go only about three thousand feet in the air. A modern bomber has a speed of 135 miles an hour or more, and will go up to 25,000 feet in the air.

It will also carry from five to ten times as much explosives as did our old planes.

The aërial torpedo, a pilotless airplane held on its course by gyroscopes in the same way a water torpedo is, and controlled if necessary by radio, can be directed with great accuracy for one hundred, two or even three hundred miles. Against a target such as New York a hit should be made every time at these distances.

With these few suggestions as to what defense against aircraft means, it must be obvious to the reader that we must hit our aërial enemy—and our water or land enemy, for that matter—as far away from our vital centers as possible. This can be accomplished only by the organization and training of a united air force.

The army, in its conception of the use of armed forces, has been in a state of arrested development for many centuries. Its theory embraces the use of the physical power of one man against another, aided by weapons which he can carry in his hand or which he can transport close to him, whose action depends on the range of visibility, or what might be termed "eye shot," for their use. The dogma of the man raised in the army school is that armies must be brought together to determine a war. This theory is now obsolete and to tie an air force to an army means the virtual extinction of its efficiency and the proper theory of its operation.

A navy, on the other hand, is not in a period of arrested development. It is in a period of declining development. The coming of air power has made necessary a tremendous curtailment of its activities on the surface of the sea. The continued development of aircraft will drive it entirely below the surface and eventually aircraft, on account of their more economical application, may even supplant the submarine.

We are the only nation to-day that has not definitely provided in its scheme of national defense for an air force to defend its territory. We can get more out of it, dollar for dollar, than we can from either of the older services. We are better suited for developing air power than any other country: our people make the best pilots, we have the best industrial plants and an abundance of raw materials. So when we are asked the question—How can we best defend New York?—the correct answer is "Provide a United Air Force for the United States."

She Didn't Mean to Do It

Alexander Woollcott

The most talked-about book of the mid-1920's was "Gentlemen Prefer Blondes," by a petite brunette named Anita Loos. Talking about it here is Alexander Humphreys Woollcott—critic, essayist, actor, and raconteur. Woollcott came often to Collier's *pages as critic and reporter of the world of drama—a droll and sophisticated observer and participant in the passing parade, who played himself in George S. Kauffman and Moss Hart's* The Man Who Came to Dinner, *and died in 1943 of a heart attack suffered while making a radio broadcast.*

December 11, 1926

A YOUNG MAN FROM YALE WHO HAD frittered away his first youth underfoot on Broadway fled the country this past fall. His eyes were tired of the blinding Midway. His ears were tired of "Remember" and "Always" and wise cracks and the jargon of the stage alleys. Beyond telling, his throat was tired of bootleg gin.

He wanted to find some spot on the face of the earth beyond reach of the hurdy-gurdy sound of the carrousel called New York. He wanted to seek peace in some corner of the world that would have in it no sight or sound or smell, no faint reminding trace, of Broadway.

So he bought him a blanket and a canoe and on his arrival in Norway he started for the fiords that skirt its coast, planning to paddle lazily northward toward the Midnight Sun, pulling up to shore and sleeping wherever dusk overtook him.

Finally he reached a village so remote that he halted, for he felt that at last he had come to the end of the world and looked over the wall. Yet there, in a four-page local paper, sandwiched between the news of the preceding day's herring catch and the list of winning numbers in the national lottery, he saw the review of a book then undergoing, it seems, a tremendous boom in all the bookstalls and libraries of Norway, a book from America called "Herrer Liker Blonde Piker." And at that he gave up, for he knew enough of the language of the land to know that even there they were reading "Gentlemen Prefer Blondes."

With a gesture indicating "It's no use" he turned his canoe south. But he must have been grinning as he went. At least he was grinning when he wrote me about it from some café a few weeks later.

"At that," he added, "they have to prefer blondes in this country or spend a lot of quiet evenings at home with their fishing tackle."

Nor would this fugitive have had much better luck had he sought retreat in any other corner of Europe. For in that small, merciless diary of Lorelei Lee, the fair-haired and predatory damsel from Little Rock, the surprised Anita Loos finds she has written a piece of laughter as oblivious of frontiers as Mark Twain in his day found his little "Jumping Frog." Now each morning the groaning postman dumps on Miss Loos' gratified doorstep a small mound of clippings, folders, quotations, cartoons, from the other side of the Atlantic.

The English hubbub she had been comparatively prepared for. Long before her book lifted its rowdy head in the sedate London shops and all the bookstalls of the English cathedral towns, one character in its frivolous pages had betrayed a lively interest in it. That was the Prince of Wales. His interest, evinced first by making the old walls of St. James' shudder with his laughter, was then expressed in a more solid way by his ordering sixteen copies from the States for distribution among his friends. I imagine you could thereby arrive at a nice approximation of the number of blondes in the royal circle. Or at least of the number of blondes who can read. And I imagine, too, that His Royal Highness prefers these first copies to the subsequent English edition for which some timorous soul had slightly tempered the indecorous allusions to the prince and to his sainted mother.

All these preliminary rumblings had, I say, rather prepared Miss Loos for the ructions she caused by merely passing through London last summer. At that time the London papers met her at the train, saw her off, published her pictures, gave daily accounts of what she had for breakfast and altogether behaved precisely as if they were New York papers and she were a rather well-known queen.

But the adventures of the book in lands where even its own admittedly rough approximation to English is neither read nor spoken is more arresting. Imagine, for instance, spending a good quiet afternoon reading "I gentiluomini preferisconco le bionde." Or, for that matter, "Gentlemen foretroeker Blondiner." Or "Herren ziehen Blondinen vor." Or "Herrarna tycka bäst on blondiner." Or even "Pourquoi les messieurs préférent les blondes." I cannot follow the trail further, for it vanishes into thickets and wildernesses of language with an alphabet so different that it could not be reproduced by ordinary typography. Miss Loos herself has received copies of her unruly brain child which left her in some doubt as to whether she should try them over on her piano or merely take them to the nearest Chinese laundry and get a few shirts with them. I think she stopped reading the foreign mail when the press notices from Hungary arrived. The Hungarians have a quaint custom of printing the first name last. She found it faintly disquieting to come upon all the references to herself as Loos Anita.

Her folks, by the way, continue stubbornly to pronounce the name as though it were spelled Loce, in the fashion originally affected by her French forebears. For the first few years she herself attempted to insist on this pronunciation, but, as all of us afflicted with weirdly spelled or weirdly pronounced names eventually discover, it's not worth the battle. Her folks, I imagine, still writhe with distaste when now even she will pronounce it Loose, but in all such matters one saves a lot of time for eating, contract bridge and other agreeable activities by saying, in effect, to the world at large, "Have it your own way."

A few paragraphs ago I spoke of "Gentlemen Prefer Blondes" as the work of the "surprised" Anita Loos. Of course it is traditional for any author who has spent a year in the travail of writing a book to start with polite surprise at the fact that anyone expresses astonishment if anyone goes even further and actually buys a copy. The layman is likely to set all this down to attitudinizing, as routine and as meaningless as a bow in a minuet. But with many members in the fellowship of the ink-stained, the writing of a book is such a tearing out of one's own vitals that the word "Finis" seems the only good word in the whole work and the heap of manuscript is an object of profound distaste.

But the surprise which bowled over Anita Loos was something special. The first chapter of "Gentlemen Prefer Blondes" was something she wrote on a train to amuse herself, without the faintest intention of publishing it at all. All her life she had been writing for a living. Ever since she was thirteen she had been turning out scenarios and titles for moving pictures, working harder than she needed to, aiming, I suppose, at elegance for her declining years. She was pretty tired of it by this time, and here she was again pulling out of Chicago on the long, tedious trip across the plains and mountains to Hollywood.

But, after all, she still had three days of freedom. So, alone in her Pullman drawing-room, she put her feet up, planted a big yellow pad on her knees, wet her pencil and began to write—began to write that first chapter in the annals of Lorelei Lee, the dumb but passionately acquisitive young lady from Little Rock whose philosophy of life is summed up in her dictum that whereas "a kiss on the hand may make you feel very good, a sapphire bracelet lasts forever." It was the diary of a hussy, embarked upon as a recess from all the censored heroines who had been Anita Loos' lot in the movies. For the first time in her life she let her pencil travel over page after page without stopping to calculate whether those pages would sell or not.

The result is "Gentlemen Prefer Blondes," which has already earned her more of fame and more of fortune than all the work she did in all the fifteen years during which she wrote with one eye on her pad and the other on the public. I feel pretty sure there is a moral in this somewhere for all who work in any of the arts, or, for that matter, for anyone who takes his life in his two hands in an effort to make it more interesting than that of the corner grocer.

Back in New York some months later Miss Loos came upon the rumpled sheets of her manuscript in the bottom of the trunk. She found herself grinning as she glanced over it and, with a chuckle, stuck it in an envelope and sent it around to George Jean Nathan. That genial neighbor expressed the opinion that most magazine editors would turn pale at the thought of printing such a misdemeanor, but that it might appeal to Ray Long, the doughty lord of the Hearst publications. So he shipped it on over to Mr. Long, from whose sanctum shortly thereafter were heard eager cries of "More, more."

To Mr. Long, I think, must go the credit of much of the vast popular success of "Gentlemen Prefer Blondes." That success, of course, cannot be measured merely by the book sales. For by November 1st four companies of a play made from the book were going full tilt in sundry parts of this country, and a production in London was under way. Then the profits anticipated from its career in the movies stagger the imagination. It has also popped out as a comic strip and, with Irving Berlin's tune, it has been reincarnated as a ballad for the music halls. Indeed, Miss Loos' wily, busy managers have done everything with it except make it into a breakfast food.

A good deal of this success is due to the title. A name so arresting, so provocative as "Gentlemen Prefer Blondes" has tremendous suction, and every once in a while someone stumbles upon a title for a song or a book or a play which even breaks loose from its moorings and goes careering around the world on a life of its own. Thus the phrase "Gentlemen Prefer Blondes" is familiarly and waggishly used to-day by countless old ladies and gentlemen who have never read the book, who never will read the book and who would be both shocked and puzzled if they did read the book.

And, oddly enough, it was not Miss Loos' title at all. She had called her piece "Fate Keeps on Happening." The title which supplemented it was in the making when she had her first reply from the editor. His note ran thus:

August twenty-seventh
1924

Dear Anita:

There's delicious humor in your story. I'd like to use it in "Harper's Bazaar," and I think you could follow it with at least one more of her adventures abroad.

The title isn't good. How would you like "A Protégée of Mr. Eisman" or "Gentlemen Always Remember Blondes"?

Sincerely,
RAY LONG.

Now after nearly three years the tide of that unpremeditated success is still at flow. Probably the book has left the world about as it found it. Perhaps a few of the Mr. Eismans have since proved more difficult to handle. Certainly the percentage of blond heads visible in theatre audiences has increased.

Yet in that manner it is worthy of note that it took a decided brunette to write the story and that, after vainly trying at least thirty golden-haired actresses in the leading role, the manager of the production on Broadway was driven to buy a wig the color of canned corn and place it on June Walker, who, in her own right, is about as blond as a ton of coal.

One-Eye Connelly

John B. Kennedy

Among the legion of accomplished and famous Americans who never found their way into Who's Who *stands James Connelly of Lowell, Massachusetts. Here, in what the editors of* Collier's *describe as "the only authoritative story of his life," reporter John B. Kennedy gives "One-Eye" Connelly his due, revealing that consummate skill, ingenuity, and brass built the warranted fame and title of the world's foremost gate crasher.*

November 26, 1927

"BY ORDER OF 'IS MAJESTY'S 'OME OFFICE the person known as 'One-Eye' Connelly is refused admittance to the British Isles."

With these fateful words a runty British immigration officer placed two large policemen aboard the Scythia. Their orders were to see to it that Mr. James Connelly of Lowell, Mass., got no nearer Liverpool than the seagoing end of the gangplank.

So, for the first time in a career of thirty years, the world's champion gate crasher came face to face with an uncrashable gate. Connelly had crossed the sea to be an eye-witness (with one-eye) of a world's championship fight—a non-paying eye-witness, as he has always been. He had seen every battle worthy of the name since John L. Sullivan reigned and seen them as an uninvited guest of the promoters. But Merrie England was in no merry mood when One-Eye arrived.

Sadly but hopefully he returned to wipe the blot from his escutcheon. Within twenty-four hours after being released from the Scythia in New York he was at the ring side for the Dempsey-Sharkey bout, disguised as a program vender.

One-Eye Connelly started life as a bare-handed gladiator, taking to fisticuffs as a primitive means of self-preservation when, as an orphaned newsboy, he tried to protect his wares from ruthless Boston bullies. Then, bantamweight champion of New England, he became a knight errant.

He was seventeen. Feeling the lure of the West, he started out for the California golconda, where a chap could fight in public without anybody being particularly eager to stop him save the fellow in the opposite corner.

He worked his way to Wisconsin, eyes whole and fancy free. Green Bay sports matched him against a lad named Jack Redmond. During the scuffle, in an oil-lit cowshed, Connelly's glove laces became undone. The referee was no stickler for ring etiquette. He let the bout proceed. Blocking a right cross, the metal tip of a lace struck the pupil of Connelly's eye. He continued, won his fight, and collected $20.

He might better have invested the prize money in a visit to an oculist instead of a tailor. While the eye caused no immediate trouble, it smarted. A week later the sight left it and the functionless lid closed down permanently. Thus, with only one good eye, Connelly set out on the career that has made him a real-life gag man whose name, while not a household word, has a flavor of the fun of life and far-going.

"I was a natural 120-pounder when I started," says he in a voice intended by nature for better things than the rasping tones of one who must get everywhere by his wits. "That made it easy to ride the thirteen-inch space on the rods of day coaches." Today he's nearer 200 pounds, yet he still rides the rods. "Aw," he explains, "you can squeeze yer stomach 'most any size when you have to."

Beating the railroad detectives and breaking long journeys by tarrying in hobo jungles (where the food is good if the language is rough) gave One-Eye Connelly a slant on society that might easily have made of him an outcast, a guerrilla evil-doer. But he had the good fortune to be blessed by an urge to enterprise—an urge which may not have made him useful, as we know that word, but which at least made him picturesque and unique.

The most money he ever had at one time was $1,400. This he made by brisk trade as a news dealer during the closing weeks of the war. The industry and shrewdness which enabled him to roll up that little fortune in a short period should, if sustained, have taken Mr. Connelly into the ranks of paying guests. The gate-crashing laurels seemed destined for some other brow. But One-Eye fell in love—with a red-headed lady. He dreamed of a three-room nest, furnished on the catch-as-catch-can basis—so he calls the installment plan.

But that dream was vain. One-Eye comes as near to sentimental display as he ever will when this sad episode slides across his memory. It's best forgotten by him, to whom it means much, and by us, to whom it means much less. Perhaps from that bloodless tragedy One-Eye's other record as the world's most continuous smoker originates.

Ever since that disappointment Mr. Connelly has been wary of dreams of a settled life. And he has gone through the years as he started: a wanderer dependent not so much upon the way or the weather as on the whereabouts of the next world-championship bout.

"I've seen the world's heavyweight title change hands seven times," says One-Eye. "And that's just one title. All told, I figure I've crashed my way into more than a hundred championship fights during the past forty years. Scores and scores of other big bouts I've been to, but I measure my history by heavyweight championship fights. Theatres, horse races, tennis and golf championships I don't count as much. They're easy. When the boys are paying $20 to $200 for ring-side seats is the time technique is necessary to crash a gate."

His first actual gate crashing was at Churchill Downs for the Kentucky Derby. The gates there, he says, have always been easy to glide through. "I use the system there now that I've used all these years, and I've never missed a Derby. Up I go to the mid-section gate during the rush, fumbling and feeling for a ticket while holding up a big crowd behind. The gatekeeper gets rattled as I keep on fumbling. Finally he pushes me aside, and in the onrush of impatient ticket holders I slip through. If this racket doesn't work at the mid-section gate, I try some other. I've never failed."

Fight gates, however, have been his enduring fascination. Disabled and disfigured in the ring, the lure of it gripped him early. Like a rejected lover, he has clung to the thrills of illusion. He sees himself in the winning mauler of every fight and wraps to his soul the solace that, if he isn't in the ring, at least he has never paid a nickel to sit or stand beside it.

New Orleans and the Corbett-Sullivan fight marked his baptism as a big league-fight gate cheater. Attempting to wheedle his way through the gate at the beginning of that festival of fights, when five world's championships were challenged and defended in the same week, an Irishman larger than Sullivan tossed him out. He employed strategy.

An hour before the Sullivan-Corbett fight he dashed up to the gate, cap peak jerked down over his blank eye. He proclaimed he had a message for Mr. Sullivan from his brother in New Orleans. The gatekeeper, awed, instructed an usher to take him to Sullivan's dressing-room.

Connelly tried to duck the usher, but found him resolute. A bellow came from an end room. Trembling, Connelly was thrust into the presence of the world's champion.

"What is it, son?" boomed John L. He sat, Connelly recalls, like a huge bear amid a crowd of sycophant jackals.

"This guy's got a message from your brother in town here," said the usher.

Connelly threw everything into a wink. Sullivan saw it—and winked back.

"Leave him stay," he bade the usher.

After the fight Connelly had no difficulty getting back to the dressing-room. The corridors were not lined with thick-eared gents. The thick-eared ones were crowding into Corbett's quarters, leaving Sullivan with a few faithful handlers to swallow the dregs of defeat.

One-Eye heard the fallen idol groaning and bellowing. Intending to thank John L. for favors received, he peeped timidly inside the doorway. Something heavy smacked and broke against the jamb. One-Eye did not stop to inquire.

Later, years later, he met John L. Sullivan again at the Jeffries-Johnson fight in Reno. Sullivan, jowled and paunchy, had a better memory than most of the gate tenders Connelly encounters. He remembered One-Eye.

"How's my brother in New Orleans?" John L. roared at him. Connelly proposed to John L. that, since he had made it possible for One-Eye to crash his first heavyweight championship gate, he repeat the courtesy.

"The guy who walks in behind you gets in free," One-Eye argued.

Sullivan, then demonstrating to an amazed country that whisky had ruined his prowess but not his geniality, let One-Eye be his valet. So Connelly once more saw the heavyweight title change hands.

He saw Fitzsimmons knock out Jim Corbett at Carson City. First he tried to attach himself to Fitzsimmons' camp. But Ruby Robert would have none of it. "One-Eye blighters are bloomin' 'oodoos," he declared. Connelly crashed that gate by picking on a dumb-looking ticket taker and posing as an overseer.

When Jeffries beat Fitzsimmons at Coney Island in 1906, One-Eye was there, sporting through on a phony deputy sheriff's badge. That was comparatively easy. Word had gone the rounds that a sheriff's raid might be expected if the fight grew brutal. Connelly breezed up to the head ticket taker and claimed he was sent from the sheriff's office to spot fakers posing as deputies. That sounded reasonable to the head ticket taker. One-Eye saw the fight.

The prospect of real adventure came when Jack Johnson and Tommy Burns were matched in Sydney, Australia.

One-Eye beat his way to Vancouver, but was compelled to part with all his savings for a steamer ride to Australia. Landing there on a sizzling hot day in December, he had just five hours to make the arena. And he didn't know a soul. Furthermore, nobody wanted to know him. Try as he would to rub up a quick acquaintance in the cool bars of Sydney, the sports failed to respond. One-Eye got the cold eye.

Despairing, with the fight an hour off, he had about decided to plunk down a golden sovereign for a seat when, milling with the crowds, he observed a stout fireman lay down his helmet to attach a riot hose to a hydrant. One-Eye borrowed the helmet—a heavy brass affair—donned it and was inside the arena before the fireman had finished his chores.

To get from Sydney, Australia, to San Francisco without fare or credentials is no easy matter. In one of Sydney's principal theatres (which he crashed), at a performance given for the benefit of a visiting English cricket team, One-Eye bawled derision while the band played "God Save the King."

Imagine a parallel insult hereabouts. The Australian police calmly haled One-Eye before the magistrates, where he proclaimed himself an American communist —and he was deported!

The six-year period between Reno, where Johnson won his title from the aging Jeffries, and Havana, where Johnson lost his title to the Kansas Colossus, Jess Willard, One-Eye Connelly filled in by practicing at minor gates barring the way to lighter championships.

To see Johnson and Willard in Cuba, he beat his way to Key West and across the straits to Havana. He crashed the fight by dolling up as a horse groom sent to watch a shipment of "platers" due at the race track where the fight was held.

"I saw Willard and Moran fight in the Garden, the poorest heavyweight show I've ever seen," he says. "I got in that one by climbing a water spout and letting myself through the garden roof.

"Toledo was frightfully hot when Willard and Dempsey fought there. I remember a fellow with refreshment rights built lemonade tanks for the mobs at the different entrances. Early in the morning Battling Nelson, who had camped inside the arena, woke up and saw one of these tanks. Figuring they were there for the hands to bathe in, he took a dip—in lemonade. They chased him out of the tub, but they didn't throw out that lemonade.

"I made that gate by walking right through. It's the only time in my life that ever happened to me."

Connelly made himself known to the new champion, Mr. Dempsey, and so was on hand when Dempsey defended his title for the first time at Benton Harbor, Mich., against ill-fated Billy Miske. One-Eye secured an easy assignment as aide to a celebrated writer hired by a large syndicate. Thus he saw the fight without paying for it.

Came the "Battle of the Century" between Dempsey and Carpentier at Boyle's

Acres in Jersey City. One-Eye made a tactical blunder by announcing to the press that he would crash this gate. Other crashers, of local but not national celebrity, like Tammany Young, were less vocal. But Rickard, angry, gave strict orders to throw out all the crashers and to keep a special eye out for One-Eye.

A dozen or so honest burghers suffering ocular afflictions were tossed from various gates, even though they held tickets. One-Eye was fired out thirteen times before he resorted to disguise by purchasing a telegraph boy's hat for $1. From the cheap section he threw his hat to the $10 seats and asked an usher's permission to get it. The usher made no objection.

One-Eye then threw his cap all the way down to the ring side until he finally landed beside his old friend Hype Igoe of the World, and acted as his copy bearer.

For the Dempsey-Gibbons scrap in Shelby, Mont., he crashed the gate by buying eighty pounds of ice and stalking in with the berg on his shoulder to supply ice water for the press.

The Dempsey-Firpo championship fight, some time later called for greater ingenuity. He found a discarded trunk up an alley. The trunk was presentable. He rang the fight park, said Madison Square Garden was calling and that a man would be up presently with a fresh supply of general admission tickets in a trunk.

He got the trunk to the fight park and marched through without difficulty.

For the Tunney-Gibbons fight One-Eye resorted to his most elaborate trick. From a given street junction he telephoned a hospital for an ambulance, warning that police lines interfered with easy access to the fight park. He met the ambulance, told the interne riding it that he'd pull out the injured man through the jam of people by the gates if the interne would wait with a stretcher. The interne agreed, and lent One-Eye his hospital hat and white jacket to expedite matters. These were gratefully tossed over the wall while One-Eye hopped down to the ring side.

Now, these exploits may seem fanciful; but I have seen Connelly in action. Over in Jersey City one night when Benny Leonard was to fight Soldier Bartfield, One-Eye broke his way into an armory when Leonard himself couldn't get through. Connelly faced the swarming fight fans and in his bull voice bawled, "Show your tickets, please!" A credulous ticket taker, accepting One-Eye as one of the emergency officials of the armory, let him in.

At the Dempsey-Tunney fight in Philadelphia he was kept out for hours.

Facing the ruin of his record, One-Eye scanned the heavens, and a rain drop struck him. He breezed through with an armful of umbrellas and the cry "Cover for the Press" just before the main go. The passing of the title found him sheltering type-thumping reporters at the edge of the ring.

So much for One-Eye, the fight fan.

When Florenz Ziegfeld put on Patricia Salmon of Shelby at the Midnight Frolic, One-Eye, curious to see the girl, crashed the theatre gate arrayed as a cowboy. The suit cost him $1 for an evening's hire and he was taken for a member of Patricia's escort. He has broken into six Broadway first nights in a row.

As a carpenter, a plumber's helper, any legitimate guise that is not a disguise, One-Eye has burst upon countless scenes. Pennsylvania was playing Illinois when Red Grange was at the height of his fame. Grange met One-Eye and offered him a ticket. One-Eye said he'd prefer to beat the gate.

While thousands fought for admittance a man in overalls with a pail of whitewash appeared outside the gates and calmly painted parking lines on the street. The work finished, he strolled to a ticket taker. "Where else do I mark?" he demanded. "Ask the boss," said the taker. "Where's he?" "Inside!"

Grange gave One-Eye an engraved signet ring in recognition of that performance. This One-Eye cherishes with the nickel which John D. Rockefeller, Sr., bestowed upon him once for a newspaper in Cincinnati before the Oil King had reached a state of fortune where he could afford dimes. One-Eye wears the nickel in a gold case for a lucky piece on his impressive watch chain.

"They've got to know me now at the small boxing clubs and the baseball clubs," says Connelly. "John McGraw, when the Giants are in a series, leaves orders for them to let me by without a ticket. I like a comfortable entrance, without having to work my way through. But tickets I can't accept."

A strange ambition, my masters; but one fulfilled. A one-eyed man, a sauntering Cyclops, who sticks his blind eye to the telescope of life and finds victory in small escape—even at peril of ten days for vagrancy between sport spectacles.

Verily it takes all sorts to make a world.

On Earth, Good Will

John B. Kennedy

The beginning of this story of a freed convict bent on vengeance is familiar enough; the ending is not.

December 29, 1928

IN A BLEAK OFFICE THAT LOOKED OUT ON a walled-in patch of soiled snow the warden gave Jarvis his farewell.

"You should be grateful to the governor, Jarvis, for commuting sentence," he said gravely. "Here's the ten dollars you get from the state. And I'm giving you fifteen dollars from the released prisoners' fund to help tide you over the holidays."

Jarvis checked a sneer. The warden was decent enough: in nine years Jarvis had never heard of him being unfair in rows between inmates, trusties and guards. Jarvis took the money.

He boarded a train at the depot. In a packed day coach he found a seat beside a dozing old man. Packages in colored paper were piled high on racks and laps. Sprigs of imitation holly and bright red ribbon stuck out everywhere.

To Jarvis, steady movement seemed unreal. It distracted him, for a while, from a plan—a plan that had become an obsession in nine years of brooding. But presently he settled into a grim concentration on his plan. It was a simple one. He was going to kill, as quickly as possible, the man who had sent him to prison.

Memory flashed back to the picture of that man. Jarvis standing between two policemen. The round, comfortable face of his judge. Gray eyes beaming through heavy lenses as he said:

". . . Congratulate yourself on being found guilty of manslaughter. The prosecutor has been kind. I sentence you to not less than twelve years and six months at hard labor in state's prison and to not more than fifteen years."

His attorney had told Jarvis that five years would be the limit. The judge couldn't go lower than that. And he wouldn't go higher. The man Jarvis had killed in a drunken row was a bad egg, with a record—a gyp gambler; and Jarvis had dependents—a wife and child.

Yet the judge's gray eyes had blinked genially—as if in sentencing Jarvis to twelve years and six months in prison—all of a man's life worth living at Jarvis' age—he was being merciful.

"The fat devil," Jarvis had muttered. "I'll square this some day!"

And he had muttered the threat ten thousand times in agonies of cell-dreams. He knew, in his heart, that the killing had been self-defense, really. He and the man he killed had been partners in the racket—

a poolroom dive. He had merely outguessed a harder crook. He didn't deserve a severe sentence.

Nine bitter years of filtering through memory the details of his case had brought a fury of oppressed innocence. His wife had died the fifth year. The warden had been willing to let him go to her; but an election campaign was in full blast and the governor had no time for pleas from prisoners. The court had committed Jarvis' fourteen-year-old daughter to a home. The same judge who had sent him up for the best years of his life. A spasm of hate trembled through his head as the train rolled on.

He left the coach and worked his way uncertainly through clamorous traffic. In glaring lights he bumped into laden passers-by who smiled at his savage mutterings. Cold slush bit through his shoes and he tripped on ice-coated crossings.

Fumbling down a dark side-street he found the place he sought. After an argument he emerged with an automatic in his pocket.

He walked north to the suburbs. The judge's house was there. Holiday-buyers packed the stores. Hooting cars slid along. The town was alive and bright with fevered shopping.

A dog bayed as he walked resolutely up a lawn-path to a home set in naked pines whose bare trunks lifted like broken swords. Shivering, he tugged at a bell. A sharp voice told him the judge was at his office.

The judge sat alone in a large, gloomy office bordered with law-books. He was bent over a desk. Jarvis could have shot him instantly. That would not have satisfied Jarvis. He wanted to see terror stare from the gray eyes in the pudgy face. As he looked at the bent white head, changing the picture he had long carried of an iron-gray bush of hair above glinting glasses, the judge spoke without turning.

"You're early, Frank," he said.

The voice was deep and gentle—not the probing blade Jarvis remembered.

"This isn't Frank!" Jarvis grated the words through set teeth.

The judge looked up. For only a moment he was startled. A flash of recognition lighted his gaze.

"Your name's Jarvis," he said. "What can I do for you?"

In a pocket Jarvis' fingers clutched the gun. A stream of profanity crossed his quivering lips.

"Stop that, Jarvis!" the judge commanded.

"You're on no bench now," Jarvis sneered. "I'm top dog, and, by God, you'll know it!"

He stepped toward the desk. The judge's hand fell on a black-bound notebook.

"Leave that be," bade Jarvis.

The judge sat back in his chair, coolly facing the ex-convict.

"Curious," he said, as though addressing others besides Jarvis, "I'd just written something there under your name. The governor granted your pardon, Jarvis. There are others. I wonder if they bear me malice?"

"It isn't me," growled Jarvis. "You're going to pay for my wife, and my youngster. Where is she?"

"Jarvis," said the judge, "I've had you in mind more often than you think. I asked the governor to parole you. I always do when a man I've sentenced has been up long enough. Your daughter—"

Jarvis jerked his hand from his pocket. Voices sounded behind him. A man stamped into the room.

"All right, Judge," he called cheerily. "All set."

The visitor was big and breezy with strength. He stared suspiciously at the ex-convict.

"We'll take this man with us, Frank," said the judge to the newcomer.

The judge passed his coat to Jarvis to hold. Then they went out and got into a car.

The car was heaped high with packages. The judge and Jarvis sat behind. They sped through business section and suburbs into open country, headlights banking the snow, chains sputtering.

Jarvis shivered. The judge, pushing a laprobe toward him, touched the cold hand that had gripped a gun. The ex-convict turned away, focused his stare through a curtain. He would wait, come back with the judge—plead for a private talk.

In a low voice the judge spoke:

"I've been thinking of you, Jarvis. You mustn't be spiteful and mean. You'll have a chance for a fresh start. But not with your daughter."

Jarvis whipped his head around. His hand thrust into his pocket.

"What's that?" he snapped.

"You sit still," the judge said.

A building loomed before them. The judge bade Jarvis help the others with the packages. Arms laden, the party walked up a long path. A door was opened. Through heated corridors they followed a smiling nun. The place smelled uncomfortably clean, like a hospital. Upstairs, one flight, two flights. Then in a brightly lit room they deposited their burdens. Jarvis stood with tight lips as other sisters entered.

Quietly the judge tapped his arm. Led by the sister who had first greeted them, he and the judge climbed to another floor. A dim light burned in a long dormitory. It was above a desk at which sat a sister, reading—while on either side, in rows of cots, children slumbered.

As Jarvis backed out his shoulder touched a green wreath hung over the threshold. The nun disappeared in the room below while Jarvis purposely delayed. He faced the judge.

"Where's my kid?" he blurted. "Where is she?"

"Upstairs," said the judge softly.

Jarvis wrenched away. The judge caught his wrist.

"Let me go," growled Jarvis. "Stick her in a pauper's dump, eh? By God!"

The judge tightened his grip.

"Just a minute, Jarvis," he warned. "Your daughter's in that dormitory, but not in bed. She's the sister on duty."

Jarvis brought up sharply. The judge's hand went to his shoulder.

"Think it over—before you want to tell her," he said.

Side by side they walked out of the place. The judge stopped by the car.

He produced cigars, passed one to Jarvis. As they lit them the judge hailed Frank, who was behind them:

"Frank, this is the fellow I spoke to you about for that job at the power plant."

Jarvis shook hands, first, with the judge. On the ride back something dropped with a clatter on the road. Only Jarvis heard it.

After Three Years

Dana Burnet

"Tell her for me that life is beautiful, Tommy. Not the things that go to adorn life, but life itself . . . Just to live, and be in love." But Tommy didn't tell her . . .

March 23, 1929

"HELLO! IS THIS—? HELLO! I WANT TO speak to Mr. Thomas Clarke. Oh! . . . Hello . . . Tommy! This is Angela. What? You do! You recognize my voice? After three years! My dear Tommy—! Oh, hello, hello! You're not going to ring off, are you? Tommy! I must speak to you, I've simply got to! . . .

"Tommy, listen. I saw the announcement of your engagement in the paper this morning. . . . Yes, in the society column. Yes, I still do—religiously! Remember how you used to say it was the only part of the paper I ever really read? What? You can? You can still see me sitting up in bed reading the society column?

"I suppose it's just habit, but I always turn first to the social news. . . . And there I saw the paragraph announcing your engagement to Miss Delafield. Is she pretty, Tommy? She is? Well. . . . Just how pretty would you say she was? Prettier than I am? What? No, of course you wouldn't say. . . . You always were gallant, Tommy, even when you were so annoyed with me you wanted to choke me. . . . And naturally you've forgotten how I look.

"You haven't? You say you what? You *saw* me? Oh, a taxicab!

"How perfectly extraordinary! And I'd only just arrived in New York! I got in two days ago from California.

"You say I haven't changed? No, I haven't, on the outside. I look just the same, I really do. But *inside* I've changed a good deal. Yes, I have. . . . Why, I was, too! I was as silly as a peacock, and just about as vain. I'm not vain any more. I'm . . . rather humble, Tommy. Humility, as a rule, comes with misfortune, doesn't it? At least that's what they say. . . . Mine came with good fortune. I'm rich, Tommy. I've got everything I ever wanted, except . . . one or two things. How did I do it? I'll tell you.

"Oh, but before I go on I want to congratulate you on your engagement. That's why I called you up. I do hope you'll be happy, Tommy. You deserve to be. I wish you all the happiness in the world. I really do!

"Well, let's see. . . . You remember I

was going to marry Dick Holt? Yes, naturally you remember, since I divorced you to marry him. But I didn't marry him, Tommy. What? You knew that? Am I what? No, I'm not married now. I've never married anyone in my life but you, Tommy. And what a mess I made of that!

"No, it wasn't partly your fault. The whole trouble was that I was so silly and selfish and so frightfully demanding. . . . All right, I'll stop. Only don't ring off, will you, darl—?

"Where was I? Oh, about Dick. Yes— Well—you see, I was going to join him in Rio and we were to be married there. I had my passage engaged. I was all packed up ready to sail. Yes, from New York. Then one morning I was reading the paper, and I saw an item about some motor stock that a big banking firm was trying to buy. The paper said this stock had been practically worthless for years, but that it had suddenly become valuable because this banking firm needed it to get control of another company they wanted to buy.

"The name of the stock struck me as rather familiar. It was Sprague Motors. Yes, Sprague Motors! Yes, yes, I did! I had a lot of it! I had a whole bundle of it, tied with a pink ribbon, in a drawer in my trunk.

"How did I get it? Uncle William left it to me in his will. A lawyer told me it was worth about ten cents a gross in Confederate money.

"So there I was, in my room at the hotel, reading about the boom in Sprague Motors. . . . What? I should say I was excited. I jumped up and ran to my trunk and got out my bundle of securities, and sure enough it was all Sprague stock.

"Well, I dressed as fast as I could, and went to a broker I knew. He almost fainted. He said: 'It's a lucky thing for you I'm an honest man! I could buy you out at the market and make a fortune reselling this stock to the syndicate that's after it!'

"Tommy! I got almost a quarter of a million dollars for that stock. I couldn't believe it for days. And then I realized the truth about my feeling for Dick. I'd never really faced it before. He was rich and attractive and he'd offered me the kind of life I'd always wanted, and I'd accepted him without thinking twice about it.

"Well, since I had plenty of money of my own I found that Dick had lost all his glamour. So the day before I was to sail I canceled my passage and telegraphed him I'd changed my mind. I went to France that year. I'm on my way to France now, Tommy.

"Yes, I'm sailing tomorrow. Tomorrow at noon. I've a suite de luxe on the Majestic, Tommy . . . I shall curl up in it like a contented cat, and dream my way across the ocean.

"What will I dream about? I don't know . . . Maybe—a little—about your wedding. I should like to see you married, Tommy. . . .

"What! Am I crying? Why, of course not! Why should I cry? I told you I was perfectly contented with my life. I live a beautiful life, Tommy, I really do. . . .

"And what about your life, my dear? You've been successful, haven't you, these past three years? And you're happy, aren't you? What? You're the happiest man in the world? Oh, Tommy, I—I'm so glad. I'm so very, very glad!

"Will you tell the girl you're going to marry that I wish her every happiness, too? Tell her for me that life is beautiful, Tommy. Not the things that go to adorn life, but life itself. . . . Just to live, and be in love. . . . To eat and sleep and work and laugh and play with someone you love. . . .

"I am *not* crying! I'm not, I'm not! But *I've* said all I have to say to you, except good-by, and I'll say that now. Good-by, Tommy! God bless you! Good by, dear! Good-by!

"Good-by, Tommy!"

The following day, about two o'clock, a man and a woman met on the promenade deck of the Majestic as she steamed out of the Narrows on her way to Europe.

"Hello, Angela!" said the man.

"Tommy!" said the woman. She put her hand to her breast. Her slender body swayed toward him. He put out his hand to steady her. "Tommy!" she said again, faintly.

"It's all right, Angela! It's all right! It's . . ."

"But, Tommy!" she cried. "What are you doing on this boat?"

"I'm going to Europe—with you."

"With me? But you—! What about your fiancée?"

"I haven't any fiancée. I put that notice in the paper myself."

"You put that—? You mean the notice of your engagement? But—oh, Tommy! But why?"

"Because," said the man, smiling, "I didn't know how else to get hold of you. I knew you were in New York because I saw you. But I had no idea where you were staying. Then I remembered that you always read the society columns in the newspapers. I telephoned the fake news of my engagement to every paper in town, feeling sure you'd read it and call me up. And you did!"

"Tommy!" said the woman called Angela. "Tommy, Tommy, Tommy, Tommy—!"

"Angela!" said the man called Tommy.

The End of the Story

J. P. Marquand

The deft irony so familiar in Marquand's later novels (H. M. Pulham, Esq., So Little Time, *etc.*) *is visible in this story of a mud-encrusted sword.*

April 6, 1929

PERHAPS THE MOST REMARKABLE THING about it all was that Mr. Grimm was always amused by the incident. He was as literal as that. He could not see that nationalities never think the same.

The house of the Orviedos was a fine old house; the roar and hum of modern Havana scarcely penetrated its three-foot walls. Señor Mercurio of Orviedo was proud of it, and proud of himself, though he was very fat and his mustache was unkempt and white. He pointed the cigar he was holding in his plump old fingers toward a rusty weapon on the wall.

"You were a connoisseur in weapons, Mr. Grimm," said he, "not so? What do you think of that sword?"

Mr. Grimm snapped his glasses on his nose, as became a retired business man with a hobby.

"Not much," he said; "the hilt's all covered with coral mud. It's a Spanish rapier of the early 17th century."

Señor Orviedo smiled tolerantly and twisted the end of his mustache.

"You have, sir," he said, "quite evidently an eye. It's not much of a sword, you say. Ah, hardly a decoration for the wall of a gentleman's salon. A rusty, dirty rapier, but the coral mud on the hilt is the mud from the grave of a very honorable gentleman, who died rather than sell his honor.

"We are an old family, sir; we've many things of which to be proud. That sword, sir, is a symbol of our house. It is the sword of young Don Pedro of Orviedo, who sailed for the New World in 1615, heading the military guard of the ship, Donna Maria, which was carrying as passengers men and women of the Holy Church. Shall I tell you his story?"

"Yes," said Mr. Grimm, "but before you go ahead, get the boy to bring me another brandy, will you?"

Señor Orviedo's face glowed with a kindly light. "Drink it," he said. "It will make your blood run the warmer in sympathy with a brave man's story. Now Don Pedro, sir, was a wild young man but handsome. Our house, I fear, has been full of wild blood. He loved a lady far above him, very indiscreetly; that was why he was sent from Spain. Her picture was in a locket hung about his neck with a gold, jewelled chain, as the church story goes, when Don Pedro set sail. He was bitter on the voyage—diced and blasphemed quite shockingly. Yet, as you shall see, he had the high spirit of religion in him, such as burned in the breasts of the great conquistadores. They glimpsed it when the pirates passed the bulwarks."

"Pirates, is it?" said Mr. Grimm.

"Ah, you smile?" said Señor Orviedo. "But there were pirates then, believe me. It was the Frenchman, L'Ollinais. Don Pedro did his best with only twenty soldiers in the guard. The twenty were killed like sheep as they ran upon the deck. But not Don Pedro. He was a wild young man but—how do you say?—neat with the sword—and he knew that he must die for the honor of his house. They ran about him, but they could not get through his guard.

"He must have been magnificent. He was in a doublet of velvet, the record says, and that heavy gold chain was about his neck and his sword bright red. They drove him to the bulwarks. He was the last man fighting but they could not knock him down. Ah, sir, you are an Anglo-Saxon; cool, devoid of what we call the sentiment. But L'Ollinais—he was a Latin, thanks to Heaven! He had sentiment to pay tribute to a brave man about to die; and the ship was his, entirely his own.

" 'Don't kill him,' he said, 'he's a brave man. Who are you, if you please?'

"The story is that Don Pedro laughed. 'What affair is it of yours?' he said.

" 'Do you desire your life?' said L'Ollinais and Don Pedro only laughed again because, you understand, he was a very brave young man, and burning with a zeal to die like a brave son of his house, since he could no longer defend the holy servants of the Mother Church.

" 'Ah,' said L'Ollinais, 'that is beautiful sentiment.' He was a Latin, you understand. 'Give us that gold chain, boy. We'll call the bargain square.'

"It was the gold chain with the picture in it of that noble lady, you comprehend. Now there was a temptation, sir. What would you have done? What would I have done under the circumstances? I trust—what Don Pedro did."

"Well," said Mr. Grimm, "what did he do?"

Señor Orviedo waved a heavy arm. "He threw that chain and the picture into the sea," he said. "Just like that, he threw it. 'But here's my sword,' he said, and he waved it close under the nose of this man, L'Ollinais, because, you comprehend, he was about to die and wished to die with the fine gesture of a gentleman."

"Waved it under his nose?"

"Beneath his nose," said Señor Orviedo, "just like that."

" 'Take it! Take it!' he said, and laughed in the fellow's face. You are of cold blood, sir. You must understand the beautiful effrontery of it, the delicacy of waving the sword beneath the nose of a man about to kill you. You may not understand the refinement of the insult but L'Ollinais understood. He did not answer but pulled a dirk from his belt and threw it quickly. So! Clean into Don Pedro's chest. Don Pedro died, sir, as a great gentleman should, with his sword in his hand."

Señor Orviedo pointed to the wall.

"There it is, sir," he said, "a rusty bit of iron but very precious. It was buried with Don Pedro but, when his bones were moved to the church aisle, the sword was given his family. It may be a small anecdote, badly told, but there is the sword of a very honorable gentleman of Spain, who would not buy his life. Do you wonder we are very proud of his memory?"

Mr. Grimm was interested. "May I have it in my hand?" he said.

"Ah, sir," said Señor Orviedo, "you are a realist—you have to touch." He unhooked the sword from the wall and handed it to Mr. Grimm. "A bit of rusty iron," said Mr. Orviedo, "but the sword of a brave man. Eh? Eh? What are you making—?"

He had a right to ask. Mr. Grimm's face was alight with a violent interest. With a penknife he was scratching at the mud-encrusted hilt.

"Great Scott!" he cried suddenly. "There's something in that yarn!"

"Sir!" Señor Orviedo's face grew purple.

"A piece of iron, is it?" cried Mr. Grimm. "Haven't you ever looked at the thing before? That hilt is jeweled, gold work. By Gad, Cellini might have made it. I will give you five thousand dollars for it without giving another scratch, Mr. Orviedo."

"Mother of Heaven!" Señor Orviedo's voice was very faint. "Will you spoil a beautiful story with talk of money, like all your race? Mother of Heaven, why did I hand you that?" And Señor Orviedo plucked the relic from the hand of Mr. Grimm, as he might have retrieved a glove from the gutter.

"Nonsense!" muttered Mr. Grimm. "But if that's how you feel, I'm sorry."

Señor Orviedo glared at Mr. Grimm. "You are sorry! Sorry!" He fingered tenderly the sword of Don Pedro. "Bah!" he sighed. "No sentiment, no feeling, none of that delicacy which goes to make—" He blinked rapidly. "Let us discuss," he said, "the possibility of a somewhat more generous offer." And with his finger nail he began to chip the coral mud from the hilt of the venerable blade.

The Four Horsemen

Knute K. Rockne

It takes talent, luck, and hard work—each in generous degree—to achieve the greatness won by the University of Notre Dame's famous backfield, the Four Horsemen, and all of these are assessed in this article. That it also takes the genius and inspiration of a great coach is not mentioned by the author, and that was characteristic of the man who was the greatest of them all. Knute Kenneth Rockne, born in Voss, Norway, came to the United States at the age of eleven, entered Notre Dame as a student at twenty-two, became a chemistry instructor and assistant football coach, was made head coach in 1918, and died in an airplane crash in Kansas in 1931. His teams won 105 games, tied 5, and lost 12.

November 1, 1930

A SLEEPY-EYED LAD, WHO LOOKED AS though he were built to be a tester in an alarm-clock factory, loafed about backfield in the Notre Dame freshman line-up for practice. With him in the backfield, his companion halfback, was a youngster who appeared to be half puzzled by everything going on. Between them was a smaller and wirier boy with a sharp, handsome face and a clear, commanding voice. These assets seemed the best the youngster had, for in his first plays during that practice game he made as many mistakes as he called signals—and he called a lot. As a rule, rookie quarterbacks do.

It was not an inspiring practice to watch. Even the likely-looking youngster at fullback, who could run like a streak, ran quite as often into the hands of tackles as through slits in the line. After watching this backfield performance for an entire quarter, I shook my head.

"Not so hot," I thought—especially when the entire four were smeared by a clumsy but willing scrub tackle who weighed about as much as the entire quartet and pounded through like an ice wagon to block a kick.

"Not so hot," I repeated, preparing to exercise the virtue of patience and wait optimistically for the season's developments. This freshman bunch could be whipped into a combination of average players. Not much more.

That was all the dream I had of them that day. And it didn't come true.

Three years later this trio, with another, took the field to the cheers of fifty thousand people at the Polo Grounds and dazzled into defeat the strongest Army eleven ever sent against anybody. The next morning Grantland Rice rose to lyric heights in celebrating their speed, rhythm and precision, winding up a litany of hallelujahs by proclaiming them "The Four Horsemen." Whereupon an enterprising young gentleman in South Bend perched the returned victors of the backfield on four borrowed nags and sold the resultant photographs to the tune of a small fortune.

These accidents will happen in the best of all possible worlds. Indeed, the football epic of the Four Horsemen is the story of an accident. How it came to pass that four young men so eminently qualified by temperament, physique and instinctive pacing to complement one another perfectly and thus produce the best coördinated and most picturesque backfield in the recent history of football—how that came about is one of the inscrutable achievements of coincidence, of which I know nothing save that it's a rather satisfying mouthful of words.

Harry Stuhldreher, the quarterback, hailed from Massillon, Ohio; Don Miller, halfback, came from Defiance, Ohio; Jimmy Crowley, the other halfback, hailed from Green Bay, Wisconsin, and Elmer Layden, the dashing, slashing fullback, had his home in Davenport, Iowa. The four did not play as backfield in their freshman year—remember, I had seen them in practice and survived the experience.

These men and the others of the freshman squad in 1921 were soundly beaten by such teams as Lake Forest Academy and the Michigan State freshmen. Stuhldreher, of the lot, had the most promise. He sounded like a leader on the field. He was a good and fearless blocker and as he gained in football knowledge he showed signs of smartness in emergencies. Layden had speed—he could run a hundred-yard dash in under ten seconds at a track meet. But speed and some kicking ability seemed to be all his football wares. Jimmy Crowley was only less humorous in play than in appearance. He looked dull and always resembled a lad about to get out of or into bed. He showed very little as a freshman—certainly none of the nimble wit that made him as celebrated for repartee as for broken-field running. Don Miller traveled, that first year, on the reputation and recommendation of his brother, "Red" Miller, the great Notre Dame halfback who made such havoc when his team beat Michigan in 1909. "Red" had sung the praises of another Miller, Jerry, who made a fine high-school record, but couldn't add to his poundage of one hundred and thirty-five and, unfortunately, grew quite deaf and so was disqualified for the tough going of big-league football. Don, an also-ran in his freshman year, surprised me when he came out for spring practice and with his fleetness and daring sized up as a halfback to cheer the heart of any coach.

In the fall of 1922, Notre Dame had lost all its veteran backs except Castner at fullback and Thomas at quarterback—one of those decimations by graduation that give coaches gray hair or, as in my case, remove what little hair they have.

This 1922 squad, the first on which the Four Horsemen got their chance, romped through its preliminary games against Kalamazoo, St. Louis, Purdue and DePauw. With the first big game looming, against Georgia Tech, Stuhldreher was promoted to alternate as quarterback with Thomas; Crowley and Layden were assigned to alternate as left halfbacks, while Castner, the veteran, remained at fullback and Don Miller received the right halfback berth. Crowley only won his place by a surprising performance against Purdue, when the sleepy one astonished Purdue a great deal and me a great deal more with the liveliest exhibition of cutting, jumping, side-stepping, change of pace and determined ball-toting that I had seen in many a day.

The Georgia Tech game of 1922 found the Four Horsemen ready to demonstrate. The experienced Castner guided them through their green patches, but practice had displayed their unusual gift for synchronization. They showed it against Georgia Tech for the first time and were largely instrumental in turning in a 13-3 victory.

Yet in that same game Stuhldreher, who had appeared most promising of the bunch, made the biggest mistake of his career—one that stamped him still an apprentice quarterback. When our team reached the five-yard line Stuhldreher passed on second down over the goal line for a touchback, and it became Tech's ball on our twenty-yard line.

Never again did Stuhldreher make a tactical error while running the team as quarterback. I have in mind the uproar that followed his spectacular or what seemed to be a spectacular error during the Tournament of Roses game against Stanford on New Year's Day in 1925.

Notre Dame was ahead, yet Stuhldreher passed straight into the hands of a Stanford player. The fact is that Stuhldreher had hurt his foot, badly. We didn't know until the game was over that he had broken a bone and was suffering agony throughout the game. Even this circumstance, of course, could not excuse passing on second down with his team leading.

But Hunsinger, our right end, had told Stuhldreher in a huddle that the Stanford halfback who should be covering him, Hunsinger, did not follow him deep into the scoring zone on Notre Dame's offensive plays. Knowing this, Stuhldreher opened up on second down and called for a forward pass from himself to Hunsinger.

Sure enough, on the play, Hunsinger got clear away from the Stanford halfback, who failed to follow him deep enough. He was clear in the open, ready to race for a touchdown on receipt of the ball. A forty-five-yard pass would have done the trick, and a forty-five-yard pass straight to the target was easy enough for Stuhldreher. But not this time. As the plucky little quarterback squared himself to shoot, bringing down the foot with the broken bone to take his stance, excruciating pain shot through him, so that instead of his usual vigorous throw the ball sailed a feeble twenty yards.

Yet Stuhldreher's tactics were sound—for so good a ball thrower. For even if Hunsinger had failed to catch the ball and it had been intercepted, a forty-five-yard pass would have been as useful as a punt. If Hunsinger had caught it, it was a sure touchdown. The worst thing that could have happened would have been an incompleted pass, which would have cost us a down. As the play took place on third down, an incompleted pass would not have hurt because Layden was there to kick the ball on the next play. And Layden was a kicker!

Stuhldreher was really a master of sound quarterback play. He could read through another team's strategy without a key to the code. Against Army in 1924 Stuhldreher found their ends were smashing in close, with the result that he sent Crowley and Miller circling the ends. In the very next game, against Princeton, he found the tackle and end on each side were very wide, so he confined his tactics all day to sharp thrusts by Layden through the thinned-out line, and cut-backs by Crowley and Miller. In the game following that, against Georgia Tech, he made gains back to our weak side, because Georgia Tech had overshifted to our strong side, thus leaving the weak side unguarded. And in the game against Wisconsin, fairly strong that year, Stuhldreher repeatedly found a gap between tackle and end that netted neat gains. To prove conclusively his versatility, when Nebraska's line in the next game was exceedingly tough before a fast, plowing backfield, Stuhldreher wasted little time or strength on line drives. He opened up a passing attack and completed ten before the final whistle, the score being 34 to 7.

This diversity of attack caused a well-known football writer to wonder what the Four Horsemen could do with a kicking game. As if in direct response they put one on in their last appearance for Notre Dame in that Tournament of Roses game against Stanford. The entire team had wilted in the heat. The boys were unable to move. They had to rely on Layden's punting, not their usual game. Layden, however, got off a pair of punts of around eighty yards which were quite useful. Stanford lost the game despite its hard, smashing play and Pop Warner was disappointed, making much of the fact that Stanford had made more first downs than Notre Dame.

To this comment, Crowley, as spontaneous spokesman for the Four Horsemen, pointed out that the score was 27 to 10, adding: "Next year in the major leagues they aren't going to count runs that come over the plate. They'll just count the men left on bases." Pop Warner, like the grand old sport he is, admitted Crowley had the laugh and that the only pay-off in football was the ball over the line and not down close to it.

Crowley was always quick at a come-back. After one big Eastern game an official who had penalized Notre Dame all afternoon to the neglect of the Eastern team, which he rarely looked at, met Crowley, and they trudged side by side into the dressing-room. The official said to Crowley:

"You were lucky to win today."

"Yes, Cyclops," said Crowley. "After watching you officiate you don't even begin to know how lucky we were."

Crowley was the gagman of the outfit, but not at first. You never saw a more serious bunch of football players than the Four Horsemen before they had really made good, or a gayer group afterward.

One afternoon Crowley came from vacation into my office. This was after fame had perched on his sloping shoulders.

"Ran into a grand high-school player in Green Bay, Coach," he said.

"Good, is he?" I asked.

"Awful good," he said.

"You really mean that, Jim?" I said.

"He's awful good," said Crowley.

"You mean—as good as you?" I asked.

"Well," said Jim, edging toward the door. "Perhaps not that—but awful good."

He vanished.

The official début of Crowley and his other Horsemen as big-leaguers was actually against Carnegie Tech. Castner, the veteran fullback who had been their bell-wether in the early games, was so seriously injured in the game against Butler—a broken hip in a flying fall—that he was out for the season.

I moved Layden from left halfback, where he had been alternating with Crowley, to fullback. These boys surprised the football fans of Pittsburgh with their perfect timing as they functioned for the first time as a unit backfield. Layden amazed me by his terrific speed as fullback. He adopted a straight line drive that made him one of the most unusual fullbacks in football. He pierced a line through sheer speed—cutting it like a knife, although each man in the opposing line outweighed him by twenty pounds.

They won. This victory, however, didn't thrill me as much as the defeat they suffered the very next game—against Nebraska. The Cornhuskers had one of the heaviest teams in their history—and they are known for very active heft. They pushed the relatively little Four Horsemen team all over the field. At the half the score was 14-0, and it would have been another touchdown if the lightweight boys from South Bend hadn't held the Nebraska heavies on their one-yard line for four straight downs. They emerged from that battering a sadly crumpled team.

But they came out fighting mad for the second half, whacked across a touchdown in the third quarter, and carried the ball to Nebraska's one-yard line toward the end of the final period. Stuhldreher called for a pass, and Layden spurted ahead to a corner of the field, where he was all set to receive and down the ball for six more points. But Stuhldreher, the alert, this time was not alert enough. Weller, the huge 250-pound Nebraska tackle, crashed through the line and smeared the 150-pound Notre Dame quarterback.

Our college alumni in Lincoln had a banquet ready for the Four Horsemen team that night. But Crowley, who came through the drumming bruised and bandaged, put it this way:

"We need a thermometer more than a feed." They went to bed to nurse their sore spots.

The Four Horsemen once were blamed for a breach of football etiquette in which they were nowise involved. This was against Wisconsin in 1924. We had the game well in hand, so in the second half the Horsemen were taken out and sent to the showers. In the final two minutes of play a substitute Notre Dame halfback went in for Crowley and strutted his stuff by running for a touchdown. As he crossed the line for the score he thumbed his nose at a Wisconsin player pursuing him. He was instantly yanked from the game. Many thought Crowley had made the vulgar gesture—but that was never Crowley's idea of wit.

His style of thought and good-humored balance of character was of the sterling stuff that wears better in adversity than in success. Against Princeton he and his three playmates were at their best. But Crowley faltered once. He had taken the ball, skirted Princeton's shock troops and began one of the rhythmic runs of the Four Horsemen. Slagle of Princeton ripped up the field to meet him. Crowley veered and Slagle nailed him from behind.

In the dressing-room between halves sleepy-eyed Jim Crowley was apologetic.

"I made a mistake," he said. "I didn't know Slagle was that fast. I should have cut back."

"That wasn't the mistake you made," I said. "That wasn't it."

"Yes, it was," he said. "I admit it. A mistake."

"No," I said. "Slagle didn't know who you were. If you had shown him those New York clippings you've been saving, telling how good you were, he wouldn't have dared come near you."

Crowley laughed louder than anybody at this. Perhaps he knew what all the team knew, that the Four Horsemen—great though they were—received a measure of praise that they should have shared with the stalwart linesmen—whom we called the Seven Mules.

This caused a few timely prods from some of the Mules. Adam Walsh, our center—a tower of strength for the Horsemen to play behind—watched them try unsuccessfully to get started on one of their famous runs against Lombard, with a second-string line to screen them. There was nothing doing, so I shot in Walsh and the other six Mules.

"What seems to be the matter, boys?" said Walsh, as he took the ball to snap back for the first scrimmage. "It seems you need a little help."

This banter helped to check the rising tide of self-esteem which only the rarest of young athletes can stem in the face of wholesale flattery. One of the Horsemen suffered just a trifle from swelled head. It was cured in short order. This particular Horseman stalked in to the squad manager and asked for a clean pair of stockings and a new belt. The manager said: "O. K., but turn in your old ones."

"What for?" said the Horseman.

Rip Miller, one of the Seven Mules, standing within earshot among five of the other six, rebuked the manager:

"What do you mean," he said, "talking that way? Don't you know who this is? This is one of the Four Horsemen."

"No-o?" said the manager, in mock awe.

"Ye-es," said Rip in more mock awe.

As the Horseman walked away, confused, manager and players stood staring, while the players nudged one another, murmuring reverently:

"He's one of the Four Horsemen."

The lad was cured. Next morning he went forthwith to the manager and said his old stockings and belt would do.

Those Horsemen were pretty good themselves at concerted kidding. Against Army in 1924 they had been warned in practice of the prowess of Garbisch, the great Army All-America center. When they met him he punctuated some of their attempts to get away. They found a neat way to irritate Garbisch. On subsequent plays, when the drive was against him, and he was smeared, one Horseman would politely inquire of another so that Garbisch, picking himself up from the ground, could overhear:

"Is that the great Mr. Garbisch?"

To which another would solemnly reply:

"Yes, that's the great Mr. Garbisch."

When on another smash the All-America center was floored, Crowley would ask of Miller in amazement:

"You don't mean to say that's the great Mr. Garbisch?"

And Miller would retort: "If the number's correct it's none other than Mr. Garbisch in person."

It didn't help Garbisch's game much.

In this Princeton game of 1923 Miller had just gone off right tackle for what looked like a good gain when he fumbled the ball, which went rolling along the ground. Quick as a flash a Princeton back, trained in the alert Bill Roper way of stooping at full speed and picking up a loose ball, scooped it up. The next thing we saw was this Princeton halfback with two interferers in front, speeding down the field. The goal line was seventy-five yards away—and no one between the runners and that goal line but Don Miller.

Wasting no time after his boner, Miller had recovered poise and was racing across field to cut off the Princeton men. The stands were in an uproar. It seemed impossible that Miller could overtake them or, if he could, that he could offer much resistance against three men.

Pressing his speed he ran in front and

to one side of the two interferers, crowding them toward the sideline. He feinted in and out to slow up the Princeton cavalcade, and did this so calculatingly that by the time they were within twenty yards or so of the Notre Dame goal line our fastest end, Clem Growe, had had time to rush up and tackle the ball carrier from behind. The touchdown was not scored, and so Miller redeemed his fumble by as heady a piece of work as any I have ever seen.

Crowley, the sleepy-looking wit, was the nerviest back I've known. He would throw himself anywhere. Also, since I'm using superlatives where they belong, he was the greatest interferer for his weight I have ever seen, and a particularly effective ball carrier on the critical third down.

Quick to block and banter opponents, the Horsemen, through their most articulate member, did not spare themselves when they failed. I tried to make Jimmy Crowley a triple-threat man. He could pass and run in great shape, but his kicking was good for just about forty yards. This was, perhaps, due to an unusual fault. He would take three steps with the ball—and that made his kicking dangerous as he held the ball too long and there was risk of the defense breaking through and blocking it. He practiced for weeks to kick almost simultaneously with receipt of the ball. So when Layden became slightly injured in the Princeton game Crowley was assigned to do the punting. On the first try, his old bad habit returned subconsciously and he took three steps. A fast-charging Princeton tackle broke through and blocked the kick, which rolled over our goal line for a safety and two points for the Tigers.

After the game was over a teammate chided Crowley:

"I see you're a triple-threat man, this year."

"Yes," snapped Crowley. "Trip, stumble or fumble."

While this joshing on the part of their squad-mates lasted, the Horsemen took the best means to offset it by joining in the chorus. On the only day in a great season that they weren't able to shine—against Northwestern at Soldiers' Field, Chicago—they expected razzing. Northwestern was an inspired team, while the Four Horsemen were off key, off color, stale and plainly unable to get anywhere. We won from Northwestern but only after a heart-catching, nip-and-tuck game.

On the train returning to South Bend a gentleman who had gazed upon the rye when it was golden barged into the car containing the squad. The conductor requested his ticket. The drunk brushed him aside.

"Where are you going?" the conductor demanded. "New York, Toledo or Cleveland?"

"I don't know," sighed the inebriate. "I guess I'm not going anywhere."

Jimmy Crowley turned to his teammates and remarked, "Must be one of the Four Horsemen."

Layden, a quiet member of the quartet, was their star on defense. His ability to intercept passes was uncanny, and it never had more value than in our Tournament of Roses game with Stanford on New Year's Day, 1925. Pop Warner—greatest originator of smart plays—had a forward pass play that enabled him to win a tie for the Coast championship even without the help of Nevers, his All-America fullback, who had been injured most of the season. Nevers was in the line-up against us—and what a game he played! Twice after Stanford had advanced to about our thirty-yard line they called for this dangerous pass out into the flat zone, and both times Layden, jumping high in the air, tipped and caught the ball and ran for touchdowns.

Each of these Horsemen shone individually on his day. As Layden's was against Stanford, so Miller's was against Princeton. Miller was the most dangerous of the quartet at right half, once in the open field. His long runs for touchdowns were a feature during his three years of play. But he was a much better defensive player than he has been given credit for being.

Examine their records closely and you'll find the Four Horsemen stand unique as a continuing combination in the backfield. They lost but two games out of thirty—both of these to the heavier Nebraska team—in 1922 and 1923. In the 1923 game their speed was seriously handicapped by the condition of the field. Nebraska had just built a new stadium, and had been unable to grow grass on the gridiron. The clay field was hard-baked, so, to prevent unnecessary bruises to the players, this field had been plowed to make it soft. A well-meant procedure, but it applied four-wheel brakes to the Horsemen.

But these lads of the colorful cavalry of Notre Dame need no alibi. The record's good enough. And the same is true of their scholastic records. They retain their interest in football while attaining success in business. All are coaching the game. Stuhldreher, the quarterback, coaches Villanova University; Don Miller, the Ohio State backfield; Jimmy Crowley, Michigan State College, and Layden, between spells at the practice of law in Pittsburgh, coaches Duquesne University. While Adam Walsh, headman of the Seven Mules that bore the brunt for the charge of the light brigade of the Four Horsemen, is an engineer and coaches the Yale line.

This quartet of backs, destined to be immortal in football, caused me labor, sometimes caused me pain, but mostly brought great joy, not only to their coach but to the spectators. Only their fame was a bit embarrassing. At their heyday I was hounded by newsmen and sob-sisters trying to get collective and individual interviews, genealogies and prophecies with, by and for them. One determined lady pursued them for pieces to appear in an obscure journal—by mail, telegraph, telephone and on foot. Finally, she caught up with Crowley.

"Who on earth is she?" he was asked.

"Oh," he said, blandly, "she's the third Horsewoman."

And biblical students of the Apocalypse will recall that the third horseman personified pestilence.

An accident of Blasco Ibañez's best-selling popularity inspired their name; by accident they were brought together. But it was no accident that made them collectively and individually fine players. That was design and hard work. The Four Horsemen have the right to ride with the gridiron great.

Freshman

Corey Ford

Corey Ford can do a top-flight job of straight reporting; he can spin a rollicking satire; or he can write tenderly of matters near a boy's heart, as he does here.

June 20, 1931

He tugged and zigzagged the heavy trunk across the floor of the bare room over to the bureau, and he turned the key in the lock and lifted up the lid and let it slam backward upon its hinges. He knelt before the trunk and began very methodically to lift the jumbled contents from the top tray, piece by piece, and put them away in the empty bureau.

He took out a pair of silver-backed military brushes and patted the bristles together and laid them on top of the bureau. Then he lifted out a safety-razor case and an unopened pack of blades, and weighed the shiny new case in his hand for a moment as his other hand stole guiltily over the downy curve of his chin. After all, a fellow would have looked pretty funny, coming to college without a razor. He'd have got a heck of a ride if the fellows had ever found out he didn't own a razor.

Beyond the open window a September breeze moved the long fringe of an elm. He thought of elm-shaded walks; the campus at dusk, and lighted dormitories, and figures hurrying under the elms in the dusk, calling to each other, lighting cigarettes, laughing; and a muscle hopped in the hard line of his jaw. He had not realized when he had packed this trunk for college, four days ago, how much he had wanted to get away from Somerville. He had not quite realized, until he began to unpack, how deeply he had always hated Somerville. He had hated it for four dull years, divided into days and subdivided into an infinity of little hours by the mumbling chimes of an obsequious clock in the tower of the Somerville High School: sending him to class; sending him home after class; sending him out again every evening at seven to work in Simmons' garage, where Bill Borden would stop for gasoline in his big red car and ignore him because his father only worked in a mill. Bill Borden, big shot at high school, president of his class, taking Elsie to ride every evening in the big red car while he stood by silently in grease-stained overalls.

He used to plan savagely how it would all be different at college; he and Bill Borden on a level, then, nobody caring in college if Bill Borden's father owned the biggest house in Somerville, and he lived on the other side of the tracks. He had even planned his return to Somerville four years later when college was over: tolerant, of course, wise and dignified, smiling casually at the band and the cheering as he stepped down from the train and shook hands with Mayor Colby, nodding, across the crowd gathered to meet him, at Elsie's adoring eyes—

He lifted out several high school textbooks from the top tray of the trunk, and his physics lab. notebook—he had figured he would need that in college—and the green-covered Freshman Catalogue, and he rose and carried them across the room to a desk by the window. There was a pad of blue-ruled notepaper on the bare desk, the top sheet partly scribbled over, and three crumpled balls of blue-ruled paper already lay on the floor beside the desk.

The catalogue flopped open as he flung it on the desk. He turned the familiar pages one by one. He had read them and reread them all summer, while he was working in Simmons' garage, planning his courses, planning the things he would do in college in September. Freshman war. Fraternity rushing. The Big Game: Sensational Run by Unknown Sophomore Scores Winning Touchdown. And Junior Week; sitting on the fraternity steps with Elsie. And Graduation.

He flipped the pages and reread the Instructions to Incoming Freshmen, his lips moving mechanically, his forehead pleating in a slight frown. ". . . in order to meet classmates and become acquainted with College Traditions, the freshman class will gather in University Hall on Friday, September twenty-first, at two o'clock." The twenty-first. Today. He had looked forward all summer to today. Two o'clock. His jaws tightened, and he grinned hard and stared fixedly past the upper edge of the catalogue.

He saw that he was looking at the blue-ruled paper on the pad, and he read the letter he had started to Elsie: "Dearest Elsie, I have started to write you several times in the last three or four days, but . . ." Suddenly he ripped off the sheet and crumpled it into a ball and dropped it onto the floor beside the three other balls of scribbled paper, and shoved back his chair briskly. He'd better finish unpacking. It was getting late. Soon be two o'clock.

He hauled out his worn football pants and jersey and laid them across a chair, and lifted out a green sweater. Then he looked back briefly over his shoulder at the closed door, and suddenly he rose and held the sweater before him, and looked in the mirror at the all-American quarter who grinned back at him from the glass, his face elaborately unaware of the tremendous white "D" on his broad chest as he strolled nonchalantly across the campus and waved easily to Elsie and Bill Borden, hurrying up the elm-shaded walk to congratulate him on that never-to-be-forgotten touchdown in the last three minutes of—

He bundled the sweater savagely into a ball and hurled it across the room at the closet. To thunder with it. He slammed the lid vindictively on the empty trunk and shoved it lightly with his foot across the floor, and stood before the bureau, pulling the silver-backed military brushes apart and jamming the bristles together again and frowning. He pulled the brushes apart once more and looked at his father's monogram on the back. His father had said, "Use 'em in college, son." He thought of his father, and suddenly he knew that he missed him. Then he looked at the barren room and he thought ". . . will gather in University Hall on Friday, September twenty-first, at two o'clock" and he grinned hard and banged the brushes together viciously, and spun on his heel and walked over to the desk.

"Dear Elsie." He halted the furious rush of his pencil across the blue-lined paper as a taxi stopped in front of the door. Through the window he saw his mother, in black, dismount slowly from the cab with a friend on either side and walk up to the house, staring dully before her. He wrote rapidly: "I suppose you will no doubt be surprised to get a letter from me back in Somerville, the fact is that I did not start for college last Saturday, after all, it is account of the sudden—" He crossed that out. "Owing to my father's—" He crossed that out. "You have read in the newspaper about what happened at the mill—"

He crumpled the blue-lined sheet into a ball and dropped it on the floor beside the four crumpled balls of paper. He heard his mother's voice faintly downstairs, as the obsequious chimes in the tower of the Somerville High School mumbled twice in the distance. At two o'clock he had to go see Simmons about getting back his job at the garage. He would finish the letter tomorrow. There was no hurry about finishing the letter.

A Man Must Fight

Gene Tunney

Wherever men follow boxing, they still talk about the seventh round of the second Tunney-Dempsey fight for the world's heavyweight championship —the round of the "long count" at Chicago. In the final instalment of his serialized autobiography, James Joseph "Gene" Tunney discusses the round, second-by-second—and goes on to reveal the philosophy of the man who retired, undefeated, to make a new career for himself as a successful businessman.

April 2, 1932

Several days before the fight I was notified by the Illinois Boxing Commission to send a representative to its offices for a conference upon the interpretation of the rules. They set no limit to the number of representatives, so I sent three—Billy Gibson, Jimmy Bronson and my lawyer, George Whiteside, of the firm of Chadbourne, Stanchfield and Levy. Gibson and Bronson I thought could take care of any professional question. In the event of any legal question arising I wanted Mr. Whiteside there. I also thought that the notes that Mr. Whiteside would take might be important later on.

George Getz, the nominal promoter, now member of the Illinois Boxing Commission, was present. Leo P. Flynn, representing Dempsey, and the three members of the Commission made up the conference. This group met every afternoon for three days. They went over all phases of the rules and Commission interpretations. Mr. Getz later told me that Leo Flynn brought up the question of a knockdown and insisted that in the event of a knockdown the man scoring it should go to the farthest neutral corner and, in the event he refused, the count would not begin until he had gone. The suspension of the count was to be the penalty for disobeying the rules. This interpretation, insisted on by Flynn, later became the cause of great discussion. Bronson claims it was not Flynn but he who introduced this point. Which one took the initiative is immaterial. That it was discussed before the fight is the important factor. Toward the close of the third conference, during a discussion of some point or other, Flynn in the midst of this group turned to George Whiteside and said, "For —— sake, let's be frank. I'm here to steal as much for my man as I can. Why don't you admit the same?"

To get the humor of this situation, one would have to know George Whiteside. George, with his malacca walking stick, chamois gloves and gray hair, has the appearance of a director of the Social Register. In address he resembles what you think a great jurist should be.

"What!" exclaimed Mr. Whiteside. "Well, that is just why I am here—to prevent your stealing anything."

Mr. Whiteside had been associated with William Travers Jerome in the District Attorney's office in New York for many years. He later proved his mettle in defending me in blackmail suits brought subsequent to my retirement.

Just before the fight started, Righeimer went to Commissioner Kelly and said, "No hoodlum is going to referee the fight. I will tell you the name of the man if you want me to."

Kelly answered, "I don't care to know his name. My only concern is that he is not a hoodlum."

A reporter for the Chicago Herald-Examiner paid a visit to the offices of the Commission at five o'clock in the afternoon and brought with him a message from the publisher to the effect that the Herald-Examiner would not tolerate the appointment of any referee of bad reputation and that if such a one were appointed referee, whether his officiating were honest or not, that paper would utilize its power for the removal of Righeimer.

John Hertz, whose home I had visited with Bernard Gimbel, assured me that Mayor Thompson's committee of seven leading business men of Chicago were determined to have two reputable business men with a knowledge of boxing act as judges for the contest. These business men were as anxious to avoid scandal as we were.

In the dressing-room the bandaging of my hands was watched by Gus Wilson and another Dempsey follower. I had argued for weeks to have the bandaging done in the ring, as it had been done in Philadelphia and for which a provision had been inserted in the contract between Rickard and me. I was overruled by Leo Flynn and the Commission. Game little Jimmy Bronson had been advised that he was *persona non grata* with the Dempsey camp, and that if he came over to Dempsey's dressing-room to watch the bandaging for me he would be assaulted. Jimmy did not mind taking the chance, but Gibson insisted that he take Captain Mike Grady with him—"just in case."

So Jimmy went to Dempsey's dressing-room, Mike Grady and Lou Brix with him. Someone had given orders that Jimmy be kept out and, to be sure that these orders were followed, assigned one Sergeant Tappscott of the Chicago police, who had been appointed Dempsey's bodyguard, to see to it. Tappscott made a brave showing, glowering at Jimmy. He was in the process of telling Bronson just what would happen to him if he persisted in entering.

"Listen, flatfoot," said Grady, jabbing a large finger into Tappscott's chest. "I'm giving you your choice; either shut your face or I'll—"

His right hand moved toward his hip. Tappscott looked at him hard.

"Yeah," went on Grady, pointing to a tiny ventilation window high up near the ceiling—"yeah, shut up or I'll make you climb out through that window. See?"

Tappscott saw. And Jimmy Bronson with Lou Brix watched Dempsey's hands bandaged.

Through some mistake in the signals I kept Jack waiting in the ring a couple of minutes. This was unintentional. Jack greeted me as I entered the ring: "How are you, Gene?" "Quite well, Jack, and you?" I replied. Soon after my arrival the announcer bellowed what had been printed a million times—"This is a fight for the world's heavyweight championship"—and announced the principals.

I was standing in my corner and made the usual gesture in acknowledgment of the cheers and jeers. Suddenly a gray-haired man, whom I had never seen before to my knowledge, climbed through the ropes and stood in a neutral corner. The announcer turned to him and shouted, "The referee, Dave Barry!"

My heart dropped into my stomach. Dave Barry? Jimmy Bronson's old antagonist and the man that Jimmy warned me against permitting to referee the match! Well, now I was in for it good and plenty. "You must make the most of it!" I told myself.

Then followed the introduction of the two judges, prominent Chicago business men, George Lytton and Sheldon Clark. I had never seen either of them before. We were called to the center of the ring. Flynn and Jerry the Greek stood with Dempsey; Gibson and Bronson with me. The referee said, "Both you boys have received a book of rules of this Boxing Commission. They are the rules under which you are going to fight. They have been discussed by your representatives, I understand, for several days at the Commission."

Gibson and Fynn assented to that.

"The rabbit and kidney blows are barred, of course," he continued. We all nodded acquiescence to that.

"Now, I want to get this one point clear," continued Barry. "In the event of a knockdown, the man scoring the knockdown will go to the farthest neutral corner. Is that clear, Jack?"—turning to Dempsey—and "Is that clear, Champ?"—turning to me. We both nodded "Yes."

"Now, in the event of a knockdown, unless the boy scoring it goes to the farthest neutral corner I will not begin the count until he does. Is that clear, Jack?"

"Yes," nodded Dempsey.

"Is that clear, Champ?"

"Yes," I said.

"When I tell you to break I want you to break clean and step back without hitting—" He paused impressively. Then: "Shake hands now and come out fighting."

We shook hands and went back to our corners. The bell rang and we came out fighting.

In my anxiety to end the fight by a knockout I threw and missed more rights than I ordinarily would have in twenty fights. I scored often with my left, only occasionally with my right. So did Dempsey. Dempsey, however, was fighting a considerably different fight from the one in Philadelphia. He was very cautious. Because of this I was unable to get him into positions that would make him a target. He left very few openings.

At the end of the fourth round I finally nailed him with one of those wild rights on the temple. He staggered back into a corner. He was considerably dazed but conscious enough to cover up. The bell rang. He went to his corner in an unsteady stride.

Sitting in my corner, I thought that the end was near and that I would probably get him in the next or following round. Much to my surprise, he answered the bell for the fifth round as clear and strong as he was at the beginning.

"He has marvelous recuperative powers!" I thought. "Well, it is only a matter of time until he will be weakened from the loss of blood."

I had opened two cuts on his face, both of which were bleeding. The fifth round passed without much heavy damage being done, though there was considerable action. I felt I was leading by a big margin on points.

We were both fencing carefully. I was trying to maneuver him into an opening so that I could get a shot at his jaw; he was attempting to cross my left lead with a long, straight right. The sixth was similar to the fifth. My right-handers were landing high and Jack's cross-counters were either missing or grazing my jaw. At close quarters I tied him up. This, however, was more to prevent his using the rabbit punch than a disinclination on my part to in-fight.

Despite repeated warnings from the referee he continued to use the rabbit blow whenever I failed to tie him up. This rabbit blow is the most dangerous blow in boxing. It was barred originally through the action of Jack Dempsey in his fight with Bill Brennan in Madison Square Garden. After Brennan had started to the canvas from a body blow, Dempsey hit him a fearful blow on the back of the neck on his way down. This left Brennan prostrate on the canvas. When I asked Carpentier what effect the rabbit blows had on him in his match with Jack he pressed his temple and said, "Zis is where zey hurt."

The rabbit blow is particularly dangerous and damaging because it is directed at the point where the base of the skull and the cervical vertebra meet—the lower brain stem, called the medulla oblongata. This nerve center is actually the center of life. It controls respiration, heart action and locomotion. Many doctors are agreed that it is the twisting of this brain stem by a blow or jolt that causes the so-called knockout. No man can stand eighty or ninety rabbit blows from the fists of a heavy hitter like Dempsey, as I did in each fight, without feeling the effects. It brings a deadening headache which seems to rest in the base of the skull. There is a numbness which reacts on the whole nervous system. The blow was barred by all boxing commissions because it is not a scientific blow that you make an opening for, but one that is used when men are locked in a clinch, animal fashion. It is about as scientific as the blow of a hugging bear. There is no defense against it but to tie up the hands of an opponent.

My bodyguard, Sergeant Bill Smith of the Chicago police department, who was in my corner, became wildly excited because the referee was apparently doing nothing to stop Dempsey's rabbit punches. Between the fifth and sixth rounds he climbed to the outer platform of the neutral corner in which the referee was making his notes and yelled. "You blankety-blank-blank, if you don't stop those rabbit punches you'll be carried out of here dead." The faithful bodyguard was feeling each blow more than I.

In the seventh round, after some fifty seconds of jabbing, feinting and mixing, I led a straight left which Dempsey crossed with a long right. This hit me high. I realized it. So did Dempsey. I danced back a step or two. Dempsey followed. With a long left swinging hook, he hit me on the right side of the chin. It was a savage punch and shook me up. To this day I cannot understand how I missed seeing it as it came.

I got furious at myself for being hit by that kind of swing. It had actually been telegraphed. How stupid of me! Such was my reaction. Suddenly a right followed which I partially rode. My back was to the ropes. I leaned against them quite relaxed. Rebounding with a spring, I raised my guard.

Dempsey slipped in with another left hook that got inside my guard and hit me as I sprang from the ropes. This blow had the added force of catching me as I hurled myself forward. It landed again on the right side of the chin. It was a terrific blow. I began sagging against the ropes. It was the fourth he had landed in quick succession.

As I slowly crumpled to the canvas, being partially supported and held up by the ropes, he followed with a hard right, a left and another right. By the time the last right landed I was just short of sitting on the canvas. Seven vicious punches in all. I have no recollection of the last three.

This was the first time in my life I had ever been knocked down. After getting to the floor I slowly went back toward a reclining position. Before my shoulder blades touched the canvas, I instinctively reached out with my left hand and, taking hold of the lower rope, pulled myself into a sitting position.

My first conscious reaction was one of comfort. Gosh, the padded floor felt good! I noticed that the distance between my eyes and the canvas seemed short—I was sitting on it. I must be down, I must be down!

"You must have been knocked down," I told myself rather foolishly. "You have been knocked down. Look here, Tunney. you must get up. Sure, sure, get up! But . . . What shall I do when I do get up?"

I looked over at my corner. Bronson and Gibson were wild-eyed, beckoning me to stay down. I nodded, recognizing them and their message. I looked up. There was the referee. I heard him say "Two." I had lots of time—lots of time.

What to do when I did get up became the problem. Although I had never been knocked down before, I had thought of the possibility of it from the early days of my career. I had decided that one of two courses might be followed to try to ward off defeat after a knockdown. Every thoughtful boxer goes on the assumption that sooner or later he will have the experience of being knocked down. To anticipate is to be prepared.

Since a man who has been knocked down usually loses the power of locomotion, it follows that he must clinch if and when he rises. I had never seen a man completely knocked out or cleanly knocked down get up and propel himself out of danger. When a complete knockout is administered the recipient usually has to have his legs lifted up so he may get through the ropes and out of the ring. Because of the belief that this partial paralysis of the legs always followed a knockdown, I decided it would be wiser to clinch with an opponent and hold on until my head cleared. Moreover, a clinch affords one a chance to take a light blow on the shoulder or chest as an excuse to go down for another count. These extra nine seconds would enable one to clear one's head entirely and get back the strength of the legs.

But now I had to dismiss this first alternative because of the danger of Dempsey's rabbit blow, which I knew he would use if I attempted to clinch when I got up, and which would probably cause a complete collapse.

There was left the other alternative. It was to gamble with an opponent. Usually after a fighter knocks another one down, particularly when it is unexpected, he gets excited in spite of himself. In this excitement and his desire to "kill" he usually leaves himself open. At this moment a well-placed punch, properly timed, is apt to turn defeat into victory.

I realized that Dempsey, by constant conscious effort in his training bouts, shadow-boxing and road work, had learned to keep his chin on his chest. This constant precautionary measure developed an instinctive habit of keeping his chin tucked down when in action.

Because of this habit, I knew that Dempsey, as he came at me for the "kill," would be a bad gamble. My blow would probably land on the top of his head or on his forehead while his would undoubtedly hit me on the chin or jaw. Another blow on either, after getting up, was not going to help me. That I realized.

Therefore, in those few seconds that I rested on the canvas waiting for the referee to say "Nine!" I had to discard the plans that I had thought of for years and expected to put to use in such an emergency as I was now in.

I determined that I must avoid allowing Dempsey to close in on me when I got up. I remembered that in the early part of the fight, as I feinted him and moved away, he would flounder after me. This was the cue to my safest course: To get up and make him chase me. Years of practice in running backward in road work would help me now.

To the average person the possibility of all this thinking, weighing, rejecting and deciding seems incredible in so short a space of time. Considering that thought in the normal person is instantaneous, I can readily understand the development of a faculty for emergency thinking.

Resilience, precision and decisiveness were needed. My years of training had provided them. Determined to get the last part of a second that was mine, I rose as the referee raised his hand to say—TEN!

There has been considerable question about the length of time I was on the floor. Many newspaper men at the ringside said that the referee lost two seconds in taking Dempsey from behind me and putting him into a neutral corner. Leo Flynn, Dempsey's chief second, said that the stopwatch in his corner registered fourteen seconds, from the time I went down until I got up. It was agreed by all the experts to accept Flynn's timing. Even photographs were taken of this magic watch, the next day, registering fourteen seconds. Wonderful provision and thoughtfulness there, dear Percival! I have never found out what the official timekeeper's watch registered. It did not matter.

Realizing, as do all professional boxers, that the first nine seconds of a knockdown belong to the man who is on the floor, I never had any thought of getting up before the referee said "Nine!" Only badly dazed boxers who have momentarily lost consciousness, and "show-offs," fail to take the nine seconds that are theirs. No boxer that I have ever known has carried a stopwatch on his wrist going into the ring. They always go by the referee's counting. Whether twenty-nine seconds or nine seconds had elapsed when the referee said "NINE!" would have made no difference to me. My signal to get off the floor was the count—nine! The action of the referee in not taking up the count immediately when I went on the floor, regardless of where Dempsey was, is another question.

Football, tennis, baseball, swimming, golf and all the popular sports have rules by which the contestants abide. There is usually an arbiter in the form of an umpire or referee to see that the rules are enforced. Dave Barry, in his refusal to count until Dempsey had moved from behind me and had gone to a neutral corner, was merely enforcing the rule insisted upon by Leo Flynn, Dempsey's manager, and agreed upon by the promoter, the commissioners and the boxers. Any other action of Barry's would have been in direct contradiction of the Illinois Boxing Commission rules, under which we boxed that night. The Commission later, in disallowing Dempsey's protest, upheld Referee Barry's handling of the situation.

Each state makes its own rules, which become a part of the law legalizing boxing. There is very little of the original Queensberry code in the various states' rules governing boxing. But each state has as part of the law the clause regarding knockdowns, so that it becomes not only an "unsporting" thing to stand behind a fallen opponent but unlawful.

Had Dempsey and I been boxing under the old London prize-ring rules, at the knockdown the round would have ended and I would have had thirty-eight seconds in which to come to scratch. The matches under the old London prize-ring rules were always to a finish with bare knuckles. The only virtue about this kind of fighting was that it put each man to the final test. They were most boring spectacles, however, for after the hands got sore and disabled the contestants became wrestlers. These ten-round fights for the world's heavyweight championship are entirely too short in which to establish truly the better man. They are decidedly disadvantageous to the skillful man who goes on the principle of the constant drop of water wearing away the stone. It could only be by sheer accident that a man of my style could knock out a man of Dempsey's strength, resistance and courage inside ten rounds. Fifteen rounds is the minimum number in which a man can establish his superiority as a champion fighter unless a knockout intervenes. However, I am in favor of twenty-round matches for heavyweight championship fights.

"Your legs are fine," was the first thought I had after rising. Dempsey was darting toward me from the corner. He was crouching forward. His head was about four feet from the floor. A savage scowl covered his face as he looked up from below his heavy eyebrows. With his right hand up as a guard, the left hand dragged along the floor until he got within hitting distance.

"This time," I said to myself, "you will catch that left and not be sucker enough to walk into it again!"

I waited until it got three quarters of the way on its course and then picked it off. In doing so, I started to circle to his right. This was to stay out of the way of his left hook.

After circling the ring once and avoiding eight or nine swings, I realized that I could circle him faster than he could follow. I bided my time, remaining physically relaxed. Presently, I decided it was time to try to nail him. I slowed up until he got within hitting distance; suddenly I lunged forward with a straight right that hit him on the temple. This was unexpected. His knees buckled a bit. We exchanged five or six blows in close before the referee separated us. I then circled to his left side.

He made several futile attempts to catch me with long swings. Slowing up again, I lunged forward with another right-hand punch and hit him on the cheek-bone. Again his knees buckled. We clinched. The referee separated us. I renewed circling to his left. He sensed that if he kept up this futile chase, he would be knocked out. Either of the two blows that I hit him had sufficient force for a knockout if placed on a more vulnerable spot.

He then decided on a grand-stand gesture. The ridiculousness of the situation can be most appreciated by a professional boxer. Here was I, just up from a count, and while avoiding his attempts to put me down again for keeps, being gestured by my opponent to come in so that he could land the finishing punch or punches!

I thought this gesture an acknowledgment of discouragement; so, cautiously moving about, I got what I thought was an opening for a right at his body. I lunged forward with the same power of the other two blows and hit him under the heart. He grunted.

I want to say here that Dempsey's actions after this blow proved to me that he possessed the stick-to-itiveness that makes him great amongst champions. He made no attempt to go down but, bending forward, his arms close to his body, weaved until the bell rang.

In the spring of 1929, while coming north on the train after promoting the Sharkey-Stribling fight at Miami Beach, Dempsey went into the compartment of Roy Howard and Ray Long, the publishers. After talking a little while about the Chicago fight and, in particular, that seventh round, Dempsey exclaimed:

"The right-hand punch under the heart that Tunney hit me when he got off the floor in the seventh round was the hardest blow I have ever received. It was not a question in my mind of being knocked out—I thought I was going to die. I could not get my breath."

Following the knockdown at the opening of the eighth round, Dempsey again demonstrated the kind of courage he has. Every newspaper account of those last three rounds describes Jack as a human punching bag. Yet, aside from the knockdown in the early part of the eighth, he was never off his feet.

When the decision was given I walked across to Jack's corner. He advanced to meet me and said, "Congratulations, Gene; it was a good fight! I did the best I could."

The following day Eddie Sullivan, alderman for my old Greenwich Village district, and Jimmy Eagleton ran into Al Capone at the railroad station. Al had come down to see some friends off for New York. Eagleton had been to his hotel, the night before the fight, where Al was showing to the out-of-town visitors the warm and generous hospitality of Chicago.

Capone said to Eagleton and Sullivan, who were about to board the train, "I lost $45,000 on the fight but I don't give a damn because Tunney is from New York. Before the fight I heard Tunney was up in his training camp with a lot of lavender boys in golf clothes and that they did not know what it was all about. I couldn't understand fellers like Gibson and Tunney coming from New York being so dumb. So I says this to the guys that told me to go and bet as much as I wanted on Dempsey and that everything was O. K. One of these guys tells me: 'They're all saps. They gotta coupla college guys up there with them runnin' the camp. Tunney's too busy wid his books. He's a mug, I tell yer!' So against my best judgment, I bet against Tunney.

"At five o'clock I had word that the Commission had switched the referee. I did not have time to get off, but what the hell! These mugs in Chicago think New Yorkers are all suckers. Why, I came out here from Brooklyn seven years ago and they ain't made a sucker of me yet."

There was talk of a return match. There was still a question in the minds of many as to who was the better man.

I felt as bad about the incident of the seventh round as Dempsey. The subsequent publicity made it obligatory for us to meet a third time. Realizing this, I decided to give Dempsey a third match, only stipulating that it should be for at least fifteen rounds.

At a conference at the Union League Club in New York between Tex Rickard, Richard Hoyt, chairman of the Board of the Madison Square Garden Corporation, Bernard F. Gimbel, George Whiteside, my lawyer, Rickard's lawyer and myself, Rickard was authorized to meet any demand that Dempsey might make that was within reason for a return engagement of fifteen rounds. It would surely have been the largest purse ever paid a challenger.

But Dempsey turned a deaf ear to Rickard's constant pleadings and finally, in a telegram which Rickard subsequently showed us, said, "Count me out, Tex."

With Dempsey out and no likely-looking opponent around, I began to lose interest. Tex did not ask to tear up the contract which he had signed a few days before the Chicago fight in which he agreed to provide an opponent for me during the year 1928 in the event I was still champion, and for which he was to pay me a guaranty of $525,000.

To meet his contract Tex selected Tom Heeney, who had the best record of all the "tournamentalists" as my opponent for that year. Sharkey would have been ideal from the point of view of gate receipts, but just when he had the match in his hand, Tom Heeney bested him, so Rickard thought. I did not see the match. After the Heeney fight Risko gained a fifteen-round decision over him. This unfortunately eliminated him as a contender. Heeney subsequently got a decision over Risko and, though Heeney turned out to be the poorest drawing card Rickard could have selected, he was entitled to the match on achievement.

Before the Heeney match I became engaged to be married. I decided this would be my last ring contest. During the training period for this fight I was completely free from annoyance and worry.

The fight with Heeney, I believe, was the most skillful performance of my career. Everything clicked in unison. Heeney was stopped in the eleventh round after putting up a most courageous resistance.

After this fight there was considerable speculation on the part of newspaper men and fans as to why I had backed away refusing to hit Heeney in the eighth round when he was in obvious pain and helpless from a blow over the left eye. It was laid to timidity by some, to sportsmanship by others, and, by the more fiction-minded, as conclusive proof of the lack of a "killer instinct"—"that indispensable quality of the successful fighter."

I have always been amused by that phrase, "killer instinct." It has been written of exhaustively as a virtue. It was coined for prize fighting; it is now being employed in describing football and other athletic contests. In pugilism it is defined as that fierce urge to beat one's opponent helpless, hang him on the ropes, push him out of the ring, knock him unconscious, kill him, win.

In my humble opinion, a great deal of what is described as the killer instinct is merely a burning desire to win, to win brutally or skillfully, fairly or foully. It is the emotional reaction to violent physical competition. The higher in human development one goes, the more controlled one finds this reaction. Acting on instinct has always meant to me a suspension of reason. How does one adhere to rules under such circumstances? All the killer-instinct boys of my acquaintance obey the rules—when the referee is looking.

For myself, I was always guided by reason in the ring. For everything I did, I had a reason. When I moved back from Heeney an experience of a friend, a splendid little fellow, had come to my mind.

While in Hollywood making "the greatest serial ever produced"—The Fighting Marine—I attended a fight show one night. Gene Delmont, my friend, who seconded me in some A.E.F. matches in France, was in the star bout. Gene went very well for the first three rounds, winning rather easily. At the beginning of the fourth, Gene stepped into a terrific right-hand punch that seemed to land on his forehead. There was an instant reversal of form. Gene backed away. He clinched. He hung on. The referee had a hard time breaking them. The crowd started razzing. Gene was stalling. The fifth round was a repetition of the fourth. Delmont's opponent started getting to him in the sixth, pounding him rather severely. The audience continued booing. The eighth, ninth and tenth rounds were tests of endurance for little Delmont. Leaving the ring, Gene got an unmerciful booing and razzing. The brave ones in the audience called him profane names.

I believed something was wrong, so I went back to the dressing-room. Gene was weeping; the names he had been called when leaving the ring had hurt. I asked him what happened in the fourth round. And this was his answer:

"I got a punch over the left eye that didn't hurt much. I thought it closed my eye. I couldn't see with it. When I got back to my corner I told one of my seconds that the eyelash was in my eye. I asked him to open the eye and turn the lash out.

" 'Your eye is open,' he said.

" 'Stop kidding me,' I said. 'I can't see a thing. Open it.'

" 'I tell you it is open,' he insisted.

"Like a death sentence I realized I was blind in that eye. The doctor now tells me I am going . . ."

And so I could not hit Heeney again.

Good-Night Lady

John B. Kennedy

The Great Depression engendered many a strange phenomenon in the American social scene—but none stranger than the dance marathon. Some entered for "kicks," or to spend a little while in the spotlight. Most entered for money—to live on. For money was hard to come by, in those difficult years—harder on the floor of the marathon dance hall, the contestants found, than almost anywhere else.

July 23, 1932

HELEN WAS WEAKENING. SHE AND HER partner had entered the dance marathon as one of seventy couples bent on endurance and reward; she had entered a plump, vivacious brunette, pretty enough and attested by doctors to be in sound physical condition. That was eleven weeks before. The seventy couples had now thinned out to five, and all these were gummy-eyed, sunken-cheeked and numb with fatigue.

A slim young man spouting through a microphone told a listening world of the scene on the dance floor.

"The seventy-eighth day of the Golden Slipper Marathon Dance Contest," he blurbed. "Only five couples left on the floor. They're stumbling, slipping, fighting to keep awake. There's Helen sleeping on her partner's shoulder. Listen to the crowd yell as a judge comes up to look her over and see if she's fainted or just dozing." (He flaunts the microphone to embrace the crying, crowing spectators squared around the dance floor.) "Helen shudders awake. But she's wilting. It won't be long now.

"Her partner takes her out for the rest period of fifteen minutes. She can hardly stand. She looks twenty years older than when she started eleven weeks ago. But eleven weeks is a long time, folks. The other couples go on. This young guy who's been dancing solo for two weeks since his partner fainted—he hasn't got any girl yet. Their mates are sticking out the grind. It's going to be a bitter finish, folks. Better come along and see it for yourselves."

They came to see it—in hundreds. Helen was the particular favorite of that particular dance marathon. Wherever those organized atrocities are held, one competitor—male or female—becomes an established favorite, especially if he or she is a durable local product, as Joe Humphreys might say. Shrewd showmen promoting the dances are as quick to focus publicity on favorites like Helen as the public is to select these favorites.

They came to see Helen quit. But she didn't. Her feet were swollen. Every touch of the patched and worn dance floor hurt them. So she hobbled around on crutches. This she did for two days and two nights. Housewives thronged the place. Helen was their heroine, and they enjoyed feeling anguish at her all-too-evident pain. Her partner, a square-shouldered young man with the stamina of a deep-sea diver, clinched to save her all the suffering he could. But that wasn't enough. A record crowd saw Helen's final agony on that floor. She came out of the rest cubicle unrevived by consommé and coffee. Bravely she tried to go on, haggard and grim. A five-piece jazz band droned maddeningly. The four other pairs of dancers stumbled about in near-coma. Helen pushed a crutch, it skidded on a smooth spot of the dance floor. Helen skidded with it, and collapsed. She was through, through so utterly that she was insensible to a small shower of bills and coins that fell about her.

Sobs came from women spectators; some shed tears; but the grind of the dance went on and on. Helen, carried away, was revived. Her partner remained, brokenly weaving about the floor, watching the other dancers like a tired jackal, waiting for a male to falter and fail so that he could step in and partner the surviving female. He danced like that, alone, for five days and nights, only emerging from his semiconscious daze to send word to Helen that if he won the prize he'd split his share with her.

That dance dragged on for another weary week. Then the climax. A jammed hall. Two couples left. Spectators divided in hysterical support of each team. A fresh band blared through the same tunes the dancers had heard for twelve solid weeks—a torture in itself. Days ago these "dancers" debased their steps to a mournful shuffle, mocked by jazz. From their twitching faces—faces that stir even in half-sleep—they might be damned souls toiling through eternity on an outer rim of Hades. A shout from the crowd—one pair collapses. A functionary steps out, chains the waists of the swerving pair together. That gives them what is technically called "contact," so that even if leaden arms can no longer be lifted in an embrace—they're still deemed to be dancing partners.

The prize of that dance was theirs—a grim-jawed young woman of thirty who might have been a circus acrobat, and a semi-bald man of about forty who could only have been what he was, a freak in mufti. Hours pass, spectators fade—and when the gate has gone, the dance ends. Two human machines are awarded the title of champion marathon dancers of their district, and the promoters have a two-way chuckle—over the profits and over the fools who make them possible.

Nobody seems to know just where this fad originated. If you visit a zoo you will find many things that resemble a marathon dance, and if you visit a marathon dance you will find many things that resemble a zoo. The swaying bear, the ambient wolf, the peripatetic lynx, to say nothing of the gibbering chimpanzee, are gluttons for motion, yet even these have sense enough to surrender to nature in replenishing sleep.

We've had rocking-chair marathons, talking marathons, roller-skating marathons and pie-eating marathons. All are equally silly, all are equally sad; but the dance marathon, more than any other, reveals human nature at its worst. It's a bug that bites participants and spectators alike.

Research reveals that the first press mention of dance marathoning issued from Indiana. There an indignant hall proprietor, seeing the use to which his premises were put, ordered the dancers and their backers to move. Another hall was hired and the dancers conveyed there in open trucks, shuffling as they rode.

Without that fillip of publicity, this newest and nuttiest of the arts might have been aborted and thousands of uncertified lunatics deprived of an opportunity for self-expression. Alert showmen have turned the fad into a well-organized business.

It works this way. They descend on a town like, say, Newark, New Jersey. They hire a dance hall, preferably in an amusement park. They hang up a first prize of $2,000, with graded prizes down to $50—about $5,000 in all. That begins the ballyhoo. Entry blanks are open to everybody, including juveniles who must have the written consent of parents or guardians. Doctors examine all applicants to find if they're fit for the grueling grind. When passed, they team up with anybody of the opposite sex who's willing. Then time is hired on a local broadcasting station; three jazz bands are assigned eight-hour shifts, and the fun begins.

The dancers come from all walks of life, and in most cases they'd be better off if they'd keep on walking. Young and pretty girls line up with middle-aged women. Boys in their late teens compete with wiry veterans of sixty. Husbands and wives occasionally enter; but their records are poor. They quickly quarrel and reproduce all the atmosphere of home to get themselves chased by the judges.

One woman entrant in Detroit spotted her estranged husband at a dance-opening with another woman. She yanked him away, danced with him for weeks. They won the prize, split it and again split up.

A motley mob by day, in a variety of sports and street costumes, the marathoners resemble a beggars' ball. At night, when the customers pay their fifty cents by the hundreds, the dancers brighten. Many of them appear in evening clothes, although it's observable that the prettier women favor pajamas.

Both sexes are quartered just off the dance floor in two dormitories, littered with wardrobe and baggage. Through with a forty-five-minute spell, they are clocked for fifteen minutes' rest. A fire siren hoots them in and out of the dormitories, where the cots are used in shifts.

Clockers guard against cheating. Two blond boys who looked like twins got away with a trick of wearing identical clothes, one going out for the other so that each, in turn, could get a full hour's sleep. The watchers were fooled, but not the other male dancers. These tolerated the deception until the marathon reached the stage where nerves began to crack. Then they exposed the boys. Disqualification followed.

The most favorable thing that can be said for the promoters of these marathons is that they feed the dancers well—eight meals a day prescribed by a dietitian. It's claimed that the boys and girls actually put on weight during a grind. Some of them were frank enough to confide that if there was nothing else in it, being fed and sheltered for six or seven weeks was an inducement in jobless times.

The men and women eat together; they are only separated in the dormitories, where close supervision is kept over them to guard against irrelevant entertainment. Yet the atmosphere of these affairs is pervaded by sex. Drinking is taboo among the dancers; spectators make up for that enforced abstinence. But every few hours bushels of cigarette stubs, mostly stained by lipstick, are swept from dance floors and rest-rooms. A slip of a girl told me that she consumed four packs a day—an indication of how the crazy contest rags the nerves. The dancers have no time out for a breath of fresh air, save during their fifteen-minute intervals. Leaving the floor for any reason during the forty-five-minute dance session brings instant disqualification.

The judges are stern, especially at the beginning of a marathon. They like to see the field thinned out because that conduces to partisanship by the spectators, and partisanship means swinging turnstiles. They are especially alert for love episodes. Jealousy crops out every now and then when a girl or a man indicates a desire to change partners. Fist fights and hair-pulling often ensue, followed by ejection of the scrappers.

Romance invariably results from each dance. A man and woman who can tolerate each other through days and days of odious propinquity have initiation into the temperamental collisions of matrimony. In logic, that should cure them of the idea. In fact, it doesn't. Wedding bells always follow the bedlam for some pairs of prancers.

Indeed, I suspect that unmarried women go into these things with an eye to making a dance partner a life partner. I asked a stout lady in an expensive evening gown what induced her to leave her home in Chicago to take up marathoning. She had been the wife of an executive of a large national corporation. There was a glint in her eye as the question was asked, coupled with a smirk when it was answered.

"I've found my man," she said, tugging the sleeve of a broad-shouldered youth almost young enough to be her son. The youth gazed desirously at a doll-like girl in vivid magenta pajamas. She ogled him listlessly. He turned to talk to her; but the middle-aged woman tugged his sleeve and trotted him away.

"Nobody's going to get my man," she chirped over a pudgy shoulder.

About the second week of the dance, all the contestants know and call one another by first names. About the fourth week of a dance, the contestants come to call one another by any names that occur to them in their irritation at bumpings, collidings and accidental tramplings.

From that fourth week on to the finish the drama's at its best—or worst. Tempers are sharpened on jagged nerves; blow-ups are frequent.

A man who had achieved a reputation in half a dozen marathons for canniness in conserving his energies and the stamina of his partners caused a riot one night in Brooklyn. He had feet that would have stopped traffic anywhere. His girl would stand on them and be carried around the floor. In turn he would rest his chin on her shoulder and sneak over a snooze. But as the weeks wore on his girl developed an annoying trick of coming out of her dance coma and clawing his face. She didn't mean to do it; but she did it well—so well that word got around and customers piled in to see the act. Before a full house she clawed once too often. The gentleman exploded, landed a haymaker and brought on a free-for-all in which the customers heartily participated until the girl was dragged away unconscious and sent to the massage table.

Tempers pop as the time flies. Couples who, in the early stages, brightened proceedings by rapid tangos or double hulas, concentrate on sticking rather than starring. They smell the prize and settle down stubbornly to win it. This engenders impatience with the side-racket specialists. These are the boys who sell their backs for advertising signs of local merchants and the dancers who juggle and sing to entice showers of coins from the spectators. One lad with a tenor voice like a circus calliope makes hundreds of dollars by singing Mother Machree at different marathons eleven times in a night in a style that should make the composer revolve in his grave. The customers toss him money with outspoken injunctions to shut up. So every time he comes out last in the crap games in which the hardier boys indulge during rest periods, he bounds to the floor and gives poor old Mother Machree another drubbing. Ringsiders always respond.

They sit there, hour after hour, watching for the weary marathoners to break down. And the weary marathoners in turn always respond. Towards the end of the grind each night witnesses some individual or couple go completely out. Many of them go quite mad, although it's granted that they don't have to go very far.

Women marathoners seem to be able to hold their mental balance longer than the men. Certainly they are more expert dancers. During lulls in the music you'll see girls teaching their partners new steps, usually some unorthodox new twist they themselves have invented. That, of course, is early in the dance. Towards the end the steps degenerate to painful plodding. Yet in those vivacious hours when the dance is young a specter lurks behind the life of the party. That specter is the lure that fills the marathon halls by night. It's really brutality, the sight of others in mental and physical anguish that gives beholders a greedy delight. It's the eternal fascination of the kill. Spiced by sex it makes a show to the taste of the tasteless.

Of course there are exceptions. At a marathon dance that had checked in more than a million customers over a period of five weeks, I spotted O. O. McIntyre, whose taste cannot be impugned, no matter what may be said about his tailor. "Odd" sat there bright-eyed—he only wears glasses to pick out his shirts. He'd been sitting there for hours and on many different days.

"Why?" I asked him.

"I like it," he said.

Millions share Mr. McIntyre's curious pleasure in these moron clinics. At the present writing there are eleven marathons in full swing in eight different cities. Jack Curley, master of the sports stockyards where wrestlers eat, drink and make mayhem, is operating dance marathons on the chain-store plan. This shrewd showman plans a series of international marathons, finals of champion couples from all over the world, to be held in New York. He has rivals, because the racket has come at the right time when a fifty-cent top price for a show is practical and popular.

"It's the softest thing I've ever struck," says the calculating but candid Mr. Curley. "As a craze it beats midget golf hollow. The customer doesn't have to do any work. There, my boy, is the secret of success in the exhibition business. Never make your customer exert himself beyond paying at the gate and getting his seat. This is ideal for promoter, participants and public. The promoter makes money because his show is continuous day and night; the participants are paid even if they don't win prizes. They have cash thrown at them by the customers and they're well fed. And the public has every variety of entertainment."

A soft racket like this was not long overlooked by the authorities. In various cities health inspectors dug up the old laws enacted to stop six-day bike racing. These prohibit participation in any athletic event by any individual for more than twelve hours continuously. Curley and his pals kicked that law in its rubber teeth by teaming up bike riders. In dance marathons they get by with that fifteen-minute rest in each hour. Besides, every entrant signs a legal release, so that, whatever happens, the promoters are covered.

Through the haze and odor of one of these marathons at its mad stage, when the boys and girls had been grinding for a solid month, a wiry man in his mid-thirties who had danced throughout in overalls staggered into the dormitory.

He was a steam-fitter by trade until the marathon bug bit him.

"I'm in this racket—for fun and money," he said. "It's going to be my life work. I never win a prize but I get my keep and about thirty bucks a week for my whistling act."

He began to whistle, piercingly—but a fellow artist socked him with a pillow and he fell over on his cot—asleep.

Outside was a pleasant-faced girl who would have been quite pretty if she hadn't been quite fat.

"What am I in this game for?" said she, with perhaps merited scorn in her tone at an obvious question. "What does a girl go into any racket for? Money, of course. I've got two babies to keep. My husband left me—to become a marathon dancer. He's playing in that one up in Boston. So I took up the racket. Oh, I only knock down about twenty dollars a week. You see, I ain't got no specialty like that gal over there. She can do the split."

Figuring hurriedly with a blunt pencil and a blunter arithmetic, this twenty bucks a week for eighteen hours a day works out at what? Too much for the pleasure given the public; too little for the pain given the patient.

How Huey Long Gets Away with It

Walter Davenport

Huey Pierce Long, in the early 1930's was the undisputed dictator of Louisiana and one of the most powerful—and dangerous—men in America. Here Walter Davenport, Collier's *able political writer (and briefly the magazine's editor) analyzes both the personality and the political mechanics of the man called variously Kingfish, Crawfish, and Catfish. Author of a specious "Share the Wealth" plan, Huey Long as U. S. Senator was reaching for national power when an assassin's bullet cut him down in 1935. A great many thoughtful citizens in and out of Louisiana breathed easier when that word came.*

June 17, 1933

TAKE THE WORD OF THE ST. TAMMANY bull, two hundred and twenty pounds of traffic cop, Huey's car comes down Canal Street like a gulf squall. Wham! and she had passed the bull, threading the stalled traffic like a squalling bobcat with dogs at its haunches. Even the cops at the crossings had to be nimble or get run down. The bull had just time to spin about like a gyroscope, halting traffic in all directions, and leap to the curb with his barn-door hand at his cap. Red lights, green lights, white lights—the hell with all that: Huey's in from Washington.

The car takes the right turn into University Place, its rear end slewing to the gutters. Then, with a squeal, a jounce and a snort that fetches it all standing like a bucking horse, the caterwauling thing comes to a stop. War-rump! Like that. The Hotel Roosevelt.

Out of the car, like a dock-walloping, blue-jawed jack-in-the-box, blurts a massive chap who looks as though he was going to be horribly disappointed if nobody tries to stop him. He takes his stand at one side of the door. From the steps of the hotel, where a dozen men stand frozen with the wide eyes and loose jaws of people expecting almost anything, a curiously narrow man with a bloodhound face and a nubbin of cigarette burning the middle of his lips, the smoke curling into the nostrils of his beak of a nose, joins the heavyweight and stands at the other side of the door. From somewhere two quietly violent lads, in shiny blue serge, appear, taking up posts in the middle of the pavement. One waves a quartet of giggling girls back. Just a minute, you dolls, just a minute.

And then out of the car steps Huey—the Honorable Huey P. Long, general manager and business agent of the state of Louisiana, United States senator, protector of the poor, Hotcha Huey (Tell 'em nothing and make 'em like it), Get-'em-while-they're-hot Huey, Let's Go Long, the hardest-working demagogue in America.

To see him for the first time is something of a shock. You would expect a picture of power, the intensity of a zealot, the burning eye of fanaticism, the uncompromising jaw of the crushing autocrat, the lean asceticism of a prophet, the austerity of a despot. But nothing like this. He's pudgy. His cheeks are blotched, flabby. His uncertain nose is red, betokening either bad circulation or entirely too much. His face is weak, willful and there is no discipline in it. But his eyes, soft, protruding robin's eggs, are nevertheless bold. Hit-and-run eyes that roll upward as he talks. And his reddish hair crackles with vigor. Out at the Club Forest in Jefferson Parish, where the vote depends upon how much Huey needs, Rudy O'Dwyer's musclemen or torpedoes tell you he's a "Take-a-chance guy who beats you to the punch by not being there when you deliver it."

Hi-yah. Huey strides across the pavement, the four guards enclosing him in their square. Hi-yah. He leaps up the steps, waving a pudgy hand to the boys. Hi-yah. Hi-yah. Through the lobby shooting that hand hither and yon in recognition and salutation. His voice is flat and aggressive and carries deference to no one. He is met and fawned on by Mr. Seymour Weiss, manager of the hotel, master of moneys for the Long political war chest, sepulcher of many secrets that the United States government has been trying with only indifferent success to disinter for more than a year, chairman of the New Orleans Dock Board, director of the ill-fated Union Indemnity Company, which bonded all Louisiana's state contractors. Mr. Weiss is suave, insinuating, blond, scrubbed pink, softly sure of himself, easily deferential. Hi-yah to him in a loud voice. And he joins the procession toward the elevators, smiling mysteriously.

There's no handshaking. Not that Huey's above handshaking but sometimes, particularly these days when hatreds have boiled to the surface and one's enemies are putting everything they have into one round-house wallop, Huey is taking no chances. It's a Hi-yah and you can take it or leave it. If you want to shake hands with the Kingfish of Louisiana (they're calling him Crawfish since he failed to make good his boast that he would waive senatorial immunity for that libel suit General Sam Ansell of Washington filed against him) you knock on the door of his suite in the hotel and prove that you should get past the strong-arm guys who open to you. Try it, fellah, try it.

Among the first things they tell you about Huey in Louisiana is that he lacks physical courage, that he sleeps behind a machine gun and that his slumbers are guarded by such stanch lads as Joe Messina, Wheaton Stillson, Two-Gun Thompson and Squinch or Squinch-Eye McGee. There's a boy for you—Squinch. Listen, mister, don't lay no hand on the senator; just don't lay no hand on no senator, pal, and you and me will be okay.

But perhaps these stories may be discounted as the wails of the growing number of Louisianians who would like, to hear them tell it, to punch the Kingfish's chin, or have made valiant efforts in that direction only to be confronted by a bodyguard as they hauled off. It is not easy to believe that he is as fearful of physical attack as they say; maybe they mistake prudence or convenience for absence of valor. After all, a state's boss and United States senator can't very well cruise around trading wallops with every Tom, Dick and Harry who thirsts for his blood. For one thing, it wastes a lot of valuable time, and black eyes and missing teeth add nothing to a statesman's appearance.

So in no time Huey is through the hotel lobby and, with a final, all-inclusive Hi-yah, he is in the elevator. None except Huey's personal suite enters that car and it makes no stops on its flight to his rooms on the eleventh floor. The guards see to that. No more of such nonsense as that which followed the running battle between Huey and the venerable ex-Governor Sanders some time ago. The old boy leaped into the elevator after the young senator and nobody is quite sure what would have happened had not a radio announcer, who was also a boxing commissioner, jammed himself between them just as Huey tore a cuff from the ancient Mr. Sanders' shirt and Mr. Sanders was digging his fingers deeply into the Long neck. A nasty mess, as you readily can appreciate, and certainly no position for a United States senator to be in.

In his suite at last, Huey makes ready for the affairs of state. It's quite warm, so he sheds his coat and vest, his necktie and shirt, hurling them from him. They are picked up by retainers who either stand there holding them or hang them in the closet. And while Huey is making himself comfortable on the bed, pillows at his back and his hands hooked behind his head, let's look over the assemblage. We'll have time because Huey is delivering himself of a few snappy commands and a brisk summary of the situation in general. Too bad we can't quote him; but, except when delivering himself for the papers, Huey isn't very quotable. To try it on paper is to lose all the salty flavor of the man's tongue. Fancy having Huey saying, "You blasted old son of a gun" or "You gosh-hanged old bluffer, what in heck are you talking about?" Too bad, but we just can't get away with it here. You probably would enjoy it.

So we'll look around while Huey unburdens his mind. There's Bob Maestri. A capable citizen, Mr. Maestri, of French and Italian blood, forty-three years old, Commissioner of Conservation for the state of Louisiana at five thousand dollars a year. Make no mistake about Mr. Maestri; he serves the Huey Long machine, not Huey. As a collector of campaign funds, you would go far to find his equal. He deals in cash, not checks. To him Senator Long is the head of the political organization he serves, that's all. He has no illusions and, as far as you can observe, no prejudices. Particularly about Huey. (Listen, my friend, you complain because promises have not been kept by this man. But listen. With this man's promises warm upon my ear, I could stand yonder on the roof of La Maison Blanche and my beard which I do not have now would reach the pavement before these promises would be kept. Therefore, my friend, it is well to look after one's own interests oneself.) That's Bob Maestri, who stands there eyeing the recumbent Kingfish with a sidewise, cynical smile.

And yonder, alert, bobbing, shrugging, is Mr. Maestri's team-mate, but younger, the president of the New Orleans Levee Board, the mercurial Abie Shushan, whose mobile face mocks Huey as Huey bids him do this and do that. Mr. Shushan is infinitely more valuable to the Long machine than you might suspect on hearing

Huey abusing the poor fellow. Is ten thousand dollars needed this moment for instant use? Mr. Shushan vanishes, makes a few magical passes and, genie-like, reappears with fifteen thousand. Did the senator demand a cigar? In a trice Mr. Shushan flips open a fresh box of dollar specials with the swift nonchalance of a magician. Senator Long is no dullard; but whereas he thinks louder, Mr. Shushan thinks faster.

These two—Messrs. Maestri and Shushan—seem to be closest to the throne. Perhaps the Honorable T. Semmes Walmsley, mayor of New Orleans, should be included with them, but opinion differs about that. Mr. Walmsley seems scarcely to be eligible for such accomplished company. Mr. Walmsley is of the ordinary run of American mayors and does the Long bidding with gratifying promptitude. With him is State Senator Harvey Peltier, Huey's hard-working leader in the upper house of a completely subjugated legislature, and Dr. Joseph A. O'Hara, who is not only president of the State Board of Health but president of the Louisiana Democratic Association. Huey's own device with which he battered down the defenses of the city of New Orleans and made it his.

Than Dr. O'Hara, not even the cynical Mr. Maestri nor the agreeable Mr. Shushan are better collectors of funds. Dr. O'Hara's forte is in persuading state employees that they should not only make a joyful noise before their lord, Huey, but shower down with anything from ten to twenty per cent of their incomes when elections are about to be indulged in. Just why state employees should have to contribute anything but their presence toward the winning of a Long candidate or a victory for Huey himself is a defiant mystery. As things are at present in Louisiana it would be almost impossible to lose if you wore the Long colors. But that's enough of Huey's audience. Presently, when he needs him, Huey will telephone Baton Rouge and Governor Oscar K. (Okay) Allen will come galloping in with hat in hand. Hi-yah, Allen, where the hell have you been?

This is no ordinary gathering. No election impends. If one did, there would be no reason for all this palaver. Elections in Louisiana are delightfully simple and informal. All you need are a few pencils and plenty of paper. All the preparation necessary is to nominate somebody (Huey takes care of that), collect fifty thousand dollars or so from the officeholders, from business men who would rather do that than have their tax assessments and rates raised and from employees of factories, stores and so forth who owe their jobs to the organization's influence upon their employers, and go to it. Nobody knows where the fifty thousand dollars gets to except the gentlemen in charge of the collections. Ask them and they even forget what day the election was held on.

No, this assemblage is far more important than that. Something far more dangerous than an opposition ticket threatens. Out on the street, boys and men are hawking scandalous sheets and pamphlets written by enemies of the senator, the Kingfish. For two bits you can buy Kidnapped by the Kingfish, a withering blast which accuses Huey of everything short of murder. You don't have to believe what is written therein but it is good entertainment.

For the asking you can have a brochure, Unmasking Crawfish Huey P. Long, wherein it is set forth that Huey is a liar, a coward, a blustering braggart, a blackmailer, a plunderer, a racketeer, an election thief—in so many words. Up in the fragrant town of Hammond, Editor Campbell is issuing weekly salvos of rich hatred wherein Huey is accused of hounding banks into bankruptcy, driving men to suicide, plunging the state into hopeless debt for which the state gets nothing. The gentle John M. Parker, once governor, once candidate for Vice President as Theodore Roosevelt's running mate, a man of such integrity and honor that not even his enemies can impute selfish motives to his opposition, is beseeching the United States Senate to expel Senator Long and his colleague, Senator Overton. The women of the state are demanding that the United States Senate resume its inquiry into the election of Overton and, as a natural corollary, its survey of the reign of the Kingfish.

They accuse Huey of being responsible for the horrible condition of the state's great banks—the Hibernia, the Canal and so on—and they are saying things about the defunct Union Indemnity and its unhappy subsidiaries that are either libelous or too close to truth to be contested. These things do a politician no good. Huey isn't taking convincing steps to refute these accusations which, day by day, gain more believers. He hasn't sued Editor Campbell in the courts; and surely no courts could be more friendly to Huey. And the Kingfish isn't taking legal steps against Mr. Shirley G. Wimberley, the young lawyer who is carpeting the country with his Unmasking pamphlets. What's the matter? Has Huey something to hide?

Here's a lawyer of high repute telling you about Huey's beautiful mansion on Audubon Boulevard in New Orleans. How did Huey get it? Where did he get the money and how much? Is it true that he got the great house from Rudy O'Dwyer of the Club Forest over in Jefferson Parish? And did Rudy get it from an unfortunate gambler, now a bootblack, who turned over the deeds to the mansion when he couldn't take up his I O U's? Well, what about it?

And here's a pamphlet that says shocking things about the origin of the money with which Huey bought himself a hundred-thousand-dollar policy in a Canadian insurance company. Just around the corner you are told that Huey's crowd, buying motor trucks for the state, charged the state treasury $102,000 more than the trucks cost—that $102,000 went into pockets and not trucks. And here's a man who tells you that in his presence a cement company was offered a contract for 2,800,000 barrels of cement for Louisiana roads if it would contribute $25,000 to the organization plus ten cents a barrel. Uncontested tales like these do a politician no good. Nor his organization either. They are either true or lies. And if they're lies, the health of the organization demands that they should be nailed.

A dealer in electric-power plants, offered to the state at twelve hundred dollars each, is asked to make it fifteen hundred and turn two hundred and fifty back to the department that asks for his bid. At least so he tells you—and he doesn't speak in whispers. Something ought to be done about such yarns—if there is anything to be done.

So you see this is no ordinary meeting in Huey's rooms in the Roosevelt. An organization can control the election machinery, it can make the laws and unmake them, it can control courts and conjure up the juries and write the decisions. But let these tales go unchallenged and the electorate is likely to run wild next

February when New Orleans nominates a mayor in the primaries. In the closed banks of Louisiana there are many millions of depositors' money. They closed while Huey himself was exhorting the public to have faith in their banks, to refrain from withdrawing their funds, that nobody would lose a dime in Louisiana banks.

And when the banks closed anyway, Huey is heard to say: "My kids have got $10,000 in cash. It's in a lock box. I've got too gol-durned much sense to put it in a savings bank. All I've got for myself is in insurance, and I've been drawing on that and putting it in a lock box." Naturally that doesn't fetch laughter to the mouths of the thousands of Louisianians who were exhorted by Huey to keep their savings and the educational funds of their children in Louisiana banks which, so go the tales, were sunk by state bonds floated by the Board of Liquidation in Baton Rouge—state bonds which couldn't be sold to an overloaded and impoverished populace and therefore grew yellow in bank vaults.

These things have to be explained, of course. But bad feeling invades the meeting as ways and means of countering the assaults on the Long rule are discussed.

Here's the condition: Louisiana boiling with rebellion, the air soupy with accusatons and vilification. They are ready to do anything they are told—provided Huey tells them. After all, it is up to him to save himself; he is the objective of the attacks, not the Democratic party. The party will survive Huey just as it has survived other leaders and bosses. His captains know that. Huey must, too. Therefore, as all the glory, all the authority, all the emoluments of name and fame have been Huey's, so now is all the responsibility. So what does he propose to do? His stalwarts, gathered there around the bed that is the Kingfish throne, await his command.

In the event that you do not know it, Huey P. Long is not loved in Louisiana even by those subordinates who have followed him to personal fortune. At this moment, hundreds of his vassals are poised to leap the moment they are convinced that he is foundering. They grin at his daring, his boldness, his contempt for precedent, convention and opposition; but they have profited by his own lessons in selfishness, in disregard for others and his blinding egotism. Where not long ago he was hailed as the Kingfish, even within his own organization he is referred to today as the Crawfish, the Tin Can Napoleon, the Catfish Cæsar, the Mud Pie Mussolini.

So there he lolls on the bed, surrounded by his satellites, who await his orders. He is suffering all the woes of absentee-landlordism, the victim of the inaction, the scandalmongering, the jealousies, the resentments and even the sabotage of his tenantry. He is not afraid so much of the voters as he is of treachery in his own crew. As governor of his state his ears and his fingers covered every parish. But Washington is far from New Orleans and Baton Rouge and the hue and cry has extended to the national capital. Even through Huey's amazing conceit, arrogance and blatant egotism, suspicion of double-crossing, of calculated deceit, deception and infidelity are seeping.

He can take care of himself at the polls. That is all provided for. In Louisiana as in other one-party states the primaries are the important thing. In Louisiana, primary elections are actually pulled out of a hat. And statesmen too. Anybody's hat will do; the make, shape, style and quality have nothing whatever to do with the result.

Your hat will serve, or mine would, were we on the scene at the time and in line for such honors.

Of course the growing but still disorganized minority in New Orleans will have it that it is Huey's hat, but that is only a figure of speech, although where virtually everything worth having belongs to Mr. Long, why quibble about the ownership of a hat? Rather let's examine these elections while we are on the subject.

Let us assume that a primary election impends in the parish of St. Bernard. Counties are parishes in Louisiana. Two eager patriots are vying for a seat in Congress. To see to it that the election shall be utterly fair to all concerned, five citizens are chosen to sit in the polling place and pass upon all who come to exercise their royal right of franchise. One candidate for Congress is Huey's. Let us have no doubt about that. He is all Huey's. Whether he is running for governor, for Congress or the state legislature, Huey has chosen him. And Mr. Long has not necessarily chosen him for his statecraft, for his sturdy championship of the rights of the masses, for his love of liberty nor for his looks. For all practical purposes he might just as well have a serial number as a name.

The other aspirant is not Huey's—just a deluded soul who has assumed that a certain number of people might enjoy voting for somebody without the brand on his flank. Of course he has no chance to win, but there are men who seem never to find that out.

Now, to acquire these five election commissioners, each candidate nominates five. Each man so nominated is pledged to sit in the polling place all day to see that his candidate does not suffer the mortification of getting no votes at all. I have talked to ladies and gentlemen in Louisiana who tell me that while they have voted regularly for years they have yet to find that anybody has ever paid the slightest attention.

Anyway the ten nominees for commissionerships (watchers) are thrown into a hat. Then some designated person, chosen on the spot, is asked to step forward, reach into the hat without peeping and extract five names. The five names thus drawn are the election commissioners. No telling, you see, which of the candidates for office will get the majority on the board of commissioners. A square deal for everybody. Such, at least, is the law.

Now, if that were all of it the chances for an honest election in Louisiana would be fairly bright. You can see for yourself. But so could the Long machine. The law has it that each candidate for the office contested for may nominate five commissioners. Therefore (and particularly when the independent candidate is a mean critter, given to fighting for his few remaining rights and of making himself thoroughly objectionable in an argument) the friends of the Long candidate rally round.

Two, five, ten or even twenty of them file for the same nomination their pal seeks. Of course they don't want the job he aspires to. They have been told by their betters that they can't have it anyway. But they can file for the nomination and each can, and does, nominate five names for commissioners. These names they drop into the hat. After the drawing they retire from the race, their functions accomplished.

You see how it is. The independent has five names in the hat. His opposition has anywhere up to a hundred. The independent's nominees for commissionerships go into the hat first. The fifty opposing nominations are dumped in afterward, completely smothering the lonely five. Then the drawing.

Now it is just a waste of time to ask why the independents don't do precisely the same thing. To begin with, it costs money to file one's name for office—anywhere from a hundred and twenty-five to a hundred and fifty dollars. And that's a mere beginning. And such is the spell the Kingfish has woven around and over the citizenry of his native state, that whatever it costs is regarded as just so much money thrown away—unless, of course, you are running on the Long ticket.

Moreover, the moneyed people who might match the Long candidates dollar for dollar indignantly reject all suggestions that they fight the devil with a poker. Such practical gentlemen as Mr. Francis Williams, the most aggressive of all of Long's political foemen, lack the financial resources to give the machine a battle on its own ground. So there you have it. Those who would fight Long with his own tools lack the cash to purchase them with; those who could are too ethical or respectable, or something.

But you get the idea. Under the conditions it is almost certain that the board of commissioners will all be true to Huey. All sorts of things can happen to the five names of the independent aspirants. Once the name of one of these anti-Long lads managed to get out of the hat wherein one hundred names of organization boys had been dropped. They called him Houdini after that. He went to the hospital before the polls closed, poor soul, the human system being able to stand just so much punishment and no more. But when he was released from the hospital he was taken into the Kingfish's political lodge by sheer force and smothered with honors because an investigation of this unprecedented situation had revealed that somehow he had insinuated his name into that hat fifteen times. He died an utterly prosaic death two years later with his family at the bedside, without having revealed the secret of his success. But Mr. Long's boys were fearfully worried for a time, not so much that this gentleman should have had his name in that hat fifteen times but rather that Mr. Long might think them lax in their stewardship of his interests.

A machine like Mr. Long's leaves as little to chance as the scheme of nature permits. Let us say that somehow a couple of independents get on a board of election commissioners down here in St. Bernard Parish, or in the Irish Channel district of Orleans Parish. Or over in Jefferson or Plaquemines. In such event the Long lads take advantage of a saving emergency clause in the law.

The polls open at six o'clock in the morning. The commissioners are supposed to be there at that hour, not a moment later. If the entire board is not on hand at the stroke of the hour, those who have sacrificed sleep to serve the public begin the day by electing substitutes for those who failed to arrive on time. And all sorts of things can have happened to the tardy ones—the independents. Just use your imagination. If you were hired to delay a man a few moments, and were well paid for it, you probably would find a way. Particularly if you had the coöperation of four or five strong assistants.

And suppose that only one commissioner arrives at the polls at six. He will be a Long man, make no mistake about that. At once he selects, from a crowd standing near by, a substitute. The two of them select a third. The trio chooses a fourth and this swift quartet takes unto itself a fifth. And there you are. Hooray for our side!

Therefore you must understand that Huey is not worrying there in his rooms in the hotel about the machinery of elections. And you can't accuse him or his followers of having done nothing to mend conditions. Indeed, they took the whole election law to the courts, saying that their opponents had found fault with it. The organization's own lawyers besought the Supreme Court of Louisiana to look the law over from stem to stern and do something about it, because if there is one thing that the Kingfish dislikes more than another it is to have his people dissatisfied. So the Supreme Court looked it over and deplored it and did something about it. It was decided that the penalty clause was unconstitutional and it was so declared. Now Louisiana has the law with no penalty clause attached. And who can say the courts did not do something about it?

You can see then that it is not the elections that worry Huey, but the way his men have of letting him down when he is up in Washington about the nation's business. Not only let him down but do utterly stupid things. For instance, the slugging of Mr. Joe Boudreaux in Baton Rouge. Nobody knows just who ordered the slugging of Mr. Boudreaux, but things like that do a political organization no good.

You see, Mr. Boudreaux and the militant Mr. Francis Williams, the liberal lawyer and constant challenger of Senator Long, were in the beautiful new capitol building which Huey built after the manner of a man erecting his own monument. They had just come from the Hotel Heidelberg, a few blocks away, where Mr. Williams had called Mr. Long things that one doesn't call a gentleman. Mr. Williams went further and proposed to punch Mr. Long in the nose. Whereat Mr. McGee—Squinch or Squinch-Eye—stepped between the somewhat abashed Senator Long and the irate Mr. Williams and, hands in coat pockets, bade Mr. Williams not to lay no hand on the senator, and, furthermore, not to lay no hand on no senator.

At the capitol, however, someone stepped up behind Mr. Williams and landed a manly wallop on Mr. Williams' jaw. In the excitement and general milling that ensued the slugger departed. But Mr. Boudreaux was escorted out of the capitol by several heavyweight champions of the Long cause and, at the bottom of the great stone steps—a fine, long sweep of perhaps fifty feet—was smashed with the butt of a .45 caliber automatic and carted off to the police station where it was found that his skull was fractured, and he was transferred to a hospital.

When the perpetrator of this valiant deed reported back to his superiors in the capitol he was mortified to hear himself addressed as a fat-head, a mug, a moron and a dumb thug. You see, Mr. Boudreaux should have been slugged at the top of the great stone flight instead of at the bottom. From the top of the steps he would have fallen all the way down. Then who could have denied that he had fallen in his efforts to escape officers of the law? And how much greater would have been the chances of his failure to recover.

But such stupid sluggings tend to irritate the senator. What about doing something to counteract the effect of all this nasty propaganda, all these ribald pamphlets, all these shouted charges that somebody romped off with the public-school funds from the state treasury? Everybody ought to know that nobody would steal the money that should have gone to educate the kiddies—not intentionally, anyway.

It just happens that the Louisiana law has it that all public moneys shall be kept in one account, under one title—the general fund. The natural outcome of a system of that sort is that he gets the money who gets there first and it is your own fault if you are late.

Now the public schools of the state had a balance in the treasury of $1,033,549.07 on January 1, 1933. But when it came time to pay the teachers and defray the other incidental expenses of teaching the young, it was discovered that someone had not only made off with that neat sum but had overdrawn the state's bank account—the general fund—to the extent of $2,452,429.89. So some of the schools had to close while others went on a thirty-five per cent diet. All this would be rectified. The schools were assured of that. But in the general excitement of bank closings and the like the rectifying was overlooked and the overdraft on March 31 had swelled to $3,341,024.34.

Something should be done to calm the people about that dismal circumstance instead of punching Francis Williams on the jaw and breaking the cranium of Joe Boudreaux. And a little brains might be applied to pleasant explanations of why, on March 31, the state of Louisiana had exactly $790,734.63 in banks to compare with a state indebtedness of $136,156,460. And that, mind you, is merely the state's indebtedness. Add what the parishes and all the subdivisions owe and you find Louisiana in debt to the extent of $395,532,463.47. Which does not include the $7,000,000 that the state has borrowed from the Reconstruction Finance Corporation for relief of the needy, or bond issues and other indebtednesses for drainage districts, which haul the total up to about $425,000,000.

So this is what the conference in Huey's hotel rooms is about—about this growing propaganda, about this incessant demand of the opposition that the Senate committee on campaign expenditures reconvene.

But it is going to be an exhausting task for the miracle-working Mr. Long. The doggedly sincere John M. Parker, who, as governor of Louisiana, freed that violated state from the domination of the Ku Klux Klan, has petitioned the United States Senate in words that not even Huey can laugh off. Let the committee reconvene, say Mr. Parker and his associates, and they will furnish proof that Huey is "the greatest menace to American decency and civilization, that he knows neither truth, honesty, nor decency. Psychiatrists have stated in my presence that he is a dangerous paranoiac."

Mr. Parker is well acquainted with Huey, having sued the Boss of Louisiana for criminal libel and having won. "Huey P. Long," says Mr. Parker to the United States Senate, "is personally dishonest, corrupt and immoral. He has created and maintained in Louisiana a system of corruption and debauchery unparalleled in the history of the state, not even excepting the so-called Louisiana Lottery. He has operated a system of so-called racketeering. He has made elections a farce. He has gained control of the legislature and no relief can be obtained from that source. He has boasted publicly that he controlled its members like a deck of cards, bought them like loads of potatoes. He escaped trial after impeachment by bribery and other corrupt methods. He has declared openly that he controlled our state courts. Relief from the courts under existing conditions is impossible. The only hope for relief is through the Senate of the United States."

It is going to take all the influence, actual or alleged, that Huey can muster to stave off a resumption of the investigation. Mr. Parker's charges are not those of a political aspirant; he seeks nothing but an even break for Louisiana, a complete investigation of conditions in a state that Huey has made his private skating rink. A nasty spot for Huey Long, who is seeking cover these days in spite of his doughty words. When he backed out of his invitation to General Ansell to sue him for slander when he called the general a "thief, a rascal and a crook," taking advantage of senatorial immunity when the general field libel proceedings, Huey lost considerable respect at home, where they still believed his boasts of fearlessness.

Thus far he has kept the investigation committee adjourned. How? Well, let's see.

Says Hitler

T. R. Ybarra

On a Spring day in 1933, two men sat together in an office in Berlin, the one talking, rapidly and eloquently, occasionally tapping his companion's knee for emphasis; the other listening. The listener, Collier's *reporter T. R. Ybarra, wrote later that he "couldn't help wondering whether . . . Hitler is definitely turning to a statesmanlike calm after years of demagogic violence. . . ." The answer was to be written in blood.*

July 1, 1933

While Berlin was still ringing with Chancellor Adolf Hitler's first big speech before the Reichstag on the foreign crisis besetting Germany and while government officials, foreigners and the Berlin public—everybody—were snatching newspapers, eagerly devouring all foreign comment and breathing a deep sigh of thanksgiving at the easing of the tension which had almost seemed a prelude to another European war, the man who had made that speech and eased that tension kept his promise to give Collier's an interview.

He found time amid Cabinet meetings, which were following one another in quick succession, to receive me in his office at the chancellery on Berlin's historic Wilhelmstrasse. Without hesitation, concisely and straight from the shoulder, Chancellor Hitler—who in the opinion of many, even his enemies, had taken his first step as a statesman after years of sensational success as a spellbinding orator possessed of the secret of lashing multitudes to hysterical patriotic frenzy—gave me a message direct from himself to the American nation, the kernel of which was a plea for better understanding among Americans for the problems now confronting Germany at home and abroad.

When he received me Hitler made a strange contrast to his Wilhelmstrasse surroundings. He had so far conformed to statesmanlike etiquette as to don the conventional garments usual at European chancelleries—which he still does reluctantly.

But beyond the anteroom of his sanctum the corridors of the chancellery were swarming with picked Nazi storm troopers in full uniform, bristling with swastikas and other insignia, their revolvers dangling in plain sight from their hips—and Nazi revolvers give the distinct impression of being carried because they are useful, not merely ornamental. These rough characters contrasted ludicrously with the officials left over from the pre-Nazi era, who were going about as if ashamed of their ceremonial toggery, looking—and doubtless feeling—like fish out of water. Coming from among the brown-shirted guards and from the street outside were other uniformed, armed Nazis constantly passing through, arousing the impression that Berlin had been captured by an army of roughnecks.

The spectacle of the biggest Brown Shirt of all, Adolf Hitler, attired as neatly and conventionally as his Beau Brummel predecessor, Franz von Papen, certainly came as a shock. I couldn't help wondering whether it was an omen presaging that Hitler is definitely turning to a statesmanlike calm after years of demagogic violence, and seeking to end the swashbuckling first phase of his régime, which was characterized by the Berlin wag as "Brown Shirt-sleeve Diplomacy."

Hitler received me in the big audience chamber of the new chancellery. It adjoins the old chancellery, where President von Hindenburg is now living while the presidential palace, a little way up Wilhelmstrasse, is being repaired. The Chancellor's eyes were clear, his bearing alert, and he allowed no signs of fatigue to become apparent. During the preceding days, Hitler had had no rest. From Templehof Field outside Berlin, where he addressed more than a million persons, he had rushed to Kiel, then to Königsberg, then to Munich. Always he traveled by airplane, to the intense worry of those around him, who constantly feared accidents. And all the while the international situation was growing more serious, the foreign ring around Germany more threatening, the clouds presaging war bigger and blacker.

Yet when he stepped forward to shake my hand you wouldn't have thought he was bothered about anything. His face was solemn—but it always is. And he didn't smile—but he seldom does.

I asked him to talk straight out to Americans. He paused a moment, then said:

"I don't believe in criticizing. It simply creates difficulties."

Then, gathering force and speed as he talked, until he almost resembled the Hitler who has so often swayed mass meetings to tumultuous enthusiasm, he continued:

"In observing the American attitude toward Germany, some things have been beyond my understanding. Certainly Americans are interested in the maintenance of peace in Europe, aren't they? Certainly they don't want to see Europe go up in flames. Certainly they have economic interests in Europe which they want consolidated. And certainly they don't want another European war which would prevent their economic development.

"This being so, how can Americans fail to realize that the very existence of weapons of aggressive warfare such as are possessed by some of the European nations constitutes in itself a menace to peace? The existence of such weapons is a threat to all nations. To safeguard herself against them, Germany should have the right to provide herself with unlimited defensive weapons. If Germany is not allowed these, Europe, which urgently needs peace, will be ruined. In the interests of peace Germany should be allowed these defensive weapons, at least so long as other nations are allowed aggressive weapons.

"Tanks are aggressive weapons. Germany has no tanks. By what right are we denied anti-tank weapons?"

Worked up by this time to a high pitch of earnestness, Hitler leaned forward, emphasizing his points by tapping my knee with two fingers of his right hand.

"Germany has no bombing planes," he continued, "yet we Germans are denied anti-aircraft defense weapons. How can Americans think it is a help for peace to have Germans unable to defend themselves from aërial attack? How can it help peace if we Germans are unable to bombard Paris while the French are able to bombard Berlin? I tell you it isn't logical. We Germans should at least be allowed to have adequate defensive weapons. This would be advantageous to the cause of peace and not detrimental."

He paused for a moment and I, knowing well the torrential nature of his eloquence when once under way, carefully refrained from interrupting with questions. For a moment Hitler sat there with knit brows and stern expression. Then, fixing his eyes again on me, he said:

"You Americans should understand the internal problems of Germany. Germany is overpopulated. You Americans too have an immigration problem. You have made restrictions against immigrants of the sort you don't want in America. Why are not Americans fair enough to admit that we Germans have the same right?

"The United States has fourteen or fifteen inhabitants per square kilometer against Germany's one hundred and thirty-seven. Much of Germany is worthless soil, sandy land—look at such regions as our arid Lüneburger Heide, which you Americans wouldn't think of trying to cultivate. Overpopulated as we are we must have the right to say what elements we don't want to admit into our country."

I asked the Chancellor to specify exactly against what elements he was talking.

"We don't want Jews from eastern Europe," he said. "It is for us Germans to decide this matter. You Americans make similar restrictions. Why don't Americans then show an understanding for questions of this kind?"

This brought us to the question whereon Hitler feels very strongly—the picture of "the Reign of Terror" painted in foreign newspapers during the first phase of his régime.

"There was no terror in Germany," he said. "How can any American believe, for instance, the tales told before the Reichstag election early this year of the terrorizing of voters by the National Socialists in view of the fact that ninety per cent of the Germans entitled to vote actually did go to the polls? Under a reign of terror people don't go to the polls. They stay home.

"Whatever violence there was is now past. Perfect calm reigns in Germany. Not a street has been destroyed, not a house. Where is this terror they talk about? What a difference when the English and the Irish fought each other in the days of the Irish rebellion! Dublin was a different-looking place from Berlin when we settled accounts with the German Communists." He leaned back and looked me straight in the eye. "Wasn't it?" he asked.

Then he turned once more to his favorite method of emphasizing points by comparing American and German conditions.

"You have—let me see—how many unemployed? Eight millions? Ten millions? At any rate, you know how serious the unemployment situation is. Well, suppose that all these millions of American unemployed were Communists taking their orders from Russia. That's the situation here in Germany. We have millions of unemployed and the great majority of them are Communists. Germany has six million Communists—ten per cent of our total population.

"I couldn't understand America's attitude at the time of the Reichstag fire a few months ago. The accusation was made that the Reichstag was set on fire by members of my party. Do Americans really believe I needed to do such a thing in my fight against Communists, even if I had wanted to do it? That's absurd. The trial of those suspected of burning the Reichstag will prove the existence of an enormous Communist conspiracy. I tell you we have Communists here in Germany who would not be allowed to go free for a moment in America! You in America wouldn't tolerate for one hour what we in Germany have been forced to endure from these Communists. Americans should view international problems from the viewpoint of other nations. They must try to get inside other people's minds. I know this isn't easy. But only thus can understanding come."

Again the Chancellor leaned forward, his voice tense with earnestness. Again he tapped my knee as he said: "Here is what I wish would happen: That American people might understand these special German problems. In my speech before the Reichstag I avoided statistics. Nevertheless, I did point out that in Germany, since the signing of the Versailles Treaty fourteen years ago, there have been 224,000 suicides—forty per day. It is incredible. Germany is in a tragic situation. In the war of 1870 against France, Germany lost only 60,000 killed."

He paused. In silence he gazed straight ahead. He seemed to be trying actually to see the Americans to whom he was addressing his words. Into his face came some of that mystical quality which has helped him to drive audiences to hysteria.

"If only all Americans," he said, coming out of his reverie and fixing his eyes on mine, "could come over here to Germany. They would look about and ask themselves where is this revolution, where is this terror, where is all this destruction and chaos I've heard about?"

Then abruptly he stood up. The interview was over. We shook hands. A moment later he was back amid the other Nazi chieftains debating the latest thorny problems confronting Germany. And I was out in the corridor among those tough-faced, hard-boiled Nazi guards with their swastikas and military boots and their ready revolvers strapped to their sides.

When I interviewed the Nazi chief, Germany was quieting down. The first phase of Hitlerism's triumph was ending, the second just beginning. The first phase consisted of kicking things to pieces. The second phase consists of sticking them together again. The first phase was characterized by anti-Jewish attacks, crushing political opposition and an intensive campaign against freedom of the press, states rights, independence of trade unions, and so on. Abroad, it had almost obliterated whatever world opinion there was favorable to Germany, also sentiment for the revision of the Versailles Treaty. The second phase is being characterized—and this even before Hitler's Reichstag speech—by unmistakable signs that the Hitlerists are worried about foreign hostility and are desirous of getting back into the good graces of the world.

Nevertheless, life in Berlin still resembled sitting on the edge of a volcano, wondering when rumblings and smoke would be replaced by lava and fire. That there is relief is beyond doubt—but it is no more genuinely satisfactory than a reprieve granted to a prisoner condemned to the gallows.

The relentless march of the Nazi steamroller continues. Scarcely a sound comes from the Hitler régime's opponents. Socialists, formerly dominant in German politics, are as silent as the grave. Centrists, so influential before, apparently have been swept into the ash-heap. And the Communists, who polled a million votes recently seem blotted out of existence.

Yet despite this Nazi predominance one cannot help thinking that the opposition must be somewhere underground, biding its time. As one observer put it, "It is simply impossible that all Centrists, all Socialists and all Communists should suddenly have lain down and died."

At the time of my talk with Hitler there was no indication of a cessation of anti-Jewish persecution. Daily lists were being published of professors dismissed from universities, many of whom are Jews with nothing else against them. A big chain-store firm and other concerns were being obliged to close temporarily because their Nazi employees had struck against Jewish control. At the headquarters of a big publishing house, a procession of striking employees surged through the corridors shouting: "We want all Jewish bosses fired." Here as elsewhere, there was nothing to do but to obey. Many Jews, being dismissed after years of faithful service, were now besieging the offices of Americans in business in Berlin seeking work. The fruits of a lifetime of toil had been snatched from them—in many cases they faced destitution—and often men who formerly had held the most important and best-paid positions were telling Americans that they were willing to do anything for wages no better than an office boy's.

There was an enormous amount of curiosity in Berlin as to whether Germany's new ruler would continue a ruthlessness at home and initiate an aggressive policy abroad, or act more in conformity with the statesmanlike note of his Reichstag speech.

Was it to be a case of Hitler Jekyll or Hitler Hyde? Would the second phase of Hitlerism be an era of constructive statesmanship or destructive violence? There was a distinct impression that if Hitler really favored Jekyll tactics he must soon have a show-down with such rabid chieftains at Goering and Goebbels, who apparently are wedded, heart and soul, to Hyde methods.

But some observers believe that the situation inside the Hitlerist ranks is another case of Frankenstein and his monster. They feel that because Hitler for years has been promising his adherents that Jews would be uprooted and all opposition crushed, and that foreigners would be shown the temper of a new Germany, he was obliged to make good his violent promises. But sometimes it certainly seemed that Adolf Frankenstein Hitler's machine was running amuck. Many of us foreigners, sitting on the rim of the German volcano, occasionally wondered whether Hitler really was boss of his own show any more.

Ancient Roman emperors used to boast that all the populace needed to be kept in leash was *panem et circenses*—bread and circuses. So far Hitlerism has given Germans many marvelous circus stunts—colossal patriotic demonstrations, unending parades, martial music, thrilling songs, constantly driving the multitudes to delirious patriotism by speakers, including Hitler, frankly using revival-meeting methods. If a change is indeed coming over Hitlerist acts at home and abroad, then it will mark the end of the circus phase of the movement. It remains to be seen whether this second phase will provide bread—both literally by finding jobs for the unemployed and restoring prosperity, and figuratively by lessening the hostility among the nations around Germany, which a few weeks ago almost became a threat of war.

The Three Wise Guys

Damon Runyon

Kansas-born Damon Runyon won fame as a sports writer, war correspondent, and newspaper columnist, but he is best remembered for the gallery of Broadway characters whom he knew, loved, translated into fiction, and endowed with rare warmth and whimsy. "The Three Wise Guys" first appeared in the Christmas issue of 1933, and again—ten years after Runyon's death—in the second last issue of Collier's *ever to appear—Christmas of 1956.*

December 23, 1933

ONE COLD WINTER AFTERNOON I AM standing at the bar in Good Time Charley's little drum in West 49th Street, partaking of a mixture of rock candy and rye whisky, and this is a most surprising thing for me to be doing, as I am by no means a rumpot, and very seldom indulge in alcoholic beverages in any way, shape, manner, or form.

But when I step into Good Time Charley's on the afternoon in question, I am feeling as if maybe I have a touch of grippe coming on, and Good Time Charley tells me that there is nothing in this world as good for a touch of grippe as rock candy and rye whisky, as it assassinates the germs at once.

It seems that Good Time Charley always keeps a stock of rock candy and rye whisky on hand for touches of the grippe, and he gives me a few doses immediately, and in fact Charley takes a few doses with me, as he says there is no telling but what I am scattering germs of my touch of the grippe all around the joint, and he must safeguard his health. We are both commencing to feel much better when the door opens, and who comes in but a guy by the name of Blondy Swanson.

This Blondy Swanson is a big, six-foot-two guy, with straw-colored hair, and pink cheeks, and he is originally out of Harlem, and it is well known to one and all that in his day he is the largest puller on the Atlantic seaboard. In fact, for upwards of ten years, Blondy is bringing wet goods into New York from Canada, and one place and another, and in all this time he never gets a fall, which is considered a phenomenal record for an operator as extensive as Blondy.

Well, Blondy steps up alongside me at the bar, and I ask him if he cares to have a few doses of rock candy and rye whisky with me and Good Time Charley, and Blondy says he will consider it a privilege and a pleasure, because, he says, he always has something of a sweet tooth. So we have these few doses, and I say to Blondy Swanson that I hope and trust that business is thriving with him.

"I have no business," Blondy Swanson says. "I retire from business."

Well, if J. Pierpont Morgan, or John D. Rockefeller, or Henry Ford step up and tell me they retire from business, I will not be more astonished than I am by this statement from Blondy Swanson, and in fact not as much. I consider Blondy's statement the most important commercial announcement I hear in many years, and naturally I ask him why he makes such a decision, and what is to become of thousands of citizens who are dependent on him for merchandise.

"Well," Blondy says, "I retire from business because I am one hundred per cent American citizen. In fact," he says, "I am a patriot. I serve my country in the late war. I am cited at Château-Thierry. I always vote the straight Democratic ticket, except," he says, "when we figure it better to elect some Republican. I always stand up when the band plays the Star-Spangled Banner. One year I even pay an income tax," Blondy says.

And of course I know that many of these things are true, although I remember hearing rumors that if the draft officer is along half an hour later than he is, he will not see Blondy for heel dust, and that what Blondy is cited for at Château-Thierry is for not robbing the dead.

But of course I do not speak of these matters to Blondy Swanson, because Blondy is not such a guy as will care to listen to rumors, and may become indignant, and when Blondy is indignant he is very difficult to get along with.

"Now," Blondy says, "I am a bootie for a long time, and supply very fine merchandise to my trade, as everybody knows, and it is a respectable business, because one and all in this country are in favor of it, except the prohibitionists. But," he says, "I can see into the future, and I can see that one of these days they are going to repeal the prohibition law, and then it will be most unpatriotic to be bringing in wet goods from foreign parts in competition with home industry. So I retire," Blondy says.

"Well, Blondy," I say, "your sentiments certainly do you credit, and if we have more citizens as high minded as you are, this will be a better country."

"Furthermore," Blondy says, "there is no money in booting any more. All the booties in this country are broke. I am broke myself," he says. "I just lose the last piece of property I own in the world, which is the twenty-five-G home I build in Atlantic City, figuring to spend the rest of my days there with Miss Clarabelle Cobb, before she takes a runout powder on me. Well," Blondy says, "if I only listen to Miss Clarabelle Cobb, I will now be an honest clerk in a gents' furnishing store, with maybe a cute little apartment up around 110th Street, and children running all around and about."

And with this, Blondy sighs heavily, and I sigh with him, because the romance of Blondy Swanson and Miss Clarabelle Cobb is well known to one and all on Broadway.

It goes back a matter of anyway six years when Blondy Swanson is making money so fast he can scarcely stop to count it, and at this time Miss Clarabelle Cobb is the most beautiful doll in this town, and many citizens almost lose their minds just gazing at her when she is a member of Mr. Georgie White's Scandals, including Blondy Swanson.

In fact, after Blondy Swanson sees Miss Clarabelle Cobb in just one performance of Mr. Georgie White's Scandals, he is never quite the same guy again. He goes to a lot of bother meeting up with Miss Clarabelle Cobb, and then he takes to hanging out around Mr. Georgie White's stage door, and sending Miss Clarabelle Cobb ten-pound boxes of candy, and floral horseshoes, and wreaths, and also packages of trinkets, including such articles as diamond bracelets, and brooches, and vanity cases, for there is no denying that Blondy is a fast guy with a dollar.

But it seems that Miss Clarabelle Cobb will not accept any of these offerings, except the candy and the flowers, and she goes so far as to return a sable coat that Blondy sends her one very cold day, and she is openly criticized for this action by some of the other dolls in Mr. Georgie White's Scandals, for they say that after all there is a limit even to eccentricity.

But Miss Clarabelle Cobb states that she is not accepting valuable offerings from any guy, and especially a guy who is engaged in trafficking in the demon rum, because she says that his money is nothing but blood money that comes from breaking the law of the land, although, as a matter of fact, this is a dead wrong rap against Blondy Swanson, as he never handles a drop of rum in his life, but only Scotch, and furthermore he keeps himself pretty well straightened out with the law.

The idea is, Miss Clarabelle Cobb comes of very religious people back in Akron, Ohio, and she is taught from childhood that rum is a terrible thing, and personally I think it is myself, except in cocktails, and furthermore, the last thing her mamma tells her when she leaves for New York is to beware of any guys who come around offering her diamond bracelets and fur coats, because her mamma says such guys are undoubtedly snakes in the grass, and probably on the make.

But while she will not accept his offerings, Miss Clarabelle Cobb does not object to going out with Blondy Swanson now and then, and putting on the chicken Mexicaine, and the lobster Newburg, and other items of this nature, and any time you put a good-looking young guy and a beautiful doll together over the chicken Mexicaine and the lobster Newburg often enough, you are apt to have a case of love on your hands.

And this is what happens to Blondy Swanson and Miss Clarabelle Cobb, and in fact they become in love more than somewhat, and Blondy Swanson is wishing to marry Miss Clarabelle Cobb, but one night over a batch of lobster Newburg, she says to him like this:

"Blondy," she says, "I love you, and," she says, "I will marry you in a minute if you get out of trafficking in rum. I will marry you if you are out of the rum business, and do not have a dime, but I will never marry you as long as you are dealing in rum, no matter if you have a hundred million."

Well, Blondy says he will get out of the racket at once, and he keeps saying this every now and then for a year or so, and the chances are that several times he means it, but when a guy is in this business in those days as strong as Blondy Swanson it is not so easy for him to get out, even if he wishes to do so. And then one day Miss Clarabelle Cobb has a talk with Blondy, and says to him as follows:

"Blondy," she says, "I still love you, but you care more for your business than you do for me. So I am going back to Ohio," she says. "I am sick and tired of Broadway, anyhow. Some day when you are really through with the terrible traffic you are now engaged in, come to me."

And with this, Miss Clarabelle Cobb takes plenty of outdoors on Blondy Swanson, and is seen no more in these parts. At first Blondy thinks she is only trying to put a little pressure on him, and will be back, but as the weeks become months, and the months finally count up into years, Blondy can see that she is by no means clowning with him. Furthermore, he never hears from her, and all he knows is she is back in Akron, Ohio.

Well, Blondy is always promising himself that he will soon pack in on hauling wet goods, and go look up Miss Clarabelle Cobb and marry her, but he keeps putting it off, and putting it off, until finally one day he hears that Miss Clarabelle Cobb marries some legitimate guy in Akron, and this is a terrible blow to Blondy, indeed, and from this day he never looks at another doll again, or anyway not much.

Naturally, I express my deep sympathy to Blondy about being broke, and I also mention that my heart bleeds for him in his loss of Miss Clarabelle Cobb, and we have a few doses of rock candy and rye whisky on both propositions, and by this time Good Time Charley runs out of rock candy, and anyway it is a lot of bother for him to be mixing it up with the rye whisky, so we have the rye whisky without the rock candy, and personally I do not notice much difference.

Well, while we are standing there at the bar having our rye whisky without the rock candy, who comes in but an old guy by the name of The Dutchman, who is known to one and all as a most illegal character in every respect. In fact, The Dutchman has no standing whatever in the community, and I am somewhat surprised to see him appear in Good Time Charley's, because The Dutchman is generally a lammie from some place, and the gendarmes everywhere are always anxious to have a chat with him. The last I hear of The Dutchman he is in college somewhere out West for highway robbery, although afterwards he tells me it is a case of mistaken identity. It seems he mistakes a copper in plain clothes for a groceryman.

The Dutchman is an old-fashioned looking guy of maybe fifty-odd, and he has gray hair, and a stubby gray beard, and he is short, and thickest, and always good-natured, even when there is no call for it, and to look at him you will think there is no more harm in him than there is in a preacher, and maybe not as much.

As The Dutchman comes in, he takes a peek all around and about as if he is looking for somebody in particular, and when he sees Blondy Swanson he moves up alongside Blondy and begins whispering to Blondy until Blondy pulls away and tells him to speak freely.

Now The Dutchman has a very interesting story, and it goes like this:

It seems that about eight or nine months back The Dutchman is mobbed up with a party of three very classy heavy guys who make quite a good thing of going around knocking off safes in small-town jugs, and post offices, and stores in small towns, and taking the money, or whatever else is valuable in these safes. This is once quite a popular custom in this country, although it dies out to some extent of late years because they improve the brand of safes so much it is a lot of bother knocking them off, but it comes back during the depression when there is no other way of making money, until it is a very prosperous business again. And of course this is very nice for old-time heavy guys, such as The Dutchman, because it gives them something to do in their old age.

Anyway, it seems that this party The Dutchman is with goes over into Pennsylvania one night on a tip from a friend and knocks off a safe in a factory office, and gets a pay roll amounting to maybe fifty G's. But it seems that while they are making their getaway in an automobile, the gendarmes take out after them, and there is a chase, during which there is considerable blasting back and forth.

Well, finally in this blasting, the three guys with The Dutchman get cooled off, and The Dutchman also gets shot up quite some, and he abandons the automobile out on an open road, taking the money, which is in a gripsack, with him, and he somehow manages to escape the gendarmes by going across country, and hiding here and there.

But The Dutchman gets pretty well petered out, what with his wounds, and trying to lug the gripsack, and one night he comes to an old deserted barn, and he decides to stash the gripsack in this barn, because there is no chance he can keep lugging it around much longer. So he takes up a few boards in the floor of the barn, and digs a nice hole in the ground underneath and plants the gripsack there, figuring to come back some day and pick it up.

Well, The Dutchman gets over into New Jersey one way and another, and lays up in a town by the name of New Brunswick until his wounds are healed, which requires considerable time as The Dutchman cannot take it nowadays as good as he can when he is younger.

Furthermore, even after The Dutchman recovers and gets to thinking of going after the stashed gripsack, he finds he is about half out of confidence, which is what happens to all guys when they commence getting old, and he figures that it may be a good idea to declare somebody else in to help him, and the first guy he thinks of is Blondy Swanson, because he knows Blondy Swanson is a very able citizen in every respect.

"Now, Blondy," The Dutchman says, "if you like my proposition, I am willing to cut you in for fifty per cent, and fifty per cent of fifty G's is by no means pretzels in these times."

"Well, Dutchman," Blondy says, "I will gladly assist you in this enterprise on the terms you state. It appeals to me as a legitimate proposition, because there is no doubt this dough is coming to you, and from now on I am strictly legit. But in the meantime, let us have some more rock candy and rye whisky, without the rock candy, while we discuss the matter further."

But it seems The Dutchman does not care for rock candy and rye whisky, even without the rock candy, so Blondy Swanson and me and Good Time Charley continue taking our doses, and Blondy keeps getting more enthusiastic about The Dutchman's proposition until finally I become enthusiastic myself, and I say I think I will go along as it is an opportunity to see new sectons of the country, while Good Time Charley states that it will always be the great regret of his life that his business keeps him from going, but that he will provide us with an ample store of rock candy and rye whisky, without the rock candy, in case we run into any touches of the grippe.

Well, anyway, this is how I come to be riding around in an old can belonging to The Dutchman on a very cold Christmas Eve with The Dutchman and Blondy Swanson, although none of us happen to think of it being Christmas Eve until we notice that there seems to be holly wreaths in windows here and there as we go bouncing along the roads, and finally we pass a little church that is all lit up, and somebody opens the door as we are passing, and we see a big Christmas tree inside the church, and it is a very pleasant sight, indeed, and in fact it makes me a little homesick, although of course the chances are I will not be seeing any Christmas trees even if I am home.

We leave Good Time Charley's along in mid-afternoon, with The Dutchman driving this old can of his, and all I seem to remember about the trip is going through a lot of little towns so fast they seem strung together, because most of the time I am dozing in the back seat.

Blondy Swanson is riding in the front seat with The Dutchman and Blondy also cops a little snooze now and then as we are going along, but whenever he happens to wake up he pokes me awake, too, so we can take a dose of rock candy and rye whisky, without the rock candy. So in many respects it is quite an enjoyable journey.

I recollect the little church because we pass it right after we go busting through a pretty fair-sized town, and I hear The Dutchman say the old barn is now only a short distance away, and by this time it is dark, and colder than a deputy sheriff's heart, and there is snow on the ground, although it is clear overhead, and I am wishing I am back in Mindy's restaurant wrapping myself around a nice T-bone steak, when I hear Blondy Swanson ask The Dutchman if he is sure he knows where he is going, as this seems to be an untraveled road, and The Dutchman states as follows:

"Why," he says, "I know I am on the right road. I am following the big star you see up ahead of us, because I remember seeing this star always in front of me when I am going along this road before."

So we kept following the star, but it turns out that it is not a star at all, but a light shining from the window of a ramshackle old frame building pretty well off to one side of the road and on a rise of ground, and when The Dutchman sees this light, he is greatly nonplussed, indeed, and speaks as follows:

"Well," he says, "this looks very much like my barn, but my barn does not call for a light in it. Let us investigate this matter before we go any farther."

So The Dutchman gets out of the old can, and slips up to one side of the building and peeks through the window, and then he comes back and motions for Blondy and me to also take a peek through this window, which is nothing but a square hole cut in the side of the building with wooden bars across it, but no window panes, and what we behold inside by the dim light of a lantern hung on a nail on a post is really most surprising.

There is no doubt whatever that we are looking at the inside of a very old barn, for there are several stalls for horses, or maybe cows, here and there, but somebody seems to be living in the barn, as we can see a table, and a couple of chairs, and a tin stove, in which there is a little fire, and on the floor in one corner what seems to be a sort of a bed.

Furthermore, there seems to be somebody lying on the bed and making quite a fuss in the way of groaning and crying and carrying on generally in a loud tone of voice, and there is no doubt that it is the voice of a doll, and anybody can tell that this doll is in some distress.

Well, here is a situation, indeed, and we move away from the barn to talk it over.

The Dutchman is greatly discouraged, because he gets to thinking that if this doll is living in the barn for any length of time, his plant may be discovered. He is willing to go away and wait awhile, but Blondy Swanson seems to be doing quite some thinking, and finally Blondy says like this:

"Why," Blondy says, "the doll in this barn seems to be sick, and only a bounder and a cad will walk away from a sick doll, especially," Blondy says, "a sick doll who is a total stranger to him. In fact, it will take a very large heel to do such a thing. The idea is for us to go inside and see if we can do anything for this sick doll," Blondy says.

Well, I say to Blondy Swanson that the chances are the Doll's ever-loving husband, or somebody, is in town, or maybe over to the nearest neighbors digging up assistance, and will be back in a jiffy, and that this is no place for us to be found.

"No," Blondy says, "it cannot be as you state. The snow on the ground is anyway a day old. There are no tracks around the door of this old joint, going or coming, and it is a cinch if anybody knows there is a sick doll here, they will have plenty of time to get help before this. I am going inside and look things over," Blondy says.

Naturally, The Dutchman and I go too, because we do not wish to be left alone outside, and it is no trouble whatever to get into the barn, as the door is unlocked, and all we have to do is walk in. And when we walk in with Blondy Swanson leading the way, the doll on the bed on the floor half raises up to look at us, and although the light of the lantern is none too good, anybody can see that this doll is nobody but Miss Clarabelle Cobb, although personally I see some change in her since she is in Mr. Georgie White's Scandals.

She stays half raised up on the bed looking at Blondy Swanson for as long as you can count ten, if you count fast, then she falls back and starts crying and carrying on again, and at this The Dutchman kneels down on the floor beside her to find out what is eating her.

All of a sudden The Dutchman jumps up and speaks to us as follows:

"Why," he says, "this is quite a delicate situation, to be sure. In fact," he says, "I must request you guys to step outside. What we really need for this case is a doctor, but it is too late to send for one. However, I will endeavor to do the best I can under the circumstances."

Then The Dutchman starts taking off his overcoat, and Blondy Swanson stands looking at him with such a strange expression on his kisser that The Dutchman laughs out loud, and says like this:

"Do not worry about anything, Blondy," The Dutchman says. "I am maybe a little out of practice since my old lady put her checks back in the rack, but she leaves eight kids alive and kicking, and I bring them all in except one, because we are seldom able to afford a croaker."

So Blondy Swanson and I step out of the barn and after a while The Dutchman calls us and we go back into the barn to find he has a big fire going in the stove, and the place nice and warm.

Miss Clarabelle Cobb is now all quieted down, and is covered with The Dutchman's overcoat, and as we come in The Dutchman tiptoes over to her and pulls back the coat and what do we see but a baby with a noggin no bigger than a crab apple and a face as wrinkled as some old pappy guy's, and The Dutchman states that it is a boy, and a very healthy one, at that.

"Furthermore," The Dutchman says, "the mamma is doing as well as can be expected. She is as strong a doll as ever I see," he says, "and all we have to do now is send out a croaker when we go through town just to make sure there are no complications. But," The Dutchman says, "I guarantee the croaker will not have much to do."

Well, the old Dutchman is as proud of this baby as if it is his own, and I do not wish to hurt his feelings, so I say the baby is a darberoo, and a great credit to him in every respect, and also to Miss Clarabelle Cobb, while Blondy Swanson just stands there looking at it as if he never sees a baby before in his life, and is greatly astonished.

It seems that Miss Clarabelle Cobb is a very strong doll, just as The Dutchman states, and in about an hour she shows signs of being wide awake, and Blondy Swanson sits down on the floor beside her, and she talks to him quite a while in a low voice, and while they are talking The Dutchman pulls up the floor in another corner of the barn, and digs around underneath a few minutes, and finally comes up with a gripsack covered with dirt, and he opens this gripsack and shows me it is filled with lovely, large coarse banknotes.

Later Blondy Swanson tells The Dutchman and me the story of Miss Clarabelle Cobb, and parts of this story are rather sad. It seems that after Miss Clarabelle Cobb goes back to her old home in Akron, Ohio, she winds up marrying a young guy by the name of Joseph Hatcher, who is a bookkeeper by trade, and has a pretty good job in Akron, so Miss Clarabelle Cobb and this Joseph Hatcher are as happy as anything together for quite a spell.

Then about a year before the night I am telling about, Joseph Hatcher is sent by his firm to these parts where we find Miss Clarabelle Cobb, to do the bookkeeping in a factory there, and one night a few months afterwards, when Joseph Hatcher is staying after hours in the factory office working on his books, a mob of wrong gees breaks into the joint, and sticks him up, and blows open the safe, taking away a large sum of money and leaving Joseph Hatcher tied up like a turkey.

When Joseph Hatcher is discovered in this predicament the next morning, what happens but the gendarmes put the sleeve on him, and place him in the pokey, saying the chances are Joseph Hatcher is in and in with the safe blowers, and that he tips them off the dough is in the safe, and it seems that the guy who is especially fond of this idea is a guy by the name of Amersham, who is manager of the factory, and a very hard-hearted guy, at that.

And now, although this is eight or nine months back, there is Joseph Hatcher still in the pokey awaiting trial, and it is 7 to 5 anywhere in town that the judge throws the book at him when he finally goes to bat, because it seems from what Miss Clarabelle Cobb tells Blondy Swanson that nearly everybody figures Joseph Hatcher is guilty.

But of course Miss Clarabelle Cobb does not put in with popular opinion about her ever-loving Joe, and she spends the next few months trying to spring him from the pokey, but she has no potatoes, and no way of getting any potatoes, so things go from bad to worse with Miss Clarabelle Cobb.

Finally, she finds herself with no place to live in town, and she happens to run into this old barn, which is on an abandoned property owned by a doctor in town by the name of Kelton, and it seems that he is a kind-hearted guy, and he gives her permission to use it any way she wishes. So Miss Clarabelle moves into the barn, and the chances are there is many a time when she wishes she is back in Mr. Georgie White's Scandals.

Now The Dutchman listens to this story with great interest, especially the part about Joseph Hatcher being left tied up in the factory office, and finally The Dutchman states as follows:

"Why, my goodness," The Dutchman says, "there is no doubt but what this is the very same young guy we are compelled to truss up the night we get this gripsack. As I recollect it, he wishes to battle for his employers' dough, and I personally tap him over the coco with a blackjack.

"But," he says, "he is by no means the guy who tips us off about the dough being there. As I remember it now, it is nobody but the guy whose name you mention in Miss Clarabelle Cobb's story. It is this guy Ambersham, the manager of the joint, and come to think of it, he is supposed to get his bit of this dough for his trouble, and it is only fair that I carry out this agreement as the executor of the estate of my late comrades, although," The Dutchman says, "I do not approve of his conduct toward this Joseph Hatcher. But," he says, "the first thing for us to do is to get a doctor out here to Miss Clarabelle Cobb, and I judge the doctor for us to get is this Doc Kelton she speaks of."

So the Dutchman takes the gripsack and we get into the old can and head back the way we come, although before we go I see Blondy Swanson bend down over Miss Clarabelle Cobb, and while I do not wish this to go any farther, I will take a paralyzed oath I see him plant a small kiss on the baby's noggin, and I hear Miss Clarabelle Cobb speak as follows:

"I will name him for you, Blondy," she says. "By the way, Blondy, what is your right name?"

"Olaf," Blondy says.

It is now along in the early morning and not many citizens are stirring as we go through town again, with Blondy in the front seat again holding the gripsack on his lap so The Dutchman can drive, but finally we find a guy in an all-night lunch counter who knows where Doc Kelton lives, and this guy stands on the running board of the old can and guides us to a house in a side street, and after pounding on the door quite a spell, we roust the Doc out and Blondy goes inside to talk with him.

He is in there quite a spell, but when he comes out he says everything is okay, and that Doc Kelton will go at once to look after Miss Clarabelle Cobb, and take her to a hospital, and Blondy states that he leaves a couple of C's with the Doc to make sure Miss Clarabelle Cobb gets the best of care.

"Well," The Dutchman says, "we can afford a couple of C's out of what we have in this gripsack, but," he says, "I am still wondering if it is not my duty to look up this Ambersham, and give him his bit."

"Dutchman," Blondy says, "I fear I have some bad news for you. The gripsack is gone. This Doc Kelton strikes me as a right guy in every respect, especially," Blondy says, "as he states to me that he always half suspects there is a wrong rap in on Miss Clarabelle Cobb's ever-loving Joe, and that if it is not for this guy Ambersham agitating all the time other citizens may suspect the same thing, and it will not be so tough for Joe.

"So," Blondy says, "I tell Doc Kelton the whole story, about Ambersham and all, and I take the liberty of leaving the gripsack with him to be returned to the rightful owners, and Doc Kelton says if he does not have Miss Clarabelle Cobb's Joe out of the sneezer, and this Ambersham on the run out of town in twenty-four hours, I can call him a liar. But," Blondy says, "let us now proceed on our way, because I only have Doc Kelton's word that he will give us twelve hours' leeway before he does anything except attend to Miss Clarabelle Cobb, as I figure you need this much time to get out of sight, Dutchman."

Well, The Dutchman does not say anything about all this news for a while, and seems to be thinking the situation over, and while he is thinking he is giving his old can a little more gas than he intends, and she is fairly popping along what seems to be the main drag of the town when a gendarme on a motorcycle comes up alongside us, and motions The Dutchman to pull over to the curb.

He is a nice-looking young gendarme, but he seems somewhat hostile as he gets off his motorcycle, and walks up to us very slow, and asks us where the fire is.

Naturally, we do not say anything in reply, which is the only thing to say to a gendarme under these circumstances; so he speaks as follows:

"What are you guys carrying in this old skillet, anyway?" he says. "Stand up, and let me look you guys over."

And then as we stand up, he peeks into the front and back of the car, and under our feet, and all he finds is a bottle which once holds some of Good Time Charley's rock candy and rye whisky without the rye whisky, but which is now very empty, and he holds this bottle up, and sniffs at the nozzle, and asks what is formerly in this bottle, and I tell him the truth when I tell him it is once full of medicine, and The Dutchman and Blondy Swanson nod their heads in support of my statement. But the gendarme takes another sniff, and then he says like this:

"Oh," he says, very sarcastic, "wise guys, eh? Three wise guys, eh? Trying to kid somebody, eh? Medicine, eh?" he says. "Well, if it is not Christmas Day I will take you in and hold you just on suspicion. But I will be Santa Claus to you, and let you go ahead, wise guys."

And then after we get a few blocks away, The Dutchman speaks as follows:

"Yes," he says, "that is what we are, to be sure. We are wise guys. If we are not wise guys, we will still have the gripsack in this car for the copper to find. And if the copper finds the gripsack, he will wish to take us to the jail house for investigation, and if he wishes to take us there I fear he will not be alive at this time, and we will be in plenty of heat around and about, and personally," The Dutchman says, "I am sick and tired of heat."

And with this The Dutchman puts a large Betsy back in a holster under his left arm, and turns on the gas, and as the old can begins leaving the lights of the town behind, I ask Blondy if he happens to notice the name of this town.

"Yes," Blondy says, "I notice it on a signboard we just passed. It is Bethlehem, Pa."

Love, Action, Laughter

Budd Schulberg

Budd Schulberg, son of a famous motion picture producer, combines a rare perspective on Hollywood with a fine, sensitive writing talent. In this story —which appeared some years before What Makes Sammy Run *made Schulberg a best-selling novelist—we meet that same Mr. Sammy Glick: "an amoral young man with a cold eye and a quick head."*

January 15, 1938

LARRY MARTIN WAS A BAREBACK RIDER in a circus who broke into the movie game in the early days as a double for a Western star who couldn't ride a horse.

The hero would always learn in a very dramatic scene that the damsel was in distress and he would run for his horse and then Larry would carry it on from there—riding to the rescue from every possible angle, all afternoon.

Every girl in the company used to look up when Larry did his stuff. He was a feverish young man with an almost primitive force. He had a strong, sensuous face, a well-trained body and an athletic mind. His agility and eagerness were electrifying. He was violent, he could walk faster than most men run, he was aggressive and nimble-brained; no wonder he climbed the Hollywood ladder two rungs at a time.

Larry spent two months riding to the rescue with the wind in his ears and the dust in his mouth before he caught on to the movie racket. One day he raced over a bump and swallowed too much dust; he coughed and spat and had an inspiration.

"Why must I keep racing through this lousy dust?" Larry asked. "Why don't you shoot lots of cameras at me at once from different angles, and get the whole chase knocked off at one crack?"

That was one of the most brilliant things that had been said in Hollywood up to that time. The director shook his head in disgust.

"When I want advice from you," he bellowed, "I'll ask for it."

Larry's suggestion had never been tried before and it was obviously ridiculous. The director told him to keep moving. Those were the days when anybody who knew how to fit a crank into a camera was a cameraman and a director was the guy who could yell the loudest.

Larry was convinced that either he or the picture business would have to go. "This game is nutty," he said. "For a calm, quiet, sensible life, give me a circus any day, you—" and he used a number of terms you won't find in the dictionary.

Just then a little man, who called himself a producer, one of the first to suspect that people would actually pay to see pictures moving on a screen, reached out and drew Larry back into the industry.

The producer told him he had heard his idea.

Larry told him he could take that idea and do with it as his imagination directed.

The producer told him his idea would cut a shooting schedule on a Western in half—he must be a genius or something.

Larry told him he thought he could direct pictures a whole lot better than that straw man behind the megaphone.

The producer said, "Kid, you've got the job. I'll put you on at seventy-five a week."

Larry said, "That's pretty cheap for a genius, but I'll take a stab at it."

Larry's stab cut deep into Hollywood. He became the industry's first great director.

Hollywood was rising like a new world out of the sea, and on its highest peak stood Larry Martin, circus performer.

Larry Martin helped to give America something to do in the evening. He was God's gift to the moment. He was an artist and a pioneer and a drunkard and a tough guy and he caught the fancy of a nation.

Dames wanted Larry Martin for a thousand reasons. Society women winked at his vulgarity—he was a target for every little girl whose insides squirmed with the itch for a career. When he walked through the studio he left a wake of sighing secretaries.

But there could be no permanence for Larry Martin; life was a grab bag—he could reach into it to his elbows—every month there was a new picture and a new salary and a new fame.

Larry's mind was always leaping ahead, inventing new camera angles, improving the lighting, speeding up the tempo and going on the most complex and rambunctious binges known to man. Larry's hair grew gray, his pictures were longer and more mature—Larry and his industry were growing up. It was 1920 and he was thirty-one—he had lived ten years in Hollywood, a lifetime long enough to span the conception and revelation of a new world that lived and trembled on a thousand silver screens.

The late twenties were a nightmare to Larry Martin. Suddenly the silent screen stood up and screamed, trying its voice like a new baby, and the sound split the earth, and futures and careers and fortunes were swallowed up—and among them, suddenly shaken from his pedestal and devoured by oblivion, was Larry Martin.

For it must be told, it cannot be explained. Hollywood swallows its children. Watch, as it bears them, suckles them and suddenly leaps upon them from the rear and gulps them down.

Time caught up with Larry Martin and gave him the razzberry as it passed him by. People told one another how sorry they were for him. His money ran out—there had always been a leak at the bottom. Then his health ran out—an unkind columnist said his mind was pickled in alcohol. One morning he woke up in a Hollywood hotel with a bad hang-over and very little more, and he looked at himself in the mirror. His face was lined with purple veins from too much drinking and his eyes were glazed and sunken with not enough forgetting.

"Larry," he said to himself, "I knew

you when. If you don't get yourself a job today, I'll see you in hell, and that's a place inhabited strictly by agents and supervisors."

He sent his suit out to be pressed. He gave the bellboy the line about its being easier to tip him in a lump sum at the end of the month. He drew his clothes on gingerly, to save the creases, and took the streetcar to Classic Pictures, Inc. Classic Pictures was the brain child of Sammy Glick, Hollywood's boy producer, an amoral young man with a cold eye and a quick head. Maybe Larry wouldn't admit it to himself, but he picked Glick because the older producers knew him too well for what he was. His virility made him sense their pity and resist this condescension.

Larry was tense inside and trying to be as casual as possible when he gave his name to Doc, the receptionist.

"Larry Martin!" Doc said. "Sure I remember you."

"That's great," said Larry—he wished people wouldn't remember him. "I want to see Sammy Glick."

"Any special business?" Doc asked.

"Hell, yes," said Larry. "I was toying with the idea of going back to work."

Doc called Glick's secretary, Judy Castle.

"Larry Martin's out here," Doc said. "An old friend of mine, remember him? He wants to see Mr. Glick."

Larry! Larry Martin?

Judy was almost thirty-five. She had been one of those secretaries on the old lot. She had the same feeling now she used to have when she watched Larry Martin drive into the studio in his Austrian limousine, the only one of its kind in the country. One day she had been sent down to give him a message on the set; she remembered how he strode across the set to her, making a riding whip whistle in the air—she remembered being frightened by his youth and his fierceness.

She was young enough to be shy and excited then, and her message slipped under her tongue. It was a desperate moment and he had put his arm around her in front of the whole company, saying, "Take it easy, sister." He was a fresh guy and she should have minded; she looked up into his face and told him the whole message and she was all mixed up. She wished it were longer and she was sweating and blushing and glad it was over just the same.

"Can you hear me? I said Larry Martin's out here," Doc repeated.

"Oh," Judy said, making a nonstop return flight. "Send him right in."

She had thought he was dead; it was just a dreadful thing to think. She looked into her mirror; it was such a silly thing to do, he wouldn't even notice her. She daubed a bit of rouge on her cheeks to hide that studio pallor.

She could hear him coming. Should she recognize him? She didn't want to hurt him. She felt choked up. She didn't want to see him again, ever. She stared at the door, waiting for him.

Larry entered as jauntily as possible. This job was now or never and he must be casual—don't let them get inside you—that's it, smile, wink at the secretary.

"Hello, honey, is the boss in?"

"He will see you in a few minutes, Mr. Martin. Won't you please have a seat?"

"Thank you," Larry said quietly.

Judy had expected him to tell an off-color story about waiting rooms. She had found the change she feared. He was like a great volcano that has become quiescent. He seemed to be a much smaller man than she had remembered. And not as handsome. The shock of thick brown hair that had given him a wild, careless look was gone. His hair was thinned now, and tamed. She was afraid it typified his whole personality.

There was a long silence. She had waited so many years to see him that she couldn't think of anything to say.

Larry waited an hour and fifteen minutes to see Mr. Glick. She wanted to remind him of the time he put his arm around her absent-mindedly on the old lot—she wanted to tell him what it meant for her still. She was copying her shorthand notes and banging the typewriter as loud as she could.

Finally she said, "You can go in now, Mr. Martin."

Larry went in and found a little fellow, a dark man with an unattractive puss, behind an enormous desk.

Sammy Glick was friendly and smiling—he came forward and shook Larry's hand softly.

Sammy knew the old-timer wanted a job; he couldn't insult him, and he hoped to pass the whole thing off as a social call.

Larry could see what Sammy was trying to do. Did this young punk think he was completely punch-drunk?

"Listen, Sammy," said Larry. "You and me know our business. I'm not the kind of a guy to beat around the bush. You've proved that you've got the courage of your convictions—you've got a fresh slant on this racket, and you're going up. I was the biggest director in the game and I wouldn't take up your time if I wasn't sure I could still deliver."

"Sure," said Sammy, "everybody knows what you've done, but the business is changing. You were tops in the blood-and-thunder days. I guess you could still give us cards and spades on meller-drammer, but times have changed. That old hokum is dead and buried; the people want something new, something fresh and light; they want young love, action, music and laughter."

"Listen," said Larry desperately. "Everybody in town says I can't come back. If you give me a break you'll be the white-haired boy."

"Why kid ourselves?" Sammy said. "I am now."

Larry beat a retreat.

"How about your second-unit stuff?" he asked. "God knows I know enough about this business to swing those—"

"But the tempo's changed," said Sammy, less politely. This was getting painful.

"All the people want now is young love, action, laughter and music," Sammy recited. "I don't think you've got the pace for that sort of thing any more."

Larry stood up. He felt leaden inside.

Sammy put his hands in his pockets. He was uncomfortable; he didn't want an old-timer like Larry Martin going out hating his guts—it hurt his pride; it wasn't good for his reputation.

"Listen," Sammy said. "We all have our ups and downs, that's the law out here." He fished into his pocket and said, "Take this hundred. You can pay it back whenever you want to."

Larry clenched his fists. This had never happened before. He was wondering if he could squash this cockroach on the blotter of his big desk.

And then something strange happened. Something hidden in Larry Martin, some alien thing that Larry did not recognize, reached out to grasp that bill. A broken voice inside him said, "Thanks, Sammy," and his hand slipped into his pocket, where the bill rested quietly, hiding from the shame.

Sammy Glick's phone rang. It was Tony Kreuger, the agent, one of his pals.

"Hello, Tony, howya, baby?" he said. "Naw, I'm not busy, go ahead."

Larry walked slowly out of the office, his chin hanging on his chest as if his neck were broken.

Judy's eyes searched him when he came out. She tried to look at him without pity, and she was able to, because she loved him. To Judy Castle he was still a force and a danger.

For Larry the show was over and he didn't have to act any more.

"Well, girlie," he said, "it looks like the curtain on the third act for me. It's all over but the piano playing as you walk out."

"What did he say?" Judy asked.

"He says he wants young love, action, music and laughter," Larry said. "He says he wants four things I ain't got."

He looked her over once more. For some crazy reason he hoped Sammy Glick didn't get to first base with her. Then he gave her an informal salute.

"Take it easy, sister," he said, and started out.

Judy watched him walking out of her life. She was frantic for a moment and then was sure.

"Larry, wait," she called.

He whirled around in surprise.

"It isn't too late," she said, "believe me, Larry."

He smiled faintly. "What's it to you?"

"Everything," she said. She knew it sounded too dramatic, but she didn't care. This was no time for caution—you don't think of subject and predicate when you've wanted a man for sixteen years.

"On the level," she said, "I used to watch for you on the old lot; it's been that long."

Larry looked at her. He believed her. "This is one screwy day," he said.

"Larry," she said, "let me see you tonight, let me help you."

"Don't waste your time," Larry said. "I'm old hat. You heard what Sammy said. I can't give you young love, action, music and laughter—that's what you want —that's what we all need."

"I never did like formulas," she retorted, "and anyway, I'll take my chances."

"No," he said, "it's crazy, it's too late."

"Don't be a sap," she insisted. "It's my turn. The old wheel has finally stopped on my number."

Judy knew there must be something about this moment that would burn them both. She knew that this was the last time, that if he walked out into the street now, and she went back to her dictation, that was the end for both of them.

"This will sound nutty," she said. "I've been in love with you for sixteen years. I was in love with you when girls buzzed around you like bees. I was in love with you when you went off on yachting parties and stayed drunk for weeks, when the scandals came and the papers had to be hushed up. I was in love when you put your arm around me on the set and forgot to look at my face. I've been in love with you for a million years, and now there's nobody else—time has given me a break, and I'm moving in."

Larry looked at her hard and wrinkles spread in ripples from his eyes as he smiled.

"You win," he said.

"Call for me at the Villa Carlotta at eight o'clock."

"Okay," he said, "what's your name?"

"Judy," she said. "Judy Castle."

"I'll be there, Judy," he said, "in tails—we're going formal."

Larry was back at eight. He had downed four highballs. His dress suit was tight around the shoulders and slightly faded. He drove up to the Villa Carlotta in a taxi; the fare was ninety cents. He gave the driver his hundred-dollar bill. The driver laughed and said, "I haven't seen one of them things since the depression."

"Okay," Larry said. "Then wait here—we can use you—we're going places."

Judy came down in a purple evening gown. She must have spent a lot of time on her face—it didn't look so round and white. She took his hand and squeezed it hard twice. She had been very excited all afternoon thinking of this and now she was subdued and slow-moving.

He helped her into the taxi elegantly and said, "To El Patio." He turned on the radio. It played too loud at first, and then too soft, and this was very funny and they laughed at it together.

In the taxi Judy said gaily, "It looks like you've got a head start on me," and Larry said, "I have a feeling this is one race we're going to end up together." The radio hummed a gay tune. Larry looked at her and said, "I wish you had forced this on me fifteen years ago," and Judy answered, "Don't be silly. It couldn't have happened then; you were too busy."

They kissed then, for the first time, and the driver looked around and grinned and said, "Here's El Patio."

"I haven't felt like this since I was a kid," Larry said as they went in. "Young love, Sammy Glick, should see us now."

Nearly everybody who eats in places like El Patio watches the door, lapping up the success with their filets, eager to see the new people who are entering the charmed circle. When Larry came in with Judy on his arm, people put their heads together and wondered who they were, and one lady thought she had seen Judy at some party the week before and then Wally Conors, Judy's boss when he was production manager for Larry on the old lot, looked up and said, "Why, that's Larry Martin—I haven't seen the old boy in years."

Conors walked over to Larry's table and seemed very glad to see him.

"Hello, Larry," he said, "where've you been keeping yourself?"

"Hello, Wally old kid, I've been traveling," Larry said.

"Abroad?" Conors asked. "Why didn't you look me up when you got back, you dog?"

"I've just been traveling from one hotel to another, jumping the rent," Larry said.

Conors threw his big head back and roared. "Still the same old Larry Martin," he said, "but on the level, you're looking swell. Things must be breaking pretty good for you."

"Can't complain," said Larry. "They want me to make a picture in England, but you know how I feel about this burg."

"Sure," said Conors. He was glancing over toward his table. He couldn't quite make Larry out, and he'd rather let it go at that before he got involved.

"By the way," Larry said, "you know Miss Castle, don't you? Used to be with us on the old lot."

"Oh, yes," said Conors vaguely, "glad to see you."

There was an awkward silence. Conors glanced over at another table and waved. "There's Lolly Parsons," he said, "I gotta see her a minute. Give me a ring, Larry, and we'll have lunch sometime."

"He and I used to be great pals," Larry said.

"I can see that," Judy said.

"See," said Larry, "they still come over to me—we're in, kid."

He picked up the menu and read it from cover to cover. It gave him a kick to see those prices again. Then he beckoned the waiter with an authoritative wave.

"Why isn't the 1921 Liebfraumilch on the wine list?" he demanded.

"I'm sorry, sir," the waiter answered, "we have the 1919."

"But the 1921 is the best year," Larry said triumphantly.

Larry leaned back. He had won his right to belong again. He ordered the 1919 and lobster Thermidor. He squeezed Judy's hand. "Baby," he said, "I haven't felt so good in years."

"You didn't have to order all that," she said, "it's too expensive. We don't need all that stuff to have a good time."

She was wondering how he could afford it. He told her not to worry, just leave everything to him.

Larry was getting drunk, and pretty soon Judy had a glow on too, and more people stopped over to say hello, and Larry leaned back very full and comfortable. He was beginning to feel his old warmth.

He asked for a phone extension and called the Glorioso and said, "Reserve a table for two for Mr. Larry Martin," and he hung up and blew Judy a kiss.

Judy was drunk with the ecstasy of all this. She had the exquisite illusion of being out with the Larry Martin they all wanted to know. And I always thought I was a little too heavy to play Cinderella, she reflected.

"Snap out of it, Judy girl," Larry said; "you're a million miles away."

And Judy snapped, giving herself to this moment. She would forget about thinking, she wouldn't look before or after. "I'm right with you, darling," she said. "Have you heard the one about the star and the producer's daughter?"

They both howled then, and started out. Larry yelling back to the headwaiter, "Next time have that 1921." And they roared with laughter, all the way out to the taxi. "Give 'er the gun," Larry shouted, "just for the hell of it."

The taxi started.

"Young love, action, music and laughter, whoopee!" Larry yelled, and then he sang the words in time to the radio, "*Young-love, action-and-music, laughter, do-dee-o-do*. Can you imagine that little shrimp saying I don't know anything about young-love, action-and-music, laugh-ter?

"Wait'll I get one good picture under my belt, I'll show that little worm—I wouldn't have him as my office boy. Judy baby, you brought me luck—I love you, we'll knock this town dead."

"We?" Judy asked.

"Sure," said Larry, "we're a setup for each other; we'll fly down to Tia Juana tonight and get hitched."

"Kiss me," Judy said.

"Are ya glad, honey? Say something."

"Hold me, Larry," she said. "Don't let me go."

The Glorioso was filling up. There was an air to that place with its smart patterns of black and white, the rustle of evening gowns, the seminude cigarette girls, the tailored moguls and their panting stooges, ingratiating agents doing business after dark, beautiful women with wet lips and cool mascara searching for something, and poised ladies who had arrived, leaning back to watch the procession. The music was playing, the room seemed flooded with theatrical passion and tango rhythm.

It was not quite real, this world into which Larry and Judy entered, holding hands and laughing—laughing because life was just too funny for words.

They were led to a table in a corner, ordered more wine and joined the dancers on the floor. As they whirled, they stole a kiss and almost fell. Somebody said, "If you want to do that, why don't you get off the floor?" It was Tony Kreuger, the tough little kid who used to be California lightweight champ until he met Sammy Glick and found out it was a softer racket to be a ten-percenter.

Larry and Judy laughed at Tony. Tony glared over at them; he didn't know who Larry was so he couldn't be too fresh until he found out.

Now Larry was making love out loud to Judy, and the waiters winked, and Judy shook her finger, but Larry only kissed it and put it aside, saying, "We got a right—this is our engagement party! Hey, waiter, another bottle of champagne for me and the bride."

When they got up to dance again, they noticed that Tony Kreuger was sitting right behind them with a blond show girl.

"Those guys give me a pain," Larry said. "A bunch of fakes. I'd like to see him get tough."

The floor show began. Larry turned his back on it and made love to Judy.

"As soon as this is over," he said, "as soon as they hang up the floor show we are heading for the last round-up."

Tony Kreuger looked over and glared. He had found out who Larry was. "Shut up," he growled.

Larry stiffened. "Who do you think you're talking to?" he said.

"Don't give me that act," Tony said. "I heard all about you from Sammy Glick. Just because he's nice enough to give you a handout today you think you can come here and be a big shot."

This was a shock to Judy. She must have loved Larry from way back because she still didn't pity him; she understood—nothing was going to come between them.

"Darling, sit down," she begged.

Her voice pierced the fog that was settling around his head.

"Sorry, baby," he said. "Let's blow—let's have some fun."

Tony felt very proud of himself; his eyes shone like a cat's.

Larry staggered out, Judy trying to help him without appearing to. They tumbled into the taxi, and Larry pulled all the bills he had left out of his pocket and told Judy to count them. She did, fearfully. There were fifty dollars left; she would like to tell him to save them, to take it easy, but there was no time, no time like the present, no time but this for young love, action, music and laughter; time was ticking, time was chasing itself around the block; this was the zero hour for real joy. So she shut her eyes again, they would loop the last loop together, and she said, "Fifty bucks, honey," and he grinned and yelled two loud words to the driver, "*Clover Club*," and he grabbed her chin and kissed her possessively and said, "Now we're gonna have some action!"

And Judy said, "I'm right with you." If Larry was going to lose his last fifty bucks, he was going to lose sight of Tony Kreuger too. This night he would lose his shame and his weariness. Judy was with him. She was going to hold onto him; he could lose everything but her.

The Clover Club is one of those quiet, swanky places where big men throw away big money with such ease you forget it is money at all. It is very exclusive, for they must be careful whom they take their money from. Larry and Judy climbed the steps to the door, and a dark face looked out at them from a peep-hole.

The face said, "Sorry, boss, don't know you."

Larry said, "That's your fault, I'm Larry Martin."

The face was puzzled. It said, "Wait a minute," and disappeared.

In a moment it bobbed up again with another face. The new face started out more diplomatically. "I'm sorry, sir, I didn't get the name."

"You better get the name," Larry said, "or you'll get a lot more than that."

Larry pranced on the step like a mad bull; he puffed fury into the air; he held his head high in the air and looked down on these guardians of the gate.

He had won. He heard the knob turning. The big door swung open to them.

Inside, Hollywood was having an expensive good time. Larry stormed in like a mad bull. Judy thought he would make everybody look at him. She caught a glimpse of Wally Conors, and there was Sammy Glick, but Hollywood has always suffered from convenient nearsightedness. Nobody turned, nobody seemed to look, the rhythm of the Clover Club flowed on unchanged.

Larry shouldered his way into the crowd at the roulette wheel, and put five dollars on forty-three.

The wheel spun and the little ball did its dance.

The wheel slowed, the little ball let each number catch it for a moment, then jumped away again, like a flirtatious girl, until it hopped securely into the arms of forty-three.

Green bills were pushed across to Larry. He picked them up and crumpled them up in his hand carelessly.

Judy said, "Try 21, that's the year we first met," and the wheel spun once, and spun again. But 21 didn't seem to show, and Judy was nervous—it had to for her sake; and the third time the ball leaped in, as if it knew it was overdue.

Larry had a couple of hundred dollars in his hand. The man next to him said, "You're getting to them," and Judy noticed that several others looked over. Larry hadn't time to look up.

Then Larry put the two hundred on red, the whole wad, and the weasel looked up in appreciation. And Judy prayed, and red it was, four hundred dollars coming across the table to them; that little ball was human, it understood them, it was coming through.

Larry and Judy and the wheel were going crazy; they were all spinning around together; they were hoping to spin forever. It seemed to Judy that they were out in a wonderful sort of snowstorm; it was snowing dollar bills; they would build a great fortress out of the stuff to wall out the world.

Larry said, "Here, Tootsy, you hold this."

She found a thousand dollars sticking to her hand; she felt as if she were coming out of a faint. There were heads crowding around; she and Larry were in the middle of a circle of amazement and envy. Larry was sprinkling chips across the boards like seeds.

Somebody asked, "Who's that lucky guy?" Everybody was beginning to wonder. Someone thought he was a big banker from the East, and then Sammy Glick came up and stood behind him and said, "Larry?—you mean Larry Martin?—he was in my office just today."

Larry had three thousand dollars and the wheel was still spinning. Wally Conors said, "Larry—he's been making pictures in England," and went through the room proudly proclaiming to everyone that his pal, Larry Martin, was rolling the wheel down Hollywood Boulevard like a hoop.

The name was hoisted above the room like a flag. Larry Martin had ten thousand dollars. Everybody saluted.

"It's time to cash in," Judy said.

It was the touch of her hand on his arm rather than the sound of her words that made him say, "Okay. I'll be back tomorrow night."

"You are back," she said. "Larry, you're back right now."

She was right. The room was buzzing with Larry Martin. With every moment and every dollar he was becoming a better director. "He can still do a better job than half these punks drawing down big dough," one producer said. "He had a great touch," another said; "he's a swell guy."

As Larry was turning in his chips, the old producer came up to him and shook his hand. "Congratulations, Larry," he said, "glad to see you back.

"Listen," the producer said. "I've got a hunch Hollywood needs you more than England does. How would you like to meet me at the Imperial tomorrow at one?"

"Okay, pal," Larry said. "See you later."

As he walked to the door, a little guy with a quick step caught up with him. "Why, hello, Mr. Glick," Judy said.

It was Sammy. He put his arm around Larry and whispered into his ear.

"Listen," he said. "I happened to hear what that guy said to you. How about dropping into my office first, about ten? I may have something hot for you."

Larry nodded. The wheel was still spinning. He was hot. He would rub one producer against another like flints. He would start a real fire again.

Larry was his old self, as he and Judy drove back to the Villa Carlotta. He was talking about his comeback, about the triumphs he would have, and Judy was silent, wondering if he would crowd her out of his world, wondering if tomorrow would find them strangers or lovers. The wheel was still rolling; she was keeping her fingers crossed; she would keep them crossed forever, remembering this night when two old-timers made a symphony out of young love, action, music and laughter.

The taxi drew up to the door of the apartment. Judy was ready to step out into the early morning and the old life.

"Pull yourself together, Tootsy," he said. "I'll pick you up at noon."

"Larry," she said, "you don't have to —the night's over—I'll understand."

"I said be ready at twelve," Larry said, "and don't keep me waiting. We've got a lot to do together—we got a one-way ticket to young love, action, music and laughter for the rest of our lives—and it looks as if Sammy Glick is going to pay our way."

Judy hurried inside; she didn't want to cry on the street, just when the sun was ending this long night in which Larry Martin had risen from his grave to come back to Hollywood and Judy Castle.

Little Stranger

Walter Henry

Regan had the fastest gun in town. Now half the townsfolk watched from behind windows and corners to see him kill the boy who wouldn't back down.

August 27, 1938

As soon as I heard about it, I went to Regan's saloon. Regan was there. He was a big man, with the coldest black eyes I've ever looked into. When I came in, he was behind the bar. I walked to the bar and said: "You going through with this business?"

He was tinkering with a gun. He gave me a dirty look. I told him what I had to tell him. It didn't take long.

When I was through with Regan, I went out and found the boy. He was leaning against a post outside the Fenton House. His horse, a scrawny pinto, was tied to the post. He must have ridden that horse twenty miles that morning; the brute was white with sweat, and he looked half dead.

When I came up, the boy turned his head and looked at me. He couldn't have been more than twenty. He wore a battered, old sombrero, and his boots weren't any too new. His face was long and narrow; it was brown, from the sun. His eyes were gray and bloodshot—and shifty. His mouth was a weak one, with lines cutting down deep on either side of it. He was just a little bowlegged, and not much to look at.

I stepped up beside him and said: "You slapped the wrong man, boy. Regan's a bad one."

He stared at me and said: "If he'd had his gun, I'd 'a' killed him. He called me a liar."

I studied his face. I knew how he felt—a boy, and a stranger without friends at that, about to meet an experienced gun fighter in a street duel. But I would never have guessed he was scared, from anything his face showed.

"Listen, stranger," I said. "Nobody knows you here. Nobody gives a damn whether you fight that man or not. Get on your horse and clear out. You've got nothing to lose."

The boy dug the toe of his boot in the dust. I noticed that his spurs were new. "I ain't yellow," he said quietly. "I'm stayin'."

I took out my watch and looked at it. Twenty-seven minutes past twelve. I had three more minutes to work in. I wanted to save this boy if I could. I couldn't take any chances.

"Regan's a bear cat on the draw," I said. "He'll beat you to it, sure as hell."

The boy didn't say anything. He pulled out the makin's, rolled a cigarette with quick, expert movements of his fingers. When he lighted the cigarette, his hands trembled.

I tried once more. "A kid like you hasn't got a Chinaman's chance against a man like Regan. For the love of God, boy, leave this town quick. Right now, while the going's good!"

"Maybe you're right, friend," he said. "And I thank you. But I think I'll stick around. What's the time?"

I looked at my watch. "Half past twelve," I said.

He threw away his cigarette butt, straightened his shoulders, pulled his hat on tight. He loosened his gun belt a little. He pulled his gun out—he was a left-hander, I noticed—tested the trigger, slipped it back into the holster.

"All set," he said, and stepped out into the street. When he got to the middle of the street, he halted, turned to his right, and started off. I thought that the lines about his mouth had deepened, and under his tan he looked pale. But his eyes were like gray ice as he walked.

He moved very slowly. He held his head rigid. He walked on the balls of his feet. He seemed to be looking straight down the center of the street. But I could see that he wasn't missing anything.

The street was about four hundred yards long, at a guess. I figured that if Regan was around now—as he'd told the boy he would be—he would probably wait in his saloon, at the other end of the street. The thing would happen as the boy passed his place and Regan stepped out.

The boy may have figured it that way, too. But he wasn't taking any chances. One slow step at a time, he moved. He kept touching the butt of his gun—just touching it. Now and then he'd stop, and look cautiously around.

I trailed him. I stayed on the sidewalk. I kept about ten yards behind him. I wasn't afraid of any wild bullets from Regan.

The Palace, a saloon—not Regan's place—was halfway down the street—only two hundred yards from where we started, but it took the boy a long time to reach it. When he reached it, he surprised me; he turned quickly and walked in.

I jumped after him. When I got inside, he was at the bar. "A shot of whisky," I heard him say to the bartender, in that dead, hard drawl of his. There were four or five punchers standing near the door. Two of them were friends of Regan. None of them said a word; none of them moved. They all seemed frozen.

The boy took the drink at one gulp. He threw a silver dollar on the bar and walked out. He passed me as though he had never seen me.

Two hundred yards more to go. It might happen at any moment now. I couldn't be sure just what would happen; I didn't know Regan well enough to dope it out.

The boy reached the center of the street, wheeled to the left, and went on toward Regan's. He moved slower than before. This time I didn't follow him. It might be safer in the doorway of the Palace; I stayed there. . . . I kept wondering what Regan was going to do.

There were five hundred people in that town. Half of them, behind closed blinds and corners, were watching.

Once, just before the boy reached a corner, he yanked out his gun. I thought we were going to have it then. Nothing happened.

When he was opposite Regan's place, one of the punchers whispered: "Now!"

I took a quick look at my watch. It was twelve thirty-seven. . . . The boy passed Regan's place. He reached the end of the street. He turned there and stood looking toward us.

I said: "Looks like the kid's wasting his time," and I went out and waited for the boy in the middle of the street.

He came back the same way he made the first trip. One step at a time, one slow step at a time, eyes straight ahead. When he reached the Palace, I trailed along again. I knew then that if it was going to happen it would happen in this last stretch. "Careful, boy," I called out. "Don't take any chances."

It seemed like an hour before we reached the pinto. I'm an old man, now, but I'll never forget how I felt as we reached that horse.

The boy got there before I did. I ran to him. I put out my hand. "Shake, boy!" I said. "Put it there! I've seen mighty few men who would do what you just did."

He didn't see my hand. He didn't even look at me. He said, "I ain't yellow," and began untying the pinto.

I hadn't planned to tell him. Now I gave it to him straight. "No," I said, "you ain't yellow, boy. But I guess I saved your life!"

He seemed mildly interested. "Yeah?" he said slowly and climbed onto his horse.

I watched him start to roll a cigarette. "Listen, young feller," I said. "I couldn't let Regan kill a boy like you. So I up and gave him some news."

"Yeah?" He flicked a quick look at me.

"Sure," I said. "I told that quitter your name was William Bonney," I laughed. "Ever hear of Bonney, boy? He's hell with a gun, they say . . . You know who I mean—*Billy the Kid!*"

The boy stared at me for a moment. He didn't change expression. "Well, now, ain't that curious, stranger," he drawled. His eyes bit into mine hard. "I *am* Billy the Kid."

And that time he cleared out . . . in a hurry.

Hornblower and His Majesty

C. S. Forester

Captain Horatio Hornblower of the Royal Navy may be better known in some circles than his originator, Cecil Scott Forester. But tracing Hornblower's career from midshipman to peer of the realm has not been the sum of Forester's achievements. He has found equal success with such diverse books as Payment Deferred (*his first novel*), The Ship, *and* The Forest and The Fort. *Born in Cairo, Egypt, Forester has spent much of his life in the United States.*

March 23, 1940

"MIND YOU, SIR HORATIO," SAID DR. MANIFOLD, "I think this treatment of His Majesty is unwise, very unwise."

"Indeed, Doctor?" said Hornblower politely.

"At the last consultation of His Majesty's physicians," said Dr. Manifold, "those of my opinion were just outvoted, but I venture to say, Sir Horatio, that although mere numbers were against me —and it was only a trifling majority, you must remember—all that are most distinguished in the world of medical science were on my side."

"Naturally," said Captain Hornblower.

"In the matter of accumulated knowledge we were overwhelmingly superior. But the question of His Majesty's health was left to a mere counting of heads. Mark my words, Sir Horatio, this business of voting by numbers, without regard to position in the world, will be the curse of humanity for centuries to come, unless something is done about it."

"That seems only too likely," said Hornblower. One of his guiltiest secrets was the fact that he fancied himself a democrat and radical, but in the exalted circles in which he moved nowadays he had little difficulty in concealing it, because everyone he met took it for granted that he was the opposite.

"A sea voyage for His Majesty!" exclaimed Dr. Manifold contemptuously. "Build up his strength! Distract him from his troubles! Fiddlesticks! A patient in His Majesty's unfortunate condition of mind should be kept low. It stands to reason. Bleeding, Sir Horatio—some ounces twice a week. A thorough course of purgatives with a low diet. Gentle confinement in the dark. That would give His Majesty's unhappy brain a chance to clear itself of its humors and to start again anew—with a *tabula rasa*, a clean sheet, sir."

"There is much in what you say, Doctor."

Hornblower was not lying when he

said that; it seemed quite a logical treatment of insanity in the year 1812. But at the same time he was moved with pity at the thought of his poor mad king exposed to that sort of brutality. His instincts revolted against it, and his reason told him that as the treatment had been tried unsuccessfully for two years now, it might be as well to experiment with the reverse.

What he was more concerned with, if the truth must be told, was the responsibility of his own position. This was his first command since his triumphant escape from captivity in France, and since he had received the accolade of the Bath at the hands of the prince regent. The command of the royal yacht during His Majesty's madness might have been a sinecure had not this decision been taken to give His Majesty a course of fresh air and change of scene. Sailing about the Channel with His Majesty on board while the sea swarmed with French and American privateers meant a grave responsibility for the captain—for him.

Hornblower looked round the decks of the Augusta, at the four stumpy six-pounders, and the two long nine-pounders fore and aft. He would not be able to make much of a defense against one of those heavily sparred, heavily gunned New England privateers. Doctor Manifold seemed to be echoing his thoughts.

"Of course," he was saying, "there is no need for me to point out to you, Captain, the need for the utmost precautions against any shock to His Majesty. You have received orders, I fancy, against firing any salute?"

Hornblower nodded.

"And there must be no bustle and no excitement. Everything must be done more quietly than is usually the case on shipboard. And you must be careful not to run into any storms."

"I shall do my best, Doctor," said Hornblower.

A midshipman who had been perched up at the main-topmast crosstrees came sliding down the backstay, touched his hat to the captain and moved hastily forward. The crew assumed an attitude of expectancy.

"Here comes the king!" exclaimed Dr. Manifold suddenly.

Hornblower merely nodded.

A little group of men on foot came slowly down the slope to the jetty against which lay the Augusta; it was not until they were no more than fifty yards away that Hornblower blew a single short note on his whistle and woke the ship to life. The side boys, in spotless white gloves and frocks, ran to their positions at the gilded gangplank. The pipes of the boatswain's notes twittered loudly. The six men and the sergeant of the marine detachment appeared miraculously upon the quarterdeck, pipe clay and buttons gleaming, the two drummers with their sticks poised beneath their noses. The crew fell in by divisions, the officers in their cocked hats and silk stockings, sword hilts and epaulets shining in the sun, in front of them. The whole of the little ship was ready and welcoming at the moment when the party reached the shore end of the gangplank, not a moment too early, not a moment too late—it was a neat piece of work.

There was a brief delay at the gangplank. His Majesty was reluctant to come on board. Hornblower saw the hesitation; he saw the plump, white hands cling to the handrails, and saw them forced free again, unobtrusively, by two of the attendants. There was a burly lord in waiting, immediately behind His Majesty, wearing a fine plum-colored coat with a laced waistcoat in a contrasting shade, crossed by the narrow ribbon of the Thistle—the bearer, presumably, of some historic name from beyond the border. He closed up behind His Majesty, closer and closer. The hands caught and clung again, and again were forced free, and the lord in waiting's ponderous stomach was planted firmly in His Majesty's back and propelled him almost unnoticeably but irresistibly along the gangplank, so that His Majesty arrived on the deck with just a shade of haste.

Every officer's hand came to the salute; the boatswain's mates set their pipes twittering loudly; the drums of the marines beat a long roll. Up to the main truck soared the royal standard, where its opulent folds flapped slowly open in the gentle wind. His Majesty had come aboard.

"Chickens and chimes. What? What?" said His Majesty. His clouded blue eyes caught sight of a sea gull wheeling against the sky, and followed it in its flight. "What? What? Ducks and Dutchmen. What? What? What?"

The little group of courtiers and attendants pressing along the gangplank gradually edged him farther onto the deck. Then his wandering glance caught sight of Hornblower standing at attention before him.

"Hillo!" said the king. A kindly smile illuminated his face. "Lessons going all right?"

"Yes, thank you, Your Majesty," said Hornblower.

The king reached up and took off Hornblower's cocked hat with its gold lace and buttons, and with his other hand he ruffled Hornblower's sparse hair.

"Don't let 'em beat you too hard," he said. "What? Don't let 'em. What? Good boys get guineas."

Dr. Manifold had approached, and was standing behind Hornblower's shoulder. The king saw him, and cowered away suddenly in fear.

"Your Majesty!" said the doctor, bowing low, but his humble tone and demeanor did nothing to reassure the frightened being before him. The little court closed up round the king and herded him slowly away as before. Hornblower caught up his cocked hat from the deck where it had fallen from the king's trembling hand, and turned away to his duties.

"Fore and main-tops'ls, there!" he called. "Cast off those warps, Mr. White!"

He felt he needed distraction after seeing the abject terror that had convulsed the face of his king at sight of the doctor who had tormented him. The air of the sea would feel cleaner than that he was breathing now.

With the royal standard at the main, and the white ensign at the peak, the Augusta nosed her way out of Newhaven Harbor to where her escort, the twenty-gun corvette Cormorant, awaited her coming. Hornblower, looking through his glass at her, thought what a vivid comment it was on the strain to which the British navy was being subjected, that His Majesty, King George III, King of Great Britain and Ireland, could be escorted to sea only by a twenty-gun corvette at a time when one hundred and twenty ships of the line and two hundred frigates flew his flag.

Times were changing. The royal standard at the main no longer sported the lilies of France—they had been quietly dropped a little while ago in favor of the harp of Ireland. And in the past six months the

British navy had suffered a succession of minor reverses such as could not be paralleled in the history of the last fifty years. The reverses could hardly continue; now that England had learned the fighting power of the United States Navy, she would certainly smother the infant sea power with a relentless blockade. But blockade could never prevent the escape of raiders and commerce destroyers—nineteen years of war with France had shown that England would have to grin and bear her losses while the slow process of strangulation went on. What he was concerned about was that the Augusta should not be one of those losses.

"Signal midshipman!" he snapped. "Augusta to Cormorant. Take station one mile to windward."

The gay flags soared up and were acknowleged by the Cormorant. In her station a mile to windward she was interposed between the Augusta and any stray raider who might try to swoop down upon her.

The Augusta crept out from the shore, and turned down-channel on her cruise. Behind her stretched the cliffs of England, the Seven Sisters and the towering height of Beachy Head. Hornblower looked over at the king and his courtiers. He watched the pathetic, white-haired figure making its way here and there with uncertain steps while the shortsighted blue eyes examined everything, and he came to the conclusion that undoubtedly Manifold was wrong in his notion of the correct treatment. Surely this life, this clean air and these simple distractions were better for a diseased mind than the bleedings and purgatives and solitary confinement which Manifold desired to inflict.

The king's course had brought him close to Hornblower, and the vague blue eyes were studying Hornblower's face again.

"Little Sophia likes the sea," he said.

"Yes, Your Majesty."

Hornblower knew that Sophia was the king's favorite daughter, dead these twenty years and more; he had heard of the happy little holidays on the Dorset coast which the king had once enjoyed with his young family. The king's brow wrinkled as he struggled with his memory.

"Little Sophia!" he said. "Where is she now? She was with me a little while ago."

"Her Royal Highness is on a journey, sir," interposed the lord in waiting—there was a perceptible Scotch accent in his voice to match the ribbon of the Thistle which he wore.

"But why? She didn't tell me anything about it," said the king.

"She left the message with me, sir. Her humblest duty and respects, sir, but she did not have time to await Your Majesty's return to say goodby in person. Her Royal Highness will be back again on Tuesday, and meanwhile hopes that Your Majesty will remember to be as quiet and good as if she were here."

"Tuesday," said the king. "Tuesday. It is a long time to wait for little Sophia, but I suppose I must. I will."

Hornblower's eyes met the lord in waiting's, and Hornblower felt his heart warming suddenly to him. The kindly little deception, the dexterous hint of the need for quiet, showed that this Scottish lord had the sense and tact necessary for his position, and his smile showed that he cherished the same kindly feelings toward the mad king as Hornblower did. Hornblower suddenly ceased to remember how much higher the Order of the Thistle ranked above the Order of the Bath which ornamented his own breast.

"His Majesty," said the lord in waiting, "wishes to command your presence at dinner."

"That gives me great pleasure, sir," said Hornblower.

That was hardly a correct statement, Hornblower found. Not that the dinner was not quite excellent, despite the fact that the royal cooks were flustered and unhandy in their unwonted situation. The food was good, and the service, allowing for the cramped space of the great cabin, efficient. But it did Hornblower's appetite no good to see the king, his table cutlery limited to a spoon, seated with a watchful attendant at each side, and eating as clumsily as a child and daubing his cheeks with bread and milk. So it was almost a relief, despite the foreboding of trouble which it brought him, when a midshipman slipped into the great cabin and whispered in his ear:

"Mr. White's respects, sir, and it's getting thick outside."

Hornblower laid aside his napkin, nodded apologetically to the lord in waiting, and hastened out; it was only when his foot was on the companion that he realized that he had completely forgotten about making his bow to the king.

Outside, as Mr. White had reported, it was undoubtedly getting thick. Long, narrow bands of haze were drifting over the surface of the sea, the surest indication of an approaching dense fog. The Cormorant to windward was already nearly invisible. With night approaching, visibility would soon be negligible. Hornblower pulled at his chin and debated what he should do. Shoreham Harbor lay to starboard, but the tide did not serve and the wind was falling; it would be risky to venture into shoal water in a fog. As with every captain in difficulties, his first instinct was to get out to sea away from the dangerous land. To seaward lay added dangers from raiders, but the chance of meeting a privateer was easily preferable to the certainty of shoal water. Hornblower gave his orders to the helmsman and called the signal midshipman.

"Augusta to Cormorant," he said. "Course south. Keep closer."

It was a distinct relief to see through the thickening haze the acknowledgment mount to the Cormorant's masthead while the corvette turned obediently and shook out her mainsail to take up her new station; a quarter of an hour later it was too thick to see across the deck, and Hornblower thanked his stars he had decided to get out to sea instead of trying for Shoreham Harbor.

"Get that bell ringing, Mr. White," he ordered sharply.

"Aye aye, sir," said an invisible Mr. White.

The loud rattle of the fog bell echoed dully in the heavy atmosphere, and the silence that ensued hung heavy as the Augusta crept slowly over the invisible water. It seemed a very long two minutes before it rang again. Seemingly close at hand the bell was answered by another on the port quarter.

"That's Cormorant, sir," said White at Hornblower's side—Hornblower did not condescend to reply to a remark futile in its obviousness. The next time the other bell sounded it seemed to be well to starboard.

"What the hell?" said White.

The direction of sound in a fog was always misleading—fog banks sometimes echoed back sound as effectively as a cliff face. The Augusta's own bell rang long and harshly, and the Cormorant's reply could only just be heard. Hornblower tried to remember all he knew about Melville of the Cormorant. Young, dashing, ambitious, he had been posted as captain after a bold cutting-out affair somewhere on the Biscay coast. But it was doubtful if his qualities were such as to enable him to perform the difficult task of keeping touch with a consort in a fog. Again the Augusta's bell rang, and this time he could hear no reply at all.

Dr. Manifold was on deck now, and approaching the sacred presence of the captain—the command of the royal yacht exposed him to these plagues, and Hornblower felt he would gladly exchange it for that of the crankiest ship of the line in the Channel fleet.

"That noise disturbs my patient, sir," said Manifold.

"I am sorry, but it is a necessary noise," answered Hornblower.

"I insist on its stopping."

"There is only one man on board here," answered Hornblower, his exasperation boiling over, "who can insist on anything. And he insists that you go below, sir."

"I *beg* your pardon, sir."

"If I have to repeat myself, sir," said Hornblower, "I will call a couple of hands to carry out what I say."

"You are a boor, sir. I have the ear of a cabinet minister, and by George, sir, I'll—"

Dr. Manifold cut his speech short as Hornblower turned to the midshipman of the quarter-deck with the evident intention of carrying out his threat. He bolted down the companion as nearly like a rabbit as his portly dignity permitted.

"Pass the word for my steward," said Hornblower as he had intended doing and, when the man came on deck, "Bring me a chair and a pea jacket."

Hornblower spent the night in the hammock chair, wrapped up in the thick coat—he was unwilling to leave the deck while this fog persisted. It was a weary vigil, and whenever he dozed off, he was awakened with a start by the clamor of the fog bell. At the end of the night, White was standing beside him.

"It must be dawn by now, sir," said White. "But I can't say it looks any different."

The fog was as thick as ever—the main yard was invisible from the deck.

"Listen!" said Hornblower, sitting up tensely. His ears had caught the faintest of sounds somewhere astern—its acute analysis told him of the wash of water, the creaking of timber, the rattle of cordage, all blended and reduced in volume so as to tell him of the presence of a ship somewhere in the near distance. Then they both heard, plainly and distinctly, a voice in the fog say, "Call the watch."

"They're speaking English," said White. "That's Cormorant, then, thank God."

"Go and stop the fog bell, quick," snapped Hornblower, and White was impressed enough by the urgency of his tone to run to do his queer bidding without question, while Hornblower still listened.

"Keep the hands quiet!" said Hornblower on White's return. "I don't want a sound on board."

There had been something odd about the pronunciation of that word "watch." The vowel was broadened in a fashion no English officer would employ. Hornblower did not believe that it was the Cormorant that lay astern there.

"Send a hand to the chains with the lead," said the voice in the fog.

"Queer," whispered White; the explanation still had not dawned upon him—he was not as quick-witted as his captain.

Hornblower walked aft and stared

through the mist over the traffrail. There was just the faintest thickening there, the merest, most inconsiderable nucleus to the fog—a ship was crossing their wake from starboard to port not twenty yards away, and unsuspecting. Hornblower watched until the nucleus had lost itself again in the fog over the port quarter.

"Mr. White," he said, "I'm going to haul my wind. Port your helm, quartermaster."

The Augusta swung around and headed on a course exactly opposite to that of the other ship. Hornblower could be confident that the distance between the two was widening steadily, though slowly; there was only the faintest of breaths of air to push the Augusta through the water.

Here came the king, up bright and early on this misty morning, attendants with him. Hornblower grudged the moments of distraction from his duty of staring into the fog. King George straddled on the slightly heaving deck like an old sailor—one way and another he must have spent a great deal of time at sea.

"Morning," said the king.

"Good morning, sir," said Hornblower.

"Foggy day, what? Thick weather, what? What?"

There was a lucidity about his manner that had been totally wanting yesterday; perhaps his day at sea had really done him good. A gleam of light came through the fog, and suddenly there was sky to be seen overhead.

"There's Cormorant, sir," said White. "No, by gad, she's not."

A mile astern a ship was to be seen, headed on an opposite course; with every second her outline became clearer and sharper. As they watched she wove around in pursuit of them, revealing herself as heavily sparred and well-armed, with twelve gun-ports a side. She was hastily setting all sail—the white pyramids of canvas grew as if by magic in a fashion that would have been creditable in a king's ship.

"Set all sail, Mr. White. Smartly now, men."

"Pretty, pretty," said the king, smiling in the sunshine; whether he was alluding to the ordered bustle of setting sail or to the appearance of the pursuing ship was not apparent.

The Augusta had all sail set as soon as the other ship, and Mr. White was paying careful attention to their trim as she ate her way close-hauled to windward. It was some time before he could spare a moment to stare through his glass at the other vessel.

"A Yankee, by gad!" he exclaimed, as the red and white bars of the flag she hoisted danced into the field of his glass.

"Hoist our colors, Mr. White. But not the royal standard."

There was no purpose in telling the American what a prize was being dangled under his nose. Hornblower peered through his glass at her. If she managed to work up within close range there was no hope for it—he would have to surrender, as the Augusta's six-pounder popguns would stand no chance against the other's heavy metal. And then? Hornblower's imagination boggled at the thought of what would happen next. What would the Americans do with a captive king—the king against whom they had fought for so many weary years a generation ago? He tried to picture the effect of the news in New York or Boston.

He was so interested in the idea that he quite forgot that he, himself, and his career were in jeopardy. American boats would swarm out to the Narrows to meet them; there would be jubilation and excitement. And then—and then—there was a tradition of hospitality and kindliness across the ocean. Faults on both sides had brought about this war, faults that might easily be forgotten when America tried—as she surely would—to make the poor old king as comfortable as possible. The unnecessary war might end in a wholly desirable peace.

For one insane moment Hornblower was almost tempted to risk it, and he was positively shocked with himself when he realized the depths of the treason with which he was dallying. It was his duty to escape with the Augusta if he could; for that matter she would be a captive by now if his quick brain had not steered her toward safety the moment he had first heard that American voice through the fog. There was a bank of fog up there to windward; once let the Augusta bury herself therein and she stood a chance of safety. That fool Melville in the Cormorant was apparently quite lost.

A puff of smoke from the American's bows, and a fountain of water a hundred yards on the starboard quarter.

"Take him below," said Hornblower curtly to the lord in waiting, with a gesture at the king.

"No!" said the king with a stamp of his foot, and Hornblower had no time for further argument.

"Clear away that nine-pounder," he said—the long nine on the quarter-deck might perhaps shoot away a spar and save them.

Another puff of smoke from the American, and this time there was a sudden howl overhead like devils in torment. She was firing with dismantling shot—lengths of chain joined to a common center, rolled in a ball and fired from a gun. In the course of the projectile's trajectory the chains swung out and circled screaming in the air, spelling destruction to any rigging they might hit.

"Come on with that gun, there! Have you all got wooden legs?" Hornblower called.

The men threw their weight on the train tackles and ran it out. The gun captain crouched over the sights. As he did so, the American allowed her head to fall away from the wind; she showed her side, and when every gun port was in view, she suddenly enveloped herself in the smoke of a full broadside. It sounded like some devils' orchestra as the air filled with the din of the dismantling shot screaming all about them. Hornblower looked anxiously upward and was astonished to see how little damage had been done; then he remembered the same astonishment in other battles. The sea was so large, the target so small by comparison—a miss was so easy, a hit so difficult. A halliard had been cut—White had already started a hand up the rigging to splice it—and a long tear appeared in the main-topsail. And the American had lost a hundred yards by yawning out of her course to deliver that broadside.

The bang of the stern chaser beside him caught him off his guard and almost startled him out of his wits—he hoped no one noticed the nervous jump which nearly lifted him from the deck. No one could see where the shot fell—at least the American showed no sign of damage. The king was standing breathing in the smell of the powder smoke that eddied round him. He was clearly enjoying himself; mad or no, he was full of the traditional courage of his family. There was no sense in repeating the order to take him below in that case, for the flimsy sides of the royal yacht would be of small avail in keeping out twelve-pounder balls.

The American was yawing again. Hornblower watched, fascinated as gun after gun of her broadside crept into view. Then came the gust of smoke and the howl of the projectiles, and an immense clatter aloft as everything seemed to go at once. The main-topsail yard lurched lop-sided, its slings shot away. The fore-top-mast was gone altogether, and hanging overside. Ropes were parted everywhere, and the little Augusta lay crippled. She was hardly able to move through the water, and the American could overhaul her at her leisure now. There could be no question of making a hopeless fight of it, not with the king on board. All he could do was to try to prolong the chase by keeping the Augusta moving as long as possible.

"Clear that raffle away, Mr. White," he said loudly and cheerfully for the benefit of the crew. "Fo'c'sle, there! Cut that wreckage clear! What are you thinking about?"

The men were leaping to their tasks, but the American was coming up, hand over hand, behind. She had lost ground to leeward through yawing, and now she was going about so as to get up to wind-ward of the chase. Her other broadside would bear soon. Hornblower decided that when it did he would have to sur-render. He found himself wondering again how the king would enjoy a visit to Boston or Philadelphia, and then shook off these idle thoughts to supervise again the work of clearing the wreckage.

And as he did so he caught a glimpse of a faint blot in the fog bank ahead. Something was looming out of it, grow-ing sharper every second. He saw the headsails of a ship; so definite was the fog bank that the headsails were illumined by the sunshine before the aftersails were visible. He knew her—she was the Cor-morant tardily retracing her course in search of her precious convoy. He cheered wildly and involuntarily, and the surprised crew, looking in the direction in which he pointed, cheered with him.

The Cormorant came flying down to them, with every sail set, but as they watched they saw her upper yards thick with men as she got in her royals ready for action. They gave her another cheer as she went by; the American was clawing up to windward trying to get the weather gauge in the approaching duel with this formidable opponent. But the fog bank had reached the Augusta by now. One or two little wreaths of mist drifted across her deck, and then she plunged deep into it, and the battle they were leaving behind was hidden from view. Hornblower heard the two opening broadsides, each one sharp and distinct—sure proof in either case of a well-disciplined crew. And then the firing changed to a long, continuous roll of artillery.

Without the king on board, Horn-blower would have turned his ship about, crippled as she was, to join in the fight, but he knew his duty. He was about to shout an order to Mr. White, when his attention was attracted by the approach of the king.

"A good boy," said His Majesty. "Good boys get guineas."

The smile on the foolish face was quite winning and charming; the king brought his hand out of the royal fob pocket and put something into Hornblower's hand. It was not a guinea. That desirable and elegant coin had disappeared from circula-tion altogether now that England was in arms against all the world. The coin epitomized the financial straits through which England was struggling; it was a Spanish silver dollar, with, struck into it, the profile of the king who had just presented it to Hornblower—queer legal currency for the wealthiest nation in the world.

"Thank you, sir," said Hornblower, doffing his hat and bowing low as the spirit of the moment dictated.

They were through the fog bank now and the sun was shining on them again, lighting up the face of the king. Far astern the long roll of artillery came to a sudden end. Perhaps one ship or the other had hauled down her colors. Perhaps at this moment the boarders were fighting hand to hand on the littered decks. Perhaps, after all, thought Hornblower, it might have been better if the Cormorant had not arrived in time for the battle. Some lives would have been saved—many more, perhaps, if peace had resulted from an enforced visit of the king to the United States. He tried once more to picture the king landing at the Battery, but even his imagination boggled at that.

They Think of Everything

Pat Frank

In the meticulous preparations for Wolfgang's mission of sabotage in wartime England, the Parachute Corps covered every contingency. Wolfgang didn't.

August 24, 1940

"In the traveling bag," said Captain Gross, checking off the items on his fingers, "you should have the following: Two shirts, two pair of blue socks, four handkerchiefs, and striped tie, razor, soap, toothbrush, the two suits, which I hope you have been wearing, and the cable cutter."

"As instructed," said Wolfgang, "I wore the suits for ten days so they would not seem strange. They are excellent suits. Made in England."

Captain Gross smiled and shook his head. "That we could not afford," he explained. "But the labels, they were made in England. Now on your person you will carry your Luger, fifty rounds, and three grenades. Most important of all, of course, is the cable cutter. Everything is packed?"

"Yes, Captain."

"You have the English money, and your papers and credentials? You have memorized the name and address of our man in Ipswich? You have not forgotten the compass? They have removed all road signs, so it will be important."

"I have everything, Captain."

"Then goodby, and good luck. Heil Hitler!"

"Heil Hitler," Wolfgang replied, saluting. He adjusted his leather parachutist's helmet, picked up his shiny brown suitcase, walked out on the dark field, and felt his way toward the deeper shadow, in many shadows, which was the big Junkers.

He took his seat in the transport, and saw that others were there before him. There were no lights, so their figures were dim and bulky and their faces unrecognizable. In a moment they were in the air.

There is not much excitement, Wolfgang considered, flying in a military transport that has no windows. Sometimes he wished he had become a pilot. But the Parachute Corps was elite, also, and no doubt when it was over he would have decorations and perhaps a commission. He could see himself lined up for the Fuehrer's personal congratulations, and unconsciously his back stiffened and his shoulders went back.

When they had been an hour in the air Wolfgang sensed they must be near their destination, the sparsely settled lowland between Orford Ness and the Deben River. He did not need a map. His map had been etched in his head. An officer stepped from the pilot's compartment and said: "In two minutes we begin. You will go out at intervals of one minute." This was so they would not fall bunched, Wolfgang knew. The plan did not call for assault, but for infiltration. Some might be captured. A few would get through. For each job there were at least two men. The Parachute Corps thought of everything. He saw that the suitcase handle was secure on his belt.

Wolfgang was closest to the door. The officer motioned to him. Wolfgang stepped to the opening, held to the metal grips and braced his feet as he had been taught, and shoved off hard into the night. The wind whipped his head back, and then he was falling easily, his chute opened wide over him.

Expertly he tugged at the shrouds, and swept down for an open field. He struck, went to his knees, recovered instantly, and spilled the wind from his parachute. He lay still on the ground, as he had been instructed, and disengaged the traveling bag.

This was fortunate, for from the direction of the road he heard voices. "I saw something moving in that field," a man's voice said. And then a girl said, her voice taut with fear: "So did I!"

"I'll see what it is," the man said reassuringly.

Wolfgang drew a stick grenade from his belt. He heard the whip of brush on the man's trousers, and then he saw his form, looming clean against the sky. Wolfgang flipped the pin and threw the grenade. The explosion seemed much louder than it ever had in practice. Wolfgang rose and ran toward them. The grenade had got them both, he saw at once. Wolfgang retrieved the suitcase and ran for a clump of trees. There was no sign of more life in the field, or on the road. He got busy.

He stripped off his uniform, changed to the gray flannel suit, tossed the unused grenades and the Luger into the suitcase and walked out onto the road as a Londoner who had been summering at Orford, and who now was fleeing the coast because of imminent invasion. His compass led him west, toward the coastal highway running to Ipswich. When he reached the highway he walked south, and, with dawn's first light, cars began to pass him.

Six, maybe seven miles now to Ipswich, and the suitcase dragged at his arm. The party man in Ipswich would point out the telephone lines leading to London. After these were cut he would be on his own. The idea of being his own commander fascinated him. He would capture a British armored car. He would race to the shore again, and perhaps take a battery from the rear.

He was so busy with his plans that he did not notice the barricade until it was too late to turn back, for he had been seen. A lorry blocked the road. There were soldiers around it, rifles slung over their shoulders. Three small cars, luggage strapped to their running boards, were halted in front of it.

A sergeant motioned to Wolfgang, and called, "This way, sir." Wolfgang walked over and saw, behind the lorry, a straggling line of men and women, some empty-handed, some carrying bags. "Sorry," the sergeant said, "but we're examining all coming this way. Won't take long. Step into line."

"Righto," Wolfgang said. "What's up?"

"Fritz's planes have been over the coast. May have dropped some damn' 'chutists."

"Nuisance, aren't they!" Wolfgang dropped his suitcase at his feet. He could open it, casually, grab the grenades, and make a fight of it.

Then he saw the Englishman just ahead in line had a suitcase much like his own. A typical Englishman, sallow, his chin weak and narrow. He would be polite, perhaps meek. A man in the Parachute Corps thinks swiftly.

Wolfgang shoved his own suitcase alongside the Englishman's, jostled the frail fellow, said, "Sorry, old man," and picked up the bag again. Only it was the Englishman's suitcase he now held. He didn't think the Englishman noticed.

Presently the sergeant came to the Englishman, and riffled through his credentials. Then he bent and opened the suitcase. The sergeant cursed, and the Territorials slammed their rifle muzzles into the Englishman's belly. The Englishman's eyes were wide and frightened, staring straight into his own, as they led him away. They didn't give him much of a chance to talk. They just took him into the woods and shot him. A soldier in civilian clothes is a spy.

The sergeant came back. His face was twitching.

"Ready for me now?" Wolfgang asked.

The sergeant didn't say anything. He examined Wolfgang's papers, felt his hips and under his arms, and then opened the suitcase that had been the Englishman's. Wolfgang looked down, numbly, at two shirts, a suit, handkerchiefs, socks, and on top of these a heavy, rubber-sheathed pair of shears, a Luger, and three stick grenades.

Four and Twenty Blackbirds

Agatha Christie

Hercule Poirot, the Belgian master of deduction invented by Agatha Miller Christie, has probably solved more crimes than did Sherlock Holmes. Prolific as she is ingenious, Mrs. Christie can roll out three fine mystery novels a year when she sets her mind to it. This is one of Poirot's briefer adventures.

November 9, 1940

Hercule Poirot was dining with his friend, Henry Bonnington, at the Gallant Endeavour in the King's Road, Chelsea.

Mr. Bonnington was fond of the Gallant Endeavour. He liked the leisurely atmosphere, he liked the food which was "plain" and "English" and "not a lot of made-up messes."

Molly, the sympathetic waitress, greeted him as an old friend. She prided herself on remembering her customers' likes and dislikes in the way of food.

"Good evening, sir," she said, as the two men took their seats at a corner table. "You're in luck today—turkey stuffed with chestnuts—that's your favorite, isn't it? And ever such a nice Stilton we've got! Will you have soup first or fish?"

The question of food and wine settled, Mr. Bonnington leaned back with a sigh and unfolded his napkin as Molly sped away.

"Good girl, that!" he said approvingly. "Was quite a beauty once—artists used to paint her. She knows about food, too—and that's a great deal more important. Women are very unsound on food as a rule. There's many a woman, if she goes out with a fellow she fancies, won't even notice what she eats. She'll just order the first thing she sees."

Hercule Poirot shook his head.

"*C'est terrible.*"

"Men aren't like that, thank goodness!" said Mr. Bonnington complacently.

"Never?" There was a twinkle in Hercule Poirot's eye.

"Well, perhaps when they're very young," conceded Mr. Bonnington. "Young puppies! Young fellows nowadays are all the same—no guts—no stamina. I've no use for the young—and they," he added with strict impartiality, "have no use for me. Perhaps they're right! But to hear some of these young fellows talk you'd think no man had a right to be *alive* after sixty! From the way they go on, you'd wonder more of them didn't help their elderly relations out of the world."

"It is possible," said Hercule Poirot, "that they do."

"Nice mind you've got, Poirot, I must say. All this police work saps your ideals."

Hercule Poirot smiled.

"Nevertheless," he said, "it would be interesting to make a table of accidental deaths over the age of sixty. I assure you it would raise some curious speculations in your mind. . . . But tell me, my friend, of your own affairs. How does the world go with you?"

"Mess!" said Mr. Bonnington. "That's what's the matter with the world nowadays. Too much mess. And too much fine language. The fine language helps to conceal the mess. Like a highly flavored sauce concealing the fact that the fish underneath it is none of the best! Give me an honest fillet of sole and no messy sauce over it."

It was given him at that moment by Molly and he grunted approval.

"You know just what I like, my girl," he said.

"Well, you come here pretty regular, don't you, sir? So I ought to know."

Hercule Poirot said: "Do people then always like the same things? Do not they like a change sometimes?"

"Not gentlemen, sir. Ladies like variety —gentlemen always like the same thing."

"What did I tell you?" grunted Bonnington. "Women are fundamentally unsound where food is concerned!"

He looked around the restaurant.

"The world's a funny place. See that odd-looking old fellow with a beard in the corner? Molly'll tell you he's always here Tuesday and Thursday nights. He has come here for close on ten years now —he's a kind of landmark in the place. Yet nobody here knows his name or where he lives or what his business is. It's odd when you come to think of it."

When the waitress brought the portions of turkey he said: "I see you've still got Old Father Time over there?"

"That's right, sir. Tuesdays and Thursdays, his days are. Not but what he came in here on a *Monday* last week! It quite upset me! I felt I'd got my dates wrong and that it must be Tuesday without my knowing it! But he came in the next night as well—so the Monday was just a kind of extra, so to speak."

"An interesting deviation from habit," murmured Poirot. "I wonder what the reason was."

"Well, sir, if you ask me, I think he'd had some kind of upset or worry."

"Why did you think that? His manner?"

"No, sir—not his manner exactly. He was very quiet as he always is. Never says much except 'Good evening' when he comes and goes. No, it was his *order*."

"His order?"

"I dare say you gentlemen will laugh at me." Molly flushed. "But when a gentleman has been here for ten years, you get to know his likes and dislikes. He never could bear suet pudding or blackberries and I've never known him to take thick soup—but on that Monday night he ordered thick tomato soup, beefsteak and kidney pudding and blackberry tart! Seemed as though he just didn't notice *what* he ordered!"

"Do you know," said Hercule Poirot, "I find that extraordinarily interesting."

Molly looked gratified and departed.

"Well, Poirot," said Henry Bonnington with a chuckle. "Let's have a few deductions from you. All in your best manner."

"I would prefer to hear yours first."

"Want me to be Watson, eh? Well, old fellow went to a doctor and the doctor changed his diet."

"To thick tomato soup, steak and kidney pudding and blackberry tart? I cannot imagine any doctor doing that."

"Don't you believe it, old boy. Doctors will put you onto anything."

"That is the only solution that occurs to you?"

Henry Bonnington said: "Well, seriously, I suppose there's only one explanation possible. Our unknown friend was in the grip of some powerful mental emotion. He was so perturbed by it that he literally did not notice what he was ordering or eating."

He paused a minute, and then said: "You'll be telling me next that you know just *what* was on his mind. You'll say perhaps that he was making up his mind to commit a murder."

He laughed at his own suggestion.

Hercule Poirot did not laugh.

He has admitted that at that moment he was seriously worried. He claims that he ought then to have had some inkling of what was likely to occur.

His friends assure him that such an idea is quite fantastic.

It was some three weeks later that Hercule Poirot and Bonnington met again—this time their meeting was in the subway.

They nodded to each other, swaying about, hanging onto adjacent straps. Then at Piccadilly Circus there was a general exodus and they found seats right at the forward end of the car—a peaceful spot since nobody passed in or out that way.

"By the way," said Mr. Bonnington. "Do you remember that old boy we noticed at the Gallant Endeavour? I shouldn't wonder if he'd hopped it to a better world. He's not been there for a whole week. Molly's quite upset about it."

Hercule Poirot sat up. His eyes flashed. "Indeed?" he said. "Indeed?"

Bonnington said: "D'you remember I suggested he'd been to a doctor and been put on a diet? Diet's nonsense of course—but I shouldn't wonder if he had consulted a doctor about his health and what the doctor said gave him a bit of a jolt. That would account for him ordering things off the menu without noticing what he was doing. Quite likely the jolt he got hurried him out of the world sooner than he would have gone otherwise. Doctors ought to be careful what they tell a chap."

"They usually are," said Hercule Poirot.

"This is my station," said Mr. Bonnington. "Bye-bye. Don't suppose we shall ever know now who the old boy was—not even his name. Funny world!"

He hurried out of the carriage.

Hercule Poirot, sitting frowning, looked as though he did not think it was such a funny world.

He went home and gave certain instructions to his faithful valet, George.

Hercule Poirot ran his finger down a list of names. It was a record of deaths within a certain area.

Poirot's finger stopped.

"Henry Gascoigne. 69. I might try him first."

Later in the day, Hercule Poirot was sitting in Dr. MacAndrew's surgery just off the King's Road. MacAndrew was a tall, red-haired Scotsman with an intelligent face.

"Gascoigne?" he said. "Yes, that's right. Eccentric old bird. Lived alone in one of those derelict old houses that are being cleared away in order to build a block of modern flats. I hadn't attended him before, but I'd seen him about and I knew who he was. It was the dairy people got the wind up first. The milk bottles began to pile up outside. In the end the people next door sent word to the police and they broke the door in and found him. He'd pitched down the stairs and broken his neck. Had on an old dressing gown with a ragged cord—might easily have tripped himself up with it."

"I see," said Hercule Poirot. "It was quite simple—an accident."

"That's right."

"Had he any relations?"

"There's a nephew. Used to come along and see his uncle about once a month. Ramsey, his name is, George Ramsey. He's a medico himself. Lives at Wimbledon."

"How long had Mr. Gascoigne been dead when you saw him?"

"Ah!" said Dr. MacAndrew. "This is where we get official. Not less than forty-eight hours and not more than seventy-two hours. He was found on the morning of the 6th. Actually, we got closer than that. He had a letter in the pocket of his dressing gown—written on the 3d—posted in Wimbledon that afternoon—would have been delivered somewhere around 9:20 P. M. That puts the time of death at after 9:20 on the evening of the 3d. That agrees with the contents of the stomach and the processes of digestion. He had had a meal about two hours before death. I examined him on the morning of the 6th and his condition was quite consistent with death having occurred about sixty hours previously—around about 10 P. M. on the 3d."

"It all seems very consistent. Tell me, when was he last seen alive?"

"He was seen in the King's Road about seven o'clock that same evening, Thursday the 3d, and he dined at the Gallant Endeavour restaurant at 7:30. It seems he always dined there on Thursdays."

"He had no other relations? Only this nephew?"

"There was a twin brother. The whole story is rather curious. They hadn't seen each other for years. As a young man Henry was by way of being an artist, you know. An extremely bad one. It seems the other brother, Anthony Gascoigne, married a very rich woman and gave up art—and the brothers quarreled over it. Hadn't seen each other since, I believe. But oddly enough, *they died on the same day*. The elder twin passed away at one o'clock on the afternoon of the 3d. Once before I've known a case of twins dying on the same day—in different parts of the world! Probably just a coincidence—but there it is."

"Is the other brother's wife alive?"

"No, she died some years ago."

"Where did Anthony Gascoigne live?"

"He had a house on Kingston Hill. He was, I believe, from what Dr. Ramsey tells me, very much of a recluse."

Hercule Poirot nodded thoughtfully.

The Scotsman looked at him keenly.

"What exactly have you got in your mind, M. Poirot?" he asked bluntly. "I've answered your questions—as was my duty seeing the credentials you brought. But I'm in the dark as to what it's all about."

Poirot said slowly: "A simple case of accidental death, that's what you said. What I have in mind is equally simple—a simple push."

Dr. MacAndrew looked startled.

"In other words, murder! Have you any grounds for that belief?"

"No," said Poirot. "It is a mere supposition."

"There must be something—" persisted the other.

Poirot did not speak.

MacAndrew said, "If it's the nephew, Ramsey, you suspect, I don't mind telling you here and now that you are barking up the wrong tree. Ramsey was playing bridge in Wimbledon from 8:30 till midnight. That came out at the inquest."

Poirot murmured: "And presumably it was verified. The police are careful."

The doctor said: "Perhaps you know something against him?"

"I didn't know that there was such a person until you mentioned him."

"Then you suspect somebody else?"

"No, no. It is not that at all. It's a case of the routine habits of the human animal. That is very important. And the dead M. Gascoigne does not fit in. It is all wrong, you see."

"I really don't understand."

Hercule Poirot smiled. He rose and the doctor rose also.

"You know," said MacAndrew, "honestly, I can't see anything the least bit suspicious about the death of Henry Gascoigne."

The little man spread out his hands.

"I'm an obstinate man—a man with a little idea—and nothing to support it! By the way, did Henry Gascoigne have false teeth?"

"No, his own teeth were in excellent preservation. Very creditable indeed at his age."

"He looked after them well—they were white and well brushed?"

"Yes, I noticed them particularly."

"Not discolored in any way?"

"No. I don't think he was a smoker if that is what you mean."

"I did not mean that precisely—it was just a long shot—which probably will not come off! Goodby, Dr. MacAndrew, and thank you for your kindness."

He shook the doctor's hand and departed.

"And now," he said, "for the long shot."

At the Gallant Endeavour, he sat down at the same table that he had shared with Bonnington. The girl who served him was not Molly. Molly, the girl told him, was away on a holiday.

It was just seven and Hercule Poirot found no difficulty in entering into conversation with the girl on the subject of old Mr. Gascoigne.

"Yes," she said. "He'd been here for years and years. But none of us girls ever knew his name. We saw about the inquest in the paper, and there was a picture of him. 'There,' I said to Molly, 'if that isn't our Old Father Time—' as we used to call him."

"He dined here on the evening of his death, did he not?"

"That's right. Thursday, the 3d. He was always here on a Thursday. Tuesdays and Thursdays—punctual as a clock."

"You don't remember, I suppose, what he had for dinner?"

"Now let me see, it was mulligatawny soup, that's right, and beefsteak pudding or was it the mutton?—no pudding, that's right, and blackberry-and-apple pie and cheese. And then to think of him going home and falling down those stairs that very same evening. A frayed dressing-gown cord they said it was as caused it. Of course, his clothes were always something awful—old-fashioned and put on anyhow, and all tattered, and yet he *had* a kind of air, all the same, as though he was *somebody!* Oh, we get all sorts of interesting customers here."

She moved off.

Hercule Poirot ate his sole.

Armed with introductions from a certain influential quarter, Hercule Poirot found no difficulty at all in dealing with the coroner for the district.

"A curious figure, the deceased man Gascoigne," he observed. "A lonely, eccentric old fellow. But his decease seems to arouse an unusual amount of attention."

He looked with some curiosity at his visitor as he spoke.

Hercule Poirot chose his words carefully: "There are circumstances connected with it, Monsieur, which make investigation desirable."

"Well, how can I help you?"

"It is, I believe, within your province to order documents produced in your court to be destroyed, or to be impounded—as you think fit. A certain letter was found in the pocket of Henry Gascoigne's dressing gown, was it not?"

"That is so."

"A letter from his nephew, Dr. George Ramsey?"

"Quite correct. The letter was produced at the inquest as helping to fix the time of death."

"Is that letter still available?"

Hercule Poirot waited rather anxiously for the reply.

When he heard that the letter was still available for examination he drew a sigh of relief.

When it was finally produced he studied it with some care. It was written in a slightly cramped handwriting with a stylographic pen. It ran as follows:

"Dear Uncle Henry:

I am sorry to tell you that I have had no success as regards Uncle Anthony. He showed no enthusiasm for a visit from you and would give me no reply to your request that he would let bygones be bygones. He is, of course, extremely ill, and his mind is inclined to wander. I should fancy that the end is very near. He seemed hardly to remember who you were.

I am sorry to have failed you, but I can assure you that I did my best.

Your affectionate nephew,

GEORGE RAMSEY."

The letter itself was dated 3d November. Poirot glanced at the envelope's postmark—4:30 P. M.

He murmured: "It is beautifully in order, is it not?" . . .

Kingston Hill was his next objective. After a little trouble, with the exercise of good-humored pertinacity, he obtained an interview with Amelia Hill, cook-housekeeper to the late Anthony Gascoigne.

Mrs. Hill was inclined to be stiff and suspicious at first, but the charming geniality of this strange-looking foreigner soon had its effect. Mrs. Amelia Hill began to unbend.

She found herself, as had so many other women before her, pouring out her troubles to a really sympathetic listener.

For fourteen years she had had charge of Mr. Gascoigne's household—*not* an easy job! No, indeed! Many a woman would have quailed under the burdens *she* had had to bear! Eccentric the poor gentleman was and no denying it. Remarkably close with his money—a kind of mania with him it was—and he as rich a gentleman as might be! But Mrs. Hill had served him faithfully, and put up with his ways, and naturally she'd expected at any rate a *remembrance*. But no—nothing at all! Just an old will that left all his money to his wife and if she predeceased him then everything to his brother, Henry. A will made years ago. It didn't seem fair!

Gradually Hercule Poirot detached her from her main theme of unsatisfied cupidity. It was indeed a heartless injustice! Mrs. Hill could not be blamed for feeling hurt and surprised. It was well known that Mr. Gascoigne was tight-fisted about money. It had even been said that the dead man had refused his only brother assistance. Mrs. Hill probably knew all about that.

"Was it that that Dr. Ramsey came to see him about?" asked Mrs. Hill. "I knew it was something about his brother, but I thought it was just that his brother wanted to be reconciled. They'd quarreled years ago."

"I understand," said Poirot, "that Mr. Gascoigne refused absolutely?"

"That's right enough," said Mrs. Hill with a nod. "*'Henry?'* he says, rather weaklike. *'What's this about Henry? Haven't seen him for years and don't want to. Quarrelsome fellow, Henry.'* Just that."

The conversation then reverted to Mrs. Hill's own special grievances, and the unfeeling attitude of the late Mr. Gascoigne's solicitor.

With some difficulty Hercule Poirot took his leave without breaking off the conversation too abruptly.

And so, just after the dinner hour, he came to Elmcrest, Dorset Road, Wimbledon, the residence of Dr. George Ramsey.

The doctor was in. Hercule Poirot was shown into the surgery and there presently Dr. George Ramsey came to him, obviously just risen from the dinner table.

"I'm not a patient, doctor," said Hercule Poirot. "And my coming here is, perhaps, somewhat of an impertinence—but I believe in plain and direct dealing. I do not care for lawyers and their long-winded roundabout methods."

He had certainly aroused Ramsey's interest. The doctor was a clean-shaven man of middle height. His hair was brown but his eyelashes were almost white, which gave his eyes a pale, boiled appearance. His manner was brisk and not without humor.

"Lawyers?" he said raising his eyebrows. "Hate the fellows! You rouse my curiosity, my dear sir. Pray sit down."

Poirot did so and then produced one of his professional cards which he handed to the doctor.

George Ramsey's white eyelashes blinked.

Poirot leaned forward confidentially. "A good many of my clients are women," he said.

"Naturally," said Dr. George Ramsey, with a slight twinkle.

"As you say, naturally," agreed Poirot. "Women distrust the official police. They prefer private investigations. They do not want to have their troubles made public. An elderly woman came to consult me a few days ago. She was unhappy about a husband she'd quarreled with many years before. This husband of hers was your uncle, the late Mr. Gascoigne."

George Ramsey's face went purple.

"My uncle? Nonsense! His wife died many years ago."

"Not your uncle, Mr. *Anthony* Gascoigne. Your uncle, Mr. *Henry* Gascoigne."

"Uncle Henry? But *he* wasn't married!"

"Oh, yes, he was," said Hercule Poirot, lying unblushingly. "Not a doubt of it. The lady even brought along her marriage certificate."

"It's a lie!" cried George Ramsey. His face was now as purple as a plum. "I don't believe it. You're an impudent liar."

"It is too bad, is it not?" said Poirot. "You have committed murder for nothing."

"Murder?" Ramsey's voice quavered. His pale eyes bulged with terror.

"By the way," said Poirot, "I see you have been eating blackberry tart again. An unwise habit. Blackberries are said to be full of vitamins, but they may be deadly in other ways. On this occasion I rather fancy they have helped to put a rope around a man's neck—your neck, Dr. Ramsey."

"You see, *mon ami*, where you went wrong was over your fundamental assumption." Hercule Poirot, beaming placidly across the table at his friend, waved an expository hand. "A man under severe mental stress doesn't choose that time to do something that he's never done before. His reflexes just follow the track of least resistance. A man who is upset about something *might* conceivably come down to dinner dressed in his pajamas—but they will be his *own* pajamas—not somebody else's.

"A man who dislikes thick soup, suet pudding and blackberries suddenly orders all three one evening. *You* say, because he is thinking of something else. But *I* say *that a man who has got something on his mind will order automatically the dish he has ordered most often before.*

"*Eh bien*, then, what other explanation could there be? I simply could not think of a reasonable explanation. And I was worried! The incident was all wrong.

"Then you told me that the man had disappeared. He had missed a Tuesday and a Thursday the first time for years. I liked that even less. A queer hypothesis sprang up in my mind. If I were right about it *the man was dead.* I made inquiries. The man *was* dead. And he was very neatly and tidily dead. In other words the bad fish was covered up with the sauce!

"He had been seen in the King's Road at seven o'clock. He had had dinner here at 7:30—two hours before he died. It all fitted in—the evidence of the stomach contents, the evidence of the letter. Much too much sauce! You couldn't see the fish at all!

"Devoted nephew wrote the letter, devoted nephew had beautiful alibi for time of death. Death very simple—a fall down the stairs. Simple accident? Or murder? Everyone says the former.

"Devoted nephew only surviving relative. Devoted nephew will inherit—but is there anything *to* inherit? Uncle notoriously poor.

"But there is a brother. And brother in his time had married a rich wife. And brother lives in a big rich house on Kingston Hill, so it would seem that rich wife must have left him all her money. You see the sequence—rich wife leaves money to Anthony, Anthony leaves money to Henry, Henry's money goes to George—a complete chain."

"All very pretty in theory," said Mr. Bonnington. "But what did you do?"

"Once you *know*—you can usually get hold of what you want. Henry had died two hours after a *meal*—that is all the inquest really bothered about. But supposing that meal was not dinner, but *lunch.* Put yourself in George's place. George wants money—badly. Anthony Gascoigne is dying—but his death is no good to George. His money goes to Henry, and Henry Gascoigne may live for years. So Henry must die too—and the sooner the better—but his death must take place *after* Anthony's, and at the same time George must have an alibi. Henry's habit of dining regularly at a restaurant on two evenings of the week suggests an alibi to George. Being a cautious fellow, he tries his plan out first. *He impersonates his uncle one Monday evening at the restaurant in question.*

"It goes without a hitch. Everyone there accepts him as his uncle. He is satisfied. He has only to wait till Uncle Anthony shows definite signs of pegging out. The time comes. He mails a letter to his uncle on the afternoon of the 2d November but dates it the 3d. He comes up to town on the afternoon of the 3d, calls on his uncle, and carries his scheme into action. A shove and down the stairs goes Uncle Henry.

"George hunts about for the letter he has written, and shoves it in the pocket of his uncle's dressing gown. At 7:30 he is at the Gallant Endeavour, beard, bushy eyebrows, all complete. Undoubtedly Mr. Henry Gascoigne is alive at 7:30. Then a rapid metamorphosis in a lavatory and back full speed in his car to Wimbledon and an evening of bridge. The perfect alibi."

Mr. Bonnington looked at him.

"But the postmark on the letter?"

"Oh, that was very simple. The postmark was smudgy. Why? It had been altered with lampblack from Nov. 2d to Nov. 3d. You would not notice it *unless you were looking for it.* And finally there were the blackbirds."

"Blackbirds?"

"Four-and-twenty blackbirds baked in a pie! Or blackberries if you prefer to be literal! George, you comprehend, was after all not quite a good enough actor. He *looked* like his uncle and *walked* like his uncle and *spoke* like his uncle and had his uncle's beard and eyebrows, but he forgot to *eat* like his uncle. He ordered the dishes that he himself liked.

"Blackberries discolor the teeth—the corpse's teeth were not discolored, and yet Henry Gascoigne ate blackberries at the Gallant Endeavour that night. But there were no blackberries in the stomach. I asked this morning. And George had been fool enough to keep the beard and the rest of the make-up. Oh! plenty of evidence once you look for it. I called on George and rattled him. That finished it! He had been eating blackberries again, by the way. A greedy fellow—cared a lot about his food. *Eh bien,* greed will hang him all right unless I am very much mistaken."

A waitress brought them two portions of blackberry-and-apple tart.

"Take it away," said Mr. Bonnington. "One can't be too careful. Bring me a small helping of sago pudding."

Death of a Truck

Talbot Johns

As a small boy he had been fiercely possessive of the little toy car. He was a bigger boy now, and the car was an army truck, dead in a snowbank.

March 21, 1942

"My dear son," she wrote, "your father and I miss you in a way that my heart can hardly tell, but we rest here at home secure and as happy as we may be, and I am proud as only a mother can be of the great and brave work you are doing for the Fatherland. Herr Kapitan Sweiger came home on leave last week and brought word that he had seen you in Poland and you were well and happy. Your panzers, he said, will be the first to enter Moscow, an honor reserved for your division by Marshal von Brauchitsch himself because of 'extraordinary valor in the face of the enemy.' We all now realize that the Fuehrer brings us another great victory, but I yearn for you, my Liebchen. . . ."

The boy dropped the spanner heavily on the rough floorboards of the great gray truck, and sighed wearily—a despairing sigh that sent a long white cloud of steam to mist the icy metal face of the dashboard and freeze instantly and magically in tiny crystals on the rough shoddy of his upturned collar. It was no use. Nothing was any use any more, because the lonely truck in the wide white desert of snow was dead. Just as Johann, sitting stiffly upright on the hard seat by his side, was dead. Johann, who had driven east twelve hundred miles, laughing, and singing of victory, and then had been five seconds late diving under the truck in this afternoon's early dusk when a wandering Russian hawk had spattered and blasted their crippled machine.

The boy felt Johann's hand. It was cold and stiff, like a clean white fish in the ice bin of the market on the Odinstrasse, and the boy shuddered for he, too, was cold.

The very world must be cold, he thought, and he could not remember when it had ever been warm. During the first weeks of this fantastic retreat he had dreamed of the round fat stove at home, the one with the little windows in the side where you could watch the flames merrily leaping. Once he had dreamed of his fathers' great steaming tankard of mulled ale, and his father's red, beaming face above it, but today that face was a face like Johann's, like the hundreds of other Johanns they had passed along the white road of cold and death.

The boy had been confused at first, for had not the Fuehrer himself said of the bearded giants, "I say that this enemy is already smashed and will never rise again!" That was months ago, when big blond Johann with the laughing blue eyes sat by his side, flipping cigarette butts scornfully at the dull, brutish prisoners who watched with open mouths the dingy, travel-worn truck from the side of the rutted road.

Now there was no confusion. There were no decisions to make. The cold and the truck were all. The boy still loved his truck—loved it as much as he hated his thin, useless coat. Crippled though it was, it now constituted his only last hold on life.

The boy did not know it was forty below zero; it would have meant nothing to him if he had. No shelter from the freezing blasts but the truck, no companion but Johann; and now Johann and the truck were dead.

"The war seems far away from us today, my Liebchen, and indeed it is hard to realize that we are steadily forging ahead toward the glorious conquest promised us. We hear that the weather is very mild in Russia for this time of year, and I can believe that, as we have had just one light snowfall. Just enough to coat the trees in a pretty mantle of pure white—you used to love them, remember? You called them candy-cane trees, and I used to tell you all about Jack Frost and his long white brush. . . ."

The truck had died that afternoon. With its high square nose buried in a drift, it died, and left a clear stillness broken only by the indiscriminate murmurings of death from the rear, and the weary chuttering of the rusty machines next in line. Shrill whistles blew up and down the column, a tired *oberleutnant* floundered up in a staff car. He stood, and the boy could see the tattered uniform coat, the legs wrapped in mufflers.

"Push it off the road!" came the sharp command to the crew of the following truck.

"*Herr Oberleutnant*, please," faltered the boy.

"Speak quickly! The column must move!"

"I can save my truck, sir," said the boy, "if I can have but half an hour. I know it well, and all its troubles."

"It carries valuable oil. Very well," the officer assented. "We will leave you at the side of the road. If you are not repaired in time, get on the last truck and save yourself."

"I must finish up my letter now, dear son, as your father is waiting for supper. Please remember me to that friend of yours—isn't his name Johann? A nice boy.

"Looking out into our yard with its beautiful carpet of white takes me back so many years (and yet, not so many, either) to one Christmas when you had a little toy automobile. How you loved it! You would sit there in the snow and pump with your little feet and get nowhere, and I remember once when some of the bigger boys came and tried to take your little car away from you, but you wouldn't let them. You held onto the wheel with your tiny hands so tightly until Mother came and chased the naughty boys away. Well, good night, my Liebchen, wherever you are, and sweet dreams. . . ."

Fifty men on horseback plodded silently along the snowy white road. They were big and bearded and well-fed; they cursed and laughed softly as they drew abreast of a stalled truck standing intact among the junk and litter of a ruined supply column.

"Chief Lieutenant," said the colonel in the lead, "take a detail and investigate that machine. Look out for traps, now."

The small squad warily reined their steaming mounts closer to the big truck.

"All in order, sir. The crew is inside, frozen."

"Get them out of there," said the colonel, "and see if we can salvage anything."

"Beg pardon, sir," said the chief lieutenant a moment later. "The driver's hands are frozen around the wheel. It is impossible to move them."

The colonel rode closer to the high cab, and looked inside. The driver's cold fists gripped the big wheel rim desperately, the thin knuckles almost standing through the parchment skin.

"Poor kid," the colonel said to the chief lieutenant. "He's only a boy."

The chief lieutenant laughed. He was examining some torn and dirty papers. "They send us babies," he said. "This one is but fifteen."

The colonel shook his head. Struck by a sudden whim he slipped off his heavy gauntleted glove, leaned over on one stirrup and gently touched the boy's cold cheek.

He swung back into his saddle. His eyes still on the boy, he saluted. He snapped, "Follow me!" and rode on through the snow.

Miracle from Heaven

MacKinlay Kantor

No contemporary American writer has a surer, finer way with the hearts of his readers than Iowa-born MacKinlay Kantor. Scenarist, war correspondent, author of such distinguished novels as Andersonville *and* The Voice of Bugle Ann, *Kantor wrote for* Collier's *this simple, deeply moving story of a prodigal's return.*

September 11, 1943

When Johnston Bush got off the evening train at Cool Meadows it was dark, and seven o'clock. A thin wind was blowing as he walked along the platform, carrying his one small bag.

There were lights over on the main street; a lot of lights in the Big-Time Drugstore on the corner, and the platform in front of the pool hall was also brightly illuminated. Johnston was walking against these lights, facing them, with his back toward the railroad yard from which the train was already laboring away. He could not clearly recognize the figure approaching him from the main street, but he thought it was Mr. Shannon from the bank, and immediately he experienced a feeling of shame for vandalisms which he had committed when younger.

One Saturday night he had thrown a rock through the window of Mr. Shannon's bank. He had done it intentionally.

His grandfather was forced to pay for the window, and Johnston himself spent two days in jail before his mother could persuade the authorities to let him come home.

This wasn't Mr. Shannon whom he met now, however. It was the Reverend Charles Hood of the Christian Church.

"Why, aren't you Johnny Bush?"

Johnston halted, grinding his fingers around the handle of his bag. The minister came back to shake hands. "I thought maybe that was you, coming from the train. We knew you were due home."

Johnston said, "Evening, Reverend."

"It's wonderful," said the Reverend Hood, still holding the boy's hand. "You picked your time right—or had it picked for you. Got back for Thanksgiving."

Johnston hadn't thought much about it before. He had thought about Thanksgiving sometimes, but not just recently.

He wanted to tell the Reverend Hood that it seemed unbelievable to be welcomed back to Cool Meadows thus heartily; but he had never been easily articulate, and a weight of emotion kept him from saying things which the Reverend Hood might have enjoyed hearing.

"It was in the newspapers, Johnny."

Johnston Bush and the minister released the grip of their hands simultaneously.

"Well," Johnston said, "I guess you know where I been."

He wanted to say a great many other things, but the cat got his tongue. He wished that he might tell the Reverend Hood and all of Cool Meadows how much he had learned, how much he had changed. . . . He wished to declare his skills and newly acquired wisdom. Johnny wanted to say, "Look at me—I'm what you might call a changed character. Never again will I throw a rock through the bank window, no matter how broke we Bushes get! Never again will I fight the marshal. Never again break a billiard cue over Jud Axline's head. Never again take Grandpa's .45 and try to shoot up the town. Never—"

But he could not say these things, nor could he say anything else. He merely shuffled his new stiff shoes; and the Reverend Hood knew that Johnston Bush wanted to hurry along.

So the minister said, "I pray that you and yours will enjoy a happy Thanksgiving. God bless you, my boy."

Johnston said soberly, "Thank you, Reverend," and turned toward the lights.

He walked on to the main street, remembering now that they had always called it "the main drag," and he wondered why main streets in little towns were called main drags.

He didn't care to enter the drugstore; there would be a lot of people in at the drugstore, and a lot of the younger fellows, probably, at the pool hall. So he kept to the opposite side of the street, striding west, his hard heels clicking sharply on new concrete before one series of stores, and then making a momentary thunder as they trod the hollow wooden sidewalk in front of Harney's Furniture and Undertaking.

He wanted some cigarettes, and before he reached the end of the block he crossed diagonally toward the yellow, steamy front of Nick's Café. That one wide window was exactly the way he remembered it, exactly the way he had thought about it when he was hungry. Yellow glow came through the flat-painted letters of the word "Café," and the letters, deep red in daytime, always looked orange at night.

Inside the restaurant, Johnston put his bag on a stool next to the glass cigar case where the cash register stood.

Nick himself approached slowly in his greasy apron behind the counter. Johnston looked down the room, and everything seemed just the same: salt and pepper, and little triangular sheaves of paper napkins at strategic intervals. All except the catsup bottles. There were no catsup bottles any longer. Catsup was almost impossible to get, in many of these little towns, and Johnston had been surprised when he found that out.

Nick was about five steps away before he recognized Johnny Bush. There were some young kids sitting away back at the other end of the long counter, and they had turned to gaze silently, as Cool Meadows people did at the approach of strangers. It was easy for them to hear what Nick said.

He exclaimed, "Johnny!" and beamed all over his fat, stubbled Greek face. Then he added in a low voice, "What you know? What you know?" as he kept pressing Johnny's hand between his own two fat ones.

The restaurant smelled of fresh hot grease and fresh-cooked eggs. It was a good smell. Johnny thought that he might sit down and have an egg-on-bun. . . . No, he would wait and eat something when he got home.

"We heard you was coming, kid."

"Sure glad to be home," said Johnny. He asked for a couple of packages of cigarettes.

"They treat you good?" asked Nick, as he got the cigarettes. "Not so good, huh? You look mighty thin. Maybe they don't feed you good where you been? Your ma—maybe she put some meat on you, huh?" Nick kept laughing, and at first he didn't want to take any money for the cigarettes, but Johnny insisted.

Nick wanted him to sit down and have a cup of Java on the house.

"No," said Johnny. "I guess maybe I better get along home."

Nick nodded wisely, and kept on beaming at Johnny while he put the packages of cigarettes deep into his pocket.

"Now maybe you be a good kid, huh? Maybe you don't shoot and get drunk and raise some troubles no more? I guess maybe this straighten you out, Johnny?"

"Sure has," said Johnny softly.

At this moment two young girls who had been seated at the other end of the counter with a couple of school-age boys came up to Johnston Bush shyly. Johnny didn't know who they were; but the one who came first, the one in a pale blue sweater and old leather jacket, looked like one of the Blacks from over around Deep Notch. She must have been just a little kid when Johnston Bush went away. Now she was at least fifteen.

She said explosively, "You're Johnston Bush, aren't you? Well, can I—can we—have your autograph?"

Johnny felt all hot and red. He didn't know quite what to do, but Nick understood easily. Nick tore a couple of sheets off his little pad of restaurant checks, and he gave a pencil to Johnny. Johnny wrote slowly and painfully. He signed his name twice. In each case he made a "Jr." after the name.

Big Jack Bush, his father, had been shot dead by the sheriff, eleven years before. Johnny wondered what Big Jack Bush would think of his grown son, writing out autographs just like a movie star.

He swallowed, and muttered, "Okay, sister," and shoved the little pieces of paper toward the girls.

They went shrilling back to their stools, telling the boys they were with, "We got it. We got it. We got his autograph!" But Johnny was out of the door and gone.

He didn't meet anyone else along the main street. He kept on west past the lumber yard, and then turned south. This narrow street, this uphill sluice that wound through the chilly night—it passed eight or ten houses, and then became the Pretty Pocket road.

All the way out to the ridge where this road intersected with the Deep Notch road, Johnny Bush kept thinking about food. Intermingled with visions of food were visions of his family. He saw his grandfather, old Albert Sidney Johnston Bush, taking a little sharp knife to trim closely against the round bone of a piece of steak, and declaring to the assembled grandchildren, as he always did, "The nearer the bone, the sweeter the meat."

He thought of infrequent delicacies which Henrietta, his mother, fixed for him when he was young. . . . Lettuce sandwiches she had made for him one time; that was the spring after his father had been killed, when Johnny tried to climb into a lumber wagon to tackle some boys who yelled an insult at him, and the man who was driving whipped up his team. Johnny fell off and broke one bone in his leg. While he was in bed his mother served him some lettuce sandwiches—thin leaf lettuce, deep green, with boiled yellow dressing spread over it, between slices of coarse homemade bread. Funny to be thinking about that on the eve of Thanksgiving.

He didn't meet a soul on the Pretty Pocket road. Up to the summit of the first ridge he picked his way carefully along the rutted buggy track. Then he came out past the last stockade of timberland and halted at the schoolhouse corner.

Johnston didn't know quite why he did it, but he found himself putting down his bag at the gate, and going up to the empty schoolhouse. Many-paned windows caught the lightness of open night. He saw stars in one of the windows as he came close, and he looked up to see how clouds were being torn apart by the cold wind.

Around two sides of the schoolhouse, almost to the woodshed at the rear . . . he turned and came back. He was having a vision—the kind of vision that experiences of the past two years had compelled him to have. He was seeing thousands of country schoolhouses scattered on ridges like this, or perhaps in valleys, throughout the United States. He thought of little kids trudging reluctantly up to all those doors every morning, and breaking forth with exultation at recess time. He wanted to cry when he thought of all those kids, going to American schools everywhere.

He thought of the pledge to the flag; that was a tradition in each corner of the country, not only just in southern Missouri where he grew up. *I pledge allegiance to the flag of the United States . . . one nation indivisible, with liberty and justice for all.*

There were little things pasted on the inside of the windowpanes. Children had cut them out of paper, and colored them with crayons, just as they used to do fifteen years before, when Johnston was a shirttail kid in that school. Pumpkins and witches and things: those were left from Halloween. But also he could see the shapes of turkeys, and those turkeys symbolized the Thanksgiving season. Come Christmas, there would be bells and Santa Clauses, greasy with red crayon.

Johnny went out to the road again; he picked up his bag and started on down the ridge. His grandfather's place wasn't very far below. A little tune walked with him as he went. First he had only the music of the thing, suggested by his visit to the schoolyard; but soon the words were there, and he was singing them through his nose as he walked.

"Over the river and through the woods,
To Grandfather's house we go.
The horse knows the way . . ."

A dog began to bark in the Bush dooryard. At first Johnston thought: Why, that can't be Ranger! What's happened to Ranger? And then he remembered how his mother had written him a month or two after he went away, telling him that old Ranger had died. There was another dog now, a new one that didn't know Johnston.

The door opened, showing a beautiful light, and someone spoke to the dog. It was Grandpa all right, and the dog came up on the steps and stood whining as the boy approached.

Grandpa asked in his deep soft voice, "Is it Johnston?"

"Yes."

He heard his mother say, "Thank God, thank God." He was up on the step and inside; the room swam around him. New dog, new lamp on the table, all sorts of new things. His mother's hair was almost completely gray now, but her face was still hard and bright, though thinner.

Their hands touched him—his grandfather on one side, his mother on the other. . . . She threw her arms around his stiff young body and put her face against his shoulder. Grandpa rubbed his ragged white handle-bar mustache, and swung away abruptly and went over by the stove. Winking fast, Johnston could see the old man fumbling in his hip pocket, dragging out a crumpled bandanna. The old man blew his nose.

"For the love of mud," said Johnston.

His mother smiled. Her face was wet.

"Mabel," said Johnston. "I can't believe—"

Mabel stood bashfully by the table, though her face was twitching. She was trying to keep from crying. She wore a plaid dress, homemade, but quite pretty. She was all grown up as to face and shape and everything.

"Yes," said Johnston's mother, "that's your baby sister—Mabel. Sure enough."

"I'm seventeen," said Mabel shrilly. She came forward and allowed him to kiss her. She was wearing perfume, and it smelled good. The perfume made him think of another girl who lived near by.

They all stood off and looked at him. Then Grandpa said, "Well, I do declare, Johnston. Thought you'd be pale and puny, after where you been. You are skinny, but you appear real good."

Johnston Bush said, "Look!" and the word came out more sharply than he intended. He tried to make his voice seem lower and kinder, though firm.

"Look here, folks. Just one thing. Please—I wish you wouldn't right now ask me a lot of questions about— You know. About everything. How I felt, and what did they give me to eat, and everything that happened. All the details: what everybody did—everything that happened. . . ." There was sweat standing on the boy's forehead.

"Course," said his grandfather soothingly, and Johnston's mother said nothing, but patted his arm. She turned and ordered Mabel briskly, "Go see what we got in the pantry, and set it out."

"I wanted them to wait supper," cried Mabel over her shoulder, "but they said the evening train was always late."

"Not very late tonight. I was lucky," Johnny told his mother. "With Mabel practically woman-grown, I suppose Marvin and Braxton are off somewhere skittering around with some girls. Imagine them big enough."

Grandpa grinned at Henrietta Bush and showed his crooked teeth.

"Maybe they got girls," said Johnston's mother, "but they haven't got them in Nimrod County. They're not here, Johnston. Both of them are up and gone to the war."

Johnston stared in amazement. "Those little jerks? They're not old enough."

"So I told them, Johnston, but I might as well have been talking manners to a couple of tomcats."

Grandpa said, as he lighted his old yellow pipe, "Got to win this war. Reckon it will take Bushes to do it."

"Marvin's at an air place in Corpus Christi, Texas," said Johnny's mother. "And Braxton's clean out at San Diego in what they call the boot camp. He prophesies it won't be long before he goes overseas."

Johnston could only murmur, in the words of Nick the Greek, "What do you know?" He sat down at the table, ready and willing, as Mabel served him. There was fried ham, cold, but very good; there were apple salad and pickles and pie and cottage cheese, and plenty of homemade bread and butter. Johnston ate his head off.

"Had a real good year," said old A.S.J. Bush, with sock feet against the stove rail. "Pretty nigh worked ourselves to the bone, but you should see the corn we picked off of the two bottom pieces. . . ."

Johnston's mother smiled across the oilcloth. "Never a lazy minute around here, Johnny. Imagine Mabel riding a cultivator last spring!"

Mabel was fiddling with the old radio in the corner, but now she shut it off. "I hate field work," she said. "It's so hard on my hands. I wear gloves, much as I can."

"She's mighty vain of her hands," said Johnston's mother. "Same as me, when I was a young thing. Still, it's apparent that us women have got to work in the fields, harder than before."

"Yes, sir!" said Grandpa. "Food will win the war!"

The song was still singing in Johnston's head. *Over the river and through the woods, to Grandfather's house* . . . This was Grandfather's house all right, and his mother's house, and his own; and tomorrow would be Thanksgiving Day. A warmth struggled up within him, a peace and thankfulness; and yet, in the same moment, and for the second time that night, he wanted to cry.

Mabel came to take away the empty plates and sauce dishes. Again Johnny smelled the perfume of her hair and body. He rose abruptly and tore open a package of cigarettes. His black brows went together in a frown.

The family waited.

"I wonder," said Johnston, "if anybody is to home over at the Vanes."

There was a steady quiet in which you could hear only sounds from the stove, and the clock's ticking. "Johnny," said his mother, "if you mean Evangeline, I wager she might be there."

"What about her old man?" blurted out Mabel.

"I know," Johnny said cautiously. "Garrison Vane never did have much time for me."

Johnston's mother whispered, "Vanjy's a right pretty girl."

Johnston was silent for a moment. Then, "Is anyone in particular playing up to her these days—I mean, going to moving pictures, and taking her around?"

"Tom, Dick, and Harry," said Mabel glibly.

They waited to see what Johnston would say to that. His mother could not help but interpose: "Fact is, I don't think she's too gone on any of them. First this one, then that. She asks about you right often, when I meet her alone."

Johnston moved over to the clock shelf. The clock was on the verge of eight-thirty. He waited expectantly and in another moment a little gong rang inside the brass and imitation marble of the old clock. He turned and grinned at the family. "Still makes that funny buzz, before and after."

"Same old clock," said Grandpa. "Same old home place; same old Nimrod County. Only one thing seems to have changed much."

"What's that?"

"Reckon you know," said Grandpa.

Johnston shrugged. "Where's the lantern?"

"Hangs on the porch."

Johnny went out to get the lantern. The dog put up its ears, watching the doorway. They heard Johnny banging around out on the porch; soon he reappeared with the lantern. He raised the glass chimney, scraped the wick with a match, and then lighted it.

He put the lantern on the table and turned around to get his overcoat and cap.

"You don't say much, you folks."

"Long suit of the Bushes never was talking, 'less they was drunk," said Grandpa.

Having put on his coat and cap, Johnston stood with a big bony hand clenched on the wire handle of the lantern. "Well," he said, "we don't get drunk any more—none of us, I guess. Only it wasn't drinking that did it. Most folks drink and behave themselves. . . . It was just I always felt kind of empty and angry, and weak, and quarrelsome. That's how I make it out, thinking about it now."

He cleared his throat. "Reckon that was the trouble with my father. High spirits, and no money, and a willingness to fight. . . . Now, take us Bushes: none of us ever stole a dime from anybody! We just got in fights, raising a ruckus. That's all we did. But it was enough to get us into trouble, and give us a bad name. . . . Lot of young folks here in this country used to act the same way. . . . It makes me feel good to think of Marvin and Braxton, young as they are, gone into the service. It will do good things for them. Then they can do good things for this country."

He took his lantern and went out, apparently heading for the Vane place by a path that went through the woods.

Grandpa and Mabel and Henrietta sat quietly for some time. Johnny's mother was wiping her eyes. Then Mabel said pertly to Grandpa, "Thought you said the Bushes' long suit wasn't talking." She turned on the radio.

When Johnny got to the Vane house he was greeted effusively by three dogs. He knew their voices, and the dogs decided that they knew him, too, when he spoke their names; and with wagging tails they escorted him across pebbly ground toward the front steps.

The door came open. Garrison Vane bulked there, tall and broad in his overalls, and with a stub of cigar in his mouth as always.

"Who is it?"

"Johnston Bush."

Mr. Vane drew a long breath. He muttered something which sounded like, "Thought it would be." Johnny put his lantern down on the bottom step, and waited.

Pretty soon he asked, "Well, do I come in, or do I go away?"

Garrison Vane moved aside from the doorway, but still held the door open. "Oh," he said, "I guess you come in."

Johnny blew out his lantern and put it on the porch. He entered the combination living room-dining room of the Vane house and Garrison Vane closed the door and then turned around to study him.

"Suit you?" asked Johnny.

Mr. Vane let his long chin quiver as if he wanted to chuckle. Johnny had seen him look that way at other people, years before, but he had never gazed on Johnny with such downright tolerance. "Far cry," Mr. Vane told him, "from the kid that was so wild and mean and tough."

"I was wild, all right."

"So they tamed you down, did they?"

"Meek as a lamb," said Johnny. He was ashamed to feel that there was sweat on his forehead again.

"Want a cigar?" asked Mr. Vane.

"No, thanks. I'll just have a cigarette," and Johnny took one out and tapped it against his thumb.

Vane asked, "You want to see Vanjy?"

"I didn't walk all the way over here the first night I was home," said Johnny easily, "just to chew the fat with you." Vane's face went into a mass of dark wrinkles as he laughed.

The tall farmer turned toward the closed kitchen door. He lifted his voice. "Vanjy, you got company." In a moment the door opened and Vanjy entered, followed by her thirteen-year-old brother and a yellow cat.

Vanjy had some sewing in her hands; she couldn't seem to make up her mind whether to hang onto the sewing or put it down on the table.

"The Mrs.," said Mr. Vane, "had a little cold, so she's gone to bed. I'll be going myself pretty quick. Don't you stick around too long, Clark," he told his son.

Vanjy and Johnston stood and looked at each other after the father had gone. The cat got up on the sofa; Clark waited awkwardly, grinning, in the background.

"You're sure a sight for sore eyes," said Johnny Bush to Vanjy. He wished to heaven that Clark would get out of there.

Vanjy had a pale skin, with quite a lot of freckles, but the freckles were pale in shade, too, and Johnston had always thought they were beautiful. Vanjy wore an old green skirt and a white blouse. She was still wearing the apron she had worn for dishwashing. Her hair, the color of fresh-cut cherry wood, was built into a high pompadour, and came down low and long and soft around her thin neck. Her green-gray eyes were startlingly large and clear.

She said, "It certainly is good to see you again. And everything. Do you want to sit down?"

"I wouldn't mind."

They seated themselves—Vanjy by the round center table, and Johnston in the biggest overstuffed chair.

"Would—would you like to play a game of some kind, Johnny?"

"I wouldn't mind," said Johnny. "Whatever suits you folks. I just came to make a friendly call."

Young Clark said, "Reckon we could play Millionaire. You know how to play Millionaire, Johnny? We play it a lot, of nights."

Johnny laughed. "Okay by me. I wouldn't want to lose my shirt, though."

Vanjy explained primly, "It isn't a gambling game, really. You use pretend money. It's here in this box. Clark got it for last Christmas."

The three of them gathered around the center table, and Vanjy opened the box containing the game of Millionaire. Her voice grew thinner and shriller all the time she explained the game. She kept her eyes down, not looking at Johnny Bush as she talked.

Just as they were preparing to roll dice for the first turn, there sounded a loud shout of, "Clark! You come to bed," from somewhere abovestairs. Clark muttered, "Shucks," but he got up dutifully, and said good night to Vanjy and Johnston Bush.

After he was gone, taking the cat with him, Vanjy sat toying uncertainly with the dice. Johnny Bush kept examining the flat cardboard chart, trying to remember what she told him about the game, but it had all gone out of his head.

"Oh, let's forget Millionaire!" he cried suddenly, and Vanjy giggled.

He could smell something lovely about her; it was perfume, and he choked to think how long he had gone in his young life without smelling a pretty girl, without even being near one.

He mumbled, "Kind of close in here, isn't it? Let's go out on the porch and get a breath of air."

Evangeline started to say something, but he didn't let her finish. He opened the front door and practically pulled her out on the porch with him. When he had shut the door she stood looking up through the gloom, and then he saw that she was smiling.

"You want me to catch my death of cold, Johnny?"

He said slowly, "I'll keep you warm. I'd be mighty good at keeping you warm." Then he lifted his arms and brought them down slowly across her shoulders, his hands locked across her slim, smooth back.

Vanjy pushed her face up toward his. . . . All the world became her face, an oval of paleness framed in soft hair, coming closer and closer as he bent toward it . . . diffused and marvelous. Her knees touched his. They both cried out softly and their faces were together. . . .

When at last he heard her chuckling and whispering delightedly, "Johnny, darling, let's come up for air!" he squared his shoulders and stood back a little, feeling that he could take the world and wring it dry. He heard himself saying, "Tomorrow's Thanksgiving. Reckon it's the greatest Thanksgiving I ever could have, in all this world," and in the same breath he realized that he had been thinking of Vanjy for many months. He had been dreaming of her, even though he hadn't realized it at the time. . . .

Back at the Bush house, very late, he put out the lamp which had been left burning in the center of the kitchen table, and went up the squeaky staircase to an open room at the head of the staircase, which had always been his. His bag was there; he almost fell over it.

He moved as quietly as possible while preparing for bed, in order to keep from waking Mabel or his mother, but soon after he was in bed he heard the floor beginning to creak in the next room, and a gray shape materialized near the foot of his bed. It was his mother, coming to him in her nightdress, with an old dressing sack around her shoulders.

She whispered, "You asleep?"

"Just got in bed," said Johnny hoarsely. "Sorry I woke you up."

"Oh, I've been awake," said his mother. "I've been laying there, counting my blessings. Just laying there thinking. . . . Johnny, did you see Evangeline?"

Johnny said, "I sure did," and gave a happy grunt and sigh, and thought about seeing Evangeline again the next afternoon, and the next night, too.

"Johnny, is everything—all right?"

"Everything's wonderful."

They both listened to the chilly whisper of night beyond the black window. They could hear a dog wow-wowing away over in Deep Notch somewhere.

Presently Henrietta Bush began to cry. Johnny stood it as long as he could; then he writhed around and sat up in bed. "Look here, woman," he said, "you're plumb wore out. You go to bed now. You got a big day tomorrow. A lot of cooking, I guess. Did you kill the old red rooster?"

His mother laughed through her tears. "We sure did, Johnny. But he sprouted turkey feathers before we killed him."

"Plenty of onions and things in the stuffing?" asked Johnny hungrily.

"Plenty, son. Plenty." Her hands were trembling as they stroked his bare arm. She whispered, "It's a miracle from heaven. You know, we thought you was dead, first off."

Johnny said nothing. He couldn't say anything just then. . . . He had been a bad son. He had not lived up to the best that his mother tried to teach him. He had always been in trouble, like his father before him; but now he was living in a new world, and everything in that world was changed. He was changed, too.

Some day possibly he'd have some kids. Well, he would take good care that they didn't think they had to get drunk, and show off, and raise a ruckus all the time.

His mother cried, "I know you don't want to talk about it, but it's just a miracle! Like Lazarus and— Oh, how did you get away? The papers just said you escaped, and then you did all those other things, but we didn't know just how it was."

Johnny watched her gray shape, rigid against the pale oblong of the window as she listened to him. He was listening to himself, too. It was like listening to a couple of other guys. . . . A couple of other guys were doing the talking.

They said, "Well, it was pretty tough being there, and we had to watch our chance. My chance came with one of the guards. It was just about dark when it happened. I got him down, and he had a kind of tommy gun, and I took it away from him. Then Palmer, and Epstein, and Donnelly and me—they were took prisoner the same time I was—they came right along. We kind of shot our way out of there."

The other guys went on and on, telling her about it. "During the night, the first Germans that caught up with us— We still had enough ammunition left. I got two of them, and the other boys got what weapons they had, and then we killed the rest. We were raring to go, by that time. Then we met that car full of German officers and— Oh, it's a lot of details," Johnny cried, softly. "A lot of military details. Let's not go into that now."

His mother murmured reverently, "A real miracle! Was it—was it true about, in the papers—they gave you a Distinguished Flying Cross?"

"Gosh sake, no!" he said. "Distinguished *Service* Cross, Ma! That's that extra ribbon on my coat—the one all blue in the middle, and white and red on the ends. I'll explain about them, one of these times. You know," he added, "I've got at least twenty-six days. Maybe more."

She whispered, "Good night, Johnny." Then she tiptoed back to her own room, and left him there, staring up at the friendly ceiling, thinking of the next day and the days to follow.

Lifeboat*

Alfred Hitchcock and Harry Sylvester

Usually a good novel is translated into a screen story. Here an unusually fine screen story has been redrafted as a novelette. As a matter of fact, the result could hardly have been less than remarkable, with John Steinbeck writing the original screen story, and Director Alfred Hitchcock and writer Harry Sylvester combining their fine talents in the novelette. Hitchcock, of course, went on to produce the picture, which was one of the outstanding dramatic achievements of the war.

November 13, 1943

Although she was, by many people's standards, a successful woman, Mrs. Porter never consciously thought of herself as lucky. And perhaps she was right; the cold, orderly and somewhat ruthless intellect which she possessed had enabled her to use her body when the intellect itself failed; her foresight had always been remarkable; in a profession that required honesty, artistic ability and a certain objectivity, she ranked high, although she possessed none of these qualities.

Her ability—nameless, in a way—had reached now its highest achievement, although Mrs. Porter did not think of it that way. For she sat, an elegant and solitary figure, on one of the thwarts of a lifeboat. Her mink coat was about her, a small hat rested on her hair, and near her feet was an alligator traveling case and the smallest practical portable typewriter. She was not even breathless. A lit cigarette held halfforgetfully between two fingers, with the other fingers of both hands she was adjusting a filter on the lens of a small but very expensive camera, to compensate for the fog which completely encircled her and made her, in the boat, the center of a circle of water not much over a hundred yards in diameter.

It was on the edge of this circle that the freighter, Frances Sweeney, was sinking. Close to two thirds of the ship was under water, but the funnel with its whistle still going, was above water, and Mrs. Porter, overexquisite, even for a woman, in small matters (although never in large ones), half wished that the boat would hurry and sink so that the whistle would be stilled. While with her fingers she hastened to affix the filter.

The fog had come quite suddenly and even ironically for all concerned, for not only was the freighter sinking but the sub-

* Based on an original screen story by John Steinbeck for 20th Century-Fox.

marine that had sunk it was already itself a steel coffin for most of its men, drifting aimlessly downward, a quarter mile beneath the sea. Even as she regretted that she had gotten no pictures of the submarine, part of her was wishing that if she was to have any companionship in the boat at all, it would be the nice young ensign who had been in command of the armed-guard crew that had sunk the submarine. But the ensign and his gun crew were already in the sight of God.

Partly because she had previously gotten some film of the ship sinking, partly because she saw another subject for her camera, Mrs. Porter shot only a few feet more of the ship. She pointed the camera almost hastily to where a man swam strongly through oil toward the boat. The oil coated him completely so that he did not look unlike a Negro. Mrs. Porter kept the camera on him all the way to the boat and even while he attempted to haul himself over the gunwale. He had the strength to do so, but oil had coated every part of him so that even when his fingers twisted into the rope scalloped around the boat, his torso slipped back into the water as he rested it on the gunwale. "For God's sake, lady," he said, "put that thing down and give me a hand!"

Mrs. Porter lowered the camera and figuratively if not literally, blinked. She picked her way closer to where the man hung and gingerly taking one oily wrist over the gunwale, pulled almost without effect. The man, an oiler named Kovac, slipped over the edge and into the boat and then stood up. He was young and muscular. He wore pants and an undershirt, both vaguely outlined under the oil. He looked at Mrs. Porter, sleek and quite comely in spite of her thirty-eight years, and then began to strip the oil off his face and arms with his hands.

"Are you all right?" Mrs. Porter said.

"I could use a cigarette," he said.

Mrs. Porter fumbled in her purse and took out a platinum cigarette case and jeweled lighter. "No danger of igniting the oil?" she said, with a little half-laugh.

"I don't think so," he said. He held her wrist to steady the lighter and when he released it, she looked around for something to wipe her hands on, and finally scraped them on the gunwale.

"I thought I was the only one left," she said. There might even have been a hint of disappointment in her tone. "I saw this boat on the side nearest the sub. Everyone else seemed to be on the other side, and I got in just as it was floating and managed to work the thing that released the davit rope." She was quite pleased.

"What do you mean, everyone else?" Kovac said. "Outside the gun crew, there weren't a dozen people above deck."

"Well, what there were," she said.

"I don't know why they had to shell the boats, too," he said, almost absently, "probably trying to silence the gun crew." He stared at her. "You're Constance Porter, ain't you?"

"That's right."

"I heard you was aboard. So you took pictures, huh?"

"Oh, I got some wonderful stuff. A lot of the freighter going down and I almost got some of the U-boat sinking, too, but the fog had started to close in." Kovac kept looking at her and, not very comfortable, she said: "Too bad I wasn't closer. I—"

"You got any film left?"

"A little," Mrs. Porter said.

"So photograph that." He pointed to where in some flotsam drifting by, a baby-bottle, half-filled with milk, swayed slowly, its nipple moving like the hand of a metronome.

"I think you're disgusting," she said.

"The feeling's mutual," he said. "I'm not going to argue about it." He turned to look out over the sea. Now that neither of them spoke, they could both hear a faint shouting as at a great distance.

"For God's sake, look out," Kovac said. He dived toward a pair of oars, brushing heavily against Mrs. Porter and knocking the camera out of her hands. It struck the edge of the gunwale and slipped into the sea. She cursed him furiously and he looked up at her from the thwart as he began to row, fascinated, vaguely amused and even surprised. "Why, I didn't know nice women knew those words," he said.

"You're those and almost everything else unspeakable that I can think of," she said.

"Calm yourself," he said. She stamped away from him and sat in the stern. Looking over his shoulder as he rowed, Kovac said: "What the hell do you know! It's that Limey radio operator. Hey, Garrett, I'll be right with you."

Garrett floated in his life jacket in a piece of sea free of oil. He was able to come over the side quite briskly by himself.

"There's more out here, Kovac," he said. "One of them's hurt. They ought to be right around here."

"This ape here," Mrs. Porter said, "just knocked my camera overboard, apparently deliberately. I—"

"Oh, hello, Mrs. Porter," Garrett said. His respect stayed with him even here. "Kovac, here," he went on, smiling a little, "is dreadfully class-conscious."

"Well, I'm going to report him when—" Mrs. Porter began but stopped when she saw neither of the others were listening to her.

"There you are, Kovac," Garrett said, tensing a little. "Just back around." The raft had been in sight of them all the while they were picking up Garrett but none of them had heard the three people on it, yelling. The shorter of the two men on the raft stood awkwardly but yelled loudest of all. He wore the rough clothes of a seaman. The tall man was in suspenders and shirt sleeves and waved his arms and clapped his hands. The woman stood behind the two men and hardly moved at all.

As the two vessels came alongside each other, Mrs. Porter stood up in the boat, her anger gone, and shook her head with a kind of mocking smile. "Well, well, Ritt," she said, "leave it to you to light right side up. Twelve boards of directors would breathe easier if they knew."

"You should talk, Connie," Rittenhouse said. "I wouldn't bet against your not having engineered the whole thing for a story."

"Hey, anyone got any liquor?" the shorter man on the raft said. He started to climb over the gunwale, then winced suddenly as one leg gave almost completely under him. Garrett helped the girl, wearing a wet, white nurse's uniform, in over the side of the boat. She did not look at anyone and hardly spoke. Mrs. Porter finally noticed that the girl's eyes were lowered to the seaman's injured leg.

They were all in the boat now and the raft was drifting away.

"Look," the nurse said to the injured man. "Smith, Gus, would you please lie down and let me get a look at your leg? If—"

"Okay, kid," Gus said. "Anything for you."

Unconsciously they formed a group around the injured man, although Kovac had taken the oars of the boat and was at one far edge of the group, while Mrs. Porter, with a kind of delicacy, hovered on the other edge.

The nurse looked up at Garrett. "Is there any sulfanilamide in the kit, Stanley?"

"I'm afraid not, Alice," Garrett said. "Some of these kits are pretty primitive by modern standards."

"Anyone got a drink?" Gus said, again.

"Sorry, son, I haven't," Mr. Rittenhouse said.

"I have a little brandy," Mrs. Porter said.

"Oh, I feel faint," Gus said, clutching at his heart and rolling his eyes. Kovac thought it quite funny and one or two of the others smiled.

"No, Gus," the nurse said. "It might start the bleeding again."

There was a yell, rising hopefully, as if the boat had just been seen by someone on the edge of the fog. All but the kneeling nurse turned and Kovac swore. "My God," he said, "it's Joe the steward."

They could see the Negro floating upright in the water, supported by his life jacket, and as the boat came closer they saw he was holding a woman's head above the water with one hand and, with the other, something none of them could believe was a baby. Closer, now, they could see he had on two life jackets awkwardly arranged, as if one had been hastily put on.

The men in the boat reached down and took the woman and the baby from the Negro and then they helped him over the side. "That woman," the Negro said, "she didn't want to be saved."

The men who had helped him in turned curiously to look at the woman. Being saved was so dramatically the most important thing in their lives at the moment, that they had to turn to the woman. She was unconscious and her wet hair streamed untidily over one cheek and shoulder.

"It's Mrs. Higgins," Stanley Garrett said. "She was going back to see her husband. Hadn't seen him since before he was at Dunkerque."

The tall man, Rittenhouse, was bending over the woman with some solicitude and the nurse had left Gus Smith for the moment and turned to the baby. The nurse knew almost immediately what was the matter with the baby; there just wasn't any point in mentioning it at the moment.

Mrs. Higgins moved and opened her eyes. She did not appear to be exhausted so much as bewildered. Her eyes moved around the boat, failing to focus until they came to the baby in the nurse's arms. Then, suddenly and quite strongly, she got up and went directly and without haste to where Alice Mackenzie held the baby, and taking it from the nurse, opened her dress and held the baby against one breast. She began to talk to it.

"Look, Mrs. Higgins—" the nurse said, and stopped.

Everyone, even Kovac and Smith, knew now what was the matter with the baby; everyone but Mrs. Higgins.

"My God!" Kovac said. He sat down and began to row again.

"Look," Smith said, in a low voice, "another customer." In spite of the momentousness of saving another person he had spoken low, as though fearful of disturbing someone. The other men went to the side of the boat where two hands clung without motion to the gunwale. Garrett and Rittenhouse, stronger now, pulled the man over the side. He came in quite limp, not unlike a sea animal of some sort in soaking, dark blue clothes, and lay prone on the planking. They turned him over and saw that his eyes were open and perceptive.

"A Jerry," Garrett said.

"Throw the bastard back," Kovac said.

"Don't be silly," Rittenhouse said. "Why, we have him as a prisoner here."

"A guy can't help what he's born," Gus Smith said.

"All of you certainly feel awful nice toward this guy considering what he's just done to you," Kovac said.

"This man was acting under orders," Mrs. Porter said. "We were an enemy ship. He—"

"The baby, too?" Kovac said.

"The baby shouldn't have been aboard," Mrs. Porter said.

"How many babies have you got?" Kovac said.

"Now, look here," Rittenhouse said. "We can't be—"

"They shouldn't have shelled the lifeboats, though," Smith said. "This guy is dressed like an officer, too. We—"

"Are you the captain?" Rittenhouse said to the German. The man, sitting up now, stared back at him.

"I talk some German," Mrs. Porter said. She spoke to the man in German and he answered her. She turned to the others and said: "He says he's just a crew member and he's grateful to us for saving his life and sorry that he had to sink our ship."

"Ask him why he shelled our lifeboats," Smith said.

Mrs. Porter talked to the German again. "He says they were the captain's orders."

"You talk German good, don't you?" Kovac said.

"I also speak French, Italian, Spanish and Russian," Mrs. Porter said. "What does that make me?"

"I wouldn't know," Kovac said. "Only down in the forecastle they're always asking how the subs know where we're going to be."

"Sure," Smith said. "The U-boat surfaces and the captain of it says: 'You're ten minutes late,' or 'You're two degrees off your course.' Stuff like that."

"What's that got to do with me?" Mrs. Porter said.

"All I know," Kovac said, "is that when I got into the lifeboat you were alone in it and all dressed like you were going some place."

"I remained much calmer than anyone else," Mrs. Porter said. "It's one of the qualities that has made me a success in my profession."

"I know what's made you a success in your profession, all right," Kovac said.

"Now, look," Rittenhouse said. "This is getting no one any place fast. We have injured people aboard and—"

"The main thing," Kovac said, still rowing, "is that this boat is too small for me and that Kraut."

"Look," Garrett said, "the man is a prisoner of war. If we treat him as he has treated us, why, the whole war is pointless."

"The baby," said Mrs. Higgins in a flat tone of voice, "is dead."

In the equally flat silence her words induced, Alice Mackenzie moved toward her and took the baby from her arms. Snarling almost inaudibly and still without haste, Mrs. Higgins walked over to the German and raked his face with her nails. Garrett and Rittenhouse held her and said something useless and even silly. She began to cry and collapsed at their feet.

"Take the oars a minute," Kovac said

to Garrett. He rose and walked over to the German. Everyone waited almost expectantly for some sort of violence. The German raised one arm defensively, but his face showed little emotion of any sort. Instead of hitting the man, Kovac began to frisk him. Apparently satisfied, he sat down, in a way almost shamefaced as he realized now that the others had more than half expected violence from him. "What's he got on him?" Rittenhouse said.

"Only a watch."

The fog was gone by evening and they could see the sun sinking into the gray water.

Over Kovac's protests they had elected Rittenhouse their leader. It was Mrs. Porter's idea first, but virtually all of the others, except Kovac, had the curious respect for Rittenhouse which most Americans have for a highly successful businessman. And those that didn't know who Rittenhouse was were prepared to accept Mrs. Porter's word for it; after all, wasn't she an internationally known reporter?

"I presume," Rittenhouse said, "that we must be pretty much due west. In the morning we'll rig the sail and get going."

"Where?" Kovac said. "The compass is shot to hell, and no one knows what our course was when we was hit."

"It was sou'east by sou'," Gus said. "I was at the wheel when it happened."

"Good," Mr. Rittenhouse said, "very good, indeed. In the morning—"

Alice Mackenzie interrupted them. "Look," she said, "we'll have to get rid of that dead baby. Mrs. Higgins is asleep now and there won't be a better time. You've got some light and you won't have any hysterics to complicate matters."

"Not me," Smith said. "I don't want to do no burying at sea."

"It's a necessity," the nurse said. "Obviously—"

"That's right," Rittenhouse said, as if agreeing to some profundity just made clear to him. He moved away and spoke to Garrett and they went over together to where Mrs. Higgins, asleep, again held her baby. From the bow of the boat, to which he had been isolated as much by accident as design, the German watched, unmoving and apparently unmoved, when the bundle was ready and almost all of them had gathered by the port gunwale.

"Does anyone know the service for burial at sea?" Rittenhouse said. When no one answered him, he said: "I guess any prayer—"

The Negro began, almost absently: "The Lord is my Shepherd. I shall not want. He maketh me to lie down in green pastures. . . . He leadeth me beside the still waters. He restoreth my soul—"

The spectacle of an American Negro saying such words of faith and hope was too much for Kovac. To Kovac it was like a man blessing someone who had struck him. He swore under his breath, but no one else and hardly he himself knew why he did so.

"Surely, goodness and mercy," Joe went on, "will follow me all the days of my life and I will dwell in the house of the Lord forever."

Kovac turned away, shaking his head. He had almost forgotten about the baby, did not even identify the splash.

When Mrs. Higgins awoke it was dark, but a low moon gave them enough light to see and identify the others in the boat. All but Alice Mackenzie avoided Mrs. Higgins now that she was awake, but out of the corners of their eyes they could see the nurse talking to her and from the character of the nod of Mrs. Higgins' head, they assumed, hopefully and gratefully, that she was reconciled to what had happened. Then, her voice quite normal, she spoke past them to the German in the bow: "You killed him, didn't you? They tried to kill him in Coventry even before he was born, and now you've finished the job." She got up again and lurched toward the man, but Garrett and Rittenhouse held her.

"Let her go if she wants to get at him," Kovac said. But his voice lacked its former passion and he kept on slowly playing the oars. As gently as they could, they eased her back into her place, and the nurse, as a kind of second thought, said that they ought to tie Mrs. Higgins there.

"Why?" Kovac said. "So she can't get at that Kraut?"

"No," the nurse said. "Not for that—for her own sake." The last two words, no one heard but herself.

Mrs. Porter said: "She needs to be tied up. She has no control of herself."

"You got good control, ain't you?" Kovac said. "Superspecial control. No babies, no troubles, no nothing, huh?"

No one answered him, and the other men reluctantly tied Mrs. Higgins, who stared upward at the moon, and did not seem to know what they were doing.

They all slept much better than they had hoped to, Kovac, Garrett and Rittenhouse each taking a three-hour watch. It was not until morning, after most of them had been awake some minutes, that Garrett noticed the rope that trailed tautly over the gunwale and then noticed Mrs. Higgins was not in the boat.

Even before they looked and saw that there was nothing else to be done except cut the rope with its terrible burden, Kovac had begun to argue with Rittenhouse about whose watch it had happened on. "It could have happened any time," Garrett said. "The moon was down about ten o'clock."

"All I know," Kovac said, "is it couldn't have happened on mine."

"Oh, you're a very righteous soul," Mrs. Porter said.

"I think we could eat a few biscuits this morning," Stanley Garrett said, with an assumed and almost insane cheerfulness. This capacity to cover tragedy with relative trivialities would increase in all of them.

Alice Mackenzie looked up from where she was bandaging Gus Smith's leg and said: "You'd better make a thorough check of what we have and then form some sort of committee to ration it."

"I've done so, already," Rittenhouse said, "and we're not too badly off. The water breaker needed a little taping up but that's been taken care of, and—"

"You just ain't going to be able to eat some of them biscuits," Joe said. "They're bad now from water and they ain't going to improve."

"About the course," Rittenhouse said.

While they were talking, the German pulled a small watch-shaped object out of his pocket and looked at it furtively, cupping one hand around it as though to shield it from the sun.

Gus Smith kept saying: "It's 115, east-southeast. The first mate gave it to me less than an hour before it happened. To hit Bermuda on the nose."

"All right," Kovac said, "which way is east-southeast? That's the sixty-four-dollar question instead of something hard like what is Winston Churchill's first name."

"Over there," Gus said. From his reclining position he gestured quite accurately.

"*Nein,*" the German said rather promptly.

"What does he know?" Kovac said.

Mrs. Porter spoke to the German again in his own tongue. As he replied to her he pointed almost due east, "He says east-southeast is in that direction," Mrs. Porter said.

"How does he know?" Kovac insisted.

"The man is just as anxious to reach land as we are," Mrs. Porter said.

"There is something to that," Rittenhouse said.

"Also," Kovac said, "he ought to know if any of his pals are around."

"No," Stanley Garrett said, "I'm sure the fellow is right."

Rittenhouse, as leader, turned almost hopefully to Garrett and said: "Okay, Sparks, you're the navigator."

The wind freshened toward morning and as the boat heeled over, two things happened. Mrs. Porter's typewriter slid along the thwart on which she had placed it, struck the gunwale and turned over once on its way into the sea. Barely awake, Mrs. Porter stared almost incredulously at where the portable had been. Kovac said: "Now they'll not only have to postpone the invasion, but they'll have to wait until you get a new typewriter." But no one paid much attention to what Kovac had said or to Mrs. Porter's unpleasant reply. The same wind which had caused the typewriter to be lost had thrown Gus Smith against the side of the boat and the tone of his screech told all of them just how bad the sailor's leg was.

Alice Mackenzie, looking not particularly tidy even in her nurse's uniform, knelt quickly alongside the man. Most of the others gathered behind her, and when she parted the slit in the leg of the dungaree pants which they had made the first day in the boat, they could see the way the leg was.

"Now, ain't that nice?" Smith said. He had raised himself on his elbows and could see the way the leg had come up under the bandages. "Well, what do you think, Alice?" he said.

"I don't know," the girl said. "I really don't know."

"Like a leg of lamb?" Smith said.

The German had come out of his isolation in the bow and was standing on the edge of the group. "Why don't you get the hell out of here?" Kovac said to him. The German kept looking at the bad leg.

"Tell him," Kovac said to Mrs. Porter, "to get forward there before I throw him overboard. I suppose you're missing your camera, huh?"

Whether Mrs. Porter was going to ignore Kovac no one could say, for the German began to speak to her himself. They conversed for fully two minutes in German and finally Gus said, "What goes with the guy?"

Mrs. Porter looked at him with what was her normal expression for inferiors and which irritated Kovac. But finally and with surprising gentleness she said: "Gus—he seems to have gangrene."

"But I knew that," Alice Mackenzie said. "I just didn't want—"

"Gangrene?" Gus Smith said.

"Yes," Mrs. Porter said, "he says your leg should be amputated if you want to live."

"My God, it's impossible!" Alice Mackenzie said.

In the little silence that followed as the nurse broke off her own speech, the German spoke again to Mrs. Porter. Turning to the others, Mrs. Porter said, "This man says he was a surgeon in civil life and he would be willing to attempt the operation."

In the little silence which occurred again, Kovac said: "What else is the guy? Maybe he'll start selling us a few railroad bonds the next thing we know."

Then all began talking, but Gus Smith lying on the boards, said loudest of all, "No dice. One leg is worse than being dead. I got a girl and I ain't going back with one leg."

"You'd rather die?" Mrs. Porter said.

"To give you a plain answer, lady," Smith said, "yes."

"My good man," Rittenhouse began and the nurse started to speak, too, but Kovac spoke over all of them, "Don't be a damn fool, Gus; you can do practically everything but dance on one leg and you can do that, too."

"Oh, for God's sake."

Then there was a little silence again, and they knew he was going to let it happen.

Moving toward the little medical kit, Alice Mackenzie seemed to start all the others into movement. The German began to roll up his sleeves and spoke again to Mrs. Porter. "If there is no antiseptic he says we might be able to do something with brandy," she told them.

"No cloud without a silver lining," Smith said. Kovac turned away and shook his head.

"There's my flask. It's not much, but it's still full," Mrs. Porter said.

"You don't miss nothing, do you?" Kovac said to her.

It took a long time. Mrs. Porter was sick and the Negro and Stanley Garrett were sick, and twice all the men had to hold the sailor down. The water became gradually rougher as the German performed his crude surgery, and finally Garrett had to go to take the tiller which they had lashed. When it was over, Smith was unconscious and the color of death, but his breathing was loud like that of a man snoring.

"The flask," Mrs. Porter said. "Where is my flask?" No one answered her.

Trying to watch what was happening as they began to bandage the man, Garrett allowed a wave to come in over the stern and the boat almost broached. Two or three inches of water rushed over the planking and they had to lift the injured man quickly and move him up toward the curve in the bow. Kovac stood up to curse Garrett, but he saw the size of the waves then and he knew that they were in for it.

As the German straightened up he saw in the faces of most of the others that which he had anticipated, a definite softening of their hearts toward himself. He thanked all of them through Mrs. Porter for their assistance and then he told them, still through her, that the operation was just an emergency and that the sailor would not be much benefited if they kept drifting endlessly about. "Who says we're drifting?" Kovac said.

Before anyone could speak, the German addressed the people again. "He says if we change our course we can reach land in two or three days. He says Bermuda is that way," Mrs. Porter said.

This time Stanley Garrett said, "I am not so sure that I agree with him. It really stands to reason that even if he knew the course to Bermuda he wouldn't give it to us."

"Why not?" Rittenhouse said.

"Why, because he would be a prisoner of war there," Garrett said.

"If we land anywhere he will be a prisoner of war," Rittenhouse said.

"Not if we land in a U-boat," Kovac said.

"How asinine!" Mrs. Porter said.

"Oh, sure," Kovac said.

"It is obvious to me," Rittenhouse said, "that the German is the only one of us who knows where we are heading."

"We'll hit quite a bit north of Bermuda if we go the way he wants us to," Stanley Garrett said.

"You have no compass," Mrs. Porter said to the Englishman.

"That's right," Garrett said. "But I've been going to sea for a long time."

"My mind is made up," Rittenhouse said. "We're doing what this man," indicating the German, "says. If he were not friendly to us he would not have performed the operation."

"I don't know," the nurse said, her eyes thoughtful. "He might not have been able to help himself when he saw the need for surgery. Now that it is over he could be reverting to type."

"Now you're just being morbid, my dear," Mrs. Porter said.

Rittenhouse took the tiller and, from that vantage point, presided over what seemed an unending argument as to which the right course was. But he took the one the German gave through Mrs. Porter. The coming of night and the roughness of the waves made him surrender the tiller to Garrett again.

In the dusk Gus Smith came to and began to scream, breaking off now and then to curse all of the others. . . .

When Kovac got up in the middle of the night to take over the watch from Stanley Garrett, he said, "I think that Kraut is trying to do a job on us."

"I think so myself," the Englishman said, "but what are we going to do about it? We decided Rittenhouse would be in charge of things."

"Throw Rittenhouse overboard too," Kovac said.

"No," Garrett said. "That's your cure for everything."

"All right," Kovac said, "what's your cure for it?"

The Englishman hesitated a moment before saying, "I noticed when the German looked at his watch, he shielded it almost overcarefully."

"Meaning what?" Kovac said.

"Why, meaning that it might be a pocket compass and not a watch."

"That," Kovac said, "we could find out easy. I'll go back and take it from the guy."

"I think that might help," Stanley Garrett said, "only try not to be rough, what with the women and Smith on our hands."

"Roughness," Kovac said, "is good." He moved carefully toward the stern, and Garrett heard the sound of a fist on bone. Kovac was back in a moment and holding his big hand under Garrett's chin, "Look, chum," he said.

In the dim light to which his eyes had become accustomed, Garrett saw clearly that Kovac had a small compass. He got little pleasure out of being right, though. The fact that he had been right also proved that the enemy was here present in the boat. The sound of Kovac's fist against a sleeping man's flesh had sickened Garrett slightly, and now it was an added and, curiously, almost unsupportable burden that the enemy was the enemy after all.

"I ought to pick the Kraut up," Kovac said, "and just drop him overboard. We'd all be better off."

"Wait until morning anyhow," Garrett

said. "We can talk to the others then."

"Giving that kind a break," Kovac said, "will be the death of us yet."

In the morning the German was sullen and frightened.

"Before we do anything about it," Rittenhouse said, "we ought to try to find out why he hid it on us."

"Why do you think he hid it?" Kovac said.

Mrs. Porter spoke in German to the man and then, turning back to the others, said: "He says it was a gift from his wife and he was afraid we'd take it from him."

"He's breaking my heart," Kovac said.

Gus Smith began to moan from the bow, and Garrett in the stern held the tiller with one hand and the end of the sail rope wrapped around the wrist of his other arm. Even Rittenhouse, more anxious to be saved than to be freed, had become irritated by the German. He had to shout to make himself heard above the abruptly stronger wind. "I want the truth about the course," he yelled. His forearm moved as though he held a gavel in his hand. "Tell him his life depends on it."

As Mrs. Porter turned to speak to the German a sudden gust of wind lifted the sail so sharply that Garrett who had been paying more attention to the argument than to the boat, was raised bodily out of the stern and dropped into the water where he clung desperately to the rope as the sail flapped and bellied, jerking him crazily about in the water.

Joe the Negro and Kovac dived for the sail rope, but the nurse had reached it first and was almost pulled overboard by the force of the wind in the sail and the man dragging in the water. Mrs. Porter was thrown forward in a headlong stumble that carried her half the length of the boat. She fell almost at Gus Smith's feet.

Rittenhouse fumbled at the tiller but with most of the people in the boat on one side, the little vessel tipped dangerously, and the German grabbed for the steering oar used when the boat was being rowed, and slipping it into the water, managed to bring the boat around facing the wind and emptying the sail.

The others managed to drag Garrett back in the boat. In the sudden fury which shook the little vessel, all but Kovac failed to keep their feet. The German, steering skillfully, yelled to Mrs. Porter and still on the bottom she translated in a half gasp for the others: "He says to put on your life belts."

In the continuing fury of the storm there was a sudden rise in its tempo. Kovac, balancing himself precariously, as if ashamed to lie or sit down like the others, was thrown sideways and struck his head glancingly on the thwart. He lay there unconscious. Water sloshed back and forth in the boat, and the loose sail whipped overhead like some blank, gross and gigantic banner. In the welter of objects floating at the bottom of the boat, the others struggled to get into their own life belts and to put jackets on Kovac and Smith.

While none of them realized it, they had now resigned themselves to the German's care. In the stern, above them, above even the storm a little, the man sat, alone fully conscious of the change that had occurred, and consciously taking satisfaction from it. The slit of his wide, thin mouth curved in a smile both curious and mechanical. Looking upward from the bow where she was trying to adjust a life belt on Smith, Alice Mackenzie had time to think that the German's mouth, with its peculiar smile, was not unlike that of a shark.

"Come on, everybody bail," the German said in English. None of the others noticed that he had spoken to them in their own tongue.

The boat pitched crazily, and the water breaker fell heavily on the boards. No one but the German and Rittenhouse noticed it, and Rittenhouse was too sick to do anything. The German half started toward the fallen breaker but did not let go of the tiller. It was too late, anyhow. The water was pouring from the broken container into the sea water washing over the boards.

Whether his sudden little shift in position was responsible, or merely some whim of the storm, the angle of the sail to the wind changed and the German was half lifted from his seat. He had not been caught unprepared as had Garrett, though, and managed to remain where he was by clinging desperately to the tiller. The mast, however, broke sharply, the noise like a gunshot in the storm. As it came down, the nurse threw herself across its path, in which Stanley Garrett lay supine on the boards. The gunwale in turn took the full force of the falling mast, but the girl's gesture lost none of its value.

"My God, Alice!" Garrett said. "What in the name of heaven did you do that for?"

"I don't know," she said, half weeping. As in a kind of shame, she put her head against his chest and hid her face.

In the bow, and not without a kind of satisfaction, Gus Smith said: "This is the works for all of us."

"No," Rittenhouse said hoarsely. "No, he'll save us. He knows just what he is doing."

Staring fixedly at the German in the stern, where the man had now cleared his arm of the sail and was steering with both hands, Gus Smith, in a feeling new to him that was not quite fear, in a mental gesture born of his own new and terrible disability, found that he agreed easily with Rittenhouse.

The storm beat on, and Kovac, whose persistent refusal to trust the man alone might have saved them, rolled unconscious at the bottom of the boat.

Three days later, on a calm sea, the German's position was even stronger. Of them all, only he, at the oars, seemed unweakened by the lack of water.

Propped high in the bow, Gus Smith could not take his eyes off the clear green sea water that held all of them. The two women lay almost inert in the stern. Rittenhouse and the Negro sat on the stern thwart near the all but useless tiller, and Kovac, from where he half reclined between them and the women, stared sullenly at the German. On his face, too, was the expression of a man long used to an implicit reliance on his own great bodily endurance, who now in amazement finds that, as it leaves him, most of his interior characteristics, of which he had been so proud, also leave him. In his own somewhat dazed and incredulous mind, Kovac kept saying over and over: "My God, how does that Kraut keep doing it when I can't even stand up?"

"Well, Willi," Rittenhouse said hoarsely, "how long should this go on?"

"Oh, not long," the German said, "not too long at all. We're getting into the cruising grounds of the mother ship of my flotilla."

"And what happens then?" Mrs. Porter said, croakingly.

"Why, you will all be guests of the

German government for the rest of the war," Willi said.

From where he lay, Kovac huskily mouthed curses and the German smiled down at him.

From where she lay in the bottom of the boat, Alice MacKenzie could see what Gus Smith was trying to do. She pulled herself tiredly to her feet and started to make her way forward over the thwarts and boards. "No, Gus," she said huskily and almost unintelligibly.

Some of the others turned to see what was the matter. Smith had taken the shoe for which he no longer had any use, and holding on to a lace had let it down over the side and was trying to dip up seawater in it. The nurse reached him and, in spite of her own condition, took the shoe easily from him.

"Only a little," Smith said. His eyes were glazed.

Looking back over his shoulders and with a hint of the curious, mechanical and sharklike smile, the German said, "He has some fever, Alice. I don't think he'll be around much longer."

Again Kovac cursed the German but did not rise.

Raising his head from where he lay amidships, Stanley Garrett, in the hoarse croaking voice peculiar now to all of them, said, "That looks like a rain cloud over there," and dropped his head again.

"Right now," the German said with his odd smile, "all clouds look like rain clouds."

The bastard, Kovac thought. How does he do it? Mrs. Porter stared dazedly and even resentfully at the German. Her admiration for and reliance on him had curiously gone.

There was no rain, but the evening brought a definite coolness in which nearly all of them but the German and Smith slept. In the illusion of strength which the coolness brought to him, Gus Smith pulled himself upright where he stood braced against the gunwale and swaying. "I'm going swimming, Willi," he said.

"Sure, Gus," the German said, quietly amused.

"See you later."

"Sure, Gus," the German said, with a kind of obscene tenderness.

Quite slowly Gus' rigid body tipped forward, the gunwale serving as a fulcrum. There was very little splash but one hoarse yell which brought Stanley Garrett up to a kneeling position. "It's Gus," Garrett said, with the pathetic stressing of the obvious sometimes seen in the weak or helpless.

"Shh," the German said, "no use waking the others, and no one will miss Gus."

The little ordinary motion of the boat was enough to twist Garrett around and drop him in a seated position in which he needed to get himself rigidly placed to support himself. "Why, damn you," he said to the German. Then he began to weep. His head came down on his arms and he lay like that until the darkness, coming, hid all of them. . . .

It was not until morning that the others knew what had happened. Even to the more sensitive of them, the feeling of horror which Garrett's words about Gus induced in them seemed remote and barely connected with their own tortured consciousness. Rittenhouse, raising his head from his hands, stared almost continuously at the horizon and squinted. "Willi," he said, half gasping, "I think I see a ship."

The German stood up and, his feet still pointed toward the stern as they had been when he had rowed, twisted the upper half of his body to stare ahead of them. As he twisted, the movement of his body loosened something held inside his jacket, and the others stared, at first uncomprehendingly, at where Mrs. Porter's brandy flask, now apparently a quarter filled with water, lay on the planking. Whether the German was aware of what had happened or not, they could not have known. In a voice of calm exultation the German said, "That's it. That's it all right, the *Valkyrie*, our mother ship. I think. I'm sure."

"Where did you get my flask?" Mrs. Porter said.

"Oh, that," the German said. "I appropriated that the day I operated on Gus. I thought I was entitled to a little extra water." He smiled. "It came in handy after the water breaker smashed. And lucky for all of you, too," he went on. "After all, if it had not been for that water and a few emergency vitamin tablets, I could not have been able to carry on and bring us successfully here." Seeing and savoring their stricken and terrible faces, he went on: "After all, the foresight of my race is well known and remarkable. We—"

It was just then and with a kind of animal scream, that Alice Mackenzie threw herself at the man. He saw her coming and raised his foot to stave her off. It was then and from the side that the Negro hit him across the back of the neck with the under edge of his open palm, in an adaptation of the rabbit punch. Rittenhouse was only a little before Kovac as the whole hoarsely screaming group lunged with their own pathetic violence at the German. The man went over backward, and Garrett, lurching to his feet, stamped on the masklike face. The knife with which the German had operated fell to the boards and Mrs. Porter got it before anyone else saw it. Kovac had seized the German's head and was twisting it sideways in a fury as the man struggled. Rittenhouse had balled his hands up into fists, but was slapping with his fists as though they were his open hands. Then, quite suddenly, there was blood on all of them, and Mrs. Porter opened her hand and the knife fell down.

"Make it quick," Rittenhouse said. "Get him overboard before those others find him here."

Weakly, the four men managed to roll the German over the side, and weakly from the stern Alice Mackenzie waved a shirt. The ship had seen them, however, and was bearing down on them. All of them stood there, their sudden fear of losing their liberty, a thing they had never thought much of before, overcoming briefly their weakness.

"I don't want to go into a concentration camp," Mrs. Porter said and began to weep.

"I hope those bastards didn't see us roll the Kraut overboard," Kovac said; "they might start looking around for the body."

They stood there, more fearful than any of them had ever been—even, when days before, it had seemed that each of them must surely die. They stood like that, crouched or braced upright.

It was Alice Mackenzie who first collapsed and began to cry; then one after another they gave way to joy, as each saw the banked stars on the flag at the vessel's stern.

Hash Mark

John McNulty

It happened on Third Avenue, in Manhattan, this story of Matty Byrnes, who hated to quit the war until he had something to show for it.

January 4, 1944

MATTY BYRNES STOOD DOWN AT THE END of the bar, fighting the mirror. That's what they call it around Third Avenue when a guy gets drinking alone, and talking to that mirror behind the stick.

"I'd rather be in Sellurno," Matty said. He looked at himself—the threadbare blue suit, the worn-out white shirt, the stringy tie that wouldn't knot up except in a lump, and the hat on his head that looked like a pancake that had fallen in the coffee.

"I'm nothin' at all," Matty said. "I don't know what the hell I am except that I'm nothin' at all. I ain't a soldier and I ain't exactly a civilian. And I ain't gonna be a bartender. I'm nothin' at all."

He poured a drink out of the whisky bottle. It was in front of him on the bar. He drank down a slug of it. Then with very slow movements, the way some men do when they're crocked, he took thirty-five cents out of his pocket and put it on a little pile of silver that was there in front of him.

"They don't need to wait on me," said Matty Byrnes, to the Matty in the mirror. "Wuzzn't I the bartender here for years? Can't I pour my own drinks? And can't I pay for my own drinks? I don't want anything from anybody. They don't need to wait on me."

Matty Byrnes was fighting the mirror.

Old Malachy Ryan, who owned the gin mill, was behind the bar. He was at the far end from Matty.

"I dunno what's the matter with him, at all," said Malachy to the regular customer leaning on the bar. "Three weeks now, he's back from the Army and either drunk or dreamy all three weeks."

"Why don't you put him back to work?" the regular asked. "He was a sourpuss, but everybody knows he was the best bartender you had."

"Put him back to work, is it?" old Malachy flared up. "I've asked him three times a day now will he come back to work, and he howls and snarls at me every time. He won't be a bartender, he says. I can't make him out at all. Look at him, talking to himself. . . . I'm gonna try him once more. I sure could use a bartender the way things are."

Old Malachy moved down the bar, passed a sailor and a couple of soldiers, and stopped and faced Matty.

"You're asking me again, are you?" Matty glared over the bar at his old boss.

"And you don't know why I don't want to come back to work? If I wasn't half tight, I wouldn't try to explain to you or anybody else. I never made a fuss about goin' into the Army, did I? Didn't want any parties or cheers or that 'Good luck, Buddy,' stuff. Did I?"

Malachy broke in easily. "No, you didn't. You just went."

"All right, I just went. Matter of fact, I wanted to go. I got nobody. I got no wife, no kids. I ought to go, the way I figure it, but no hollerin', no Boy Scout stuff."

"No," said Malachy, to keep him going. "No Boy Scout stuff."

Matty kept quiet for a minute. His head seemed to be clearing up a little, remembering something.

"All right, I'll tell you," he said finally. "I did a flop on a hike. I was all right. I just passed out; that's all. I'd 'a' been all right. I come to in a few minutes. But the harm was done. They was a young lieutenant. He'd been on Third Avenue and he was kind of easy on me. It was him put in for me to leave the Army. And I had to leave it."

"But listen, Matty," said Malachy, "you done what you could. You went away, and they threw you out. You done what you could."

"It ain't enough," said Matty. He looked directly at Malachy and he seemed sober as ever a man was. "Those times I was in camp, something come to me what it was all about. Never mind the gripin' and getting sick of the drillin'. Never mind the Army's a lousy place at times. Never mind that! Something come to me, just the same, what it's all about. I think it was at retreat I used to know what it was about—like what we was doing all over the world was up on a screen in the sky up over the flag.

"Retreat is where you stand altogether when the flag comes down late in the afternoon, and if it's in camp, a band plays. If it ain't right in camp or there's no band, the's a bugle plays retreat. That's when it would come to me—that I'd say to myself: This is great. We're all together and we got to do this, and all of us is Americans. To hell with the little things! You know what I mean at all?"

"Yuh," said Malachy.

Matty poured a slug out of the bottle. "Then I got thrun out," he said. "They sent me home. Everybody said, 'You're a lucky guy,' and I joined in with them saying it. . . . So I'm home. I got only this suit to put on, this hat, and one string of a tie. Look at it!"

"You can get some clothes if you go to work again for me," said Malachy.

"No!" barked Matty. "You miss the whole point of it. I don't wanna tend bar. It don't seem right. I ought to be doing somethin'."

"How many times I got to tell you?" put in Malachy. "You done what you could."

"But I got nothin' to show for it!" Matty almost yelled. "And t'hell with you and bartendin'."

Matty weaved out of the gin mill and onto Third Avenue.

That was months ago. Nobody around the gin mill saw Matty all that time, and nobody heard from him, either—until about a week ago, when a couple of regulars were looking over the tabloids one night at the end of the bar.

"Wait a minute!" one guy said, staring at a picture in the tab. "Is that Matty Byrnes, or ain't it?"

The words over the picture said: "Survivors in Tanker Sinking." The second guy from the end, left to right—the right end—certainly looked like Matty, and the story with the picture told about this here tanker getting hit and these fellows in the picture having a tough time. Some had to swim through oil that caught on fire on the water. These fellows had been in a hospital for weeks, but they just let the picture out, the paper said.

"It looks like Matty to me," said Malachy. "Lemme have that." And he cut out the picture with the knife they use to cut lemons for drinks.

That was a Thursday night. So it must've been Saturday, because it was a couple days later, that in walks Matty Byrnes, pretty pale and pooped-out looking, but sober, and not sourpuss or dreamy, either. He hardly said hello, before he ups to Malachy.

"You still need a barkeep? Where's that white coat?"

Malachy nearly broke his neck getting a coat from under the back bar and handing it to him. It was that quick. Hardly a hello, but in two seconds, Matty was on the job.

"I'm glad you changed your mind," said Malachy, as Matty strode around in back of the stick. "What happened?"

"Nothing," said Matty. "I just don't feel so bad any more that they threw me out of the Army."

Before the others in the place could see, Malachy took out the folded picture from the paper. "Is this you," he asked, "or ain't it?"

"It could be, and it couldn't," said Matty. "They're a fine-looking bunch of men, ain't they?"

"They are," said Malachy. "Is one of them you?"

"No Boy Scout stuff!" said Matty. He walked up behind the bar and, as he did, he rolled up one sleeve of his coat and leaned one hand gently on the bar. On his right arm was an irregular scar, new-looking, but healed. It looked like a burn.

"What the hell, Matty!" said Malachy, as he saw the rolled-up sleeve. "What's that?"

"Hash mark," said Matty, and he turned down the sleeve and walked up to the customers.

"Oh," said Malachy. "Something to show for it, huh? Welcome home, Matty!"

Polish Death Camp

Jan Karski

The author felt impelled to apologize for the incredibility of this article when it appeared. That was before official post-war investigations disclosed the indisputable facts about Belsen, Buchenwald, and the other human slaughter-houses. Of this story, an editor's note says: "A patriot disguised as a guard bribed his way into the Nazi execution grounds at Belzec. Here, for the first time, is his eyewitness story of the Nazi's systematic slaughter of Jews, based on his official report to London and Washington."

October 14, 1944

As a member of the underground, I was ordered to leave Warsaw and report to the Polish government and the Allied authorities about conditions in Poland. My orders came from the delegate of the Polish government acting somewhere in Poland and from the commander in chief of the underground army. Jewish leaders confided to me their written report but they insisted that in order to be able to tell the truth I should see with my own eyes what actually happened to the Jews in Poland. They arranged for me to visit one of the Jewish death camps.

The camp was near the town of Belzec, about 100 miles east of Warsaw, and was well known all over Poland because of the tales of horror that were circulated about it. The common report was that every Jew who reached it, without exception, was doomed to death.

I was to go on a day when executions were scheduled. Information was easy to obtain because many of the Estonian, Latvian and Ukrainian attendants who worked there under Gestapo supervision were in the service of the Jewish organizations—not from any humane or political consideration, but for money.

I was to wear the uniform of one of the Estonians, who would stay home while I went with his papers. I was assured that chaos, corruption and panic prevailed in the camp to such an extent that there was no chance of my disguise being penetrated. Moreover, the whole expedition was perfectly organized in advance. I would go through a door habitually guarded only by Germans and Ukrainians, for an Estonian might sense a stranger in me.

The Estonian uniform itself constituted a pass, so that my papers would probably not be inspected. To make the camouflage more foolproof, still another bribed Estonian militiaman would accompany me. Since I knew German, I could talk with the German guards if it became necessary; and they, too, could be bribed.

The plan seemed simple and flawless. I agreed without any hesitation and without the slightest fear of being caught.

Early in the morning I left Warsaw in the company of a Jew who worked outside the ghetto in the Jewish underground movement. We arrived in Belzec shortly after midday and went directly to the place where the Estonian was supposed to be waiting. It was a little grocery store that had once belonged to a Jew. The Jew had been killed and since then it was being run, with the permission of the German authorities, by a local farmer who was, of course, a member of the underground.

My Estonian uniform was there waiting for me, but the man to whom it belonged had evidently decided it was more prudent to remain away. However, he had left me a complete outfit: trousers, long boots, a belt, a tie and a cap. The idea of letting his personal papers be used had apparently given him qualms, too. Instead he had left me the papers of one of his colleagues who had probably returned to his native Estonia and had taken the opportunity to sell his papers. I was not surprised. Selling papers was an established business in Poland, not at all frowned upon. The uniform and the shoes fitted me but the cap came down to my ears. I stuffed it with paper. Then I asked my companion how I looked. He said I looked like a model Estonian militiaman.

An hour or two later the Estonian who was to accompany me arrived. He confirmed that the camp was so disorganized, chaotic and indifferently managed that I could stroll about in perfect freedom. I was to stick to the place assigned me throughout the executions and in that way I would miss nothing. After the executions all the guards would be leaving the camp. I was to join them, mingling with the mob of mixed attendants but avoiding the Estonians. He reiterated the latter precaution solemnly, warning me that if I had any close contact with them it would be easy for them to recognize me as not "their man."

The camp was about a mile and a half from the store. We started walking rapidly, taking a side lane to avoid meeting people. It took about twenty minutes to get to the camp, but we became aware of its presence in less than half that time. About a mile away from the camp we began to hear shouts, shots and screams.

"What's happening?" I asked. "What's the meaning of all that noise?"

"The Jews are hot," he said grinning as though he had said something witty.

I must have glared at him, for he changed his tone abruptly.

"What could it be?" He shrugged. "They are bringing in a 'batch' today."

I knew what he meant and did not inquire further. We walked on while the noise increased alarmingly. From time to time a series of long screams or a particularly inhuman groan would set the hair on my scalp bristling.

"What are the chances of anyone's escaping?" I asked my companion, hoping to hear an optimistic answer.

"None at all," he answered, dashing my hopes to the ground. "Once they get this far, their goose is cooked."

"You mean there isn't a single chance of anybody's escaping from the camp, even with the way things are there?"

"Well, from the camp itself, maybe. But not alone. With a guard like me helping, it can be done. But it's a terrible risk," he said, wagging his head solemnly. "The Jew and I could both get killed."

We trudged on, the Estonian watching me out of the corner of his eye.

"Of course," he said craftily, "if a Jew

pays well—very well—it can be done. But it is very risky, it has to be handled right . . ."

"How can they pay? They don't have any money on them, do they?"

"Say, we don't try to get money out of them. We ain't so dumb. We get paid in advance. It's strictly a cash proposition. We don't even deal with those in the camp"—he gestured contemptuously in the direction of the noise—"we do business with people on the outside, like you. If somebody comes to me and tells me that such and such a Jew is going to arrive and that he wants him 'cheated out'—well, if he is willing to fork out plenty of hard cash in advance, then I do what I can."

"Have you saved many Jews so far?" I asked.

"Not as many as I'd like, but a few, anyhow."

"Are there many more good men like you there who are so willing to save the Jews?"

"Save them? Say, who wants to save them?" He looked at me in bewilderment as though I were talking unheard-of nonsense. "But if they pay, that's a different story. We can all use some money."

I did not venture to disagree. It would have been hopeless to try to persuade him of anything different. I looked at his heavy, rather good-natured face and wondered how the war had come to develop such cruel habits in him. From what I had seen he seemed to be a simple, average man, not particularly good or bad. His hands were the calloused but supple hands of a good farmer. In normal times that was what he probably was—and a good father, a family man and a churchgoer besides. Now, under the pressure of the Gestapo and the cajoleries of the Nazis, with everyone about him engaged in a greedy competition that knew no limits, he had been changed into a professional butcher of human beings. He had caught onto his trade well and discussed its niceties, used its professional jargon as coolly as a carpenter discussing his craft.

"And what are you here for?" The question was both shrewd and innocent.

"I'd like to 'save' some Jews too," I said with an air of conspiracy. "With your help, of course. That's why I've come to the camp, to see how everything works."

"Well, don't you go trying to do anything without us."

"Don't be silly. Why should I work without you? We both want to make money and we can help each other. We would be foolish to work against each other."

This satisfied him and I now had the status of a younger colleague.

As we approached to within a few hundred yards of the camp, the shouts, cries and shots cut off further conversation. I noticed an unpleasant stench that seemed to have come from decomposing bodies mixed with horse manure. This may have been an illusion. The Estonian was, in any case, completely impervious to it. He even began to hum some sort of folk tune to himself. We passed through a small grove of decrepit-looking trees and emerged directly in front of the loud, sobbing, reeking camp of death.

It was on a large, flat plain and occupied about a square mile. It was surrounded on all sides by a formidable barbed-wire fence, nearly two yards in height and in good repair. Inside the fence, at intervals of about fifteen yards, guards were standing, holding rifles with bayonets ready for use. Around the outside of the fence, militiamen circulated on constant patrol. The camp itself contained a few small sheds or barracks. The rest of the area was completely covered by a dense, pulsating, throbbing, noisy human mass—starved, stinking, gesticulating, insane human beings in constant agitated motion. Through them, forcing paths if necessary with their rifle butts, walked the German police and the militiamen. They walked in silence, their faces bored and indifferent. They looked like shepherds bringing in a flock to the market. They had the tired, vaguely disguised appearance of men doing a routine, tedious job.

Into the fence a few passages had been cut, and gates made of poles tied together with barbed wire swung back to make an entrance. Each gate was guarded by two men who slouched about carelessly. We stopped for a moment to collect ourselves. I noticed off to my left the railroad tracks which passed about a hundred yards from the camp. From the camp to the track a sort of raised passage had been built from old boards. On the track a dusty freight train waited, motionless.

The Estonian followed my gaze with the interest of a person seeing what kind of an impression his home made on a visitor. He proceeded eagerly to enlighten me:

"That's the train they'll load them on. You'll see it all."

We came to a gate. Two German noncoms were standing there talking. I could hear snatches of their conversation. They seemed to be talking about a night they had spent in a near-by town. I hung back a bit. The Estonian seemed to think I was losing my nerve.

"Go ahead," he whispered impatiently into my ear. "Don't be afraid. They won't even inspect your papers. They don't care about the likes of you."

We walked up to the gate and saluted the noncoms vigorously. They returned the salute indifferently and we passed through.

"Follow me," he said, quite loudly. "I'll take you to a good spot."

We passed an old Jew, a man of about sixty, sitting on the ground without a stitch of clothing on him. I was not sure whether his clothes had been torn off or whether he, himself, had thrown them away in a fit of madness. Silent, motionless, he sat on the ground, no one paying him the slightest attention. Not a muscle or fiber in his whole body moved except for his preternaturally animated eyes, which blinked rapidly and incessantly. Not far from him a small child, clad in a few rags, was lying on the ground. He was all alone and crouched quivering on the ground, staring up with the large, frightened eyes of a rabbit. No one paid any attention to him, either.

The Jewish mass vibrated, trembled and moved to and fro as if united in a single, insane rhythmic trance. They waved their hands, shouted, quarreled, cursed and spat at one another. Hunger, thirst, fear and exhaustion had driven them all insane. I had been told that they were usually left in the camp for three or four days without food or a drop of water. They were all former inhabitants of the Warsaw ghetto.

There was no organization or order of any kind. None of them could possibly help or share with one another and they soon lost any self-control or any sense whatsoever except the bare instinct of self-preservation. They had become, at this stage, completely dehumanized. It was, moreover, typical autumn weather, cold, raw and rainy. The sheds could not accommodate more than two to three thousand people and every "batch" included more than five thousand. This meant that there were always two to three thousand men, women and children scattered about in the open, suffering exposure as well as everything else.

The chaos, the squalor, the hideousness of it all were simply indescribable. There was a suffocating stench of sweat, filth, decay, damp straw and excrement. To get to my post we had to squeeze our way through this mob. It was a ghastly ordeal. I had to push foot by foot through the crowd and step over the limbs of those who were lying prone. It was like forcing my way through a mass of death and decomposition made even more horrible by its agonized pulsations. My companion had the skill of long practice, evading the bodies on the ground and winding his way through the mass with the ease of a contortionist. Distracted and clumsy, I would brush against people or step on a figure that reacted like an animal; quickly, often with a moan or a yelp. Each time this occurred I would be seized by a fit of nausea and come to a stop. But my guide kept urging and hustling me along.

In this way we crossed the entire camp and finally stopped about twenty yards from the gate which opened on the passage leading to the train. It was a comparatively uncrowded spot. I felt immeasurably relieved at having finished my stumbling, sweating journey. The guide was standing at my side, saying something, giving me advice. I hardly heard him. He raised his voice:

"Look here. You are going to stay here. I'll walk on a little farther. You know what you are supposed to do. Remember to keep away from Estonians. Don't forget, if there's any trouble, you don't know me and I don't know you."

I nodded vaguely at him. He shook his head and walked off.

I remained there perhaps half an hour, watching this spectacle of human misery. At each moment I felt the impulse to run and flee. I had to force myself to remain indifferent, to practice stratagems to convince myself that I was not one of the condemned. Finally, I noticed a change in the motion of the guards. They walked less and they all seemed to be glancing in the same direction—at the passage to the track which was quite close to me.

I turned toward it myself. Two German policemen came to the gate with a tall, bulky SS man. He barked out an order and they began to open the gate. It was very heavy. He shouted at them impatiently. They worked at it frantically and finally shoved it open. They dashed down the passage as though they were afraid the SS man might come after them, and took up their positions where the passage ended. The whole system had been worked out with crude effectiveness. The outlet of the passage was blocked off by two cars of the freight train, so that any attempt on the part of one of the Jews to break out of the mob would have been completely impossible.

The SS man turned to the crowd, planted himself with his feet wide apart and his hands on his hips and loosed a roar that must have actually hurt his ribs. It could be heard far above the hellish babble that came from the crowd:

"*Ruhe, ruhe!* Quiet, quiet! All Jews will board this train to be taken to a place where work awaits them. Keep order. Do not push. Anyone who attempts to resist or create a panic will be shot."

He stopped speaking and looked challengingly at the helpless mob that hardly seemed to know what was happening. Suddenly, accompanying the movement with a loud, hearty laugh, he yanked out his gun and fired three random shots into the crowd. A single, stricken groan answered him. He replaced the gun in his holster, smiled and set himself for another roar:

"*Alle Juden. 'raus—'raus!*"

For a moment the crowd was silent. Those nearest the SS man recoiled from the shots and tried to dodge, panic-stricken, toward the rear. But this was resisted by the mob as a volley of shots from the rear sent the whole mass surging forward madly, screaming in pain and fear. The shots continued without letup from the rear and now from the sides, too, narrowing the mob down and driving it in a savage scramble onto the passageway. In utter panic they rushed down the passageway, trampling it so furiously that it threatened to fall apart.

Then new shots were heard. The two policemen at the entrance to the train were now firing into the oncoming throng corralled in the passageway, in order to slow them down and prevent them from demolishing the flimsy structure. The SS man added his roar to the bedlam.

"*Ordnung, ordnung!*" He bellowed like a madman.

"Order, order!" The two policemen echoed him hoarsely, firing straight into the faces of the Jews running to the trains. Impelled and controlled by this ring of fire, they filled the two cars quickly.

And now came the most horrible episode of all. The military rule stipulates that a freight car may carry eight horses or forty soldiers. Without any baggage at all, a maximum of a hundred passengers pressing against one another could be crowded into a car. The Germans had simply issued orders that 120 to 130 Jews had to enter each car. Those orders were now being carried out. Alternately swinging and firing their rifles, the policemen were forcing still more people into the two cars which were already overfull. The shots continued to ring out in the rear, and the driven mob surged forward, exerting an irresistible pressure against those nearest the train. These unfortunates, crazed by what they had been through, scourged by the policemen and shoved forward by the milling mob, then began to climb on the heads and shoulders of those in the trains.

These latter were helpless since they had the weight of the entire advancing throng against them. They howled with anguish at those who, clutching at their hair and clothes for support, trampling on necks, faces and shoulders, breaking bones and shouting with insensate fury, attempted to clamber over them. More than another score of men, women and children crushed into the cars in this fashion. Then the policemen slammed the doors across the arms and legs that still protruded, and pushed the iron bars in place.

The two cars were now crammed to bursting with tightly packed human flesh. All this while the entire camp reverberated with a tremendous volume of sound in which groans and screams mingled with shots, curses and bellowed commands.

Nor was this all. I know that many people will not believe me, but I saw it, and it is not exaggerated. I have no other proofs, no photographs. All I can say is that I saw it, and it is the truth.

The floors of the car had been covered with a thick, white powder. It was quicklime. Quicklime is simply unslaked lime or calcium oxide that has been dehydrated. Anyone who has seen cement being mixed knows what occurs when water is poured on lime. The mixture bubbles and steams as the powder combines with the water, generating a searing heat.

The lime served a double purpose in the Nazi economy of brutality: the moist flesh coming in contact with the lime is quickly dehydrated and burned. The occupants of the cars would be literally burned to death before long, the flesh eaten from their bones. Thus the Jews would "die in agony," fulfilling the promise Himmler had issued "in accord with the will of the Fuehrer," in Warsaw in 1942. Secondly, the lime would prevent the decomposing bodies from spreading disease. It was efficient and inexpensive—a perfect chosen agent for its purpose.

It took three hours to fill up the entire train. It was twilight when the forty-six cars were packed. From one end to the other the train, with its quivering cargo of flesh, seemed to throb, vibrate, rock and jump as if bewitched. There would be a strangely uniform momentary lull and then the train would begin to moan and sob, wail and howl. Inside the camp a few score dead bodies and a few in the final throes of death remained. German policemen walked around at leisure with smoking guns, pumping bullets into anything that moaned or moved. Soon none were left alive. In the now quiet camp the only sounds were the inhuman screams that echoed from the moving train. Then these, too, ceased. All that was now left was the stench of excrement and rotting straw and a queer, sickening, acidulous odor which, I thought, may have come from the quantities of blood that had stained the ground.

As I listened to the dwindling outcries from the train I thought of the destination toward which it was speeding. My informants had minutely described the entire journey. The train would travel about eight miles and finally come to a halt in an empty, barren field. Then nothing at all would happen. The train would stand stock-still, patiently waiting while death penetrated into every corner of its interior. This would take from two to four days.

When quicklime, asphyxiation and injuries had silenced every outcry, a group of men would appear. They would be young strong Jews, assigned to the task of cleaning out these cars until their own turn to ride in them should arrive. Under a strong guard they would unseal the cars and expel the heaps of decomposing bodies. The mounds of flesh that they piled up would then be burned and the remnants buried in a single huge hole. The cleaning, burning and burial would consume one or two full days.

The entire process of disposal would take, then, from three to six days. During this period the camp would have recruited new victims. The train would return and the whole cycle would be repeated.

I was still standing near the gate, gazing after the no longer visible train, when I felt a rough hand on my shoulder. The Estonian was back again.

"Wake up, wake up!" he was scolding hoarsely. "Don't stand there with your mouth open. Come on, hurry, or we'll both be caught. Follow me and be quick about it."

I followed him at a distance, feeling completely benumbed. When we reached the gate he reported to a German officer and pointed at me. I heard the officer say, "*Sehr gut, gehen sie*," and then we passed through the gate.

The Estonian and I walked a while together and then separated. I walked to the store as quickly as I could, running when there was no one about to see me. I reached the grocery store so breathless that the owner became alarmed. I reassured him while I threw off my uniform, boots, stockings and underwear. I ran into the kitchen and locked the door. In a little while my bewildered and worried host called out to me:

"Hey, what are you doing in there?"

"Don't worry. I'll be right out."

When I came out, he promptly entered the kitchen and called back in despair:

"What the devil have you been doing? The whole kitchen is flooded!"

"I washed myself," I replied, "that is all. I was very dirty."

Then I collapsed. I was completely, violently, rackingly sick. Even today, when I remember those scenes, I become nauseated.

Prayer for Children

Francis J. Spellman

The Christmas issue of Collier's *for 1944 contained this "Prayer for Children" by Cardinal (then Archbishop) Francis J. Spellman. The rights and proceeds of the Prayer went to the New York Foundling Hospital.*

December 30, 1944

How strange seems Christmas in the frame of war!
How feebly through our dreadful night, the star
Of Bethlehem its deathless radiance shows!
How blasphemous the roar of guns and planes
Upon the silence of this sacred eve
Which Christian faith makes consecrate to Him
Who came to be the Prince of Peace, and gain,
Not by brute force, but by the might of love,
The kingdom of men's souls, with sacrifice
Divine! Deeply, we believe there is no hope
For men, save in His gift of Self for them;
Nor is there love surpassing Love enshrined
In Bethlehem. For only God, Who was
Himself a Child, can light the road to peace.

We do not sense the toll of war, the price
Man pays for putting faith in force of arms,
Till we have seen war's children and their woe,
The innocent who reap of Herod's wrath.
It is the children; they are lambs of God.
They are our generation's sacrifice
For immolation on the altars raised,
Not to the loving fatherhood of God,
But to the cold and cruel cult of Mars.
Dear Christ, some of the altars we have built,
With all the skill that science could command,
With all the speed our genius could beget,
Have graven golden images enshrined.
Blind hatreds fog the Tablets of the Law.
Dragons' teeth are seed for children, sired
For War's brute reaping. Cycle without end!
Once more, it is the innocent who die.

Oh, wilt not Thou, Who wast Thyself a Babe,
Implant in deadened souls Thy mercy's life,
That we may labor in this darksome hour
To save Thy children for a better day,

And thus ourselves be found unworthy less
Than now, of mercy at Thy Judgment seat!
Thy Spirit wrote, "A little child shall lead";
And now the day is here for Thee, a Child,
To lead us stricken peoples back to peace,
To pour within America's great soul
Desire both strong and pregnant with resolve
To save from out the ruins of our hates,
Our children, innocent of wrong. 'Tis late,
Yet this most precious gift we beg of Thee!

Somewhere—the place it matters not—somewhere
I saw a child, hungry and thin of face—
Eyes in whose pools life's joy no longer stirred,
Lips that were dead to laughter's eager kiss,
Yet parted fiercely to a crust of bread.
And since that time I walk in ceaseless dread,
Dread that the child I saw, and all the hosts
Of children in a world at play with death,
May die; or, living, live in bitterness.
Thy love, Thy Blood alone can quell man's wrath,
Thy Spirit, only, feed men's famished souls.

O Christ, have pity on Thy little ones,
From out a million broken homes they cry
To Thee, the Friend of Children, and their God.
They truly, even as Thou how long ago,
For sins that others wrought, are sentenced now.
O God, today, above the cries of war,
Hear Thou Thy children's prayer, and grant to us
Thy peace, God's peace—
and bread for starving children!

Revenge

Samuel Blas

A honeymoon was blasted by sudden tragedy. The events that followed make this one of the most remarkable short stories ever to appear in Collier's.

January 11, 1947

TWILIGHT IS SETTLING IN THE VALLEY. *Far below us pale lights are beginning to flicker and the spreading pattern of the city slowly comes alive. As the winding road narrows to the mountaintop the motor sound grows louder in the thin air, within the enclosing silence through which we move.*

In the pale blue haze on my left the deepening dusk mingles with the vast silence that seems to suspend the day. A square yellow sign ahead blazes in our headlights: DANGER! SHARP CURVE AHEAD. The mountain wall leans close to the road. On Elsa's side the low branches of a solitary tree rush by, scraping the top of the car.

Elsa, too, is part of the surrounding silence. Beside me she stares straight ahead at the highway. For a long time now she has not spoken; she neither smiles nor is sorrowful. Her expression is grave, almost serene, as if there were no such things as tears or laughter.

But this morning she smiled. A half day's journey away, in the cool morning of a quiet glade she stepped from our trailer door and smiled softly as she waved me off to town. She blushed when I turned back a step to kiss her again. And when I finally drove off, the sweet touch of her hand still tingled in my palm.

Life was wonderful. I drove happily to the small town near by to buy provisions. We had decided to stay a few days more in this pleasant spot we had found. There could be no better place to finish out our honeymoon. As I neared the town I thought it would be fun to add a gift for Elsa to the stuff that I would carry back to the camp.

It was nearing lunchtime when I started back. I had piled groceries enough in the car to last us a week. While I waited for a traffic light to change, a newsboy came by. I bought a paper. It carried a headline reporting the capture of an escaped convict near by. The subcaption said that his companion was still at large. "Presumed Hiding In the Woods Near Campbelltown."

I ran quickly through the rest of the item. When the light turned I moved out fast and put on speed. Campbelltown was a place that lay beyond our camp, but too near to suit me, in the circumstances. I felt uneasy, with Elsa alone in the trailer. It was possible, of course, that the fugitive convict might be in our vicinity; but what disturbed me more was the thought that Elsa might have picked up the news on our radio. If she had, she would be frightened. I stepped on the accelerator.

The road twisted and turned around thinly wooded ridges and hills, and as I swung each curve I chided myself for leaving Elsa alone. I reminded myself that she had insisted I shop without her. "I have a surprise for dinner," she had said with the only artfulness she knew—a shy, secret smile. My attention returned to the road.

The winding turns ended and the last stretch was a long, straight drive sheltered by a canopy of tall trees that somehow eased my anxiety. Not much further now. I imagined the way she would welcome me. She would stanchly deny that she had been afraid but she would hold my arm tightly. And then all of a sudden she would forget the whole thing. She would smile happily and tell me to close my eyes. How I loved that smile!

In the short while that I had known her and in the single month of our marriage I had grown to cherish that smile and the soft, rich laughter that sometimes accompanied it. So strange, that warm directness with which she shared my life, for in the presence of other men there was only shyness. I think that she was afraid of men. Something in her slender glowing warmth made their blood stir. She knew that, faintly, innocently. When the bold ones stared at her she would ask me to hold her close and never tell me why.

The sun was near high noon when the road broke out of the trees into the clearing. I rolled onto the grass and parked, feeling relieved because I had come so quickly. I pulled up the hand brake and looked to the trailer, expecting to see Elsa's welcoming figure there. My complacency ended. There in the clear fall sunlight I saw wisps of smoke about our home, thin plumes slipping through the unlatched door.

Wild red leaves fluttered across the grass. And a wavering silence to which I listened stupidly. Then I ran to the door and swung it open violently.

An acrid fog swirled about me, making me choke and cough. A curling heavy mist clung to the ceiling. I swung the door wider and flailed my arms to clear the air. And as the fog lifted and shifted I saw with some relief that there was no fire. Our dinner was smoking and burning upon the stove. Three chops—I can see them yet—shriveled and black in a blackened frying pan; string beans in a burning pot, brown where the water had been; and in the oven, where I later found it, a crumbling burnt blob that must once have been Elsa's first cake—the surprise she had promised me.

Panic got hold of me.

"Elsa!" I called.

There was no reply.

"Elsa!" I repeated. "Elsa!"

But only the crackle of the burning pot answered me, and outside a thin echo wandered in the woods. I shut off the burners. The crackling persisted as if in defiance, then it ceased. I turned uneasily toward the door that led to our dining alcove in the rear, stopping short at sight of the waiting table with its knives and forks and plates in neat array. But no Elsa. But of course. She wouldn't, she couldn't have been there or the dinner would not have burned.

Trying to understand what had happened I rejected a dozen answers at once. She would never have left the dinner to burn for any sort of errand. Nor were there neighbors about with whom to fall into forgetful conversation. We were alone. Then as I stood there in the silence I suddenly heard that faint sound, a rising and falling as of someone weakly breathing. Behind the curtain that secluded our bed—Elsa!

I faced about and tore aside the curtain—

There she lay. Pale, still. I kneeled beside her. She was barely breathing.

"Elsa," I whispered.

She seemed neither to move nor to make any sound, yet I knew she was breathing, for I had heard her. I rubbed her wrists and temples. I shook her gently, then fearfully. She stirred a little.

I wanted to get a doctor, yet I was afraid to leave. Then I remembered the brandy. I fumbled in the cupboard and my hand trembled as I poured a glassful and spooned a little between her lips.

At last it took effect. Her lips moved. Her expression altered, she sputtered, she coughed, and her eyes opened weakly.

At first they were blank. A long second passed while I held her hands tightly. Then, as if awareness had just touched her, horror filled her eyes and she moaned.

Then as I gathered her into my arms and let the sheet that covered her fall away, I saw that she was naked—completely.

There were bruises on her body, as if someone had beaten her: cruel bruises on her shoulders where callous fingers had pressed; angry marks where heavy fists had struck her.

Those numb moments beside my wife are not easily recalled, filled as they are with shame and a fierce anger. When at last she stirred again in my arms I held her tight and looked beyond her so that she would not see the anguish in my eyes. For long minutes she shivered; then she sobbed pitifully. Finally the tears and trembling stopped.

In a flat voice that frightened me she said, "*He killed me . . . he killed me.*"

How I gathered the tangled threads of those dreadful hours I cannot entirely remember. For a long time I cradled and comforted her, as though she were a child. After a while she seemed to respond. But then, when she shuddered again, my indignation mounted; I lost control and stormed at her with furious questions: "Who?" I demanded. "Who?" and "When?" and "How?" Until haltingly the brutal story came out. How a salesman knocked—

"A salesman?"

"Yes."

"Are you sure? Did he carry a suitcase, a display?"

"Yes."

A salesman. Then it was not the convict. Nothing reasonable. It was an ordinary man, ordinary.

How he knocked, interrupting her cooking; how he smiled patly and edged inside, eying her boldly while he chattered about kitchenware. How he touched her arm and seized her and how when she resisted he beat her; and—and how she finally fainted away.

As she talked she seemed to fall under a spell of horror that produced in her a curious calm. She repeated. "He killed me, he killed me . . ." until I had to shake her to make her stop. Her eyes, I saw, stared straight ahead as she said over those dreadful words and it seemed as though she saw that man, that menacing figure, in the hopeless distance.

I never thought once of the police. Only one impulse was in me, a dreadful agonizing craving for revenge. "I'll find him!" I swore. "I'll kill him . . ."

Her hand clutched mine as if to restrain me, but when she felt the anger in my grip her mood abruptly changed and she said quietly, "Yes . . . yes." And when I hesitantly asked whether she would come with me, help me find him, she nodded, almost eagerly I thought.

We drove to the outskirts of the town, where she listened carefully to my instructions, nodding with a sort of unearthly calm.

"We'll drive slowly," I told her. And this we did for perhaps a half hour, examining every passer-by as we moved back and forth through the unhurried streets. The sun still hung heavy above us as we turned a third time down the town's main artery.

In the wide street were a few parked cars, and a thin afternoon crowd was lazily inspecting the shop windows. A man lounging near the hotel disinterestedly picked his teeth. It seemed to me he observed our slow progress curiously. I directed my wife's attention to him but she gravely shook her head. Then suddenly she gripped my arm. Her lips fell open and her face paled. She pointed at a shabby car parked near the hotel. A man was locking the car door.

"*That's him!*" she whispered.

My blood quickened.

"Are you sure?" I asked finally. Her eyes followed him as he put the keys in his pocket and turned toward the hotel.

"*That's him,*" she insisted, "*that's him. . . .*"

I pulled to the curb in front of his car and stepped out quickly. "Wait here," I said. "Don't move—" I looked about me with assumed carelessness. The lounger, I saw, was facing the other way. No one else seemed to notice me. I sauntered into the lobby, a few steps behind my man. I decided to wait for him near the elevator, and sure enough he was soon standing beside me absently fingering his room key.

Luck was with me, for as the car went up I glimpsed his room number on the key in his hand. I had planned to get out with him and openly follow him to his room. Instead I rode to the floor above his, made my way to the stairway, down one level, through the hallways to his room and knocked softly, an unexpected and unknown visitor.

I was calm then as he answered my knock. I spoke to him through the door and represented myself as the buyer for a local store. He opened the door wide. "Why, come in," he said; he wore a welcoming grin that infuriated me.

I went in; took the hammer from the waistband of my trousers and, as he turned to walk ahead of me, I smashed him mightily on the back of his head.

A great cry escaped him; then a dismal sigh that collapsed with him to the floor. He lay still.

I stared at the crumpled figure and my fury subsided, spent by that single avenging blow. A clock ticked into my consciousness. My eyes wandered absently to the simple dresser, the bed, the silent telephone. In my hand the hammer was edged with blood. I tucked it back in my trousers and dropped the skirt of my coat over it. With my handkerchief I turned the knob of the door. Curiosity prompted me to glance again at the still figure on the floor, but I no longer cared. It might be hours before anything happened. I might be suspected or I might not. None of these conjectures bothered me. I was reasonably safe from suspicion; that I knew; except perhaps from this—this ordinary individual. I turned and went out quickly, closing the door behind me. And with that closed door behind me, in that quiet carpeted hallway, I at last felt clean, free of obsessing shame.

I went back upstairs, rang for the elevator and rode down quietly. The very sleepiness of this town made my ambling exit from the hotel unnoticeable.

Elsa was still in the car, patient, gazing straight ahead, just as I had left her.

"It's done," I said.

Her head barely turned in my direction and she nodded slowly. She said one word: "Good."

Poor Elsa. So altered with shame and shock that she had grown a shell which I could not pierce. She sat silently in the car while, back at our camp, I hooked up the trailer and made ready for a journey. Even the lunch I fixed for her she barely touched, nibbling once or twice, then staring into space. Perhaps when we were away from this terrible place . . .

It was evening when we stopped again. I drove furiously past a dozen small villages, hurrying toward the city that lies, now, below and behind us at the foot of the mountain. I hoped to find in its busy streets some distraction from our lonely secret, to lose some of this horror there, perhaps in some lively bar or in a theater; perhaps in a good night's rest. Then the strain of the dreadful day took charge. A good night's sleep was all I craved. But not in the trailer; not yet.

Elsa agreed indifferently. We rolled ahead and merged with the traffic in the city. We would park the trailer and stop at the best hotel. We would have a hot bath, then dinner in our room and perhaps a bottle of wine. And a good sleep, a good sleep . . . "Would you like that?" I asked her.

I thought her expression softened; certainly a tear glistened in her eye. I wanted right then to hold her in my arms, to caress her and comfort her. I pointed to a hotel we were approaching.

"Would you like that one?" I asked.

Her glance followed my pointing finger. She paled. She gripped my arm tightly and her lips parted. She stared straight ahead. Oh, God! She stared straight ahead and pointed at a man in the street—

"*That's him*," she whispered. "*That's him* . . ."

The Trap

Howard Bloomfield

A man with a gun stalks a man with no weapon except his wits. Only one of the two would ever leave the island.

April 19, 1947

THE WAY THAT ARMSTRONG DESTIN TRIED to put George Turner overboard was simple, and yet it held a trick, a touch of drama. The trick was misdirection: a focusing of the eye on one spot, and not letting the right hand know what the left hand is doing.

The old Nassau sloop wallowed along with a broad arrow of foam at the bow and a gay bubble and froth sweeping out under the fat stern, because the trade wind could make any boat move, even though the boat waved foul grasses from its bottom like this sloop of Destin's. George Turner felt himself living in the middle of a color film and, at times, during the past two days, he had closed his eyes and opened them again, convincing himself of a vividness that was a blow on the eyeballs. The foam was so white, the sky so blue; and the dozens of sandy keys were golden chips on a sea of jade satin. And some of the keys wore dark green tufts of vegetation, though empty of human life—the Bahamas hold scores and hundreds of such tiny low islands, useless but pretty.

This was old stuff to Destin, but to George Turner it was adventure. Turner was a slight, wiry man, with brown face and brown hair, and brown eyes behind his glasses. His face gave an occasional pleased twitch, and his eyes blinked like an owl's. He kept thinking that pirate ships had sailed these waters, and it was easy to picture one here, prowling boldly, full of fighting men who were not at all like himself, men more like Destin.

The sun was beginning to set, and here it was a bigger red ball than elsewhere, and a red-and-gold cloud was a brighter and longer banner.

"Damned beautiful," said George Turner, jerking his fishing rod at the sunset. "And a good moon to come. We can go on sailing, huh?"

"Sure," said Destin. "Get us there sooner." Destin was taking him to a place where they could look down through clear water and see the ribs of an old wreck and the shape of a cannon.

Destin got up from the tiller, planted one foot across it to steer by, and stretched and yawned lazily. He was a bigger man than Turner, but the difference was more striking than that. He was a strong male animal, even if he seemed a sort of gentleman on the surface. Aside from the long knife scar down his forearm, it was plain to see that Destin had been in dangers and tight places and had fought his own fights and made his own laws.

As Destin put his right hand over his yawning mouth, a gleam in his ring caught his eye. The ring was a heavy band of gold, with a green stone that was square and large. Destin held out his hand, turning it, letting the light strike into the stone.

"You ever notice this ring?" he asked George Turner. "It was found in an old wreck. I got the ring off a dead man, down in Port-au-Prince. I took it for a souvenir. Look at this engraving—I think it's Spanish."

While Turner stepped to him, Destin made his hand into a fist and remarked, "Not a bad brass knuckle, if a man ever needs one." He relaxed the fist and spread out his fingers. Turner gazed down at the worn, indistinct chasing either side of the stone.

"The man I took the ring from tried to kill me, when I wasn't expecting a thing," said Destin. "Do you notice, right next to the stone—"

Then George Turner was staggering, reeling, on the very edge of the stern, flailing his fishing rod for balance. The unexpected shove by Destin's left hand would have sent him overboard at once, except that he had tensed a little to hear Destin's story of killing the man; except that earlier that day a barracuda had staggered him by its savage strike, so that Turner had since kept himself braced when he held the rod.

In his wild gyration he saw that Destin's fist was cocked again, and behind it Destin's face was astonishingly savage. Turner smashed the heavy deep-sea reel on his rod against that face for he had succeeded in swaying inward on the boat. Then Destin wrenched the rod down, but Turner, on his feet again, whipped a fish knife from the sheath at his belt. It opened a red streak on Destin's arm, and Destin turned and jumped down into the cabin.

Turner gasped, trying to realize what had happened. It had been only a few bewildering seconds since he was staring at Destin's ring, and now Destin was bleeding in the cabin. Turner stood in paralysis of fright, and then he thought of the revolver on a shelf below, and of Destin's hand snatching up the gun.

Turner raced forward in a panic to get off the boat, to dive and swim madly away. The sloop, its tiller free, was rounding into the wind, the sails shaking and banging. But it could come under control again in a minute, and follow and overtake him like a porpoise charging upon a fish. He slashed the main halyard. The big leg-of-mutton sail came down like a snowslide, a rotten topping lift broke, the boom was a thick club smiting the cabin roof. Destin was just coming up out of the hatchway when the boom struck his shoulder and knocked him below.

Turner slashed the jib halyard. The jib, on its slanting head stay, came down in a gentler folding fall.

The mainsail lay all over the hatchway like a great canvas rug, and the rug heaved up over a crawling form. George Turner delayed his departure one instant more, to run back and snatch the fishing rod. He swung the heavy reel down on the moving bulge and the bulge backed into the cabin.

Then Turner in his fear went overboard. The water closed round him in a cool safe bath and swept some of his fright away. A strange crashing sound had entered his ears when he drove, because the cork helmet was still on his head, held by a strap under his chin. He had his glasses, too, hooked over his ears.

He swam furiously at first, and instinct told him to go upwind, because the sloop would be drifting away down the wind. When he looked back, the sloop was only a hundred yards away, a dark bulk. Though the night would not come for a while, the boat was dark because it lay against the red stain of sunset, in reddening water. Destin was not yet on deck.

Turner sprinted again. A slow ground swell heaved and fell, like a leisurely breathing of the sea. A man would be hidden in the hollow, and Turner tried to stay there, but he could not swim quite fast enough, and so he went under in a dead man's float when he felt himself being lifted, and began to swim again when he was lowered. Out of breath, he trod water for another look. Destin was on deck, walking and turning slowly, no doubt searching the water. Farther away than Turner had expected, until he thought again of the downwind drift of the boat. The red was turning leaden on the water, and dulling in the sky.

Turner remembered the dinghy lashed upside down on deck, and he wished he were in it. There had been time—it seemed now—to get it overboard. Turner was bitter that he had not thought there was time. He could not even remember if he had thought of the dinghy at all; and the bitterness engulfed him and made him feel heavy and tired in the water. It was too late now to think of all the things he should have done. But Destin would not be treading out here in a thickening gloom. If it had happened to Destin, Destin would still be on the sloop, and the only man alive.

Turner wondered if Destin would come after him in the dinghy. Unless he came soon and fast, he would risk losing the sloop in the night. Unless—Turner's brain kept making quick snaps at the situation, like the snaps of a cornered dog—unless Destin should hang up a lantern first, so he could find the sloop again. Destin couldn't come after him in the sloop without a job of rigging first, because the severed halyards had whipped aloft and run out of the blocks. Thinking of that, the immediate fear of Destin went out of George Turner. He swam along slowly on his back, keeping his feet toward the dull maroon in the west. That color faded so rapidly, while stars came out in a slow sprinkle, that he picked a star to keep him straight on his course to nowhere.

The water was comfortably warm. Turner remembered reading once of a man who floated in the Gulf Stream for a week and was saved—true, he was unconscious and supported by a life preserver. But Turner thought he had at least a few hours ahead of him. The human body was ninety-eight per cent—was it more?—water, and flotation was only a matter of ounces. He floated quite easily so long as he lay on his back as if in a loose strait jacket, but if he tried to turn the water gushed into his nose and mouth.

The pith helmet that was now under the back of his head seemed to help a bit, though it might slowly become a soggy thing. Already he imagined that a part of the brim flapped loosely against his neck as each push of his hands moved him onward a little more. He removed his waterproof wrist watch, his belt and the sheath that had held the knife, but these were motions that sunk his face and left him out of breath.

He was dressed only in shirt and shorts and sandals. He thought of stuffing the helmet inside his shirt, but it gave him a weak comfort under his head, as if his head were really lying on something. And perhaps the sandals helped a bit, being of a composition cork sole. But a man could float, without helmet or sandals. A man had a few ounces of buoyancy in himself.

Turner tried to think reasonably about it. Life was a few ounces that would rather float; Death was a few ounces that would rather sink. He was in a big, warm swimming pool. He was lying on a kind of fluid couch, pushing himself along it by his hands, and covered all over but for his eyes and nose and mouth. But a swimming pool has sides and ends, and a ladder for climbing out, and a swimming pool holds no sharks and barracuda. He tried not to think about that, because it was a frantic thought. But it was very difficult not to wonder what might be moving below him, surveying him, as he inched along in this great black space with his eyes fixed on a star.

So Turner was immensely lonely. He imagined he heard friends wondering aloud what had become of him. He saw an office in Pittsburgh where soot fell on papers ready for him to sign, where familiar faces of men and women turned to one another and talked about him, not knowing that a man named Destin had dissolved a partnership with abrupt violence. Turner was utterly shaken—he had liked to be with Destin, had secretly admired Destin's strength and his adventurous life. Now Turner was only two eyes and two nostrils in a black liquid world because he had put funds with Destin in a beef-cattle venture on a large island near Nassau—a plausible-looking experiment, a joint account with some cautious safeguard. Cautions against everything except one big thing that had never occurred to Turner: that he should suddenly be dead and it would all belong to Destin. The familiar faces wouldn't know about that, or that Destin had suggested this quiet side trip to see a wreck that might hold a treasure.

George Turner thought the night grew a little brighter, and trod water to stare eastward where the moon rose full. He searched the horizon for an island he thought might be there, and saw nothing but the silver path of the moon across the water. He then sobbed suddenly, and wanted to scream and claw at the water and go down, swallow water and fill his lungs and have the thing over—and told himself to go on pushing with his hands, and that all these islands were very low.

A new and startling sound came through the water that so quietly lapped and patted around his face. It was a slashing noise, like canvas being ripped, of something coming toward him very fast, and Turner went rigid, though trembling violently. In his rigidity his feet sank down until he was almost upright, and then, the slashing coming very close to him, he screamed and beat his arms and legs and tried to climb out of the water. He fought himself into exhaustion, and then saw the moonlight glisten on the shining black hides of a school of porpoise leaping and diving past him.

After that Turner was very tired. He rested on his back, his hands moving as if they belonged to someone else, his eyes on the star and his head toward the low moon, until he heard another sound ahead of him. This was a gurgling, rather rhythmical and musical sound. He trod water to look, and found his feet standing on sand.

Through a lapping froth he went ashore

on the island, which was one of the three he had seen within several miles while he slashed the halyards; and this was undoubtedly the one to the eastward.

The island was about three quarters of a mile long, and half as wide, and a broad rim of sandy beach ran all around it. Turner followed the beach, walking to get warm—the breeze chill on his wet skin—until he came to his own footprints again. So low was the island that, under the bright moon, he could see across it from beach to beach. In the middle were tufts of wiry grass and one low clump of bushes. That might shade a man who crawled into it; that might make a hideaway, if a man could hide at the end of a track of footprints. Some sea birds went up with crazy screams as Turner walked among nests. Here was food, when a man began to starve. The thicket was thorny, and he went back to the beach. He lay on the warm sand and pulled it over him like a blanket.

Along the windward beach stretched a snake of sea grasses and kelp. Turner heaved up out of the sand and prowled carefully. A heavy timber of ship's deadwood, studded with rusted spikes, lay rooted in the beach. Here and there was some odd useless thing, dropped off a steamer long ago and perhaps hundreds of miles away. An electric light bulb. Three rum bottles. A little vial that had held someone's tonic, or vitamin pills. Turner snatched up four coconuts and shook each at his ear, hoping to hear a liquid thud inside. Each was light, empty, dry as an old skull, and he flung it down.

Something round and big crawled out of the sea, moved patiently up the beach, and began to settle into the sand. A sea turtle, feeling the pressure of eggs. A man could eat, now and then, on this island. He could roof over some bushes with seaweed. Likely he could get a fire for cooking, with water in a curved shoulder of a bottle to make a burning glass. He might even unravel a fishing line out of his clothes. He could get himself some scraps of food. But there wasn't any water.

Turner broke a bottle on a spike and began to dig near the bushes. Below the sand was a crumbling coral rock that became harder, then too hard. He imagined dampness in the bottom of the hole. He decided it was only cooler than the surface sand.

Turner began to arrange seaweed into letters ten paces long on the beach. Sea draped its grasses in slow twists along the sand. The angular lines of H E L P would show better than S O S from the air. Someday someone in a plane would go over; perhaps a sportsman, making a wide swing, then circling and staring at a big word H E L P. Turner began another message for the man who came down to investigate, if the man came too late. In small letters he traced out *Armstrong Destin killed George Turner*, and began to build up the letters with shells, into ridges. But now the moon was dropping low, and the night turned darker. He lay down to wait for daylight.

When the sun came up, Destin's sails were a fluttering white tent two miles away. The sloop was anchored off a sandy key. The little white dinghy moved to the beach. It was hard for Turner to follow the dinghy at that distance, and Destin he could hardly see at all—a small black mark on the sand. The dinghy moved off the beach. The sloop began to sail. Destin was looking over the few near-by islands before he sailed away, rowing in and glancing about for footprints. And now he sailed toward Turner's island.

Turner fell on the sand and beat it with his fists. He poured out hoarse curses at the boat. A man might try to hide. But it would be at the end of a plain trail. Turner stared at the sloop, the fat curve of sail, the white curl round the bow, with wincing eyes. He was a thin brown animal with a leg caught in a trap of sand, watching the hunter come. He sat down in the middle of the island and pushed up a sand wall around him, like a breastwork. It was a fort but with no defense. His pith helmet and his face were fixed still above it as he watched the sloop grow, the jib coming distinct from the mainsail, the figure of Destin standing up. The sloop held food and water. Turner remembered just where they were: the canned goods, the crate of fruit, the big galvanized tank beneath the deck. The cigarettes, the bottles of rum. They were all only a quarter of a mile away when Destin dropped the sails. The anchor made a brief white splash.

The dinghy trailed behind the sloop. Destin jumped down into it and began to row, turned his head, and pulled the oars harder. Destin knew. Turner watched the powerful back and arms move with the blades, and when the head did not turn again, Turner knew that Destin was very sure of himself. Destin would speak to him quite calmly. Destin might say, "Sorry, old man. You've only managed to string the thing out." He would be calm and steady with the pistol.

String the thing out. But if he strung it out, he would die of thirst. All that Destin really had to do was to sit on his boat and let him die. Turner saw that he must try to be calm and conserve his strength. He had an emptiness in his stomach that wasn't really hunger, and he hadn't yet so very much thirst. The day was brightening beautifully, the sea sparkling, the breeze cool, the sky very blue and the clouds very white above him and Destin.

Turner slipped out of the back of his sand pit, and on the far beach filled a bottle with sea water. The splash over his hands and wrists, the water round his ankles, made him more conscious of the dryness in his throat. He went in a crouch along the beach until the clump of bushes was between him and the dinghy. Into the dry hole he had dug, he emptied the bottle. The water stood still for a moment, and then began to seep away. Turner filled the bottle again on the beach, and crawled back into his pit.

He sat up and looked over the top at Destin, who now was pulling the dinghy up on the sand.

"Destin!" he called.

Destin looked toward him briefly, without reply. He had seen the big word on the sand. He walked around it deliberately and cast a slow look round the sky. Evidently he came to the smaller message that Turner had started, for his feet made some measured kicks and sent up spurts of sand. Then with wide sweeps of his legs he went through the letters H E L P, driving the letters out of shape. Taking the revolver out of his trousers, he walked toward Turner. He called, "Good morning!"

Turner was not much exposed in his sand pit, only his head up, a glint of sunlight on his glasses, and his legs were tense under him. A hundred yards and no closer, he thought—about the length of a football field. He got up and began to walk away from Destin. He carried the bottle of sea water like a precious thing. Destin fired. Then they were both running.

Turner thought he could hold his own with Destin in running, though he was much less of a man in every other way. But he was lighter, and in Pittsburgh he had liked to play tennis. He saw some flicks in the sand ahead, and counted the shots until there were six. He looked back, and Destin was not so close as he had been. The distance had opened very definitely. Destin stopped, taking a box from his pocket, and reloaded.

Destin sat down. Turner was quite out of breath himself, and so he lay on the sand, pulling a heap up under his shoulders for a head rest, to relax as comfortably as he could. A hundred yards was a very long revolver shot. It called for luck, even if the target stood still.

There had been a box of cartridges beside the gun on the shelf, and a box held twenty-five. Two or three had been fired at a shark. Perhaps there was another box.

Destin had a white bandage on his arm. Turner could not be sure at the distance, but he thought there was a red streak across his face, the nose swollen, where the reel had struck. Destin's broad shoulders heaved slowly as he rested, watching Turner. Turner held the bottle at his mouth, and did not swallow. Even the motion made his throat drier. Destin stood up to glare at him with both hands on hips, and then looked at the clump of bushes, as the only likely place for water.

When Destin walked away, Turner ran toward the dinghy. The attempt was hopeless, as Destin had kept himself closer to the boat. But it made Destin sprint for an instant, and fire another shot. Destin pushed the dinghy out and rowed along the beach, and Turner walked beside him, though across a wide reach of sand. Turner saw now that he might make it difficult for Destin to go far from his boat. At least he could give Destin a problem to solve.

Destin saw the problem, too, when he pulled in to the beach abreast of the low thicket. Turner watched him from a hundred yards away. Destin chased him up the beach, shot three times, and one of the bullets made a hiss. Then Destin walked toward the bushes. Turner ran back toward the dinghy. Destin ran back, too.

The thicket was at least two hundred yards from the beach. Destin took the oars from the boat, and started again. And Turner's heart leaped, hoping that Destin would rely on having the oars. He slipped toward the dinghy as Destin left it, thinking he could push it ahead of him by swimming, get into it and paddle with his hands. Destin came back on a run, but clumsily, because it was difficult to run with the oars, and fired a long shot.

Turner thought that Destin must be very angry. Destin sat near the boat a while. Then he shoved it off, and rowed toward his sloop.

Lifting the bottle again, Turner walked to the thicket. He stopped at the hole he had dug. He might have felt some elation at baffling Destin, but now he felt only an aching thirst. He had thought that Destin might examine the hole, feel some dampness, and wonder. But Destin could not approach the place. Turner poured the water over his face and chest, and noticed that Destin had stopped rowing. He shoved the bottle down into the dry hole, and then walked with it toward some sea-bird nests.

Eggs held moisture. A score of birds wheeled and screamed and dived at Turner, who carried a dozen eggs to his sand pit in his helmet.

He cracked two together, finding one liquid, and swallowed it, with fingers closed over his nose. But he retched; the egg came up. Then he remembered the mound, the scuffed place, the turtle had left. He dug with his hands. The leathery skin of eggs broke in his teeth with a relieving wet salve. He covered the place carefully and marked it with a shell. He stuffed wiry grass into his mouth, and it made a tough chewing gum.

Turner lay in the edge of the water. A man could not evaporate so much water when he was immersed, and perhaps he would absorb a little. The constant lapping and bubbling was maddening.

After a time he went back to the wreckage of his word. The sand was very hot, and it was fortunate he had his sandals. The heat soared round him in shimmering bands. On the sloop Destin was undoubtedly eating, drinking and having a smoke, training his binoculars on Turner. When Turner had raked the seaweed all into ridges again, and the letters were sharp on bare sand, and when he had walked around it in final perusal, Destin rowed ashore.

Turner watched over the rim of his sand pit while Destin struck a match. The seaweed was mostly dry, though some was still green. But there was plenty more of it, rolling in the edge of the water. The seaweed burned. But it sent up a thickening smudge, like a windrow of hay flaming and smoldering, trailing off the key like steamer smoke. Destin did not like that. He kicked the fire apart, flung sand on it, and kicked a path through the remaining letters.

"Are you here again?" called Turner. "Then let's play another set."

He seemed very calm, waiting for Destin. But the calm was a weakness, a dizziness of heat and thirst. He let Destin come almost too close, or the shot was lucky. It tossed sand up into Turner's face. It buried in the low sand wall just in front of his chest, and Turner jumped up and ran.

Two other shots passed him. When he glanced back, Destin was hammering after him, his face dark, running at a strong, ruthless gait, driving his legs with a will power that was ready to run his heart out. Turner couldn't leave him, though he had panic in his body. The distance closed a little. It was very hard to run in sand, sinking to the ankles, gulping air that was too hot to ease the lungs. He was almost ready to fling himself down when another shot sounded. He turned his head. Destin had stopped. Destin aimed at him, emptied the revolver, sat down to rock his head and body slowly, to open his mouth like a fish.

Turner was relieved that Destin sat for such a long while before he tried to approach again. Turner tilted the mockery of a bottle, stood up with an appearance of lightness, and walked away. Destin left the beach to Turner. Destin took the center of the ring, and the center was too small for them both. He kept Turner moving round the rim—Turner taking two and three steps to his one—trying to pin him in one spot against the sea. There was little running, except when Turner had to make quick spurts to hold his distance. Turner's head and eyeballs ached, and at times his legs stumbled; but whenever there was an appearance of a chance, or whenever Destin wanted to rest, he moved doggedly toward the boat. Once

Destin roared in rage, and at last he went to the shore and sat in the stern of the dinghy.

Turner lay in the water once more, rolling his burned face under, filling his mouth and blowing it out, and soaking some coolness into his skin. The water bottle was hot. He immersed it to cool. He could get through today. He had had luck against Destin, but tomorrow he could not escape. Tomorrow he would be too weak; he would collapse on the burning sand.

Destin slid the dinghy to sea. Turner sat up and felt the temperature of his bottle, and put it to his mouth.

"Turner!" shouted Destin. "See you tomorrow!"

Turner called back, "Sweet dreams!"

What was the ruse for tonight? he wondered. Would Destin come ashore, trying to catch him asleep? Would he risk leaving the dinghy on the moonlit beach while he searched? Turner considered whether he should himself try to swim out, whether he had the strength—a fly crawling to a spider. Destin would get himself a little drunk tonight, and scowl at the moon and the island. Only one thing was certain. Destin dared not leave.

The sun had not yet gone down. Turner looked around the empty sky, and began to restore his word on the beach.

At daybreak Destin rowed in to the seaweed printing. He kicked out the bellies of the letters once more, but with a difference in his motions this time, not swinging his arms with the violence of his kicks, but keeping a hand behind his back in concealment from the sand pit. Then he made his steps casually slow, as if a long day were ahead and there was no need for haste. The hand remained behind him in a careless way, while he walked toward the defenseless breastwork. Once he stopped to yawn.

Turner saw that the slow approach had taken Destin a little closer to the sand pit than usual.

Turner saw this, from a comfortable distance, when he emerged from the sand and raised himself through the seaweed in the end of one leg of the letter H.

Turner saw Destin kneel and aim at the helmet, with the glint of spectacles beneath it, and fire. Destin had lashed some kind of stock to the revolver, that nestled snugly like a rifle butt into his shoulder, and evidently greatly increased the accuracy of his aim. For the helmet, the glasses, rolled down out of sight. Turner supposed that there was a hole right through the skull-dry coconut.

The dinghy was only a few steps away, and as Turner pushed it out he saw that Destin was running, in triumph at last, to the sand pit.

An uncontrollable shivering ran over Turner as he rowed. But he wasn't cold—each grain of sand and fleck of seaweed touched a nerve end in his burned skin. But this was from the hours of waiting.

The water in the sloop's tank was warm, yet it had a deliciousness, and ecstatic seep of life in his parched throat. Turner reminded himself not to drink too much at once. He went on deck to raise the jib, because that was the easy sail. The jib would move the boat sufficiently until he had eaten and drunk enough strength into himself to hoist the mainsail. The windlass was heavy enough work for now, and he did not trouble to bring the anchor all the way up. The sloop began to move.

Turner would conscientiously report Destin at the first chance, he decided, though it might be a few days, and the government could send out a plane to rescue him and let him explain. And if Destin grew too impatient with his thirst, then—Turner's trembling ceased of a sudden—Destin had a gun.

Turner drank another glass of water, sipping each wonderful drop, and sucked the juices out of a spaodilla plum, and presently looked at the island through the binoculars. He regretted his glasses, but the binoculars focused clearly.

The plane would be able to find Destin, because Destin had an armful of seaweed and was restoring the big word H E L P on the beach.

Long-Distance Call

Jack Finney

Jack Finney (who also wrote "Contents of the Dead Man's Pocket," P. 547) can spin a yarn of breathtaking suspense, or, as here, a light-hearted tale out of the endless drama of men-and-women. In each case, he follows no formula but his own.

November 8, 1948

LYING ON THE DAVENPORT, HIS STOCKING feet up on the cushions, Mr. Timberlake Ryan lowered his magazine to his lap. He narrowed his eyes, one black brow raised, then he grinned maliciously.

He stood up, tall and thin, unplugged the small ivory radio on the table beside him and carried it out to the desk in the hall, setting it down beside the telephone. He plugged it in, and turned the dial till he found some dance music, a hot slow-pulsed trumpet solo. He turned the volume down low, and picked up the phone.

"I want to call Philadelphia, Operator. Person to person; Mrs. Eve Ryan," and gave her a number. While he waited, he turned up the radio and the music poured out, high pure notes in a slow steady beat. Tim rolled his eyes and his shoulders to the rhythm, dancing a few steps with the phone.

"Here's your party," sang the operator presently.

"Hello?" his wife's far-off voice said questioningly, and he could see her in his mind, small and blond, her blue eyes disturbed at the long-distance call. "Hello—Tim?"

He stooped, bringing the mouthpiece of the phone closer to the moaning radio. "H'lo," he said, and his speech, now, was faintly blurred. "H'lo, Eve? This Tim. H'are you?" He glanced into the wall mirror; his jaw hung slack, his eyes were wide and vacant, in unconscious imitation of the foolish expression of a drunk. He grinned.

"Hello, darling," she said eagerly. "I *thought* you might call tonight. How are you?"

He turned up the volume of the radio still more. "Fine," he said, "fine. Frilldig happystace."

"What? Tim, I can't hear you; what's that music? Where are you, Tim?"

"Here," he said. "At this place. 'M here at this place. I called you up."

"Place?" said Eve. "What place?"

Get your coat and . . . get your . . . hat, the brassy notes wailed. "Freggis," said Tim. "Freggis ellyget. Here at this place. All my money gone."

"*What* place? Tim, I can hardly make out a word you're saying!"

"Wait," he said. "Wait'll I close phone booth door here." He turned down the radio a little. "Hear me?" he said. "Hear me now? Closed door phone booth."

"That's better. Tim, what's the m—"

He turned up the volume suddenly and raised his voice angrily, holding the phone away from his mouth. "Le'go my arm!" He turned down the radio and spoke quietly, forlornly, into the phone. "Can't seem find my money. Lost. All gone. Won't le'me outta here. Here't this place. Freggis. Freggis happystace."

"*What* place!" she said, annoyed finally. "Tim, what's the *matter* with you! Where *are* you?"

"Home," he said in a perfectly clear distinct tone. He turned down the radio and spoke as though he were surprised at Eve's question. "I'm here at home listening to the radio? Why? Where'd you think I'd be?"

There was a silence at the other end of the line for a moment, then Eve spoke quietly. "I'll murder you," she said. "I will positively kill you the moment I get home."

"And when's that going to be?" he said softly. He grinned. "It better be soon. You can see the risks you're running; I'll fall in with evil companions. When you coming home?" he said.

"What's the matter?" He could tell she was smiling. "You getting lonesome?"

"No, I'm having a wonderful time." He laughed suddenly, a high-pitched giggle. "Cut it out!" he yelled. He turned away from the phone and spoke in a hoarse rapid whisper. "Quit tickling me! Get back in bed; you'll catch cold!" He spoke into the phone again. "No, I'm not lonesome at all."

"Well, in that case I can stay another week."

"No; better not."

"Why?"

"Weeds are growing in the corners, birds are nesting in piles of old newspapers —eagles, I think—and quack grass is springing up on the bedroom floor. A few more days and the place'll get away from me. You better come home. Maybe tomorrow? How's your sister, by the way; and her child recidivists?"

"Child what?"

"Recidivists."

"What's that mean?"

"Incurable criminals."

"Oh, the kids are fine. The whole family's fine; we're having a wonderful visit. Tim"—her voice was serious, concerned—"what are you doing?"

"Nothing. Just lying around. Reading."

"What'd you do last night?"

"Same. The Leggetts called me, for some bridge. But I didn't feel like it."

"Well, Tim, I wish you'd *do* something. I hate the thought of you all alone, not doing anything, or having any fun. Did you have a good dinner?"

"Yes, I found some bread; moldy on the outside, but not bad inside. And some dried-up cheese—"

"No, really, Tim. Did you eat out?"

"Yeah, a fine dinner."

"Well, I really wish you'd get out of the apartment and *do* something. It's early yet; just nine o'clock. And it's Friday night."

"Do what? Go to some lousy movie? Or do you want me to make a tour of the night clubs?"

"Yes," she said firmly, "that's exactly what I wish you *would* do."

"By myself?"

"No," she said judiciously, and paused, considering. "Why don't you call Nancy Blatchford? She'd love to hear from you, I know. And she'd love to go."

"Nancy, is it?" His voice was interested. "That's quite a girl you've picked for me. Think you can trust me?"

"I think so," she said dryly. "Tim, why don't you call her? She's a very good dancer."

"So are you," he said brusquely, "and if you'll come home here tomorrow, I can go out with my own wife. Regular old Saturday-night stuff; a real celebration. How about that?" He guessed what her answer was going to be and as she replied, he twisted the dial of the radio rapidly till he found what he was looking for.

"I'll be home," said Eve. "I'm taking the seven seventeen in the morning."

Tim turned the volume on full, brought the phone up to the radio; a burst of applause sprang from the speaker. "That's the reaction in New York," he said, "to your very intelligent decision." His voice lowered. "Night, honey," he said softly. "I'll be waiting for you." . . .

Tim lay on the davenport again, his magazine in his lap. He had tried to resume his reading and given it up. Now more than ever, after his phone call to Eve he was weary of being alone, tired of the silent apartment. He lighted a cigarette and lay back again, facing the windows, looking at the night outside, and aware of a curious resentment, a feeling of irritation at something, he didn't know what.

He got up, walked to the windows, and stood looking down at the moving lights of the cars streaming past. As he watched, the lights changed and from a waiting car directly below, he heard the clear soft music of a radio; a girl singing, quietly, sadly. The cars started up again and rolled on, the radio music fading, and it seemed to him that in all the city only he was alone; that everyone else was on the move outside his windows on the way to fun and excitement.

Eve's suggestion came to his mind, suddenly, like a good idea. He *would* like to get out of this empty apartment; to go dancing, and hear some music at firsthand. It was a good night for it, the right *kind* of night, and he wondered if Nancy would be surprised if he should call. She was pleasant, good-looking; a young widow, bright and vivacious, and they both liked her. Should I call? he thought, and knew he was going to, and he turned, walked out to the hall, looked up her number and dialed.

But before her phone could ring, he broke the connection and stood, holding the telephone, surprised at himself, and aware of a puzzling growing sense of excitement. Suddenly he understood his vague irritation for a few moments before. He was annoyed, he realized, that his wife should trust him so completely. That without a qualm or worry, and far from home, she should blithely send him out into the city and select his companion for him besides; a young, attractive, almost beautiful woman at that.

A tame duck on a string, that's me, he thought, and now another name entered his mind. It had been there, in fact, for quite some time he realized; Ginnie, Virginia Haley. And now he understood his growing excitement. For Ginnie—he'd met her at an office party some months before, a free-lance commercial artist, intelligent, smartly dressed, and, he remembered, an excellent dancer—Ginnie was a very attractive girl. Well, he thought, a little defiantly, Nancy, Ginnie; what's the difference? But he knew there was a difference, and that the difference was this: Ginnie was a girl Eve had never seen, whose existence, in fact, she wasn't even aware of. Ginnie's name was in the book and she answered the call.

And when presently Ginnie said yes, she would like to go dancing, Tim's hand, holding a cigarette, was trembling a little. Once again he felt the old almost-forgotten excitement of going out with a new girl. And when later he walked through the cool night air toward the garage for his car, hatless and wearing a tuxedo, he felt elated. . . .

The evening began just right. They sat in a quiet and nearly empty bar, in the lull before the theaters closed, and talking leisurely nonsense, took time to become reacquainted. Ginnie, her hair blue-black, eyes shining, her skin very white against her vivid gown, was even more attractive than Tim remembered.

"I drove down from New Haven this afternoon," he said, "in an open car, cutting my last class in English Lit." He grinned and took a sip of his drink. "I borrowed my roommate's tuxedo, and all I need now is a crew haircut."

Ginnie smiled, a slow sweet smile. "It was hardly worth while," she said. "I have to be back in the girls' dorm at twelve."

"Not tonight." Tim shook his head. "Call up and say you're staying with a cousin."

"You know what happened to the last girl who did that."

"She has no diploma, it's true, but she's the proud mother of a happy family. You know"—Tim smiled—"when I *was* a kid at school, there was a boy, no older than the rest of us though he seemed to be, who dated, quote, an older woman in New York. She was all of twenty-five, an artist, too, as I recall, and a very smart and glamorous creature. We looked up to that boy; he had our respect." Tim smiled and looked at Ginnie admiringly. "If they could only see me now."

"Yes," said Ginnie, "now you, too, are a debonair man of the world." She studied him for a moment. "Your roommate's tuxedo fits you very well. I like them. Men should wear them more often."

"No." Tim looked down at the black coat and fingered one shiny lapel. "Too funeral. I always have the feeling when I put one on that I should lie down, fold my hands, and wait for people to tiptoe in, look at me sadly, and murmur, 'It's what he would have wanted.' "

"What is?"

"I don't know." He shrugged a shoulder, grinning. "Yes, I do. I want a plum-colored coat with silver buttons. People had the right idea a hundred and fifty years ago; they knew how to dress. I have always wanted a tricornered hat and a wardrobe of coats, plum-colored, bottle-green, sky-blue. All with big silver buttons."

"And knee breeches?"

"No, my legs are too skinny."

"I think they wore padding."

"Mine would slip, I know; probably at a reception for General Washington. I have trouble that way; I'm always losing a garter. No, I'll settle for the coats, with pants to match. Maybe I'll carry a porcelain snuffbox. And if I have to wear a wig, okay."

"Don't do that." Ginnie rattled the ice cubes in her glass, and took a sip of her drink. "You have very nice hair."

"I have?" Tim grinned. "That's wonderful. Keep it up; nothing I like better than good honest flattery."

Ginnie raised her brows. "Even the refugees from English Lit, Mr. Ryan, know that the man usually flatters the girl. It's a very old custom, particularly among the silver-button knee-breeches set."

"I know," Tim said, "but it's really too easy in your case. Starting, however, with what I can see, your hair is a spun mist of shimmering ebony."

Ginnie nodded, judiciously, approvingly. "Go on. That's pretty good."

"It is, isn't it?" Tim raised his brows appreciatively. "Your lips," he continued, "are marvelous, of course, and so"—he leaned back on the bar stool—"are your hips. Your—"

"Okay," said Ginnie, "maybe we'd better take it easy on the flattery for a while until you get used to it."

They ordered another drink, and Tim felt good; relaxed and at ease, enjoying himself. He was aware once or twice, as they continued to talk, that Ginnie glanced at him speculatively, and he knew that she liked him and was having fun, and the evening stretched ahead in his mind full of promise and pleasure.

They sat for an hour or more, and discovered, after a time, that both of them loved to rumba. And presently, when the bar began to fill, they drove leisurely across toward a place Tim knew of where the rumba was played and danced, exclusively and expertly.

The place was small, dim, low-ceilinged, and the air was bad. Tables lined both walls at which couples, facing outward, sat side by side on red-leather wall seats. Other tables filled the space between, jammed together from the entrance to the very edge of the dance floor. And the floor itself was packed.

But the music was right; they seemed actually to feel it beating softly against the surface of their bodies as they moved to its rhythm, overridden and ruled by the dry surflike monotony of the whispering *maracas* . . . beat-beat-beat-beat, beat-beat, an excited audible pulse.

All over the floor, heads—eyes lost in rhythm—seemed hardly to move. But just below, shoulders swayed slightly; at a lower level, hips rolled with more abandon, and lower still, knees pumped rapidly; while down at the floor, toes darted and heels shot out, raising and clicking on the polished wood in a precise and disciplined frenzy.

They sat down, Ginnie shaking her head and exhaling slowly in a parody of weariness, smiling at Tim. Tim smiled back and they turned and watched the dancers in a relaxed communion of silence, time flowing past unnoticed, meaningless. Presently Ginnie turned to Tim again and spoke.

"I'm having fun," she said softly, "really fun. I haven't liked anything so much for a very long time."

"So am I," said Tim, and he paused, thinking, rubbing at the moisture on the side of his glass. "You know," he said, "I have the feeling that there is a little group of us tonight in New York who are having a particularly happy time. The hours go and we hardly notice it, moving from one place to another, our paths crossing and recrossing, and for us, the true initiates, it's going to go on forever. The sun may rise for everyone else, people may go to work again in nonexistent office buildings, but for us it will still be nighttime and fun. You believe that?"

"Of course," said Ginnie, and her face was serious, her eyes wide, staring at her own thoughts. "It's so obvious that I will never again see another newspaper. Or pay a gas bill. Or drop a coin in a turnstile, or get up in the morning. Those things are part of another shadowy world not possibly strong enough to overcome this one." She turned her eyes to Tim again, smiled, and added, "If you know what I mean."

"Precisely," said Tim. He swallowed the last of his drink, looked at her and grinned. "The conversation after two in the morning is always beautifully lucid and filled with diamond clear subtleties perfectly expressed and instantly understood. It's always seemed a shame to me that they can't quite be recalled in the confused thinking of daylight."

The music began again, one of the band members singing in high wistful Spanish, and they listened. Then, after a time, they danced once more. Tim wondered as they moved to the tight rattle of the gourds, whether their dancing and the music were really as fine as they seemed. He decided they were, or at least if they weren't, that he didn't care. But when finally the music ended again, he had had, he felt, enough. They had been there a long time and he wanted to move, now, to go on to something else, and when they reached their table again, he knew what it was.

"Know what I'd like?" he said to Ginnie. "If you feel like it. I'd like to drive in Central Park, right about now. Slowly, and with the top down. That sound like anything to you?"

"Yes," said Ginnie, "I'd like to. I think it's time to feel real air on my face again. I can't really believe there are trees any more, and I'd like to find out." She rose and Tim stood up with her. "Be back in five minutes," she said. "Maybe ten."

Tim sat down at their table to wait, listening to the music, humming the tune under his breath, and feeling, he was aware, not merely good but cocky; pleased and somehow triumphant.

He felt a sudden impulse to phone Eve. He got up and began moving through the crowded tables toward the phone booths outside. He knew that on Eve's last night, even at this hour, they'd probably all be up, still talking, and that he wouldn't be disturbing them; but he wondered why he should be making this call. He was having a good time and he wanted to communicate something of this, to share it with Eve, he told himself, and he knew this was true. But it wasn't the whole truth, and he knew that, too, and he grinned.

He grinned again when Eve answered the phone. "This Tim," he said. " 'M at this place. This place here—"

"Now, cut it out," she said. "What is it this time?"

"Well," he said quietly, his mouth close to the phone, "I just didn't want you to worry about me, so I thought I'd better tell you that I'm out at a night club with a beautiful woman."

"Oh, that's *good,* Tim," she said, and he knew that she thought so. "With Nancy?"

"No," he said casually. "I didn't call Nancy." He paused for a moment. "Well," he continued, "I don't want to keep you. I just didn't want you to worry. See you tomorrow. 'By."

"Wait, Tim! Tim, you still there?"

"Yes," he said. "What is it?"

"Well—"

"Yes?"

"Nothing," she said. "I—I'm—glad you're having fun."

"I certainly am," he said, and grinned wickedly. "This was a wonderful idea—of yours. Well, I'll see you in the morning. 'By, honey," he said pleasantly, casually.

"Goodby," said Eve, and her voice, he thought, seemed a little wistful.

When he returned to their table, Ginnie was waiting.

"I was phoning my wife," he told her. "My trouble is that my wife understands me."

"That's bad, Tim," said Ginnie, and she produced a small mirror from her handbag.

"It is," said Tim. "I told her I was out with a beautiful woman; thought I'd make her jealous. But I'm afraid, all in all, that she thinks it's just dandy. She trusts me, you see; Old Faithful Tim. Naturally, a man resents that, and it means, of course, that I've got to do something about it. I've got to do my damnedest to seduce you."

"Naturally," said Ginnie. With a little finger, she began smoothing the lipstick on her lower lip, held taut against her teeth, and staring intently into her mirror. "But I don't think I can be of much assistance," she said abstractedly. She folded her lips inward for a moment, pressing them tightly together, then studied the result in her mirror. "Certainly not just to help a man, no matter how attractive, get even with his wife."

"You see?" said Tim mournfully. "It's true; my wife is right. I don't even know *how* to get into trouble!"

Their tone was frivolous, light; Tim was joking, so was Ginnie, and both of them knew it. And yet, Tim realized, he was enjoying it very much and remembering other times, before he was married, when he hadn't been joking at all. And he wondered if he were entirely pretending now. He should, he thought, change the tenor of their conversation, yet he was reluctant to end it. Instead, he looked around for their waiter, saw him making his way to their table, and he waited, leaning back in his chair, his eyes on the man until he arrived. Tim paid the check, left a tip, then turned back to Ginnie. He looked at her for a moment, gravely. "To the park?" he said, and Ginnie nodded and smiled and got up. . . . .

Outside, it was suddenly very late. It looked late, smelled late, the city asleep now, almost competely, in the one deep hour of the twenty-four in which it nearly achieves a silence. Fifth Avenue was dark and empty; they could hear the sound of their tires on the pavement. They turned, presently, into the park, surrounded by the city, to hear the occasional chirp of a bird. The car moved slowly, almost driving itself over the winding roadway, and they saw a squirrel dart over the road in the dim beam of their headlights.

The radio was on, tuned very low, the air moved softly, coolly, over their faces and through their hair, and overhead in dim circles of lamplight as they passed. It seemed natural that Tim, one hand resting on the wheel of the car, hardly needing to guide it, should have his other arm around Ginnie's shoulders.

They drove for a time in silence, hearing the radio, enjoying the night, following the road where it took them. Sometimes they passed the same spot twice, at other times the car turned into new stretches of roadway, under the trees. They crossed tiny bridges, they passed a lagoon, and presently the road curved, passed through a low stone wall, and the car was in a street, quiet and empty, beside the park. Tim lifted his arm, put the car out of gear, and it coasted slowly and stopped, under a low overhanging tree, beside the stone wall of the park. He shut off the motor, turned to Ginnie, as she turned to him, and he kissed her.

He drew back, then, and looked at her; she was very lovely, her face tender, smiling softly.

Tim looked at her for a moment but said nothing, then he kissed her again, slowly. He liked it; very much; and when he drew back again finally, he looked at her almost fiercely, scowling a little, as he leaned back against the leather of the cushion. He picked up her hand lying on the seat beside him and looked at it, his thumb running gently over her knuckles. "You're a very special girl, Ginnie," he said, and she looked at him, smiling, but didn't answer. "Let's drive for a minute," Tim said, and he turned on the key and started the car.

They moved ahead, westward, very slowly, Tim's foot not touching the accelerator. He turned for a moment and looked at Ginnie. "I don't know where this car thinks it's going," he said. "Shall I give it its head?"

"Might try it," said Ginnie. "It's a very smart car."

"But eccentric," said Tim. "It does the damnedest things."

They stopped at a lonely traffic light and Tim spoke again, staring ahead through the windshield. "Are you tired?"

"No," said Ginnie. "I should be but I'm not."

The light changed but Tim didn't move. "You can sleep in the afternoon, can't you?" He glanced up at the sky, already graying. "It's going to be a nice morning; no time for sleeping."

"That's right," said Ginnie, "it isn't."

"Then look." Tim turned to face her. "I don't know how you'll feel about this." He hesitated and looked away toward the floor.

"What is it?" she said gently. "I have a feeling I know and that I'm going to say yes, but I want to be sure."

"Please tell me, if you aren't interested, but"—he turned and looked at Ginnie again—"I'd like to go and pick up Eve; drive straight on to Philadelphia. There's time before her train leaves." He smiled at her now, and raised his brows appealingly. "And I'd like you to come along."

Ginnie smiled back. "Long-distance call," she murmured, "in more ways than one. That's what I thought you had in mind"—she looked at him, amused—"and I think I knew it before you did. Let's do," she said. "I'd like to."

"Good," said Tim, and started the car up, driving through the light westward toward the Hudson.

And that morning, on the road to New York, a filling-station attendant, a Good Humor man and the waitress at a roadside restaurant each wondered for the rest of the day about the car driven by the man wearing a tuxedo and accompanied by two girls, a brunette in a striking evening dress and a petite blonde in a tweed traveling suit, all of them laughing, very hilarious, all of them having a very good time.

What You Owe Your Country

General Omar N. Bradley

Years before the first Sputnik jolted Americans into an awareness of certain flaws in the way we were training our youth for citizenship, a great soldier and statesman, Omar N. Bradley, was pondering the problem. In the light of all that has been learned since, no man today could analyze the problem more lucidly than did General Bradley in this article written in 1949. General Bradley led troops in World War II as a Corps, Army, and Army Group commander, became Chief of Staff in 1949, was appointed General of the Armies in 1950, holds honorary degrees from many universities and high decorations from many countries.

February 26, 1949

EVEN IN JUNE THE CHANNEL WATERS were icy as I splashed through the life-belt-littered surf and scrambled aboard the landing craft. Its Diesels shuddered as the helmsman—a stocky, frowning youngster in wet-weather gear—coaxed his clumsy boat from the beach and headed toward the line of ships offshore.

By noon on this second day on Omaha Beach, we had cracked the German crust and were pushing into the hedgerows. Now, with a marked map under my arm, I was hitching a ride back to headquarters. Offshore in deep water a thin-skinned PT boat waited to carry me out to the cruiser Augusta.

On the wet open bottom of our tiny craft a dozen litters had been loaded. And on those litters a dozen wounded youngsters lay wrapped in blankets already soggy from the spray. All of them in their raw twenties, they lay quiet, uncomplaining, awaiting transfer to a hospital ship.

Ten years before, when the German guns that had torn their bodies were being heralded by the booming mobs of Munich, those 12 youngsters were in knee pants, wandering through a depression toward their rendezvous on Omaha Beach. And while their parents struggled uncomprehendingly through the fear and uncertainty of that economic storm, their generation was being rudely hustled from adolescence into a war.

There I remember, in the pitching bottom of that nameless craft lay the fragments of a generation rashly condemned for having been "corrupted" by the ease of democracy and "debased" by the luxury of freedom. But those 12 men had learned on D-Day—as hideously as man can learn—that freedom is not free, that democracy can exact stern repayment from those who share in its bounty.

In time of war, the competitive struggle that powers a free society such as ours is enveloped by common danger. Just as life is held most dear by the man who faces death, so are the institutions of a free nation cherished most jealously when they are threatened by aggression. Confronted by war, the American people scamper hastily home to the fundamental realization that it shall profit a man nothing to gain possessions, knowledge and power if he loses the freedom in which they are rooted.

But when danger has passed and our enemies at last lie crushed, the individual once more asserts his priority claim to self-interest. The right to profit, the right to get more, obscures the war-born realization that an individual's welfare is plainly tied to the welfare of his nation. We quickly forget that if freedom is to produce security as well as the bountiful life, then its roots must be continuously nourished by sacrifice, devotion and service.

Because of the exaggerated emphasis we have attached to the omnipotence of the dollar, too many of us have already accepted the dangerous illusion that we can buy off our responsibilities as citizens in the payment of taxes.

A nation's strength is not to be found in its treasury statements. It lies instead in the national character of its people, in their willingness to sacrifice leisure, comfort, and a share of their talents for the welfare of the nation of which they are part.

Self-government is not a luxury on which men may grow fat and indulgent. Rather it is an instrument by which men can—if they have the wisdom—safeguard their individual freedom and employ that freedom in pursuit of happiness and fair reward for their ingenuity, labor and intellect. Because self-government is an instrument which demands unceasingly the services, the energies, the participation of those who would benefit by it, self-government is weighted as heavily with obligation as it is with privilege.

Our democracy is much like a tall stand of timber. We cannot cut from it more than we plant in it without periling its survival. And forests—like gardens—cannot be bought. They must be cultivated by toil and nourished by the sweat of those who would keep them.

If we dare look on our government simply as a legacy left to us for our benefit, enrichment, and ease—then we shall someday awaken to find that our nation has rotted as quickly as our character has decayed. Democratic self-government tries its people with a sterner challenge than any other system in the world. Scorning the brutal coercion of totalitarian states, it asks generosity and brotherhood of its people. It asks that they co-operate willingly and voluntarily for their common welfare in order that each may benefit equitably according to his merits.

And while the imperfections of our democratic government—like all man-made institutions—have brought injustices to some, advantages to others, it nevertheless has helped us to achieve greater personal dignity and more material wealth than any nation in the world.

At a time when peoples throughout the world are being courted by an aggressive stateism that would have them abdicate their personal share in government and entrust their welfare to rule by clique, the American people must put their faith in not less—but more—personal responsibility in the affairs of their community and nation.

Because personal freedom does not grant to the individual, license to trespass upon the rights of others, a democracy must protect by regulation the common welfare of its people against transgressions by special interests. And as our American economy matures, we have found it necessary to insure greater equality of opportunity by the wise intervention of government into the enterprise of individuals. The depth of this invasion into the freedom of the individual, however, must be limited by compromise. For in our effort to provide equality of opportunity through sufficient government, we cannot abuse this power lest we stunt initiative through too much government.

While in the Veterans Administration immediately after the war, I was several times chided by hard-shelled friends for justifying the enormous social desirability of the G.I. Bill. To some mossbacks who had plunged profitably into the production tasks of the war, even our readjustment program was viewed suspiciously—and secretly with alarm. I am reminded of one entrepreneur who made a wartime fortune in wheat. Although he conceded the need for "some" government aid to veterans on their return, he still blandly contended that I was spending money "on just another Washington handout to make government wards of these kids."

Few tories went that far. But even while they enthusiastically accept the G.I. Bill and most of the social advances made in the last two decades, many men of good will today admit to a fear that our wartime generation has become too dependent upon government, that initiative has waned, and that too many of us are inclined to see Washington as the source of the bountiful life.

Apart from its economic implications, this habit of turning to Washington with our troubles conceals a political danger as well. For, once we make a crutch of government, we are on the way to becoming political cripples.

If we look to government purely for its benefits and deny it our obligations, then we shall be poorly prepared to assert the superiority of democratic government over the absolute powers of stateism. Overdependency on government is the road to enslavement.

When men become so addicted to the benefits of government that they lose sight of their responsibilities, then that government is in danger of being seized by any leader or minority group that can promise greater benefits to the people in return for abandonment of their rights. Or when men become so intent upon selfish exploitation of their rights that our majority interests are sidetracked in favor of a greedy minority, then also is our freedom threatened. For only so long as freedom remains a force for the welfare of all our people will men cherish it in their hearts and defend it with their lives.

Our earlier insistence on opportunity for enterprise has given way to a demand for economic security. And ruefully though the older generation may view this cautious shift in interest, it has no one to blame but itself. For it was the freebooting business anarchy of my generation that brought on the Great Depression. And it was largely that depression which stimulated this passion for security we find among young men today. During the early 1930s when the nation showed its fear, the mark of that panic was stamped upon the memory of our World War II generation. First during the depression and afterward in the war, they were steadily the victims of error and default on the part of their parents.

On the other hand, the youthful postwar soldier—his average age is 22—is clearly a product of prosperity. A youngster of 12 when war broke out, he romped through adolescence during the frenzied period of war production with considerably more money and less parental supervision than his brother before him. He came of age in an era of full employment when employers were bargaining for men. Frequently he was the child of itinerant parents, raised on time-and-a-half overtime wages in the shadows of shipyards and aircraft plants.

Like his depression predecessor—he, too, is the product of his times. But what vastly different times they were.

While exploring a human relations program for the training of these recruits, we in the Veterans Administration went first to an eminent psychologist to learn what manner of man was coming into our ranks. The scholar's verdict was a harsh one—harsher perhaps than these youngsters deserve.

"The postwar soldier," he said, summarizing his observations, "is younger than his wartime brother, healthier, better schooled, and more adept at learning."

But with an estimate that alerted us to the size of our job, the professor added, "He is also plainly undisciplined, jealously aware of his rights but not of his responsibilities. Moreover, he is mercenary and antagonistic to authority in almost any form."

The conclusion we drew was an inevitable one.

Not only was the Army challenged to make soldiers of these men, but it was also faced with the task of first making them better citizens, making them aware of the responsibilities that accrued to them as adult Americans.

For most of them, service in the Army is an initial payment on the privileges they have already enjoyed in growing up, privileges they shall have to balance with obligations the rest of their lives.

At Fort Myer, where I have my home, I sometimes slip down to the tiny post movie. Dressed in a tacky prewar civilian suit I am treated to soldier talk, especially when the lights are out. One evening, several months ago, an 18-year-old youngster, who let it be known he was a one-year volunteer, complained to his companion that he had put his neck in the noose when he came willingly into the Army.

"What's it going to get me?" he asked. "Not even the G.I. Bill. My old man was in the first World War—and what did he get out of it?"

By some standards, the young man was a realist. He was simply asking the question it is the fashion to ask today:

"What's in it for me? How do I come out?"

It is time we provided the answer for that youngster and thousands like him, time we reminded him—as well as ourselves—that freedom is not a prize to be given a man for his distinguished achievement in having been born an American.

If we are delinquent in the business of being good citizens—and there are many who contend that we are—then we must learn why it is we believe democracy has become a free ride without the need for earning our way.

Probably the greatest single cause for delinquency in citizenship can be traced to our declining sense of responsibility in the home, the church, the school and the community in which we live.

While most delinquents turned remorseful suddenly feel the need for doing more for "democracy" and turn their eyes toward the mountainous issues that crowd our national scene, few have the humility to start down where citizenship counts.

Because the family is the basic unit of our society, it is there that responsibility begins. Unless the young man of this new generation can feel that the security, the well-being and happiness of his family is in part a responsibility of his, there is no hope in tutoring him later on his broader obligations. For citizenship is a progressive education that starts in the home and works its way toward the dizzying heights of national and world responsibility.

Much as we welcome the leisurely comforts of indoor plumbing, oil heat, electric lights, and the family car, we nevertheless lost a primary lesson in good citizenship when 20th-century city convenience rendered the tradition of chores old-fashioned. The necessity for doing one's daily round of little jobs made a youngster of earlier generations feel part of the household and planted in his young mind the seed of responsibility to someone other than himself.

Back home in the flat farmlands of Missouri, life on a schoolmaster's wages was not calculated to make one rich or idle. But however busy his modest life might be, still my father had time to take me through crisp cornfields hunting coveys of quail when I was a youngster of seven. And by the time I had grown to 12, he had given me a shotgun of my own.

Even at that time our life was an itinerant one. My father rambled from schoolhouse to schoolhouse, first in the soft-coal fields of Randolph County, then in the rich farm lands of Fayette. At the end of each short six-month term, he took an interim job. Sometimes we lived on a farm, sometimes in town, where Dad ran the mutual telephone exchange.

For a period of several years we farmed 200 bottom-land acres. During the school year, Dad would set off each Sunday afternoon and walk eight miles to the family with whom he boarded nearest the schoolhouse. And each Friday afternoon when school was out, with a book under his arm, he would walk eight miles back to our farm to work on the week end with Mother and me.

My chores were neither painful nor unpleasant. Each morning I filled the woodbox with chips and kindling for the big kitchen stove. I kept the buckets filled with water from the deep well out in back. When there were cows in the barn, I helped with the milking. And during the years we kept 200 chickens, I helped Mother feed them, kept the hen-house clean, and counted new records in fresh white eggs. Once a week we went together to town carrying a great tin bucket of those gleaming eggs. They fetched ten cents a dozen.

At the end of each summer I sharpened my knife and ran through the woods in search of bee trees. Whenever I found a busy beehive concealed in a hollow tree I would mark it carefully in my mind and run off to the farmhouse to ask permission to cut the tree down.

If the farmer agreed—and they always did—I would scamper happily back to the tree and scar its bark with a great gashing cross. That was my sign of a claim and there the tree stood safe from other bee seekers until we returned to cut it down. One August I put down, in the great earthen crocks Mother gave me, 200 pounds of that wild bee honey.

Throughout the time I was growing up, I knew that if there was no wood by the stove, no water in the kitchen, there would be no breakfast of home-cured ham, warm milk and bright yellow-yolked eggs. If I didn't find the bee trees, there would be no honey-bread after school. And if I didn't help Mother clean the lamps, there would be no light for the evening.

The advent of apartment dwelling and the modernization of our living habits has made too many of today's youngsters look upon their home as a shelter, a meal ticket, a refuge during their period of adolescence. A family is no longer a group whose members depend on one another for companionship and association. Their leisure time is divided. In cities, neighborliness has all but disappeared, a relic of the suburbs and the country.

Even the integrity of the family has been damaged in the rising rate of divorce. The urge of each individual in the family to pamper his own wants, to seek leisure-time companions of his own choice, has put the emphasis on selfishness and suffocated the instincts of good citizenship at the very source.

The church, too, has suffered in our automobile age. No longer is it the civic and social center of the community. Today it must compete with a score of diversions within range of our driving. The impermanence of transient family groups has denied to millions a family church in which they can take a share of responsibility in its activities and problems.

A friend only recently told me of the small congregation to which he belongs. During the depression, when the church was hard pressed by mortgage payments and too poor to keep a janitor, each member of the vestry devoted one Saturday each month to cleaning and scrubbing the building for the Sunday service. Because the church required sacrifice those who loved it best worked the hardest and loved it all the more.

Today that church is fully paid for, the mortgage burned, and a janitor paid to keep it clean. The congregation contributes far more liberally than it did before because now it can afford to. But the devotion of its members has faded with a waning of their obligations. Two dollars in the Sunday offering has replaced those Saturday afternoons. And another of the compelling obligations which produces a sense of responsibility in that community is gone.

Like many another speaker who is called upon too often, it is difficult for me to avoid occasional comment on education. When I recall the political illiteracy of our young troops at the start of the war, I am moved to charge education with gross dereliction in its responsibility to teach knowledge of the human values at issue in the world.

When the Army struggled through the summer of 1941 with rebellious and unhappy soldiers who muttered constantly of their raw deal, it became apparent that the fault lay not with the Army but with the failure of the American people to grasp the significance of the second World War.

Unlike too many critics of education, however, I cannot lay the blame on the doorstep of education alone. Rather it must be shared with the people as a whole. Their shocking apathy to the condition of their schools and the sterility of their curricula is responsible even today for the political immaturity, the economic ignorance, the philosophical indifference and the spiritual insolvency of so many young men.

Throughout Europe, wherever our armies were stationed, the people were bewildered by Americans who appeared indifferent to the political and philosophical origins and nature of the most powerful and progressive nation in the world.

Unhappily, when driven into a corner intellectually, our soldiers were forced to fall back on our wage scales, our automobiles, our refrigerators—and eventually and triumphantly to the American bathroom—for their defense. Here is an indictment, not only of American education—but of the irresponsible indifference of citizens who have permitted this vacuum to remain.

Recently, when I charged education with these derelictions, my audience of first citizens nodded comfortably and agreed. I turned on them.

"How many of you," I asked, "are members of a school board?"

Of the more than 60 men in the room, not one raised his hand.

"How many of you," I continued, "know the name of your child's teacher?"

There was a showing of a scant half dozen hands.

"How many of you," I pressed, "have ever asked your child's teacher home to dinner to measure her worth for yourself?"

Not a single hand went up.

Here, then, was an audience of successful business and professional men, too busy each in his own daily affairs to determine for himself the character and quality of education furnished his sons and daughters.

Victims of the checkbook habit, each was quite content to let it go simply by paying the bills.

This is citizenship by the dollar sign; it cannot and will not work.

Until the American people shake themselves out of this appalling lethargy and make their schools—together with the selection, the welfare, and rewards of their teachers—a matter of their personal and intimate concern, we shall go forth to do battle psychologically with the aggressive legions of stateism woefully trained and poorly equipped, handicapped from the outset.

To those military-minded men who are militarists by instinct rather than profession and who say that our weaknesses result from a failure of discipline in our young men, I must reply with this vigorous denial.

Men cannot be impressed into good citizenship. If they are to cherish the freedoms that come to them under democratic self-government, they cannot be disciplined into devotion. Instead they must be taught to value the great spiritual possessions to which they are born, by assuming from childhood a share of responsibility for safeguarding those possessions. Good citizenship springs from an appreciation of the great values of our institutions and from active participation in them.

It is immoral for us to claim freedom of the ballot unless we are ready to share that freedom with every other American. It is ungodly for us to claim freedom of religion, unless we are prepared to be tolerant of all beliefs that differ from ours. It is hypocritical to insist upon freedom of opinion unless we grant equal freedom to those who oppose us. And it is fraudulent to insist upon freedom of the press if we deny that right to other people.

Democratic institutions will continue to prosper and flourish only so long as they are fed on freedom for all, not on abridgment for some.

We are engaged in a contest today over the integrity of the individual versus the integrity of the state. It is a contest as startlingly dramatic as the air lift into Berlin, as obscurely insignificant as the attitudes of a single man. It is a contest in which ideas are as important as the atom bomb. It is a contest that can conceivably last to the end of our lifetime.

Theoretically the odds lie with us.

For where the state is an instrument of government employed by individuals for their common welfare, the progress of the state is propelled by the progress of the individual. And there can be no doubt in our minds that a free people—unfettered by fears, threats, and terror—will advance farther and faster in spiritual truths, social improvement, and material reward than any slave people, irrespective of the lash under which they labor.

The state is an invention of men. It has neither intellect, nor conscience, nor morals. It is an inanimate machine. And where the machine is master of the man it is simply fueled by his obedience, his fatigue and his terror. Its laws are the creature of dogma rather than the letters of justice. Its philosophy is spurious because it lives not on the spirit but on the oppression of its people.

A democracy such as ours cannot be defeated in this struggle; it can only lose by default.

It can only lose if our people deny through indifference and neglect their personal responsibilities for its security and growth.

Our danger lies not so much in a fifth column whose enmity is avowed. It lies in a first column of well-meaning American citizens. A first column of unconscionable men who are one hundred per cent Americans in their daily protestations and ten per cent citizens in their daily routine of neglect.

Last Kiss

F. Scott Fitzgerald

This story was written in 1940, the year Fitzgerald died. It has a quality about it—a deep melancholy, a puzzled despair at life's broken promises—that seems to reflect Fitzgerald's own bewildered disillusionment after his brilliant triumphs as apostle of the Jazz Age.

April 16, 1949

THE SOUND OF REVELRY FELL SWEET upon James Leonard's ear. He alighted, a little awed by his new limousine, and walked down the red carpet through the crowd. Faces strained forward, weird in the split glare of the drum lights—but after a moment they lost interest in him. Once Jim had been annoyed by his anonymity in Hollywood. Now he was pleased with it.

Elsie Donohue, a tall, lovely, gangling girl, had a seat reserved for him at her table. "If I had no chance before," she said, "what chance have I got now that you're so important?" She was half teasing—but only half.

"You're a stubborn man," she said. "When we first met, you put me in the undesirable class. Why?" She tossed her shoulders despairingly as Jim's eyes lingered on a little Chinese beauty at the next table. "You're looking at Ching Loo Poo-poo, Ching Loo Poo-poo! And for five long years I've come out to this ghastly town—"

"They couldn't keep you away," Jim objected. "It's on your swing around—the Stork Club, Palm Beach and Dave Chasen's."

Tonight something in him wanted to be quiet. Jim was thirty-five and suddenly on the winning side of all this. He was one of those who said how pictures should go, what they should say. It was a fine pure feeling to be on top.

One was very sure that everything was for the best, that the lights shone upon fair ladies and brave men, that pianos dripped the right notes and that the young lips singing them spoke for happy hearts.

They absolutely must be happy, these beautiful faces. And then in a twilight rumba, a face passed Jim's table that was not quite happy. It had gone before Jim formulated this opinion, yet it remained fixed on his memory for some seconds. It was the head of a girl almost as tall as he was, with opaque brown eyes and cheeks as porcelain as those of the little Chinese.

"At least you're back with the white race," said Elsie, following his eyes.

Jim wanted to answer sharply: *You've had your day—three husbands. How about me? Thirty-five and still trying to match every woman with a childhood love who died, still finding fatally in every girl the similarities and not the differences.*

The next time the lights were dim he wandered through the tables to the entrance hall. Here and there friends hailed him—more than the usual number of course, because his rise had been in the Reporter that morning, but Jim had made other steps up and he was used to that. It was a charity ball, and by the stairs was the man who imitated wallpaper about to go in and do a number, and Bob Bordley with a sandwich board on his back: At Ten Tonight in the Hollywood Bowl SONJA HENIE Will Skate on HOT SOUP.

By the bar Jim saw the producer whom he was displacing tomorrow having an unsuspecting drink with the agent who had contrived his ruin. Next to the agent was the girl whose face had seemed sad as she danced by in the rumba.

"Oh, Jim," said the agent, "Pamela Knighton—your future star."

She turned to him with professional eagerness. What the agent's voice had said to her was: "Look alive! This *is* somebody."

"Pamela's joined my stable," said the agent. "I want her to change her name to Boots."

"I thought you said Toots," the girl laughed.

"Toots or Boots. It's the *oo-oo* sound. Cutie shoots Toots. Judge Hoots. No conviction possible. Pamela is English. Her real name is Sybil Higgins."

It seemed to Jim that the deposed producer was looking at him with an infinite something in his eyes—not hatred, not jealousy, but a profound and curious astonishment that asked: Why? Why? For Heaven's sake, why? More disturbed by this than by enmity, Jim surprised himself by asking the English girl to dance. As they faced each other on the floor his exultation of the early evening came back.

"Hollywood's a good place," he said, as if to forestall any criticism from her. "You'll like it. Most English girls do—they don't expect too much. I've had luck working with English girls."

"Are you a director?"

"I've been everything—from press agent on. I've just signed a producer's contract that begins tomorrow."

"I like it here," she said after a minute. "You can't help expecting things. But if they don't come I could always teach school again."

Jim leaned back and looked at her—his impression was of pink-and-silver frost. She was so far from a schoolmarm, even a schoolmarm in a Western, that he laughed. But again he saw that there was something sad and a little lost within the triangle formed by lips and eyes.

"Whom are you with tonight?" he asked.

"Joe Becker," she answered, naming the agent. "Myself and three other girls."

"Look—I have to go out for half an hour. To see a man—this is not phony. Believe me. Will you come along for company and night air?"

She nodded.

On the way they passed Elsie Donohue, who looked inscrutably at the girl and shook her head slightly at Jim. Out in the clear California night he liked his big car for the first time, liked it better than driving himself. The streets through which they rolled were quiet at this hour. Miss Knighton waited for him to speak.

"What did you teach in school?" he asked.

"Sums. Two and two are four and all that."

"It's a long jump from that to Hollywood."

"It's a long story."

"It can't be very long—you're about eighteen."

"Twenty." Anxiously she asked, "Do you think that's too old?"

"Lord, no! It's a beautiful age. I know—I'm twenty-one myself and the arteries haven't hardened much."

She looked at him gravely, estimating his age and keeping it to herself.

"I want to hear the long story," he said.

She sighed. "Well, a lot of old men fell in love with me. Old, old men—I was an old man's darling."

"You mean old gaffers of twenty-two?"

"They were between sixty and seventy. This is all true. So I became a gold digger and dug enough money out of them to go to New York. I walked into 21 the first day and Joe Becker saw me."

"Then you've never been in pictures?" he asked.

"Oh, yes—I had a test this morning," she told him.

Jim smiled. "And you don't feel bad taking money from all those old men?" he inquired.

"Not really," she said, matter-of-fact. "They enjoyed giving it to me. Anyhow it wasn't really money. When they wanted to give me presents I'd send them to a certain jeweler, and afterward I'd take the presents back to the jeweler and get four fifths of the cash."

"Why, you little chiseler!"

"Yes," she admitted. "Somebody told me how. I'm out for all I can get."

"Didn't they mind—the old men, I mean—when you didn't wear their presents?"

"Oh, I'd wear them—once. Old men don't see very well, or remember. But that's why I haven't any jewelry of my own." She broke off. "This I'm wearing is rented."

Jim looked at her again and then laughed aloud. "I wouldn't worry about it. California's full of old men."

They had twisted into a residential district. As they turned a corner Jim picked up the speaking tube. "Stop here." He turned to Pamela, "I have some dirty work to do."

He looked at his watch, got out and went up the street to a building with the names of several doctors on a sign. He went past the building walking slowly, and presently a man came out of the building and followed him. In the darkness between two lamps Jim went close, handed him an envelope and spoke concisely. The man walked off in the opposite direction and Jim returned to the car.

"I'm having all the old men bumped off," he explained. "There's some things worse than death."

"Oh, I'm not free now," she assured him. "I'm engaged."

"Oh." After a minute he asked, "To an Englishman?"

"Well—naturally. Did you think—" She stopped herself but too late.

"Are we that uninteresting?" he asked.

"Oh, no." Her casual tone made it worse. And when she smiled, at the moment when a street light shone in and dressed her beauty up to a white radiance, it was more annoying still.

"Now you tell *me* something," she asked. "Tell me the mystery."

"Just money," he answered almost absently. "That little Greek doctor keeps telling a certain lady that her appendix is bad—we need her in a picture. So we bought him off. It's the last time I'll ever do anyone else's dirty work."

She frowned. "Does she really need her appendix out?"

He shrugged. "Probably not. At least that rat wouldn't know. He's her brother-in-law and he wants the money."

After a long time Pamela spoke judicially. "An Englishman wouldn't do that."

"Some would," he said shortly, "—and some Americans wouldn't."

"An English gentleman wouldn't," she insisted.

"Aren't you getting off on the wrong foot," he suggested, "if you're going to work here?"

"Oh, I like Americans all right—the civilized ones."

From her look Jim took this to include him, but far from being appeased he had a sense of outrage. "You're taking chances," he said. "In fact, I don't see how you dared come out with me. I might have had feathers under my hat."

"You didn't bring a hat," she said placidly. "Besides, Joe Becker said to. There might be something in it for me."

After all he was a producer and you didn't reach eminence by losing your temper—except on purpose. "I'm sure there's something in it for you," he said, listening to a stealthily treacherous purr creep into his voice.

"Are you?" she demanded. "Do you think I'll stand out at all—or am I just one of the thousands?"

"You stand out already," he continued on the same note. "Everyone at the dance was looking at you." He wondered if this was even faintly true. Was it only he who had fancied some uniqueness? "You're a new type," he went on. "A face like yours might give American pictures a—a more civilized tone."

This was his arrow—but to his vast surprise it glanced off.

"Oh, do you think so?" she cried. "Are you going to give me a chance?"

"Why, certainly." It was hard to believe that the irony in his voice was missing its mark. "But after tonight there'll be so much competition that—"

"Oh, I'd rather work for you," she declared. "I'll tell Joe Becker—"

"Don't tell him anything," he interrupted.

"Oh, I won't. I'll do just as you say," she promised.

Her eyes were wide and expectant. Disturbed, he felt that words were being put in his mouth or slipping from him unintended. That so much innocence and so much predatory toughness could go side by side behind this gentle English voice.

"You'd be wasted in bits," he began. "The thing is to get a fat part—" He broke off and started again, "You've got such a strong personality that—"

"Oh, don't!" He saw tears blinking in the corners of her eyes. "Let me just keep this to sleep on tonight. You call me in the morning—or when you need me."

The car came to rest at the carpet strip in front of the dance. Seeing Pamela, the crowd bulged forward grotesquely, autograph books at the ready. Failing to recognize her, it sighed back behind the ropes.

In the ballroom he danced her to Becker's table.

"I won't say a word," she whispered. From her evening case she took a card with the name of her hotel penciled on it. "If any other offers come I'll refuse them."

"Oh, no," he said quickly.

"Oh, yes." She smiled brightly at him and for an instant the feeling Jim had had on seeing her came back. It was an impression of a rich warm sympathy, of youth and suffering side by side. He braced himself for a final quick slash to burst the scarcely created bubble.

"After a year or so—" he began. But the music and her voice overrode him.

"I'll wait for you to call. You're the—you're the most civilized American I've ever met."

She turned her back as if embarrassed by the magnificence of her compliment. Jim started back to his table—then seeing Elsie Donohue talking to a woman across his empty chair, he turned obliquely away. The room, the evening had gone raucous—the blend of music and voices seemed inharmonious and accidental and his eyes covering the room saw only jealousies and hatreds—egos tapping like drumbeats up to a fanfare. He was not above the battle as he had thought.

He started for the coatroom thinking of the note he would dispatch by waiter to his hostess: "You were dancing." Then he found himself almost upon Pamela Knighton's table, and turning again he took another route toward the door.

A picture executive can do without intelligence but he cannot do without tact. Tact now absorbed Jim Leonard to the exclusion of everything else. Power should have pushed diplomacy into the background, leaving him free, but instead it intensified all his human relations—with the executives, with the directors, writers, actors and technical men assigned to his unit, with department heads, censors and "men from the East" besides. So the stalling off of one lone English girl, with no weapon except the telephone and a little note that reached him from the entrance desk, should have been no problem at all.

Just passing by the studio and thought of you and of our ride. There have been some offers but I keep stalling Joe Becker. If I move I will let you know.

A city full of youth and hope spoke in it—in its two transparent lies, the brave falsity of its tone. It didn't matter to her—all the money and glory beyond the impregnable walls. She had just been passing by—just passing by.

That was after two weeks. In another week Joe Becker dropped in to see him. "About that little English girl, Pamela Knighton—remember? How'd she strike you?"

"Very nice."

"For some reason she didn't want me to talk to you." Joe looked out the window. "So I suppose you didn't get along so well that night."

"Sure we did."

"The girl's engaged, you see, to some guy in England."

"She told me that," said Jim, annoyed. "I didn't make any passes at her if that's what you're getting at."

"Don't worry—I understand those things. I just wanted to tell you something about her."

"Nobody else interested?"

"She's only been here a month. Everybody's got to start. I just want to tell you that when she came into 21 that day the barflies dropped like—like flies. Let me tell you—in one minute she was the talk of café society."

"It must have been great," Jim said dryly.

"It was. And Lamarr was there that day too. Listen—Pam was all alone, and she had on English clothes, I guess, nothing you'd look at twice—rabbit fur. But she shone through it like a diamond."

"Yeah?"

"Strong women," Joe went on, "wept into their Vichyssoise. Elsa Maxwell—"

"Joe, this is a busy morning."

"Will you look at her test?"

"Tests are for make-up men," said Jim, impatiently. "I never believe a good test. And I always suspect a bad one."

"Got your own ideas, eh?"

"About that," Jim admitted. "There've been a lot of bad guesses in projection rooms."

"Behind desks, too," said Joe rising.

A second note came after another week: "*When I phoned yesterday one secretary said you were away and one said you were in conference. If this is a run-around tell me. I'm not getting any younger. Twenty-one is staring me in the face—and you must have bumped off all the old men.*"

Her face had grown dim now. He remembered the delicate cheeks, the haunted eyes, as from a picture seen a long time ago. It was easy to dictate a letter that told of changed plans, of new casting, of difficulties which made it impossible—

He didn't feel good about it but at least it was finished business. Having a sandwich in his neighborhood drugstore that night, he looked back at his month's work as good. He had reeked of tact. His unit functioned smoothly. The shades who controlled his destiny would soon see.

There were only a few people in the drugstore. Pamela Knighton was the girl at the magazine rack. She looked up at him, startled, over a copy of The Illustrated London News.

Knowing of the letter that lay for signature on his desk Jim wished he could pretend not to see her. He turned slightly aside, held his breath, listened. But though she had seen him, nothing happened, and hating his Hollywood cowardice he turned again presently and lifted his hat.

"You're up late," he said.

Pamela searched his face momentarily. "I live around the corner," she said. "I've just moved—I wrote you today."

"I live near here, too."

She replaced the magazine in the rack. Jim's tact fled. He felt suddenly old and harassed and asked the wrong question.

"How do things go?" he asked.

"Oh, very well," she said. "I'm in a play—a real play at the New Faces theater in Pasadena. For the experience."

"Oh, that's very wise."

"We open in two weeks. I was hoping you could come."

They walked out the door together and stood in the glow of the red neon sign. Across the autumn street newsboys were shouting the result of the night football.

"Which way?" she asked.

The other way from you, he thought, but when she indicated her direction he walked with her. It was months since he had seen Sunset Boulevard, and the mention of Pasadena made him think of when he had first come to California ten years ago, something green and cool.

Pamela stopped before some tiny bungalows around a central court. "Good night," she said. "Don't let it worry you if you can't help me. Joe has explained how things are, with the war and all. I know you wanted to."

He nodded solemnly—despising himself.

"Are you married?" she asked.

"No."

"Then kiss me good night."

As he hesitated she said, "I like to be kissed good night. I sleep better."

He put his arms around her shyly and bent down to her lips, just touching them—and thinking hard of the letter on his desk which he couldn't send now—and liking holding her.

"You see it's nothing," she said. "Just friendly. Just good night."

On his way to the corner Jim said aloud, "Well, I'll be damned," and kept repeating the sinister prophecy to himself for some time after he was in bed.

On the third night of Pamela's play Jim went to Pasadena and bought a seat in the last row. A likely crowd was jostling into the theater and he felt glad that she would play to a full house, but at the door he found that it was a revival of Room Service—Pamela's play was in the Experiment Hall up the stairs.

Meekly he climbed to a tiny auditorium and was the first arrival except for fluttering ushers and voices chattering amid the hammers backstage. He considered a discreet retirement but was reassured by the arrival of a group of five, among them Joe Becker's chief assistant. The lights went out; a gong was beaten; to an audience of six the play began.

It was about some Mexicans who were being deprived of relief. Concepcione (Pamela Knighton) was having a child by an oil magnate. In the old Horatio Alger tradition, Pedro was reading Marx so someday he could be a bureaucrat and have offices at Palm Springs.

Pedro: We stay here. Better Boss Ford than Renegade Trotsky."

Concepcione: (*Miss Knighton*): *"But who will live to inherit?"*

Pedro: "Perhaps the great-grandchildren, or the grandchildren of the great-grandchildren. Quién sabe?"

Through the gloomy charade Jim watched Pamela; in front of him the party of five leaned together and whispered after her scenes. Was she good? Jim had no notion—he should have taken someone along, or brought in his chauffeur. What with pictures drawing upon half the world for talent there was scarcely a phenomenon as a "natural." There were only possibilities—and luck. He was luck. He was maybe this girl's luck—if he felt that her pull at his insides was universal.

Stars were no longer created by one man's casual desire as in the silent days, but stock girls were, tests were, chances were. When the curtain finally dropped, domestically as a Venetian blind, he went backstage by the simple process of walking through a door on the side. She was waiting for him.

"I was hoping you wouldn't come tonight," she said. "We've flopped. But the first night it was full and I looked for you."

"You were fine," he said stiffly.

"Oh, no. You should have seen me then."

"I saw enough," he said suddenly. "I can give you a little part. Will you come to the studio tomorrow?"

He watched her expression. Once more it surprised him. Out of her eyes, out of the curve of her mouth gleamed a sudden and overwhelming pity.

"Oh," she said. "Oh, I'm terribly sorry. Joe brought some people over and next day I signed up with Bernie Wise."

"You *did?*"

"I knew you wanted me and at first I didn't realize you were just a sort of supervisor. I thought you had more power—you know?" She could not have chosen sharper words out of deliberate mischief. "Oh, I like you better *personally,*" she assured him. "You're much more civilized than Bernie Wise."

All right then he was civilized. He could at least pull out gracefully. "Can I drive you back to Hollywood?"

They rode through an October night soft as April. When they crossed a bridge, its walls topped with wire screens, he gestured toward it and she nodded.

"I know what it is," she said. "But how stupid! English people don't commit suicide when they don't get what they want."

"I know. They come to America."

She laughed and looked at him appraisingly. Oh, she could do something with him all right. She let her hand rest upon his.

"Kiss tonight?" he suggested after a while.

Pamela glanced at the chauffeur insulated in his compartment. "Kiss tonight," she said. . . .

He flew East next day, looking for a young actress just like Pamela Knighton. He looked so hard that any eyes with an aspect of lovely melancholy, any bright English voice, predisposed him; he wandered as far afield as a stock company in Erie and a student play at Wellesley—it came to seem a desperate matter that he should find someone exactly like this girl. Then when a telegram called him impatiently back to Hollywood, he found Pamela dumped in his lap.

"You got a second chance, Jim," said Joe Becker. "Don't miss it again."

"What was the matter over there?"

"They had no part for her. They're in a mess—change of management. So we tore up the contract."

Mike Harris, the studio head, investigated the matter. Why was Bernie Wise, a shrewd picture man, willing to let her go?

"Bernie says she can't act," he reported to Jim. "And what's more she makes trouble. I keep thinking of Simone and those two Austrian girls."

"I've seen her act," insisted Jim. "And I've got a place for her. I don't even want to build her up yet. I want to spot her in this little part and let you see."

A week later Jim pushed open the padded door of Stage III and walked in. Extras in dress clothes turned toward him in the semidarkness; eyes widened.

"Where's Bob Griffin?"

"In that bungalow with Miss Knighton."

They were sitting side by side on a couch in the glare of the make-up light, and from the resistance in Pamela's face Jim knew the trouble was serious.

"It's *nothing*," Bob insisted heartily. "We get along like a couple of kittens, don't we, Pam? Sometimes I roll over her but she doesn't mind."

"You smell of onions," said Pamela.

Griffin tried again. "There's an English way and an American way. We're looking for the happy mean—that's all."

"There's a nice way and a silly way," Pamela said shortly. "I don't want to begin by looking like a fool."

"Leave us alone, will you, Bob?" Jim said.

"Sure. All the time in the world."

Jim had not seen her in this busy week of tests and fittings and rehearsals, and he thought now how little he knew about her and she of them.

"Bob seems to be in your hair," he said.

"He wants me to say things no sane person would say."

"All right—maybe so," he agreed. "Pamela, since you've been working here have you ever blown up in your lines?"

"Why—everybody does sometimes."

"Listen, Pamela—Bob Griffin gets almost ten times as much money as you do —for a particular reason. Not because he's the most brilliant director in Hollywood—he isn't—but because he never blows up in his lines."

"He's not an actor," she said, puzzled.

"I mean his lines in real life. I picked him for this picture because once in a while I blow up. But not Bob. He signed a contract for an unholy amount of money—which he doesn't deserve, which nobody deserves. But smoothness is the fourth dimension of this business and Bob has forgotten the word 'I.' People of three times his talent—producers and troupers and directors—go down the sink because they can't forget it."

"I know I'm being lectured to," she said uncertainly. "But I don't seem to understand. An actress has her own personality—"

He nodded. "And we pay her five times what she could get for it anywhere else—*if* she'll only keep it off the floor where it trips the rest of us up. You're tripping us all up, Pamela."

I thought you were my friend, her eyes said.

He talked to her a few minutes more. Everything he said he believed with all his heart, but because he had twice kissed those lips, he saw that it was support and protection they wanted from him. All he had done was to make her a little shocked that he was not on her side. Feeling rather baffled, and sorry for her loneliness he went to the door of the bungalow and called: "Hey, Bob!"

Jim went about other business. He got back to his office to find Mike Harris waiting.

"Again that girl's making trouble."

"I've been over there."

"I mean in the last five minutes!" cried Harris. "Since you left she's made trouble! Bob Griffin had to stop shooting for the day. He's on his way over."

Bob came in. "There's one type you can't seem to get at—can't find what makes them that way. I'm afraid it's either Pamela or me."

There was a moment's silence. Mike Harris, upset by the whole situation, suspected that Jim was having an affair with the girl.

"Give me till tomorrow morning," said Jim. "I think I can find what's back of this."

Griffin hesitated but there was a personal appeal in Jim's eyes—an appeal to associations of a decade. "All right, Jim," he agreed.

When they had gone Jim called Pamela's number. What he had almost expected happened, but his heart sank none the less when a man's voice answered the phone. . . .

Excepting a trained nurse, an actress is the easiest prey for the unscrupulous male. Jim had learned that in the background of their troubles or their failures there was often some plausible confidence man, some soured musician, who asserted his masculinity by way of interference, midnight nagging, bad advice. The technique of the man was to belittle the woman's job and to question endlessly the motives and intelligence of those for whom she worked.

Jim was thinking of all this when he reached the bungalow hotel in Beverly Hills where Pamela had moved. It was after six. In the court a cold fountain splashed senselessly against the December fog and he heard Major Bowes's voice loud from three radios.

When the door of the apartment opened Jim stared. The man was old—a bent and withered Englishman with ruddy winter color dying in his face. He wore an old dressing gown and slippers and he asked Jim to sit down with an air of being at home. Pamela would be in shortly.

"Are you a relative?" Jim asked wonderingly.

"No, Pamela and I met here in Hollywood. We were strangers in a strange land. Are you employed in pictures, Mr. —Mr.—"

"Leonard," said Jim. "Yes. At present I'm Pamela's boss."

A change came into the man's eyes—the watery blink became conspicuous, there was a stiffening of the old lids. The lips curled down and backward and Jim was gazing into an expression of utter malignancy. Then the features became old and bland again.

"I hope Pamela is being handled properly?"

"You've been in pictures?" Jim asked.

"Till my health broke down. But I am still on the rolls at Central Casting and I know everything about this business and the souls of those who own it—" He broke off.

The door opened and Pamela came in. "Well, hello," she said in surprise. "You've met? The Honorable Chauncey Ward—Mr. Leonard."

Her glowing beauty, borne in from outside like something snatched from wind and weather, made Jim breathless for a moment.

"I thought you told me my sins this afternoon," she said with a touch of defiance.

"I wanted to talk to you away from the studio."

"Don't accept a salary cut," the old man said. "That's an old trick."

"It's not that, Mr. Ward," said Pamela. "Mr. Leonard has been my friend up to now. But today the director tried to make a fool of me, and Mr. Leonard backed him up."

"They all hang together," said Mr. Ward.

"I wonder—" began Jim. "Could I possibly talk to you alone?"

"I trust Mr. Ward," said Pamela frowning. "He's been over here twenty-five years and he's practically my business manager."

Jim wondered from what deep loneliness this relationship had sprung. "I hear there was more trouble on the set," he said.

"Trouble!" She was wide-eyed. "Griffin's assistant swore at me and I heard it. So I walked out. And if Griffin sent apologies by you I don't want them—our relation is going to be strictly business from now on."

"He didn't send apologies," said Jim uncomfortably. "He sent an ultimatum."

"An ultimatum!" she exclaimed. "I've got a contract, and you're his boss, aren't you?"

"To an extent," said Jim, "—but, of course, making pictures is a joint matter—"

"Then let me try another director."

"Fight for your rights," said Mr. Ward. "That's the only thing that impresses them."

"You're doing your best to wreck this girl," said Jim quietly.

"You can't frighten me," snapped Ward. "I've seen your type before."

Jim looked again at Pamela. There was exactly nothing he could do. Had they been in love, had it ever seemed the time to encourage the spark between them, he might have reached her now. But it was too late. In the Hollywood darkness outside he seemed to feel the swift wheels of the industry turning. He knew that when the studio opened tomorrow, Mike Harris would have new plans that did not include Pamela at all.

For a moment longer he hesitated. He was a well-liked man, still young, and with a wide approval. He could buck them about this girl, send her to a dramatic teacher. He could not bear to see her make such a mistake. On the other hand he was afraid that somewhere people had yielded to her too much, spoiled her for this sort of career.

"Hollywood isn't a very civilized place," said Pamela.

"It's a jungle," agreed Mr. Ward. "Full of prowling beasts of prey."

Jim rose. "Well, this one will prowl out," he said. "Pam, I'm very sorry. Feeling like you do, I think you'd be wise to go back to England and get married."

For a moment a flicker of doubt was in her eyes. But her confidence, her young egotism, was greater than her judgment—she did not realize that this very minute was opportunity and she was losing it forever.

For she had lost it when Jim turned and went out. It was weeks before she knew how it happened. She received her salary for some months—Jim saw to that—but she did not set foot on that lot again. Nor on any other. She was placed quietly on that black list that is not written down but that functions at backgammon games after dinner, or on the way to the races. Men of influence stared at her with interest at restaurants here and there but all their inquiries about her reached the same dead end.

She never gave up during the following months—even long after Becker had lost interest and she was in want, and no longer seen in the places where people go to be looked at. It was not from grief or discouragement but only through commonplace circumstances that in June she died. . . .

When Jim heard about it, it seemed incredible and terrible. He learned accidentally that she was in the hospital with pneumonia—he telephoned and found that she was dead. "Sybil Higgins, actress, English. Age twenty-one."

She had given old Ward as the person to be informed and Jim managed to get him enough money to cover the funeral expenses, on the pretext that some old salary was still owing. Afraid that Ward might guess the source of the money he did not go to the funeral but a week later he drove out to the grave.

It was a long bright June day and he stayed there an hour. All over the city there were young people just breathing and being happy and it seemed senseless that the little English girl was not one of them. He kept on trying and trying to twist things about so that they would come out right for her but it was too late. He said goodby aloud and promised that he would come again.

Back at the studio he reserved a projection room and asked for her tests and for the bits of film that had been shot on her picture. He sat in a big leather chair in the darkness and pressed the button for it to begin.

In the test Pamela was dressed as he had seen her that first night at the dance. She looked very happy and he was glad she had had at least that much happiness. The reel of takes from the picture began and ran jerkily with the sound of Bob Griffin's voice off scene and with prop boys showing the number of blocks for the scenes. Then Jim started as the next to the last one came up, and he saw her turn from the camera and whisper: "I'd rather die than do it that way."

Jim got up and went back to his office where he opened the three notes he had from her and read them again.

"*—just passing by the studio and thought of you and of our ride.*"

Just passing by. During the spring she had called him twice on the phone, he knew, and he had wanted to see her. But he could do nothing for her and could not bear to tell her so.

"I am not very brave," Jim said to himself. Even now there was fear in his heart that this would haunt him like that memory of his youth, and he did not want to be unhappy.

Several days later he worked late in the dubbing room, and afterward he dropped into his neighborhood drugstore for a sandwich. It was a warm night and there were many young people at the soda counter. He was paying his check when he became aware that a figure was standing by the magazine rack looking at him over the edge of a magazine. He stopped—he did not want to turn for a closer look only to find the resemblance at an end. Nor did he want to go away.

He heard the sound of a page turning and then out of the corner of his eye he saw the magazine cover, The Illustrated London News.

He felt no fear—he was thinking too quickly, too desperately. If this were real and he could snatch her back, start from there, from that night.

"Your change, Mr. Leonard."

"Thank you."

Still without looking he started for the door and then he heard the magazine close, drop to a pile and he heard someone breathe close to his side. Newsboys were calling an extra across the street and after a moment he turned the wrong way, her way, and he heard her following—so plain that he slowed his pace with the sense that she had trouble keeping up with him.

In front of the apartment court he took her in his arms and drew her radiant beauty close.

"Kiss me good night," she said. "I like to be kissed good night. I sleep better."

Then sleep, he thought, as he turned away—sleep. I couldn't fix it. I tried to fix it. When you brought your beauty here I didn't want to throw it away, but I did somehow. There is nothing left for you now but sleep.

The Challenge

William R. Scott

Courage, in man or boy, is the conquest of fear—and once Erwin had learned that, he discovered another eternal fact of life in this sensitively-told story of a boy's fight.

January 21, 1950

THE AWFUL WORDS HUNG IN THE COLD afternoon air, and it seemed to him that all life was suspended on the schoolyard, that the world had paused in its turning while everyone watched and waited to see what Tommy Hicks would do. Tommy had thrown a snowball made, not from fresh snow, but from watery slush, packed down like a rock. It had hit Erwin's back, and in a wild moment of hurt and quick indignation, he had cursed Tommy. It was a time of reckoning, and Erwin crumpled and withered inwardly at the thought of the appalling violence which would, inevitably, be directed straight at his plump self.

"You better take that back, Fat," Tommy Hicks said ominously.

Erwin wanted to flee, he wanted abjectly to retract what he had said. He wanted, above all, to avoid a collision with Tommy Hicks, whose reputation as the toughest kid in the grade school was based on performance, not bluff. But the same thing in him that prevented his running away also prevented him from displaying the soiled white feather of apology.

"Well," he said, groping for words to justify his impulsive lapse from caution. "Well, my gosh—any guy that uses water-soaked snowballs—well, heck fire, that's dirty."

"Take it back," Tommy said.

There were exhortations from the quickly gathered onlookers, the spectators who loved a good fight so long as they weren't in it. "Make 'em crawl, Tom, he ast fer it!" "Hey, Fat, you ain't scared, are you—*much!*" There was a brief explosion of derisive laughter, and then the crowd encouraged stalled violence to get under way.

Erwin stood in the slush, a large, plump boy of twelve, his ears red from cold and humiliation, his plump hands, blue and wet from handling snowballs, fluttering and twitching nervously at his sides. He blinked at Tommy with bewildered eyes that watered partly from the stinging breeze and partly from a desire to cry. It was as if he had become two people—one who cowered inside him and whimpered and watched in fascinated terror; the other who stood dumbly in the slush, with cold, numb fingers and a mute tongue that refused to obey his frightened self. A minute ago the world had been an exciting place and he had been a fearless warrior storming the enemy barricades; now everything was reduced to a frightening reality. Now it was simply Tommy Hicks and himself, and public opinion.

"You takin' it back, Fat?" Tommy's hands were red fists hanging.

Lookit 'im, scared silly! G'wan, fight! Whassa matter, you guys both yella or somethin'?

Erwin turned on the pack in torment, mumbling incoherent challenges. Why didn't they keep still, why couldn't they leave him alone? He saw a few of the bolder girls in the jostling circle of trouble-hungry boys, and their giggles turned the dagger in his side. He was trapped, and he was afraid, and there was no clean way out of it. He knew what to expect if he begged out of the imminent encounter—self-loathing, and the scorn of the boys who would see in him the image of themselves, who only escaped a like disgrace because they had never incurred Tommy's legendary wrath.

Somewhere on the fringes of the crowd was a boy called Sissy Perkins who had cried his way out of a fight at the beginning of the school year. Sissy had no friends; he was not allowed in the boys' games; he was a shabby object of cold scorn. There, but for the grace of kowtowing and bootlicking, went any one of a dozen other boys now clamoring for action around Tommy and Erwin; but their luck had held and their time of decision hadn't yet arrived. Erwin's had, and although he was terribly afraid of Tommy Hicks, he was also afraid of ugly public cowardice.

I don't care, he thought wildly. Let them hate me. I'll run away from home, go where nobody will recognize me, where nobody will say I'm yellow.

Every instinct of survival in him lent weight to his desire to keep from fighting Tommy Hicks. Wasn't it known that—although he was only in the sixth grade and not quite twelve yet—Tommy could whip anybody? Even the eighth-grade guys didn't mess around with him, boy. Tommy had a flaming and foolhardy courage that made him always the leader in daring, in risking his bones; he did stuff none of the other kids had nerve enough to attempt. Nobody rode a bareback horse at such a breakneck gallop. He dived from dizzy heights among the elm branches into Crystal Creek's dangerously shallow pools and poked under the muddy creek banks for catfish, turtles, snakes, or whatever came to hand. But more to the point, his sharp, rocky knuckles could bruise and scrape and smash and bloody a guy all up in no time.

Erwin was shocked when a voice said weakly, "I ain't gonna take it back," and he recognized his own voice. There was a strange withdrawn look in Tommy's eyes now that intimidated him more than anything else about his threatening expression. "I ain't takin' it back," the voice said again, and it was Erwin all right.

The vultures swooped and pounced again. "Well, whatta ya waitin' fer, Tom? Din't you hear old Fat say he'd fight you, huh?" Bob Enright's voice cut through the others. Tommy whirled and took two steps through the slush toward Bob, whose face all at once went slack with shock.

"You're doin' some big talkin', guy," Tommy said harshly. "You ack like you're anxious to get in a fight or somethin'."

"Aw, heck no, Tom," Bob said. "I just—well, everybody else was talkin', too. I was just talkin'."

Hope stirred in Erwin's tight breast. Let Tommy get sidetracked. Let him forget all about what he'd been called.

But Tommy turned back to Erwin. "Nobody's callin' me what you did and gettin' away with it," he said, moving toward Erwin, stiff-legged, tensed.

And then the bell rang. Recess was over. Let him hit me once and be done with it, Erwin thought, for now he ain't got time to beat me up the way he likes to beat up guys he fights. The bell kept ringing, the voice of authority that could bring a temporary armistice to the bitterest schoolyard war, and Tommy Hicks was not impatient. He could wait.

"All right then," he said. "I'll get you at four o'clock, Fat."

Erwin was possessed of a devil, that spoke words for him that he didn't want spoken. "I'll be here, don't worry, guy," he said.

Don't worry! *Tommy* shouldn't worry!

In line, with Tommy's dark head a safe distance in front of him, Erwin looked around at the familiar scene. It was real, not a dream; there would be no blessed awakening. Recess was ended but the fear persisted. The two-storied brick building was the same he'd come out of minutes ago. The patches of metal-gray cinders showing through the sooty snow and slush were the same; the pale, clean blue of the sky was unaltered, and beneath its high serene indifference the school's inmates hadn't changed: boys and girls, bored, giddy, loud, withdrawn, bold and hearty or pale and sniffling, they trudged with practiced regimentation through the double doors and into the gloomy schoolhouse. Everything was the same as before, but a terrible change had occurred in Erwin, and the others were strangers now, enemies lusting for his blood.

North, beyond the schoolyard and the muddy east-west road, behind the distant hay barn in the stubble field, were the bare willows of Crystal Creek, where the ice was rotting but still firm enough for sliding. Erwin's throat was thick with the wish to be there.

Back of him, running east from the schoolyard under a tunnel of naked maples, the street led to home and safety, a long block and a half away. Last year there had been a gangling, loutish country boy named Claude, three years older than Erwin, who had chased him all the way home from school now and then. Erwin had convinced himself it was a race and not a rout; he'd taken a measure of comfort from knowing he could outrun Claude, whose family, luckily, had moved away during the summer vacation. Now, more than anything under the cold winter sun, Erwin wanted to turn tail and outrun Tommy Hicks and all the lesser enemies to the haven of home and Mama, who didn't believe in fighting.

But if he ran now, something worse than getting beat up would follow him home, into his very bed, his last refuge from strange and disturbing images. And, so, knees hinged with jelly, he went into the schoolhouse and up the creaking wooden stairs. In Miss Carter's seventh- and eighth-grade room he found his seat, conscious of the knowing eyes and the snickers. He slumped into his seat, sunk in a black and bottomless pit of gloomy apprehension. Four o'clock, four o'clock, his mind mumbled.

He gripped his hands and stared out the windows at the small town sprawling north and south beyond the schoolyard. Two blocks away, at the other end of his street, was the Santa Fe depot, where his father worked. He yearned for his father.

A switching engine moved in front of the depot, and he wished he were on that train, going away forever. He sat there, achingly empty inside, and thought of all the places he'd like to be. Any of a thousand would do. Anywhere but here and now.

"Erwin Wilkerson," Miss Carter said. "Pay attention."

"Yes, ma'am," he said dully, staring at the blackboard.

"Erwin, don't you feel well? You look as if you might be ill."

Snickers and titters ran around the room like mice in an attic. "I fail to see the humor of my remark," Miss Carter said. "Erwin, I asked if you weren't feeling well."

Ah, salvation, escape! All he had to do was confess illness and she'd send him home, and he wouldn't be there at four o'clock. But the proud and evil thing in him spoke first. "I feel okay, Miss Carter."

"Very well," she said. "Then pay attention, Erwin."

But that was asking too much. Can a prisoner display interest in civics when the guillotine awaits? Can multiplication distract the mind when disaster lurks on the clock's face? . . .

Erwin had never had a fight, unless you counted the one-sided affairs with his older brother, Glenn, in which he refused to fight back. It was crazy, but he didn't want to *hurt* Glenn. He earnestly believed that he was terribly afraid of really *hurting* Glenn, who was nearly two years older than himself and who had no compunction whatsoever about hurting Erwin. Once, in a fury of impatience, Glenn had cried: "Dammit, Erwin, why don't you fight back? You're bigger than I am!" But Erwin could not say why. It sounded too crazy.

There was no hope for him. It was the longest, sickest afternoon of his life. It was worse than any of the times—like the first day he had come home with wet hair, while the creek was still out of bounds by parental decree—when his mother would make him sit on a chair all afternoon, waiting for punishment to be meted out by his father when he got home from the depot.

It was worse than the time his father had looked at him narrowly and said, "Calvin Parks knows who the kids are that've been swiping his watermelons, and he's going to have them all put in jail." Nothing had come of that, but he'd sweated for a few days. This was worse than facing life imprisonment for stealing Calvin Parks's watermelons. It was worse than looking forward to his father's razor strap, which made a loud noise but didn't really hurt.

There was no clock in the classroom. The janitor was timekeeper for the coming fight; his bell would sound the call to battle at four o'clock. After a half hour had passed, Erwin began listening for the bell, his heart pounding loud in his ears. It seemed to his taut nerves that each second was the *now*, that time had finally devoured his brief reprieve, the bell would ring. As the heartbeat seconds robbed him of safety, he strained and sighed and ached from the interminable, unbearable waiting. And it was now, *now*.

But he wasn't ready for it when it came. Suddenly the brass-throated bell rang, and Erwin jerked upright in his seat sweating and panting. Oh, no, please! he thought. Not yet, not yet! But the bell was undeniably ringing, ringing and ringing with a hysterical, alarming insistency.

"All right, students," Miss Carter said briskly, "we'll march out in orderly fashion. No jostling, no rushing, no talking. We're having a fire drill."

Erwin sagged. Fire drill. Then it wasn't four o'clock after all. Just a fire drill. A good old fire drill. He marched out with the others, feeling shaken and weak, thinking: Oh, let it be for real. Let the schoolhouse really burn down and everybody get so excited nobody will remember about four o'clock. Especially Tommy.

But the schoolhouse wasn't on fire, and they went outside and stood around and marched back in again; in an orderly fashion, and in the hall Erwin felt Tommy Hicks's glance following him up the creaky stairs. But when he slumped into his seat again, he was somehow relieved of the awful strain of waiting. The fire drill had recalled him from his gloomy introspection; it would be impossible for him to react again so rawly to the bell. And when, in a few minutes, the bell rang again, it was anticlimax, it did almost nothing to him.

In a sort of trance he got up and went out, his eyes meeting Miss Carter's perplexed glance and slipping away. He descended the stairs with the others, with the calm and measured voice of the bell telling everyone to go home, everyone but Erwin and Tommy and the blood-lusting, the violence-craving, the trouble-hungry. Everybody go on home now, the bell seemed to say, except those who want to watch Tommy Hicks pulverize Fatty Wilkerson.

Hey, you ever see a guy get beat to death with just bare fists? Hey, stick around, then. You ever see a guy with a broken jaw and his nose splattered all over his face and his eyes swole shut and his teeth all busted out and his ribs caved in and blood running out of his eyes and his ears, huh? Say, hang around, then.

Erwin didn't run, but, on the other hand, he didn't march out in an orderly fashion, either. He didn't saunter or tarry. He moved briskly, thinking: If he ain't out there I'll just act like I forgot about it, I'll just go on home. And oh, he thought with anguish, don't let him be out there!

If the fight took place, he had no strategy. There were no last-minute bits of technical advice that might help him avoid pulverization. His only tactics were to hope and pray that Tommy wasn't out there and, if he wasn't, to just go on home. It was even possible, he thought wistfully, that Tommy had forgotten, that all them other guys had forgotten, too.

Hey, listen! Forget a thing like that? You kiddin' or something? Forget a bullfight, a deadly duel, a gory accident, a lynching, a bone-splintering, blood-spattering homicide? Listen, you ever see a guy with his head busted open and his brains runnin' out? A fat guy?

Oh, they were waiting all right. They had scurried from classrooms to intercept his flight, to make sure—as someone said from the anonymous safety of the crowd—to make sure it was a clean fight without nothin' dirty gettin' pulled off, like bitin' or kickin' or gougin' eyes and stuff like that. A good, clean, bloody fight, see? They waited across from the schoolyard under the bleak, nude branches of the maple trees. Archie and Joe and Pete and Cotton. Nate, Jack, Herman, Jelly, Elbert, Ralph, Bob, Kermit and Squeechy, Buck and Flip and Clinton and Snake and Rex and Poochy and Delbert and Al and Sam. They were all there, the whole enthusiastic pack of them.

But Tommy Hicks wasn't there yet. He was in no hurry, Tommy.

"Slow down, Fat. You ain't forgot, have you, Fat? About Tommy?"

"Well, listen, if he ain't here, I can't wait all night," he said.

"Who says all night? Holy cats, give 'im time. You scared, Fat?"

"I ain't scared," Erwin said desperately, "only I promised I'd get home early. I got a lot of chores to take care of. Cripes, I can't hang around here all night. It looks like he ain't comin'."

But they wouldn't let him go. Nobody laid a hand on him, nobody blocked his path. They kept him there with words. Okay, they said. If he was yella, okay, then he better get it in high gear before old Tom showed up. Go on, head for home, Fido. Be a yella-bellied coward.

What was so terrible about being scared, Erwin wondered miserably. It was so easy and natural to be scared. But he couldn't make his feet betray that proud and evil thing inside him. He didn't want to wait, waiting longer was impossible. But he couldn't make himself run away. . . .

Tommy was later and later, and Erwin kept telling the mob: "Well, I ain't gonna wait no longer. I got chores to do at home." But he stayed, because they tied him hand and foot with taunts, they shackled him with names, and they milled and stamped and roamed about in the slush.

And then, after ten slow minutes, Tommy came out of the schoolhouse and turned north across the now deserted school grounds, his eyes on the ground, deep in thought, oblivious.

The mob was indignant. *Hey, wait a minute. He can't do that to us, for cripes' sake!* They wanted to see blood spilled, flesh bruised. And suddenly Erwin was consumed by a terrible rage that included them all. He hated them, all of them, because they insisted on seeing him humiliated, beaten insensible. He stared over their heads as Tommy hesitated, turned, and came trudging toward them. Erwin looked at the schoolhouse, and saw Miss Carter's pretty, serious face at a window on the second floor, and he had a moment of hope. But then he knew there would be no end to his nightmare through Miss Carter, for didn't the teachers always hang around the school until five or later? None of them would be coming up the street for an hour, at least, and a guy didn't need an hour to be pulverized in.

He looked at the hungering, bright-eyed rabble, hating them for forcing disaster upon him, and he wanted to kill them, every single darn' one of them. But he still didn't want to fight Tommy.

Now Tommy was sucked into the whirlpool of boy-flesh, trapped as Erwin was trapped. Tommy Hicks had no more choice than Erwin had, and he knew it. So he said wearily, "Let's go up the street a ways. We'd git reported for fightin' here."

The crowd enfolded them lovingly, protecting them from everything but the crowd and themselves. The mob hemmed them in and escorted them up the wintry street; the mob stopped and formed a tight circle around them.

Tommy Hicks was nobody's fool; he looked at Erwin now with a sort of regretful acceptance. Erwin was an inch or two taller, many pounds heavier—just bigger. Tommy knew his own capabilities; Erwin didn't know his. If Erwin had been in any condition for thinking, he might have thought of the coincidence of Tommy's previous fights; they had all been with boys who were thin and wiry like himself, not bulky stout boys like Erwin.

"Well, go ahead, start," Tommy said without enthusiasm.

"You start," Erwin croaked. "You're

the one that wanted to fight in the f-first place."

Aw, knock off the talk. Whassa matter? Bust 'im; g'wan, fight!

"Well, you called me a dirty name," Tommy said.

"Well, I wouldn't of if you hadn't busted me one in the back with a water-soaked snowball. Well, my gosh, that's dirty."

Aw, cripes! Let's have some action. C'mon, durnit, fight!

Two things happened simultaneously. Erwin's fury at the treacherous gang flooded over his fear, and someone behind Tommy gave him a sudden push, sending him forward off balance. Seeing Tommy's lunge, hating the whole world, Erwin lashed out, with all of his weight and fury and desperation behind the blow, and his plump, sturdy fist smacked into Tommy's face and Tommy reversed his direction, staggering back against the barrier of bodies.

As the shorter and smaller boy straightened up, looking stunned and unhappy, blood began welling thinly from his split eyebrow. The crowd gasped with pleased horror, and Erwin stared unbelievingly. He'd actually hit Tommy and made him bleed. All at once he felt a kind of exhilaration, a glowing exultation that filled the emptiness inside him. Cripes! Well, doggone!

So now, when Tommy advanced upon him, white-faced, his pride and his reputation in jeopardy, Erwin didn't retreat. Instead he himself moved forward, swinging his plump arms awkwardly and without skill, but flailing with a sort of frantic exuberance, and his fists smashed soddenly into Tommy's face and head, and he didn't know that he was being hit in return. Bony, hard knuckles skidded off his cheekbone, leaving it raw and burning, but Erwin kept striking and hammering and pummeling and punching and *fighting*, with a singing in his mind and heart. Who's yellow? I'm not yellow. Gee whizz!

Kill 'im! Bust 'im. G'wan, hit 'im some more. Fight, fight, fight!

Suddenly, in desperation, Tommy caught him around the waist and hung on, and Erwin heaved and panted and wrested the smaller boy away, shoving him back. Tommy came upright again and drove in, his face set in a stubborn grimace, and Erwin struck with more deliberation, with more intent and purpose and better results, getting through Tommy's lifted arms. Tommy's hard fists bludgeoned his arms and chest before the wiry arms once more encircled his pudgy waist and clung tenaciously.

They strained and gasped and swayed and struggled. Erwin thrust Tommy from him again, and again Tommy crouched and came back, and it went on and on and on, Tommy forever coming back, driving and diving and hanging on, clutching Erwin until superior weight and lesser hurt threw him off and away. Each time, Erwin hit him coming in, and now Tommy's fists were striking his body with little force. Tommy tried to throw him to the ground and it was no use. Tommy tried to trip him but went staggering himself. They fought in silence except for the grunts and gasps and slithering feet of the gladiators and the panting movement of the crowd.

Strike the white, stubborn, bruised face coming at him; struggle, break away, and then begin all over again. And all at once a new kind of terror was born in Erwin because his beaten opponent wouldn't admit he was beaten. Tommy's face was lumpy and raw and marked with blood from a split eyebrow and cut lip; his nose bled thinly but steadily, but he wouldn't stop. No words passed his mashed lips, but his stony eyes said: "I'm not whipped."

Erwin was sick of the damage he'd done to Tommy; he stopped trying to hit the other boy. And a conscience came awake here and there in the mob. "Come on, you guys, stop fightin'. C'mon, let's break it up, you guys."

But nobody tried to separate them, and Tommy wiped blood from his face with a torn sleeve, spat on the ground and turned on the crowd.

"I ain't lost yet," he gasped, and renewed the fight with such dogged, relentless stubbornness that Erwin's face was now a stiff mask of panic. Oh, make him give up, he prayed. Oh, why doesn't somebody stop him?

"You crazy nut," Erwin sobbed. "Oh, you crazy nut."

"I ain't whipped," Tommy whispered through battered lips.

"I don't want to hit you no more," Erwin said frantically. "I don't want to hurt you no more, Tommy."

And then, abruptly, his prayers were answered, and it was over. Miss Carter was suddenly there, blasting a path through the crowd with indignant authority crackling around her like sheet lightning. She grabbed Tommy and Erwin by the arms, shaking them.

"Stop it this instant!" she said. "Fighting," she said. "I'm ashamed of you. Common street brawlers." She scolded and shook, but in her eyes were anguish and compassion, and the bewilderment of all women when men clash in senseless, prideful combat. Oh, foolish, foolish, foolish boys, her eyes seemed to say. Tearing and beating each other. And for what? A silly point of honor; a matter of false, stupid, deranged pride.

Erwin felt only relief. Go ahead, nag me, he thought. Just hang onto that guy. Don't turn him loose, is all I ask.

Erwin had changed a lot in a very short while. Now he had a great swelling enthusiasm for the future, because not only had the proud and evil thing that was in him made him fight and regain his own self-respect, but from now on he would also command the respect of others. Even as Miss Carter scolded him, he was thinking: There ain't gonna be no more callin' me "Fatty" from now on. Maybe I can't keep the girls from doin' it, but them guys better knock it off.

". . . report this to the principal," Miss Carter was saying. "You both know what that means."

Yeah, a whipping tomorrow at school, because they hadn't gone home yet when they had the fight. The grade-school principal, gray, bespectacled Miss Krogstadt, would whip him and Tommy with her paddle. But she didn't whip hard, and besides, all of a sudden, he wasn't scared of a whipping.

"Now, shake hands and make up," Miss Carter commanded.

Gladly, gladly. I'm glad I fought this guy, I'm glad I ain't yellow, I'm tickled to death I beat him up, but cripes, I sure don't want no more troube with him, Erwin thought. He stuck out his skinned and pudgy right hand. Tommy looked at it stubbornly for a long moment.

"Tommy," Miss Carter said.

He glowered at her, and then he took Erwin's hand. "Well, I wasn't whipped yet," he said.

Among the onlookers, safely immune from the punishment Erwin and Tommy would get tomorrow, Bob Enright crowed scornfully. "If you wasn't whipped," he said, "then I never seen a guy that was."

Tommy turned his battered face toward the boy. "Tomorrow night look in a mirror, guy," he said. "You'll see one then."

"Look in a mirror yourself," Bob Enright said, but scorn had been replaced by an uncertainty that robbed the words of effectiveness.

Miss Carter turned to the crowd. "Disperse," she said. "Go to your homes, boys." They lingered, reluctant to leave the stadium even if the game had ended. "Boys!" Miss Carter said. "I shan't tell you again."

Aw, this ain't the schoolyard. Where's she get that stuff? But they dispersed. *Boy, wasn't that a fight! How about that, old Fat beatin' up on Tommy like that? I sure wouldn't wanna tangle with Fat Wilkerson, boy. Listen, I'd hate to be Bob Enright tomorrow, boy.*

Erwin, looking at Tommy, felt pity and compassion and respect for him, and the affection of a boy for another boy he need no longer fear. "Tommy, I didn't mean what I called you," he muttered. "I take it back, what I said at recess."

Tommy kicked at the ground. "Aw, forget it," he said. "I didn't aim to hit you with that water-soaked snowball, either."

"Aw, it wasn't really water-soaked," Erwin grumbled.

"Erwin, go home," Miss Carter said, her voice stern but gentle. "Tommy, come back to the schoolhouse and I'll try to make you a little more presentable. What would your mother say if you walked in on her in that condition?" She smiled. "You're a mess."

"Well, so long," Erwin said, looking at Tommy.

"So long," Tommy said.

"You both ought to be thoroughly ashamed of yourselves," Miss Carter said, but her tone held no conviction. They might be a lot of other things, but they were not ashamed.

The Men Who Put the Heart in Heartbreak Ridge

Stan Carter

The Korean War—first ever fought in the name of the United Nations—was as devoid of glamor as it was rich in historical significance. Stan Carter, then a twenty-seven-year-old Associated Press reporter, tells how it was with the American and French soldiers of the 23rd Regiment of the U. S. Second Division, during the thirty days and twenty-nine nights of struggle for Heartbreak Ridge. The regiment lost about half its strength in killed and wounded; the Communists suffered some ten thousand casualties before the meager handful that was left gave up the struggle.

December 15, 1951

THE TIRED, UNSHAVEN MAJOR LOOKED up at the chaplain and grinned ruefully. "They're taking a beating, Father," he said. "They're giving a beating, too, but not many men are left."

It was in the desperate, early days on Heartbreak Ridge, where American and French soldiers of the 23d Infantry Regiment were fighting the longest and most costly hill battle of the Korean war. The major had just walked down off Heartbreak Ridge. He seemed beaten and without hope.

These men thought their mission was suicide. Yet they crawled again and again up sheer mountainsides over the bodies of their dead comrades into the face of Communist fire. In a battle that raged for 30 days and 29 nights, the 23d Regiment of the U.S. Second Division wrested Heartbreak Ridge from a numerically superior enemy. In the 23d Regiment, 1,650 men, about half the unit's combat troops, were killed or wounded.

The 9th Infantry Regiment suffered 200 more casualties in three days at the beginning of the battle. Probably 10,000 North Koreans were killed or wounded.

There were men who personally knocked out Communist machine-gun nests with grenades, men who carried wounded and dead out through fire, men who fought continuously until they were completely exhausted. And there were men who stood up in formation and attacked in formation through a barrage of enemy fire.

"There's scarcely been a battle like it—ever," said Colonel James Y. Adams, of Monterey, California, commander of the 23d Regiment.

Sergeant James E. Lunsford, of East Bernstadt, Kentucky, and Corporal James Skaggs, of Columbus, Ohio, were killed going into a Communist bunker with nothing in their hands but knives.

Private First Class Franklin D. Roton, of Sheridan, Wyoming, had been a medic just three and a half days. He was standing on the ridge, tending a wounded man. A North Korean tossed a grenade. Roton threw himself over his patient to shield him from the blast and was wounded by grenade fragments.

Corporal Manley Hand, of Sanford, Michigan, continued to fire his machine gun while North Koreans swarmed around his company's position. The North Koreans threw grenades into his foxhole. Three times Hand picked them up and threw them back at the enemy. The fourth grenade exploded and killed him while he was raising his arm to hurl it away.

I was with the 23d Regiment during most of the battle. It lasted from September 12th to October 12th, while the Korean armistice talks foundered on charges and countercharges of violations of the Kaesong neutral zone. Heartbreak Ridge was named during the first week of the battle, when every Allied attack was turned back with withering Communist fire. A wounded soldier at a forward aid station shuddered, "It's a heartbreak, it's a heartbreak," and the name stuck.

The North Koreans had turned a four-mile-long ridge line 18 miles above Yanggu in eastern Korea into a fortress with 1,000 log and dirt bunkers so sturdy that even direct artillery hits sometimes bounced off. The terrain was the most difficult in Korea. There were three major peaks on the ridge line—one at the south, one at the north and one in the center.

There were countless small ridges, or fingers, running off toward the valleys on the east, and the west. Picture it as the spinal column of a fish, with hundreds of vertebrae.

Before the battle Heartbreak Ridge was covered with trees and undergrowth. At the end it was bald except for a few shell-splintered tree stumps.

The center, the tallest peak, was flat on top. Its southern slope was steep and could be crisscrossed by fire from the bunkers on the summit. The northern approach was an almost straight up-and-down cliff. The northernmost peak had a needlelike summit, with six Communist bunkers dug into the needle. South of the needle there was a bowl-like crater with 20 more bunkers. A flat, narrow ridge line led to the crater from the south. It was absolutely flat and open, with nothing on it to hide behind.

On each of the fingers, or smaller ridge lines, leading away toward the east and west, there were more bunkers placed so that they commanded all the approaches to Heartbreak Ridge. It took two and a half hours to climb the center peak of Heartbreak Ridge, and up to 10 hours to carry a wounded man down the steep trail.

Heartbreak Ridge was part of the main line of resistance the Communists established during the Kaesong truce talks. It commanded the major Communist supply route. The North Koreans were gathering troops and supplies in the Mundung-ni Valley, just west of Heartbreak Ridge, and they had concentrated mortars and artillery pieces in the Satae-ri Valley, east of Heartbreak Ridge.

"We watched the build-up on Heartbreak Ridge and we knew we'd have to do something about it," Colonel Adams said.

"It was astride their main supply route. If we could get it, it would be a dagger pointing to their heart. We could control the roads leading north," said Major General Robert N. Young, of Washington, D.C., commander of the Second Division.

But the 23d Regiment encountered resistance stiffer than anything it had expected. North Koreans fired at them from bunkers up to eight feet thick, with baffle doors fixed so that grenades could not be thrown in through the entrances. At times the Communist artillery fire was heavier than our own. North Koreans with burp guns sniped at Americans and Frenchmen from behind trees. The North Koreans carried pocketfuls of grenades and threw them like rocks. Sometimes they rolled grenades down the slopes in the path of advancing Allied troops.

There was fighting at one point or another on the ridge every day during the month the battle lasted. Communist artillery and mortar fire hit in the draws and narrow valleys below the ridge. There was the clatter of machine-gun fire and the crack of rifle above. Once when I tried to climb the ridge, seven Communist shells struck the path in front of me and behind me. I tried three approaches and an artillery round exploded in each of the three little mountain draws. I turned back, 100 yards short of my goal. As a correspondent, I could leave Heartbreak Ridge whenever I wanted, but the soldiers I encountered on the mountainside had to keep climbing toward the top.

To gain an anchor point for the attack on the ridge itself, Baker Company of the 23d Regiment seized Hill 702 east of Heartbreak Ridge in a six-hour battle on September 12th. All the guns of the Second Division bombarded Heartbreak Ridge that day to soften it up for the infantry assault. At dawn September 13th the Third Battalion of the 23d started up a finger leading from the east to a point on Heartbreak Ridge just south of the northernmost peak. It got to the top of the ridge the next day, but for three days the Communists clung to bunkers inside the battalion's perimeter, and there was continual stiff, hand-to-hand fighting before the foothold on Heartbreak Ridge was secured.

The Second Battalion tried a dozen approaches in an attempt to assault the center peak of Heartbreak Ridge, but it came under deadly Communist fire on every little finger and ridge line leading up toward the peak. Eventually it had to give up the attempt. Direct fire from tank guns destroyed most of the Communist bunkers at the southern end of Heartbreak Ridge, and a battalion of the 9th Regiment was able to take the southernmost peak with only four casualties.

But in the next three days the 9th Regiment lost 200 men from Communist mortar and artillery fire while barely holding on to the peak. The First Battalion, attacking from the southern peak north along the ridge line toward the center peak, was pushed back repeatedly by extremely savage Communist counterattacks. The casualties were heavy.

On the morning of September 15th the Communists overran Charlie Company of the First Battalion in a counterattack. The company had to withdraw, leaving behind two of its machine guns. The last time two of our men were seen, they were standing before their foxholes, fist-fighting with the Reds. Another man of Charlie Company killed a North Korean with an entrenching tool.

Three days later the Third Battalion got to the top of the northernmost peak in a night attack with flame throwers. At 1:00 A.M., September 19th, the Communists counterattacked. The Americans were still holding on to the summit at 6:00 A.M. and it looked as though they would be able to hold the hill. At 8:00 A.M., the enemy overran the American positions and killed everyone on the hill.

The First Battalion continued to attack the center peak from the south. On the fifth attempt, on September 23d, three men crawled to the summit of the high mountain. By evening, 21 Americans were on the summit, but the North Koreans were still inside bunkers on the mountaintop. With the weapons they had, the Americans could not get the Communists out. Early on the morning of September 24th, the Communists counterattacked. The Reds came out of the bunkers on the mountaintop and from the ridges to the west. Few of the Americans got off the hill alive.

About 4:30 A.M., the North Koreans swept down from the mountaintop and surrounded the remainder of the First Battalion on the southern slope. It took until dawn for the weary Americans to fight their way out of the trap, but at the end of the engagement there were 250 to 300 enemy dead in front of the First Battalion's positions.

On September 29th, Navy planes bombed, strafed and poured napalm on the center peak and the ridge west of it for a half hour. Then for a half hour the Second Division's artillery pasted the peak. After the shelling, the French battalion launched an all-out assault on the peak from the north while the First Battalion attacked it from the south. The First Battalion was stopped in its tracks by intense enemy fire. In the first 15 minutes of their attack the French suffered 100 casualties. Six French soldiers crawled up the sheer northern slope of the mountain and spread a square of red cloth on the summit to indicate to Allied airmen that the ground was ours. Then they were killed by the Reds.

All three regiments of the Second Division began a limited objective attack the night of October 5th. The Americans and French in the 23d Regiment assaulted the center peak of Heartbreak Ridge and the smaller ridge lines west of it. A tank task force of the 23d drove up the Satae-ri Valley east of Heartbreak Ridge, drawing the bulk of Communist artillery fire away from the ridge itself. The 9th and 38th Regiments attacked in the Mundung-ni Valley and the mountains west of Heartbreak Ridge. At 6:00 A.M., October 6th, the center peak of Heartbreak Ridge was ours.

"The thing that cracked it was the attack in the west," said Colonel Adams. "It left the enemy uncertain and unable to concentrate his fire on Heartbreak."

The North Koreans had been told to defend Heartbreak Ridge to the death and that was what they were doing. On the night of October 8th, the enemy made an extremely violent counterattack against the Third Battalion, holding positions west of the northernmost peak of Heartbreak Ridge. The worst of it lasted 20 minutes. Waves of North Koreans poured in on the Americans, screaming unintelligible words. The Communist attack was broken after the Americans had suffered 90 casualties and the North Koreans had suffered many hundreds.

Fifty tanks of the 72d Tank Battalion and two companies of the 38th Infantry Regiment broke through Communist lines west of Heartbreak Ridge. The task force drove up the Mundung-ni Valley, flanking the Communists on the ridge.

At four o'clock in the afternoon of October 11th, American and French troops of the 23d assaulted the last Communist-held peak at the north end of Heartbreak Ridge. Allied artillery laid a curtain of fire behind the hill to prevent the Communists from receiving reinforcements from the north, but Allied infantrymen moving up the flat, open ridge line toward the peak were pinned down by intense Communist fire. A Chinese soldier was captured, but it appeared that the bulk of Communists on Heartbreak Ridge were North Koreans to the last. American troops on the ridges west of the peak joined in the attack on the last Red-held hill, and at dawn on October 12th they linked up with American and French elements attacking from the south.

Later that morning—at 8:00 A.M.—Colonel Adams announced jubilantly, "We've got it!"

It was just a question of time before the last die-hard Communists must surrender or die. There were still 35 North Koreans holed up in three bunkers on the summit, but they were surrounded by the Americans and French. The 23d spent the rest of October 12th mopping up. At dawn on October 13th, the last Communist resistance on Heartbreak Ridge ceased.

The men of the 23d Regiment had fought in some of the bitterest battles of the Korean war: they fought at Kunu-ri in November, they turned back the Chinese onslaught at Chipyong in February, they were the blocking force in May when the Second Division almost singlehandedly repulsed the last major Communist offensive on the Eastern Front. But today they say that never have they seen or heard of a battle as savage as the battle of Heartbreak Ridge. Colonel Adams said it was the toughest fight in the 90-year history of the 23d Regiment.

"The Red defense was fanatical," Colonel Adams told me. "If they were my troops I'd be so proud of them I couldn't see straight. We tried every finger, every approach. We crawled—that's right, crawled—you can't climb up that ridge.

"There have never been American troops who have fought harder. Those French are wonderful, too. Once they start, nothing will stop them."

General Young said, "The Communists were fanatical. The terrain was the most difficult in the world. The gallantry of the men and officers of the 23d Regiment has been the outstanding feature."

There will never be a complete list of the heroes of Heartbreak Ridge. Colonel Adams said 100 men deserved the Congressional Medal of Honor for their bravery. The names of many of them are unknown.

There was a Puerto Rican boy who hobbled off the ridge on the stump of his leg after his foot had been shot away by Communist mortar fire. He said no to an officer who wanted to call for a stretcher. The stretcher-bearers were needed more urgently on the top of the ridge where the really seriously wounded were, he said.

Master Sergeant Gaither Nicklas, of Clarkson, Tennessee, went four times into Communist-held territory to evacuate wounded men of his platoon. He went from foxhole to foxhole through intense fire searching for Americans. He miraculously escaped injury that day, but later he was wounded critically.

The medics went up to 72 hours without sleep, constantly tending and caring for wounded men. The First Battalion ran out of medical supplies twice because of the large number of wounded. The morphine and plasma were gone. The men gathered their individual first-aid kits into a stockpile and still they ran out of supplies. In the midst of small-arms and mortar fire the medics sat on top of the ground, taking care of the wounded.

Machine-gun fire from a Communist bunker three stories high stopped every American advance toward the tall, center peak. On September 22d, Lieutenant P. C. Mitchell, Jr., of Dalton, Illinois, led a patrol down the side of the ridge, around to the north, and back on top of the bunker. Lieutenant Mitchell was killed by enemy mortar fire while placing a machine gun on the ridge in full view of the enemy.

"I think Mitchell was responsible in great part for the high morale of the men," said Captain William S. Jordan, of Santa Clara, California, commander of Baker Company. "He was a superb battlefield leader. Every man in the First Battalion had blood in his eye because of the death of Lieutenant Mitchell."

A week before the battle ended, a helicopter landing spot was cleared on the center peak. Three Army helicopter pilots dodged Communist mortar and small-arms fire again and again to pick up the wounded. At times the Communists held positions within 300 yards of the area.

The 23d Regiment was being supplied on the isolated ridge partially by light L-19-type observation planes of the Second Division air section. Dodging enemy fire, they swept in low over Heartbreak Ridge and dropped cases of C rations as close as they could to the Americans' foxholes. Major Robert Boatright, of Santa Monica, California, was credited by grinning infantrymen with killing two North Koreans when he accidentally dropped a C ration box behind enemy lines.

One boy—no one knows his name—was shot in the stomach five times, but he kept charging forward into the enemy until he fell over.

Corporal Billy R. Burkhard, of Knoxville, Tennessee, was a cook who was killed because he volunteered to go up on the ridge to help out his buddies.

Private Clifford R. High, of Manteca, California, reorganized his platoon after the lieutenant that led it was killed. He assumed command on his own initiative and led the platoon to the top of the last Communist-held hill. Once during the action he was knocked unconscious by the concussion of a grenade explosion and was reported by his men as dead. He regained consciousness and led the platoon on to its objective.

"But getting down and saying this fellow was a hero or that fellow was a hero—gee, it's hard," said Lieutenant Raymond Riddle, of Dearborn, Michigan. "You see so much. They're doing it for their buddies. The men had spent so many lives and so many wounded getting what they held they just weren't willing to give it up."

Crossing the Last Frontier

Dr. Wernher von Braun

Dr. von Braun, son of a German baron, was wartime technical director of the German Rocket Research Center at Peenemuende, in charge of construction of the great V-2 rockets. He came to America after the war to become technical director of the Army Ordnance Guided Missiles Development Center at Huntsville, Alabama, and this nation's outstanding authority on rocketry. Five years before the first man-made satellite went into orbit, he wrote this detailed account of how man will mount a space-platform, and proceed from there to the conquest of the last frontier.

March 22, 1952

WITHIN THE NEXT 10 OR 15 YEARS, THE earth will have a new companion in the skies, a man-made satellite that could be either the greatest force for peace ever devised, or one of the most terrible weapons of war—depending on who makes and controls it. Inhabited by humans, and visible from the ground as a fast-moving star, it will sweep around the earth at an incredible rate of speed in that dark void beyond the atmosphere which is known as "space."

In the opinion of many top experts, this artificial moon—which will be carried into space, piece by piece, by rocket ships—will travel along a celestial route 1,075 miles above the earth, completing a trip around the globe every two hours. Nature will provide the motive power; a neat balance between its speed and the earth's gravitational pull will keep it on course (just as the moon is fixed in its orbit by the same two factors). The speed at which the 250-foot-wide, "wheel"-shaped satellite will move will be an almost unbelievable 4.4 miles per second, or 15,840 miles per hour—20 times the speed of sound. However, this terrific velocity will not be apparent to its occupants. To them, the space station will appear to be a perfectly steady platform.

From this platform, a trip to the moon itself will be just a step, as scientists reckon distance in space.

The choice of the so-called "two-hour" orbit—in preference to a faster one, closer to the earth, or a slower one like the 29-day orbit of the moon—has one major advantage: although far enough up to avoid the hazards of the earth's atmosphere, it is close enough to afford a superb observation post.

Technicians in this space station—using specially designed, powerful telescopes attached to large optical screens, radarscopes and cameras—will keep under constant inspection every ocean, continent, country and city. Even small towns will be clearly visible through optical instruments that will give the watchers in space the same vantage point enjoyed by a man in an observation plane only 5,000 feet off the ground.

Nothing will go unobserved. Within each two-hour period, as the earth revolves inside the satellite's orbit, one twelfth of the globe's territory will pass into the view of the space station's occupants; within each 24-hour period, the entire surface of the earth will have been visible.

Over North America, for example, the space station might pass over the East Coast at, say 10:00 A.M., and, after having completed a full revolution around the earth, would—because the earth itself has turned meanwhile—pass over the West Coast two hours later. In the course of that one revolution it would have been north as far as Nome, Alaska, and south almost to Little America on the Antarctic Continent. At 10:00 A.M. the next day, it would appear once again over the East Coast.

Despite the vast territory thus covered, selected spots on the earth could receive pinpoint examination. For example, troop maneuvers, planes being readied on the flight deck of an aircraft carrier, or bombers forming into groups over an airfield will be clearly discernible. Because of the telescopic eyes and cameras of the space station, it will be almost impossible for any nation to hide warlike preparations for any length of time.

These things we know from high-altitude photographs and astronomical studies: to the naked eye, the earth, more than 1,000 miles below, will appear as a gigantic, glowing globe. It will be an awe-inspiring sight. On the earth's "day" side, the space station's crew will see glaring white patches of overcast reflecting the light of the sun. The continents will stand out in shades of gray and brown bordering the brilliant blue of the seas. North America will look like a great patchwork of brown, gray and green reaching all the way to the snow-covered Rockies. And one polar cap—whichever happens to be enjoying summer at the time—will show as a blinding white, too brilliant to look at with the naked eye.

On the earth's "night" side, the world's cities will be clearly visible as twinkling points of light. Surrounded by the hazy aura of its atmosphere—that great ocean of air in which we live—the earth will be framed by the absolute black of space.

Development of the space station is as inevitable as the rising of the sun; man has already poked his nose into space and he is not likely to pull it back.

On the 14th of September, 1944, a German V-2 rocket, launched from a small island in the Baltic, soared to a peak altitude of 109 miles. Two years later, on December 17, 1946, another V-2, fired at the Army Ordnance's White Sands Proving Ground, New Mexico, reached a height of 114 miles—more than five times the highest altitude ever attained by a meteorological sounding balloon. And on the 24th of February, 1949, a "two-stage rocket" (a small rocket named the "WAC Corporal," fired from the nose of a V-2 acting as carrier or "first stage") soared up to a height of 250 miles—roughly the distance between New York and Washington, but straight up!

These projectiles utilize the same principle of propulsion as the jet airplane. It is based on Isaac Newton's third law of motion, which can be stated this way: for every action there must be a reaction of equal force, but in the opposite direction. A good example is the firing of a bullet from a rifle. When you pull the trigger and the bullet speeds out of the barrel, there is a recoil which slams the rifle butt back against your shoulder. If the rifle were lighter and the explosion of the cartridge more powerful, the gun might go flying over your shoulder for a considerable distance.

This is the way a rocket works. The body of the rocket is like the rifle barrel; the gases ejected from its tail are like the bullet. And the power of a rocket is measured not in horsepower, but in pounds or tons of recoil—called "thrust." Because it depends on the recoil principle, this method of propulsion does not require air.

There is nothing mysterious about making use of this principle as the first step toward making our space station a reality. On the basis of present engineering knowledge, only a determined effort and the money to back it up are required. And if we don't do it, another nation—possibly less peace-minded—will. If we were to begin it immediately, and could keep going at top speed, the whole program would take about 10 years. The estimated cost would be $4,000,000,000—about twice the cost of developing the atomic bomb, but less than one quarter the price of military materials ordered by the Defense Department during the last half of 1951.

Our first need would be a huge rocket capable of carrying a crew and some 30 or 40 tons of cargo into the "two-hour" orbit. This can be built. To understand how, we again use the modern gun as an example.

A shell swiftly attains a certain speed within the gun barrel, then merely coasts through a curved path toward its target. A long-range rocket also requires its initial speed during a comparatively short time, then is carried by momentum.

For example, the V-2 rocket in a 200-mile flight is under power for only 65 seconds, during which it travels 20 miles. At the end of this 65-second period of propulsion it reaches a cut-off speed of 3,600 miles per hour; it coasts the remaining 180 miles. Logically, therefore, if we want to step up the range of a rocket, we must increase its speed during the period of powered flight. If we could step up its cut-off speed to 8,280 miles per hour, it would travel 1,000 miles.

To make a shell hit its target, the gun barrel has to be elevated and pointed in the proper direction. If the barrel were pointed straight up into the sky, the shell would climb to a certain altitude and then simply fall back, landing quite close to the gun. Exactly the same thing happens when a rocket is fired vertically. But to make the rocket reach a distant target after its vertical take-off, it must be tilted after it reaches a certain height above the ground. In rockets capable of carrying a crew and cargo, the tilting would be done by swivel-mounted rocket motors, which, by blasting sideways, would cause the rocket to veer.

Employing this method, at a cut-off speed of 17,460 miles per hour, a rocket would coast halfway around the globe before striking ground. And by boosting to just a little higher cut-off speed—4.86 miles per second or 17,500 miles per hour—its coasting path, after the power had been cut off, would match the curvature of the earth. The rocket would actually be "falling around the earth," because its speed and the earth's gravitational pull would balance exactly.

It would never fall back to the ground, for it would now be an artificial satellite, circling according to the same laws that govern the moon's path about the earth.

Making it do this would require delicate timing—but when you think of the split-second predictions of the eclipses, you will grant that there can hardly be any branch of natural science more accurate than the one dealing with the motion of heavenly bodies.

Will it be possible to attain this fantastic speed of 17,500 miles per hour necessary to reach our chosen two-hour orbit? This is almost five times as fast as the V-2. Of course, we can replace the V-2's alcohol and liquid oxygen by more powerful propellants, and even, by improving the design, reduce the rocket's dead weight and thereby boost the speed by some 40 or 50 per cent; but we would still have a long way to go.

The WAC Corporal, starting from the nose of a V-2 and climbing to 250 miles, has shown us what we must do if we want to step up drastically the speed of a rocket. The WAC started its own rocket motor the moment the V-2 carrying it had reached its maximum speed. It thereby added its own speed to that already achieved by the first stage. As mentioned earlier, such a piggyback arrangement is called a "two-stage rocket"; and by putting a two-stage rocket on another, still larger, booster, we get a three-stage rocket. A three-stage rocket, then, could treble the speed attainable by one rocket stage alone (which would give it enough speed to become a satellite).

In fact, it could do even better. The three-stage rocket may be considered as a rocket with three sets of motors; after the first set has given its utmost, and has expired, it is jettisoned—and so is the second set, in its turn. The third stage, or nose, of the rocket continues on its way, relieved of all that excess weight.

Besides the loss of the first two stages, other factors make the rocket's journey easier the higher it goes. First, the atmosphere is dense, and tends to hinder the passage of the rocket; once past it, the going is faster. Second, the rocket motors operate more efficiently in the rarefied upper layers of the atmosphere. Third, after passing through the densest portion of the atmosphere, the rocket no longer need climb vertically.

Imagine the size of this huge three-stage rocket ship: it stands 265 feet tall, approximately the height of a 24-story office building. Its base measures 65 feet in diameter. And the over-all weight of this monster rocket ship is 14,000,000 pounds, or 7,000 tons—about the same weight as a light destroyer.

Its three huge power plants are driven by a combination of nitric acid and hydrazine, the latter being a liquid compound of nitrogen and hydrogen, somewhat resembling its better-known cousin, ammonia. These propellants are fed into the rocket motors by means of turbopumps.

Fifty-one rocket motors, pushing with a combined thrust of 14,000 tons, power the first stage (tail section). These motors consume a total of 5,250 tons of propellants in the incredibly short time of 84 seconds. Thus, in less than a minute and a half, the rocket loses 75 per cent of its total original weight!

The second stage (middle section), mounted on top of the first, has 34 rocket motors with a total thrust of 1,750 tons, and burns 770 tons of propellants. It operates for only 124 seconds.

The third and final stage (nose section) —carrying the crew, equipment and pay load—has five rocket motors with a combined thrust of 220 tons. This "body" or cabin stage of the rocket ship carries 90 tons of propellants, including ample reserves for the return trip to earth. In addition, it is capable of carrying a cargo or pay load of about 36 tons into our two-hour orbit 1,075 miles above sea level. (Also, in expectation of the return trip, the nose section will have wings something like an airplane's. They will be used only during the descent, after re-entering the earth's atmosphere.)

Years before the actual take-off, smaller rocket ships, called instrument carriers, will have been sent up to the two-hour orbit. They will circle there, sending back information by the same electronic method already in use with current rockets. Based on the data thus obtained, scientists, astronomers, and engineers, along with experts from the armed forces, will plan the complete development of the huge cargo-carrying rocket ship.

The choice of the take-off site poses another problem. Because of the vast amount of auxiliary equipment—such as fuel storage tanks and machine shops, and other items like radio, radar, astronomical and meteorological stations—an extensive area is required. Furthermore, it is essential, for reasons which will be explained later, that the rocket ship fly over the ocean during the early part of the flight. The tiny U.S. possession known as Johnston Island, in the Pacific, or the Air Force Proving Ground at Cocoa, Florida, are presently considered by the experts to be suitable sites.

At the launching area, the heavy rocket ship is assembled on a great platform. Then the platform is wheeled into place over a tunnel-like "jet deflector" which drains off the fiery gases of the first stage's rocket motors. Finally, with a mighty roar which is heard many miles away, the rocket ship slowly takes off—so slowly, in fact, that in the first second it travels less than 15 feet. Gradually, however, it begins to pick up speed, and 20 seconds later it has disappeared into the clouds.

Because of the terrific acceleration which will be experienced one minute later, the crew—located, of course, in the nose—will be lying flat in "contour" chairs at take-off, facing up. Throughout the whole of its flight to the two-hour orbit, the rocket is under the control of an automatic gyropilot. The timing of its flight and the various maneuvers which take place have to be so precise that only a machine can be trusted to do the job.

After a short interval, the automatic pilot tilts the rocket into a shallow path. By 84 seconds after take-off, when the fuels of the first stage (tail section) are nearly exhausted, the rocket ship is climbing at a gentle angle of 20.5 degrees.

When it reaches an altitude of 24.9 miles it will have a speed of 1.46 miles per second, or 5,256 miles per hour. To enable the upper stages to break away from the tail or first stage, the tail's power has to be throttled down to almost zero. The motors of the second stage now begin to operate, and the connection between the now-useless first stage and the rest of the rocket ship is severed. The tail section drops behind, while the two upper stages of the rocket ship forge ahead.

After the separation, a ring-shaped ribbon parachute, made of fine steel wire mesh, is automatically released by the first stage. This chute has a diameter of 217 feet and gradually it slows down the tail section. But under its own momentum, this empty hull continues to climb, reaching a height of 40 miles before slowly descending. It is because the tail section could be irreparably damaged if it struck solid ground (and might be dangerous, besides) that the initial part of the trip must be over the sea. After the first stage lands in the water, it is collected and brought back to the launching site.

The same procedure is repeated 124 seconds later. The second stage (middle section) is dropped into the ocean. The rocket ship by this time has attained an altitude of 40 miles and is 332 miles from the take-off site. It also has reached a tremendous speed—14,364 miles per hour.

Now the third and last stage—the nose section or cabin-equipped space ship proper—proceeds under the power of its own rocket motors. Just 84 seconds after the dropping of the second stage, the rocket ship, now moving at 18,468 miles per hour, reaches a height of 63.3 miles above the earth.

At this point we must recall the comparison between the rocket and the coasting rifle shell to understand what occurs. The moment the rocket reaches a speed of 18,468 miles per hour, at an altitude of 63.3 miles, the motors are cut off, even though the fuel supply is by no means exhausted. The rocket ship continues on an unpowered trajectory until it reaches 1,075 miles above the earth. This is the high point, or "apogee"; in this case it is exactly halfway around the globe from the cut-off place. The rocket ship is now in the two-hour orbit where we intend to build the space station.

Just one more maneuver has to be performed, however. In coasting up from 63.3 miles to 1,075 miles, the rocket ship has been slowed by the earth's gravitational pull to 14,770 miles per hour. This is not sufficient to keep the ship in our chosen orbit. If we do not increase the speed, the craft will swing back halfway around the earth to the 63.3-mile altitude. Then it would continue on past the earth until, as it curves around to the other side of the globe, it would be back at the same apogee, at the 1,075-mile altitude.

The rocket ship would already be a satellite and behave like a second moon in the heavens, swinging on its elliptical path over and over for a long time. One might well ask: Why not be satisfied with this? The reason is that part of this particular orbit is in the atmosphere at only 63.3 miles. And while the air resistance there is very low, in time it would cause the rocket ship to fall back to earth.

Our chosen two-hour orbit is one which, at *all* points, is exactly 1,075 miles above the earth. The last maneuver, which stabilizes the rocket ship in this orbit, is accomplished by turning on the rocket motors for about 15 seconds. The velocity is thus increased by 1,030 miles per hour, bringing the total speed to 15,800 miles per hour. This is the speed necessary for remaining in the orbit permanently. We have reached our goal.

An extraordinary fact about the flight from the earth is this: it has taken only 56 minutes, during which the rocket ship was powered for only five minutes.

From our vantage point, 1,075 miles up, the earth, to the rocket ship's crew, appears to be rotating once every two hours. This apparent fast spin of the globe is the only indication of the tremendous speed at which the rocket ship is moving. The earth, of course, still requires a full 24 hours to complete one revolution on its axis, but the rocket ship is making 12 revolutions around the earth during the time the earth makes one.

We now begin to unload the 36 tons of cargo which we have carried up with us. But how and where shall we unload the material? There is nothing but the blackness of empty space all around us.

We simply dump it out of the ship. For the cargo, too, has become a satellite! So have the crew members. Wearing grotesque-looking pressurized suits and carrying oxygen for breathing, they can now leave the rocket ship and float about unsupported.

Just as a man on the ground is not conscious of the fact that he is moving with the earth around the sun at the rate of 66,600 miles per hour, so the men in the space ship are not aware of the fantastic speed with which they are going around the earth. Unlike men on the ground, however, the men in space do not experience any gravitational pull. If one of them, while working, should drift off into space, it will be far less serious than slipping off a scaffold. Drifting off merely means that the man has acquired a very slight speed in an unforeseen direction.

He can stop himself in the same manner in which any speed is increased or stopped in space—by reaction. He might do this, theoretically, by firing a revolver in the direction of his inadvertent movement. But in actual practice the suit will be equipped with a small rocket motor. He could also propel himself by squirting some compressed oxygen from a tank on his back. It is highly probable, however, that each crew member will have a safety line securing him to the rocket as he works. The tools he uses will also be secured to him by lines; otherwise they might float away into space.

The spacemen—for that is what the crew members now are—will begin sorting the equipment brought up. Floating in strange positions among structural units and machinery, their work will proceed in absolute silence, for there is no air to carry sound. Only when two people are working on the same piece of material, both actually touching it, will one be able to hear the noises made by another, because sound is conducted by most materials. They will, however, be able to converse with built-in "walkie-talkie" radio equipment. The cargo moves easily; there is no weight, and no friction. To push it, our crew member need only turn on his rocket motor (if he shoved a heavy piece of equipment without rocket power, he might fly backward!).

Obviously the pay load of our rocket ship—though equivalent to that of two huge Super Constellations—will not be sufficient to begin construction of the huge, three-decked, 250-foot-wide space station. Many more loads will be required. Other rocket ships, all timed to arrive at the same point in a continuous procession as the work progresses, will carry up the remainder of the prefabricated satellite. This will be an expensive proposition. Each rocket trip will cost more than half a million dollars *for propellants alone*. Thus, weight and shipping space limitations will greatly affect the specifications of a space station.

In at least one design, the station consists of 20 sections made of flexible nylon-and-plastic fabric. Each of these sections is an independent unit which later, after assembly into a closed ring, will provide compartmentation similar to that found in submarines. To save shipping space, these sections will be carried to the orbit in a collapsed condition. After the "wheel" has been put together and sealed, it will then be inflated like an automobile tire to slightly less than normal atmospheric pressure. This pressure will not only provide a breathable atmosphere within the ring but will give the whole structure its necessary rigidity. The atmosphere will, of course, have to be renewed as the men inside exhaust it.

On solid earth, most of our daily activities are conditioned by gravity. We put something on a table and it stays there, because the earth attracts it, pulling it against the table. When we pour a glass of milk, gravity draws it out of the bottle and we catch the falling liquid in a glass. In space, however, everything is weightless. And this includes man.

This odd condition in no way spells danger, at least for a limited period of time. We experience weightlessness for short periods when we jump from a diving board into a pool. To be sure, there are some medical men who are concerned at the prospect of permanent weightlessness —not because of any known danger, but because of the unknown possibilities. Most experts discount these nameless fears.

However, there can be no doubt that permanent weightlessness might often prove inconvenient. What we require, therefore, is a "synthetic" gravity within the space station. And we can produce centrifugal force—which acts as a substitute for gravity—by making the "wheel" slowly spin about its hub (a part of which can be made stationary).

To the space station proper, we attach a tiny rocket motor which can produce enough power to rotate the satellite. Since there is no resistance which would slow the "wheel" down, the rocket motor does not have to function continuously. It will operate only long enough to give the desired rotation. Then it is shut off.

Now, how fast would we like our station to spin? That depends on how much "synthetic gravity" we want. If our 250-foot ring performed one full revolution every 12.3 seconds, we would get a synthetic gravity equal to that which we normally experience on the ground. This is known as "one gravity" or, abbreviated, "1 g." For a number of reasons, it may be advantageous not to produce one full "g." Consequently, the ring can spin more slowly; for example, it might make one full revolution every 22 seconds, which would result in a "synthetic gravity" of about one third of normal surface gravity.

The centrifugal force created by the slow spin of the space station forces everything out from the hub. No matter where the crew members sit, stand or walk inside, their heads will always point toward the hub. In other words, the inside wall of the "wheel's" outer rim serves as the floor.

How about the temperature within the space station? Maybe you, too, have heard the old fairy tale that outer space is extremely cold—absolute zero. It's cold, all right, but not that cold—and not in the satellite. The ironical fact is that the engineering problem in this respect will be to keep the space station comfortably cool, rather than to heat it up. In outer space, the temperature of any structure depends entirely on its absorption and dissipation of the sun's rays. The space station happens to be in the unfortunate position of receiving not only direct heat from the sun but also reflected heat from the earth.

If we paint the space station white, it will then absorb a minimum of solar heat. Being surrounded by a perfect vacuum, it will be, except for its shape, a sort of thermos bottle, which keeps hot what is hot, and cold what is cold.

In addition, we can scatter over the surface of the space station a number of black patches which, in turn, can be covered by shutters closely resembling white Venetian blinds. When these blinds are open on the sunny side, the black patches will absorb more heat and warm up the station. When the blinds are open on the shaded side, the black patches will radiate more heat into space, thereby cooling the station. Operate all these blinds with little electric motors, hook them to a thermostat, and tie the whole system in with the station's air-conditioning plant—and there's your temperature control system.

Inflating the space station with air will, as we have indicated, provide a breathable atmosphere for a limited time only. The crew will consume oxygen at a rate of approximately three pounds per man per day. At intervals, therefore, this life-giving oxygen will have to be replenished by supply ships from earth. At the same time, carbon dioxide and toxic or odorous products must be constantly removed from the air-circulation system. The air must also be dehumidified, inasmuch as through breathing and perspiration each crew member will lose more than three pounds of water per day to the air system (just as men do on earth).

This water can be collected in a dehumidifier, from which it can economically be salvaged, purified and reused.

Both the air-conditioning and water-recover units need power. So do the radar systems, radio transmitters, astronomical equipment, electronic cookers and other machinery. As a source for this power we have the sun. On the earth, solar power is reliable in only a few places where clouds rarely obscure the sky, but in space there are no clouds, and the sun is the simplest answer to the station's power needs.

Our power plant will consist of a condensing mirror and a boiler. The condensing mirror will be a highly polished sheet metal trough running around the "wheel." The position of the space station can be arranged so that the side to which the mirror is attached will always point toward the sun. The mirror then focuses the sun's rays on a steel pipe which runs the length of the mirrored trough. Liquid mercury is fed under pressure into one end of this pipe and hot mercury vapor is taken out at the other end. This vapor drives a turbogenerator which produces about 500 kilowatts of electricity.

Of course, the mercury vapor has to be used over and over again, so after it has done its work in the turbine it is returned to the "boiler" pipe in the mirror. Before this can be done, the vapor has to be condensed back into liquid mercury by cooling. This is achieved by passing the vapor through pipes located behind the mirror in the shade. These pipes dissipate the heat of the vapor into space.

Thus we have within the space station a complete, synthetic environment capable of sustaining man in space. Of course, man will face hazards—some of them, like cosmic radiation and possible collision with meteorites, potentially severe. These problems are being studied, however, and they are considered far from insurmountable.

Our "wheel" will not be alone in the two-hour orbit. There will nearly always be one or two rocket ships unloading supplies. They will be parked some distance away, to avoid the possibility of damaging the space station by collision or by the blast from the vehicle's rocket motors. To ferry men and materials from rocket ship to space station, small rocket-powered metal craft of limited range, shaped very much like overgrown watermelons, will be used. These "space taxis" will be pressurized and, after boarding them, passengers can remove their space suits.

On approaching the space station, the

tiny shuttle-craft will drive directly into an air lock at the top or bottom of the stationary hub. The space taxi will be built to fit exactly into the air lock, sealing the opening like a plug. The occupants can then enter the space station proper without having been exposed to the airlessness of space at any time since leaving the air lock of the rocket ship.

There will also be a space observatory, a small structure some distance away from the main satellite, housing telescopic cameras for taking long-exposure photographs. (The space station itself will carry extremely powerful cameras, but its spin, though slow, will permit only short exposures.) The space observatory will not be manned, for if it were, the movements of an operator would disturb the alignment. Floating outside the structure in space suits, technicians will load a camera with special plates or film, and then withdraw. The camera will be aimed and the shutter snapped by remote radio control from the space station.

Most of the pictures taken of the earth, however, will be by the space station's cameras. The observatory will be used mainly to record the outer reaches of the universe, from the neighboring planets to the distant galaxies of stars. This mapping of the heavens will produce results which no observatory on earth could possibly duplicate. And, while the scientists are probing the secrets of the universe with their cameras, they will also be planning another trip through space—this time to examine the moon.

Suppose we take the power plant out of our rocket ship's last stage and attach it to a lightweight skeleton frame of aluminum girders. Then we suspend some large collapsible fuel containers in this structure and fill them with propellants. Finally, we connect some plumbing and wiring and top the whole structure with a cabin for the crew, completely equipped with air and water regeneration systems, and navigation and guidance equipment.

The result will be an oddly shaped vehicle, not much larger than the rocket ship's third stage, but capable of carrying a crew of several people to a point beyond the rear side of the moon, then back to the space station. This vehicle will bear little resemblance to the moon rockets depicted in science fiction. There is a very simple reason: conventional streamlining is not necessary in space.

The space station, as mentioned previously, has a speed of 15,840 miles per hour. Our round-the-moon ship, to leave the two-hour orbit, has to have a speed of 22,100 miles per hour, to cover the 238,000-mile distance to the moon. This additional speed is acquired by means of a short rocket blast, lasting barely two minutes. This throws the round-the-moon ship into a long arc or ellipse, with its remotest point beyond the moon. The space ship will then coast out this distance, unpowered, like a thrown stone. It will lose speed all along the way, due to the steady action of the earth's gravitational pull—which, though weakening with distance, extends far out into space.

Roughly five days after departure, the space ship will come almost to a standstill. And if we have timed our departure correctly, the moon will now pass some 200 miles below us, with the earth on its far side. On this one trip we can photograph most of the unknown half of the moon, the half which has never been seen from the earth. Furthermore, we now have an excellent opportunity to view the earth from the farthest point yet; at this distance, it appears not unlike a miniature reproduction of itself (from the vicinity of the moon, the earth will look about four times as large as the full moon does to earth-bound man).

It is not necessary to turn on the space ship's motors for the return trip. The moon's gravity is too slight to affect us substantially; like the shell which was fired vertically, we simply "fall back" to the space station's orbit. The long five-day "fall" causes the space ship to regain its initial sped of 22,100 miles per hour. This is 6,340 miles per hour faster than the speed of the space station, but, as we have fallen back tail first, we simply turn on the motors for just two minutes, which reduces our speed to the correct rate which permits us to re-enter the two-hour orbit.

Besides its use as a springboard for the exploration of the solar system, and as a watchdog of the peace, the space station will have many other functions. Meteorologists, by observing cloud patterns over large areas of the earth, will be able to predict the resultant weather more easily, more accurately and further into the future. Navigators on the seas and in the air will utilize the space station as a "fix," for it will always be recognizable.

But there will also be another possible use for the space station—and a most terrifying one. It can be converted into a terribly effective atomic bomb carrier. Small winged rocket missiles with atomic war heads could be launched from the station in such a manner that they would strike their targets at supersonic speeds. By simultaneous radar tracking of both missile and target, these atomic-headed rockets could be accurately guided to any spot on the earth.

In view of the station's ability to pass over all inhabited regions on earth, such atom-bombing techniques would offer the satellite's builders the most important tactical and strategic advance in military history. Furthermore, its observers probably could spot, in plenty of time, any attempt by an enemy to launch a rocket aimed at colliding with the giant "wheel" and intercept it.

We have discussed how to get from the ground to the two-hour orbit, how to build the space station and how to get a look at the unknown half of the moon by way of a round trip from our station in space. But how do we return to earth?

Unlike the ascent to the orbit, which was controlled by an automatic pilot, the descent is in the hands of an experienced "space pilot."

To leave the two-hour orbit in the third stage, or nose section, of the rocket ship, the pilot slows down the vehicle in the same manner in which the returning round-the-moon ship slowed down. He reduces the speed by 1,070 miles per hour. Unpowered, the rocket ship then swings back toward the earth. After 51 minutes, during which we half circumnavigate the globe, the rocket ship enters the upper layers of the atmosphere. Again, it has fallen tail first; now the pilot turns it so that it enters the atmosphere nose first.

About 50 miles above the earth, due to our downward, gravity-powered swing from the space station's orbit, our speed has increased to 18,500 miles per hour. At this altitude there is already considerable air resistance.

With its wings and control surfaces, the rocket closely resembles an airplane. At first, however, the wings do not have to carry the rocket ship. On the contrary, they must prevent it from soaring out of the atmosphere and back into the space station's orbit again.

His eyes glued to the altimeter, the pilot will push his control stick forward and force the ship to stay at an altitude of exactly 50 miles. At this height, the air resistance gradually slows the rocket ship down. Only then can the descent into the denser atmosphere begin; from there on, the wings bear more and more of the ship's weight. After covering a distance of about 10,000 miles in the atmosphere, the rocket's speed will still be as high as 13,300 miles per hour. After another 3,000 miles, the speed will be down to 5,760 miles per hour. The rocket ship will by now have descended to a height of 29 miles.

The progress of the ship through the upper atmosphere has been so fast that air friction has heated the outer metal skin of body and wings to a temperature of about 1,300 degrees Fahrenheit. The rocket ship has actually turned color, from steel blue to cherry red! This should not cause undue concern, however, inasmuch as we have heat-resistant steels which can easily endure such temperatures. The canopy and windows will be built of double-paned glass with a liquid coolant flowing between the panes. And the crew and cargo spaces will be properly heat-insulated and cooled by means of a refrigerator-type air-conditioning system. Similar problems have already been solved, on a somewhat smaller scale, in present-day supersonic airplanes.

At a point 15 miles above the earth, the rocket ship finally slows down to the speed of sound—roughly 750 miles per hour. From here on, it spirals down to the ground like a normal airplane. It can land on conventional landing gear, on a runway adjacent to the launching site. The touch-down speed will be approximately 65 miles per hour, which is less than that of today's airliners. And if the pilot should miss the runway, a small rocket motor will enable him to circle once more and make a second approach.

After a thorough checkup, the third stage will be ready for another ascent into the orbit. The first and second stages (or tail and middle sections), which were parachuted down to the ocean, have been collected in specially made seagoing dry docks. They were calculated to fall at 189 miles and 906 miles respectively from the launching site. They will be found relatively undamaged, because at a point 150 feet above the water their parachute fall was broken by a set of cordite rockets which were automatically set off by a proximity fuse.

They, too, undergo a thorough inspection with some replacement of parts damaged by the ditching. Then all three stages are put together again in a tower-like hangar, right on the launching platform, and, after refueling and a final check, platform and ship are wheeled out to the launching site—ready for another journey into man's oldest and last frontier: the heavens themselves.

San Francisco: April 18, 1906

Robert O'Brien

Fifty years after Jack London's eyewitness story of the San Francisco earthquake and fire (Page 114) Robert O'Brien reconstructed the events of that memorable day for Collier's. *Blending the results of exhaustive research with his own great narrative skill, O'Brien—in the editor's judgment—brought the story alive more vividly than anyone before him.*

March 30, 1956

THOSE WHO LIVED TO TELL THE TALE remembered that Wednesday, April 18, 1906, came in on the fairest of dawns. It was a dawn filled with tremulous, pale-green light and bird song, and quite lovely enough for the birth of a world, or the death of one.

Across the Far West and down the Pacific littoral, everything stood still, everything stood expectant, everything waited for the majestic sun to come rising up beyond the curve of the continent, the way it always does in this kind of daybreak, as if to a crescendo of triumphant golden trumpets.

By the shore of the Pacific, on the ranches, in the mountain cabins, beside the vineyards and orange groves, in the hamlets and towns and cities, the people slept, or drowsily picked up the tempo, the rhythm, of another day of living.

High in Paradise Valley, in the desolate buttes north of Winnemucca, Nevada, a rancher sat his horse and watered his cattle beside a dark, dawn-still pond. Four hundred miles west to the tumbling surf and still another 150 miles at sea, the schooner John A. Campbell heeled lazily before the fresh morning breeze, steering for the Golden Gate.

South of San Francisco, a cramming Stanford student scowled over his textbook in a dormitory room. In the telephone company office at Salinas, an operator chatted sleepily with her friend on the switchboard 180 miles down the coast at San Luis Obispo. Awake in his bunk in a Sierra shack 50 miles east of Bakersfield a mountaineer idly studied the tooling on the holster of the six-shooter that hung from a nail above his head.

Beside her peaceful bay and across her more than 40 hills, San Francisco also waited. To many she was many things—third-ranking commercial center in the United States, gateway to the Orient, skyscrapered metropolis of the Western shore. Others remembered her as a bad town, a bawdy town, a hell-raising boom camp and as rollicking and wild a port as any on the seven seas—a town with a past, a warmhearted hoyden of a town with spangles in her hair.

But as many more would never forget her because they had known her the way she was in April. She had filled their hearts with springtime light and laughter, with song and soft desires. She had cast her April spell and on such mornings as this had made them poets and adventurers and enchanted them forever.

Graceful and touching rose her spires in the breathless air. The smoke drifted drowsily from her cottage breakfast fires. Milkmen's horses clip-clopped along the quiet streets. Here and there a cable car clattered through a crossing.

Four hundred thousand strong, her people were, and known the world around for their devotion to this blithe and bonny city, their bright-lipped Pacific queen.

In rose-covered shanties on Telegraph Hill, in reeking waterfront warrens, in the teeming tenements of Chinatown and the gilt-and-crystal splendor of Nob Hill mansions they slept, in tindery flats South of Market Street, in solid, bow-windowed homes of Russian Hill and Pacific Heights and Cow Hollow. On their bureaus, in downstairs halls, on living-room mantels and kitchen shelves, their clocks ticked on.

In a bedroom adjoining his wife's above Engine No. 1 in Bush Street, fifty-four-year-old fire chief Dennis T. Sullivan lay abed as if bodily felled. He had fought a three-alarm fire at Bay and Mason Streets that night, and had turned in without finishing his report.

In an airy, second-floor bedroom west of Van Ness Avenue, a novelist who had come from Carmel the day before to confer with her publisher's agent slept deeply, and without dreams.

On the southern slope of Nob Hill, Arnold Genthe, the talented portrait photographer, reposed amid his books and his collection of ancient Chinese porcelains. He had arrived home after midnight from the Metropolitan Opera Company's production of Carmen, and the last thing he remembered before dropping off was a confused composite—the lighted stage of Mission Street's Grand Opera House, tiers of diamond-bedecked ladies and their attentive escorts, the theater's high, glittering chandelier, and, superimposed against them all, the weaving mesmeric baton of conductor Arturo Vigna.

The company's chief conductor, Alfred Hertz, slept soundly in a room on the sixth floor of the Palace Hotel, a few steps from the chamber of Enrico Caruso. The stocky tenor, who had thrilled the brilliant audience with his dashing Don José, was deep in abandoned sleep, head flung back on a sea of pillows, mouth open, sonorously snoring.

On the fourth floor of a seven-story hotel not quite so elegant as the Palace slept a reporter for the San Francisco Call. Strewn on the floor, where he had dropped it before turning off his light, was a late edition of that morning's paper. A headline reported that San Franciscans had raised $1,048 for the relief of sufferers in the recent eruption of Mount Vesuvius. The weather box said, "Fair and warmer. Light north wind."

The U.S. Weather Bureau forecaster who had filed this report was sound asleep, too. Neatly arranged on his bedside table were his astronomically timed watch, a pencil, a clean pad of paper and a small electric torch. Every night for 20 years he had placed them that way beside his bed, in case something should happen that he would need to record for science.

Six blocks north of Genthe's studio, on the northern ridge of Nob Hill, the home of Brigadier General Frederick Funston, acting commander of the Army's Pacific Division, was dim and quiet. General Funston had been studying a lengthy memorandum; he read until the type swam before his eyes, then snapped off his light and immediately fell into deep slumber. The hands of the night-stand clock stood at precisely eleven minutes after five.

Down on Sansome Street two men unlocked a door and entered a type foundry. They put their lunch pails on a bench and took off their hats and coats and tied on grimy aprons.

"Looks like another scorcher, don't it, Ed?" one of them said.

"Yeah," Ed replied. He glanced out a window. The eastern sky was filled with promise. "Hot and hazy," he grinned, "and a day to be fishing off the heads."

The watch at the scientist's bedside and the clock on the general's night stand ticked away—ticked off another 60 seconds—and hung poised at twelve minutes after five.

At that moment it happened.

The stresses, the unimaginable tensions, had accumulated miles down, in earth drifts made millions of years ago. Now the hour struck, the instant arrived when the earth's crust could no longer bear the strain, and gave way and cracked along the San Andreas Fault.

It was an old break. Scientists knew it well. For years the tremors and stirrings along its vertical walls told them something big was building up. And now it was here. In one tectonic jolt, one wall slipped in one direction, the other wall moved in the opposite direction. The grinding thrusts, the agony, the tearing wrench split the earth open in a wound 270 miles long.

The rip came in from the sea, striking northwest to southeast and traveling at three miles a second. It hit first the rugged bulge of the Humboldt County coast, some 200 miles north of San Francisco. It crossed the redwood country, the bleak mountain spurs, the black shale bluffs, and passed into the sea again.

Along the ocean floor it broke past the crescent Mendocino Beach and came ashore again at Point Arena. Down the lonely benchlands and along the leaning sandstone bluffs it slashed its gigantic plowshare furrow. It knifed through the sandspits of Bodega Head, and raced across pastures to the fishing village of Bolinas, where it vanished again into the sea. It emerged once more at the beetling cliffs above Mussel Rock, eight miles south of San Francisco. Then it struck across the peninsula uplands, down valleys and a chain of lakes and through the Coast Range notches to the old mission settlement of San Juan Bautista. There, in a marsh, the great wound ended.

The disturbance centered from 12 to 25 miles below the earth's surface and exploded with cosmic force. The earth quaked as if it had been struck a fantastic blow from outer space. Tremors radiated across mountains and under seas.

In a matter of minutes seismographs in distant lands—South Africa and Siberia, Japan and Argentina—would quiver and begin recording perhaps the most stupendous temblor ever experienced by man.

As if they had heard a shot, the cattle at the pond in Paradise Valley, north of Winnemucca, raised their heads. They stood frozen, ears up. Momentarily, the pond's glassy surface ruffled, as if a breeze passed by. But the air was quite still.

Far at sea, the John A. Campbell shuddered. Her crew piled out of their bunks in alarm; undoubtedly she had rammed a derelict, perhaps even a whale. They ran to the rail and stared at the sea. Nothing. Her keel dragged, her stern trembled for an instant, then she sailed on as serenely as before.

In Medford, Oregon, an unlatched door in a dawn-dim house creaked slowly open, then just as slowly closed. In a house on the coast at Coquille a ceiling lamp cord swung a few times east to west, then stopped. In ghost-town cabins in the Mother Lode foothills, rocking chairs spectrally rocked, and at that moment, with a rumble as of distant thunder, great falls of rock and shale detached themselves from the False Cape cliffs of Humboldt County and fell a thousand feet into the sea.

In San Luis Obispo the telephone operator heard a scream and the Salinas connection went dead in her headset. The pistol holster swung back and forth from its nail in Isabella, church bells pealed in Pescadero, and deep in their Coast Range canyons 500-year-old redwoods lashed furiously at the windless sky and split asunder and crashed to earth.

In a museum in San Francisco, the mummies of Egyptian princes, inviolate for 60 centuries, crumbled in a twinkling to dust. Bay Area seismograph pens covered their plates with a frenzy of scrawls, or left the plates entirely. Fire Chief Sullivan, awakening to the sound of avalanching bricks, leaped from bed and burst through the door to Mrs. Sullivan's room. The turret of the hotel next door had punched through the roof and carried away part of her bedroom floor. Blinded by mortar dust, Sullivan lost his balance and pitched into the blackness.

On its remote and rocky headland where it had stood since 1870, the 110-foot Point Arena lighthouse cracked in the middle. High in its lantern room its massive lenses and reflectors crashed to the floor.

As a schoolteacher watched open-mouthed from her window, a 10-foot wave formed on Tomales Bay and rolled shoreward, and a two-story hotel and its stables at the bay's edge tilted and slid gently into the water. In a Marin County dairy corral the earth opened beneath a cow, then closed again, leaving only her hind hoofs and tail sticking out.

The conductor of the Point Reyes local train sang out, "All aboard!" to the empty station, swung aboard a coach and yanked the signal cord, and at that moment his train—locomotive and all—flipped like a hooked trout, and suddenly lay on its side among the right-of-way poppies.

Genthe awoke to the smashing of his Chinese porcelains. Books cascaded from their shelves. His bed shook violently, as if a lunatic poltergeist were intent on spilling him to the floor.

The scientist who had waited 20 years to record a phenomenon for science groped for his watch and pencil to note the minute, but they rocked out of reach. The previous precise seconds ticked into chaos.

A cataract of bricks crushed the Stanford student at his desk. A landslide engulfed a Santa Cruz mountain sawmill, and buried alive nine men and a mastiff.

In the marshy lowlands south of San Francisco, the great iron pipes carrying the city's water supply from its peninsula reservoirs buckled and snapped and were twisted and crushed and even telescoped. White fountains plumed from the breaks into the morning air.

In her airy, second-floor bedroom the lady author awoke to see her marble-topped bureau lunging across the room; it rose first on one caster, then on another, then wagged its top, "like a table at a séance," she thought.

Six million dollars' worth of stone and brickwork shook off the San Francisco city hall and left its frame standing amid the shattered columns like a monstrous bird cage. Conductor Hertz's Palace Hotel room tossed like a ship's cabin in a line squall. Hertz sprang to the protection of the doorframe and cocked an ear to the orchestration of the temblor. It was, he concluded, a *mezzo forte* roll on a gong or cymbal.

He pulled on some clothes and ran downstairs into the wild hubbub of the lobby and the great Palm Court. In one corner a Chinese houseboy calmly dusted the lobby chairs. Caruso, in a fur coat, a bath towel around his golden throat, embraced Hertz. The tenor was sobbing.

"Alfredo!" he cried. "We are lost!"

The two men clung to each other, and waited for the end of the world.

At the Angel Island Light Station in San Francisco Bay it sounded as though an express train had left the rails and was charging at full speed down the ties. Twelve hundred chimneys toppled simultaneously in San Rafael. The Presidio tide gauge began to drop and kept dropping until four inches of water drained out through the Golden Gate from the 450 square miles of San Francisco Bay. In San Jose the heavy brass pendulum of a Western Union clock beat frantically back and forth against the walls of its wooden prison.

There were two great shocks in San Francisco, the first starting (as accurately as could be determined) at 5:12 A.M. The quaking sharpened in intensity for 30 seconds, held its peak for more than 10 seconds, then abruptly ceased. A lull of about 10 seconds followed. Then came a devastating second shock of equal intensity. This lasted for 15 seconds, then passed off in shuddering aftertremors that would occur at an average rate of one an hour for the next 24 hours.

The two shocks ripped with satanic power and purpose into the sandy artificial lands reclaimed from Yerba Buena Cove, and from the swamps, tideflats, creek beds and reeded lagoons in the South of Market and Mission districts.

In terms of people, these two districts represented the warm, the vital, the happy and humble heart of San Francisco. Their tumble-down tenements and flimsily anchored cottages were the homes of mill hands and factory workers, shipwrights and foundrymen and printers—the Irish and the Scotch, the Swedes and the Poles and the sons and daughters of a dozen other countries. This is where they lived, they and their patient, strong-backed wives and their many children.

Their bare bedrooms and calico-curtained parlors came crashing down about their heads in the vast clattering immemorial collapse of the earthquake. Scores of them lay pinned and broken-limbed and helpless in the basement debris, and the rest ran numbly into the alleys and streets, leaving their flaring gas jets, their broken flues and breakfast fires behind them.

In this soft insubstantial earth, the temblor waves tore apart the gridiron pipes of the water system. Gas mains ruptured and exploded. Steel streetcar tracks writhed like wounded snakes. Asphalt buckled. Cobbled streets caved in and sank 10 feet below their grades. In Valencia Street, along the filled-in bed of the old Mission creek, a score of roomers perished as the rickety underpinnings of the Valencia Street Hotel gave way. The hotel collapsed like a telescope. Survivors stepped out of fourth-floor windows at street level.

The roof peaks of buildings fell in and spread their rafters and the rafters in turn kicked out the walls. Without their walls the roofs kept on falling and the buildings simply flattened out.

This was the way it was at the type foundry in Sansome Street, and the foundryman named Ed and the other one were trapped between two upright type racks. They began to shout long-drawn calls for help.

A warehouse in lower Mission Street also collapsed in this manner and one of its brick walls rained down upon a herd of steers that cowboys were driving to a cattle boat. A black, wide-horned brute bolted clear and ran around a corner and into Beale Street. A jittery policeman drew his pistol and shot it three times. Bellowing, it ran down the heaving pavement into Market Street.

General Funston awoke clearheaded and aware that a catastrophe was taking place. He began swiftly to dress.

In his downtown hotel room the reporter heard the earthquake coming with the sound of tearing silk. A blasting concussion shook the building. Plaster showered down.

He staggered to the window, and as he reached it the window and its sash and the fire escape outside the window fell silently away from the room. The sky beyond was the pale, tender green of dawn.

A shadow swooped down the side of the building and vanished into the roofs of a row of wooden houses, and ragged holes appeared in the roofs. He looked up. The shadow had been the brick wall of the upper three stories of his hotel.

He got dressed. The lobby was filled with staring, gray-faced men and women. He shouldered past them and went out into the street. . . .

Out in the residential districts, the rooftops of houses on the hills still saw-toothed firmly against the daybreak sky line, but on the "made-ground" in the swales between the hills they had shaken down entirely or sagged in one direction or another like drunken slatterns.

People fled into their suddenly Humpty Dumpty world, and stood shivering in their nightclothes in the dawn. The earthquake had aimed its blind, malevolent force at each one of them. It had seized each one and rattled his bones as if it meant to kill him in a maniacal frenzy. Standing there, they looked around and listened and tried to relate what they saw and heard to the sane, solid, dependable world they had lived in all their lives.

Across the street was a lodginghouse without a front wall, its abandoned rooms and halls exposed in cross section like the chambers of a biology-class ant colony. In the square was a dowager in nightgown and spangled opera cloak, with a silver teapot in her hand.

Here was the old lady from down the street holding a bird cage with four kittens in it. There was a man hurrying along the sidewalk with coat, hat, suitcase and no trousers.

"Quite a rocker, wasn't it?"

"She'll have to shake harder 'n that to bring this town down!"

" 'Twarn't nothin' to the quake in '68."

Teeth chattering, shaking in sudden bursts of chills, they uttered the platitudes and giggled as if it had been nothing, really, at all; but the lady two houses down had got up 10 minutes ago to put out the milk can and now her bed was buried under three tons of bricks that would have crushed her to jelly if it hadn't been for the milk can, and she was laughing about it and no one could make her stop.

Stocky, bearded General Funston, in civilian clothes, ran down his front steps. The streets were filling with people, but there were no cable cars on the hills. The ropes in the slots were silent. The tracks stretched empty as far as he could see.

He hastened down Jones Street to California, past the towered and turreted mansions of the Central Pacific railroad barons and Comstock silver kings—the $450,000 redwood château of the Crockers, the brownstone palace of the Floods, the gabled villa of the Townes, the $2,500,000, 35-room Gothic castle that housed the Mark Hopkins Institute of Art. Beside the Fairmont Hotel, that rose in a white citadel above the streets and squares of the old Gold Rush town, the general stopped to catch his breath.

Below him, Market Street, 120 feet wide and three miles long, cut straight across the city from the waterfront to Twin Peaks. Beyond Market and south to the ship channels and the stockyards stretched the factories, and lodginghouses, churches, saloons and corner groceries, the grimy parks, clapboard schools and tinderbox homes of the workers. Two or three miles south and east, the streets trailed off into cow pastures along the rolling spurs of Twin Peaks.

The general himself, there on Nob Hill, stood roughly in the center of the city's second great division, north of Market Street. Compact, closely built since pioneer days, it encompassed the financial and shopping districts, the theaters and hotels, Chinatown, the waterfront warehouses and wharves, the steep streets and hillside houses of Nob, Russian and Telegraph Hills, the dives, cribs and rat-ridden gin mills of the Barbary Coast, the North Beach shacks and tenements of the Mexican, Spanish and Italian quarters, the piers, lateen-rigged fishing boats and net-festooned bulkheads of Fisherman's Wharf.

The section north of Market extended on his left to the bay, and, behind him, to Van Ness Avenue. This was a residential boulevard, 125 feet wide, that left Market Street halfway to the Peaks, and struck north for two miles to the bay at Fort Mason.

Beyond Van Ness, to the seaside dunes and the palm-shaded barracks of the Presidio, ranged San Francisco's third general area: the long, quiet streets of the Western Addition, the modest homes of the inner Richmond and Sunset districts, the green lawns and stately pavilions of Golden Gate Park.

The general had indeed been swift; it was five twenty-nine o'clock; far across the hills the sun was coming up in a blaze of red and gold. But fire was swifter still. Here and there, in a dozen different places across the lower city and South of Market, he saw the young scarlet forkings of flame playing above the roofs and cottagetops. Black smoke drifted languidly into the lovely morning air.

The general stared, appalled. The tongues licked greedily higher. The insolent smoke bloomed like an evil flower in the sky. The general broke into a run down the steep California Street grade.

A bank was burning at Sansome Street. An engine company was already there, its hoses down in the street. But the hoses were flat, the gleaming nozzles dry. The firemen ran from one hydrant to another.

"Where's your water?" the general asked.

"The quake broke all the mains."

The general was of well-tempered steel. But keen and resilient as he was, it took a second to recover. For what the fireman had said was that San Francisco was doomed.

For an instant, he felt a fleeting admiration. An enemy general, bent on wiping the city from the face of the earth, would have been a genius to conceive a plan so classic, so stunningly simple, as coldly beautiful as an ending in chess.

General Funston found a policeman and identified himself. "Where is Mayor Schmitz? I must telephone him at once."

The policeman shook his head. "All lines are dead, sir."

"Then find him. Tell him General Funston is turning out 1,700 armed Regulars. They will report to the Hall of Justice by seven forty-five o'clock. They will be at his complete disposal."

The general raised his arm in a brusque salute, then quickly made his way back up the hill. . . .

Jangle of ambulance bells, clatter of galloping fire horses, rumble of engine wheels on cobblestones, shouts of rallying men rose in strident medley over the South of Market streets.

Wagons, carts and here and there a high-wheeled, brass-lamped Franklin or Pope-Hartford automobile with goggled driver jounced along the littered pavements with earthquake victims for the already hard-pressed nurses and doctors of the emergency hospital in Mechanics Pavilion, across the square from the ruins of city hall.

In Southern Pacific Hospital, fire chief Sullivan, unconscious and dying from injuries received in his fall, would never know how his men broke their hearts for him in the bitter and hopeless battle, and down in the South of Market alleys the flames raced with a ravenous snarl into the flimsy dwellings, the rows of splintered kindling. The unfortunates trapped and at their mercy screamed, or stoically waited, or closed their eyes and prayed.

Photographer Arnold Genthe, in riding habit, walked along Powell Street to Union Square. It presented a reassuring sight. The palms rustled pleasantly in the light air. The familiar, 13-story façade of the Hotel St. Francis loomed sheer and solid, like a Yosemite cliff.

People in makeshift garb milled across the square's two acres, many of them refugees from the Palace who found it comforting to stand free of tall buildings and overhanging cornices. Members of the opera company were there: Sembrich and Fremstad, Hertz, the great Scotti, Caruso in his fur coat, scowling and trilling to test his voice, and carrying under his arm a large, autographed portrait of President Theodore Roosevelt. Twenty-four-year-old John Barrymore, in town with Richard Harding Davis's The Dictator, strolled about in flawless full dress and told amusingly how the quake had interrupted his down-tender love scene with the fiancée of a Venetian glass collector.

Nine separate conflagrations, each one of which would ordinarily have been rated a general-alarm fire, blazed south of Market Street. Toward the waterfront three others crackled along narrow streets.

Here and there, by freak of fortune, a hydrant still functioned, or water from broken mains formed a sump, or there was an artesian well or cistern. Firemen tapped any source they could find. It was bitter going. Time after time a company seemed on the verge of winning. Then its water supply went dry, and the blaze roared higher than before.

A Western Union operator, probing and testing for a live wire in the Bay Area's communication system, found one atop a telegraph pole in West Oakland. It was open to Sacramento. As the smoke mounted the sky above San Francisco like a volcanic cloud, he perched there and tapped out his message to the world.

Mayor Eugene E. Schmitz, with rich black beard and snapping black eyes and the sword of a graft investigation hanging over his impressive head, paced the lobby of the Hall of Justice, across Kearny Street from Portsmouth Square.

A onetime theater orchestra fiddler, he had been blatantly unfit for office. Many looked upon him as a weakling, a pawn, a sawdust mayor. But now he was astounding his severest critics. From somewhere in his makeup, he summoned forth a hero.

At this moment, under his orders, General Funston's troops were deploying on the double, with full cartridge belts and fixed bayonets, to protect lives and property. Couriers were abroad calling a crisis Committee of Fifty into session at 3:00 P.M. at the Hall of Justice. Meanwhile, in a voice charged with authority, he laid down the law.

No water to check the fires? Get dynamiters from the Army. Get dynamite from the powder company at Pinole. Bring it down the bay by tugboat. Blow up buildings in the path of the flames. That was how they controlled the big fire in Baltimore.

Drunkenness and disorder in the streets? "I forbid the sale of alcohol . . ." Looting? The mayor dictated a proclamation: "The Federal Troops, the members of the Regular Police Force and all Special Police Officers have been authorized by me to KILL any and all persons found engaged in Looting or in the Commission of Any Other Crime. . . ."

South of Market Street the landmarks were beginning to go. One incredible sweep of flame was now destroying Metropolitan Hall, the Lincoln Grammar School and The Emporium, the largest department store west of Chicago.

Across Fifth Street, the square, three-story, granite-and-sandstone United States Mint, with $220,000,000 in its vaults, stood lonely and indestructible in a wallowing sea of fire. Behind its barred iron shutters 40 men choked in refinery fumes and wet down sills and sashes to keep the flames at bay.

Two blocks east on Mission Street the blazing roof of the Grand Opera House crashed down upon the stage where Carmen had danced and died the night before.

The fire leaped the alley behind the theater to the power shed of Market Street's proudest skyscraper, the 18-story Call Building. A mighty draft sucked the fire through the tunnel and up the skyscraper's elevator shaft. With the wild scream of a thousand windows shattering at once, the building burst into a 300-foot gusher of pulverized fire.

Down toward the waterfront the fire had crossed Market to join the earliest blazes that General Funston had seen from Nob Hill. Now in one advancing comber of flame they rolled unchecked over the ramshackle warehouses and wholesale sheds of Drumm and Battery Streets.

A block north a band of rescuers tugged impotently at the wreckage of the type foundry at Sansome and Clay Streets. They had been working for hours to free the two trapped men. They were near the limit of their endurance. No help was in sight. They stopped and with ashen faces stared at one another. The flames roared closer.

"Good-by! God help you!" they cried, and ran away.

From the mass of debris rose a muffled shout of despair. "For the love of Christ, give us a pistol!"

But the street was deserted. . . .

So now the bonny city, the proud city, the lovely happy city was burning to death, and it was a heartbreaking hour, a passing of things loved and lived with, an hour of farewell and good-by forever.

A new sight appeared on the streets, and a new sound mingled in the tumult of death and destruction: the straw-bedded wagons flying red flags and laden with dynamite cases, and the hunched figures of the crews, silhouetted against the glow as they ran with their charges into the buildings, and then the thumping boom as the charge exploded, and then the slow collapse of walls, the unfurling of clouds of dust, the fall and crash of roofs.

During the forenoon the people had sat in the hilly streets, looking down on the fires, at the backdrop of smoke they hung against the sky. In the Gold Rush days, San Francisco had caught fire six times, and six times had all but burned to the ground. Each time, the pioneers went to work in the smoking ruins and rebuilt her.

After the sixth great fire, they chose a symbol for San Francisco—the phoenix, the mythical bird that burned to death, then emerged reborn from its own ashes, and flew upward, swifter-winged and more beautiful than ever.

The San Franciscans recalled their fathers and grandfathers telling them about the phoenix. "Remember it," the old men said. "It's part of your heritage."

But San Francisco then had been a primitive settlement of tents and crate-wood shacks, made for boom-camp bon-fires. Now she was a modern metropolis, substantial, enduring. Someone, something, would save her—if nothing else, the wind and fog from the sea.

Genthe, with a borrowed Kodak, walked among them taking their pictures—the women in wide hats, long gored skirts and puff-sleeved shirtwaists; the men in derbys and dark suits, the children in sailor hats and long black stockings. And beside them in the street, quite forgotten for the moment, the sewing machine, the victrola, the basketful of pans, the roll of blankets that they had pulled or carried from their homes in the moment of the earthquake, and before all this began.

The spectacle bewitched them. They told themselves that none of this was real. They were dreaming. They sat waiting to wake up—or for the rising wind.

But no wind came. Instead the holocaust soared fiercer and higher heavenward. They felt its heat on their faces. It advanced toward the hills on which they sat, in an unbroken front three miles long. They stirred uneasily. Ashes began to drift down. A fetid smell filled the air. Slowly, in twos and threes, they stood up. They began to comprehend that it was true. And to understand that no miracle was going to save them.

Stone-faced, they hurried away then, headed for the open spaces of the parks and the Presidio. By the tens of thousands they toiled across the hills, sweating and panting in the hot stifling air, in the fall of ash and cinders. The trunks, bedsprings, cots and crates in which they dragged their belongings gave off a long-drawn, never-ending, rasping screech. Children wailed and clung to their mothers' skirts. Besides them all, out-distancing them, trotted packs of silent dogs with dripping jaws and lolling tongues.

Rumors, tidings of catastrophe, flew up and down the lines. Chicago was in flames. A tidal wave had engulfed Seattle. New York had toppled into the sea. Confusion and chaos were besetting the world. San Francisco's fate was merely a tick of the clock of doomsday.

Behind them, fire of a magnitude never before experienced by man was reaching toward its climax in vast, heaven-soaring banners of smoke and flame. There was no wind. Yet from every compass point fire-generated drafts flowed toward the city. Meeting above the streets, they turned skyward, whipping the flames to fresher vigor and carrying with them in their enormous up-rush a curtain or pall of smoke that was now visible a hundred miles at sea.

Down in the streets, in the blocks of blazing structures, the flames were the flames of a fire that was destroying property at the rate of $1,000,000 every ten minutes. They burned with blast-furnace heat ranging up to 2,000 degrees Fahrenheit. Sash weights and window glass turned liquid. Steel bars were welded solid. Porcelainware softened and dripped in blobs, like colored wax.

At two o'clock that afternoon the lady novelist, one of thousands packed in Jefferson Square west of Van Ness, wrote down her notes on a pad of white paper.

She had seen an Italian woman kneeling in the yard of a demolished house. The woman was weeping and praying. The crowd passed her by without a glance. On a heap of clothes nearby lay a two- or three-year-old girl, with a doll cradled in her arms. It did not occur to the lady novelist until later that the child was not breathing.

A young man passed a grocery store. Its door was sprung loose, its plate glass had fallen out and the young man and his mother and fiancée had no food. He gathered an armload of canned goods, and stepped back into the street, and a National Guardsman shot him dead for looting.

Then, with the note she had saved for last, she finished the page. On the front steps of an abandoned house she had seen a young Chinese mother nursing a baby. The mother's face was besmirched, and drawn with weariness. Her own child slept in swaddling blankets beside her. The child at her breast was white.

At three o'clock the Palace, the bonanza caravanserai and the pride and joy of three generations of San Franciscans, went blazing up in glory.

They were blasting along Kearny Street, near the half-wrecked Hall of Justice, and Mayor Schmitz held the meeting of his Committee of Fifty across the street in Portsmouth Square. Striding among the dynamite kegs, he outlined his plans for the relief of the refugees, the hospitalization of the injured, the maintenance of public health and safety, the striking of a last-ditch resistance line along Van Ness Avenue.

The committeemen might have been

resurrected from vigilante days. Grim-faced and solemn, yet with a flint-edged courage that would never surrender San Francisco, they sat beneath the poplars with the ashes pattering down on the square and the city burning behind them.

Down one end of the square ranged the raw mounds of 39 hastily dug graves, and up the hill in back of the old Monumental firehouse the flimsy tong rooms and banner-hung bazaars, the joss houses and honeycombed cellars and tenements of Chinatown awaited their fate.

There, prone in a cobbled alley called "The Street of a Thousand Flowers," was the carcass of the great black steer. Bawling in pain from its bullet wounds, flanks bright with blood, it had looked for a field, a meadow, a corral, and labored up a hill, and came to a throng of Chinese milling in the street.

Howls of terror broke from them at the sight of the gory beast. The legend that four bulls held up the world was true! This was one of them, and he had run away! That was why the earth had trembled!

"Go back! Bull, go back under the world!" they cried, reaching for stones. "Your brothers need you!"

They drove the dying steer down Dupont Street. It staggered into "The Street of a Thousand Flowers." There it fell before the pelting stones and lashing sticks, and soon lay still.

Then the Chinese fled west by the thousands up Clay and Washington and Jackson Streets in a procession set to the crashing of temple gongs and the wail of moon fiddle—stolid coolies bearing pole-slung baskets of quacking white ducks and jute bags of rice and tea; round-faced children shuffling in embroidered slippers; mincing slave girls carrying cosmetic pots and lily bulbs; pig-tailed merchants sweating under brassbound chests; lily-footed wives in brocaded satins, teetering along, arms outstretched for balance, in their tiny shoes and for the first time in their lives appearing on a public street with their husbands.

The flaming billows leaped skyward at their backs. Below the square, the theater where little Lotta Crabtree's buck and wing had brought the miners cheering to their feet was blazing, and the old saloons of Montgomery Street's "Ambrosial Path," and the three-story, iron-shuttered, brick buildings the pioneers had built after the Gold Rush fires.

In one of them that dynamiters had marked for blasting sat a stern, dark-haired man in his thirties. On the desk before him was a cocked revolver. The door burst open. It framed an Army lieutenant. At his back stood his crew, dynamite cases on their shoulders. The lieutenant ordered the man to leave at once.

The man picked up his pistol. He was deadly calm.

"Lieutenant, I am not leaving. This was my father's building. This was his office, and his desk. If you think I am going to desert them, you are mistaken. I am telling you that if one of your men tries to lay a stick of dynamite in these rooms, I'll blow his brains out . . ."

The lieutenant hesitated, and then with his crew was gone. The man put down his pistol and locked the steel doors and shutters. Then he soaked his sacks and curtains in the water-filled fire buckets, and prepared to make his stand.

By seven o'clock the fire front was advancing methodically at the rate of two blocks an hour along Bush and Sutter Streets. The editorial staffs of the Call and the Chronicle held a conference. Executives reported that their presses were useless. The plan was to prepare copy in San Francisco and send it by launch to Oakland. There, on Thursday, in the plant of an Oakland paper, they would issue a joint paper until other arrangements could be worked out. The conference adjourned.

"All Chronicle men," said the Chronicle editor, "will meet at 1:00 P.M. tomorrow at the Chronicle Building—if there is a Chronicle Building." The Call editor said good night to his men. "All Call men will meet at 1:00 P.M. tomorrow at the Fairmont Hotel—if there is a tomorrow."

The fire was a monster that now, at its leisure, was eating its prey. What it could not devour or feed upon—concrete, brick, steel—it tumbled into rubble or left behind in ravaged smoke-blackened shells. The throbbing glare it cast across the night heaven was an awe-inspiring sight. Residents of San Jose, 40 miles south, stood outside their homes and read newspapers in the ruddy glimmer.

In the squares on the heights west of Van Ness, on the grassy meadows of Golden Gate Park, in sheltered Presidio hollows, the refugees—some 250,000 of them—numbly watched the glowing sky, or talked, or tried to rest.

In the makeshift hospital tents men died and were borne on litters to makeshift graves. Doctors and Red Cross nurses, limp with fatigue, set broken bones and administered drugs, bandaged wounds and delivered babies.

There was no disorder. People walked slowly through the camps calling the names of lost loved ones. Someone sang, or played a salvaged piano. The refugees tried to cheer one another up. But sadness was everywhere in the air.

At midnight, Union Square was empty. Fire advanced on it rapidly from three directions. For blocks around, massive buildings sat dark and abandoned. They had a remote, meditative air, as if they were brooding to themselves. There was no water. There was nothing anyone could do. The light fall of ash drifted down like soft gray snow. The only sound was the sound of the hungry flames. . . .

Tomorrow dawned, after all. The morning smoke, flickering with orange and lavender lights, boiled majestically heavenward in a vast cumulus that reared 10,000 feet into the motionless air. The rising sun turned its billowing summits a creamy white against the blue, like the caps of trade-wind clouds at sea.

And now an outside world, that didn't quite know yet what had happened, was involved. It knew only that San Francisco was in trouble, and her people needed help, and it was responding.

The Navy's Pacific Squadron steamed into the bay and put ashore blue-jackets and Marines. Regulars from the Presidio of Monterey were marching north. Mule trains of food, clothing and medical supplies filed south from the barracks at Fort Vancouver. U.S. Revenue tugs and fireboats converged on the waterfront. Relief trains sped from Los Angeles and Portland. Red Cross funds, supplies and fieldworkers were on their way from the East.

It was, in truth, San Francisco's darkest hour.

A quarter of a million men, women and children, stupefied with exhaustion and shock, their homes destroyed or in danger of destruction, lived a nomad existence in open spaces, and over them all hovered the dread specter of typhoid and smallpox. Another 70,000 had fled or were fleeing to the safety of the Oakland and Berkeley beaches and the communities of Marin County. Still another 20,000 or 30,000 had boarded trains, or were in headlong exodus to the south in a variety of other vehicles or on foot.

Behind them they left the heart of a metropolis in Carthaginian ruin. Banks, commercial buildings, schools, churches, hotels, stores, warehouses—all were destroyed or under tons of rubble. The telephone system, except for improvised military lines, was useless. Every telegraph office was gone. One million books had burned. Two hundred and sixty-one miles of railways were paralyzed.

And incredibly, the nightmare of sound and fatigue and fury continued as if it would never end until every trace of the living city had been obliterated.

The vortex swept up the southern slope of Nob Hill and up from Chinatown to the ridgetop where General Funston had stood looking down at the rising smoke wisps, the lifetime ago that was yesterday morning, and now the lofty aeries of the rich, with their costly woods, their cut-crystal chandeliers and lace-canopied beds, were blazing as brightly as the hovels of Chinatown had burned.

Their inhabitants had fled to Burlingame in silver-mounted broughams, or to New York or Newport or Europe, and it would be years before they came back and some would never come back at all.

But now in the afternoon of the second day, the fire worked its way westward. Troopers on guard fell back along the hill-crest, driving homeowners before them.

An elderly man said, "I was worth $600,000 yesterday. All I have left is my house, and in another 15 minutes that'll go with the rest of them." An Irish policeman from South of Market, who didn't have anything left either, consoled him.

At that moment they were brothers. The cast of the drama was so vast identities had become meaningless. The great and the famous of yesterday blended back into the crowd today. The dowager stood in line for soup with the scrubwoman.

The firemen pumping from sumps and wells and partially repaired mains, and indomitable men and women with mops and wet blankets had stopped the fire that morning South of Market, out on the hill beyond Mission Dolores and east in a ragged line to Townsend Street. Along Townsend Street to the Bay fire tugs turned it back with sea water from the China Basin channel.

But down the western slopes of Nob Hill the fire blazed 75 feet high on a front 14 blocks long. Consuming a house, a tier of flats, a store, at the rate of one every three minutes, it crackled toward Van Ness Avenue, and the heights and valleys of the Western Addition beyond.

The fire seemed to be traveling from housetop to housetop in a macabre game of leapfrog with the beleaguered firemen, who now fought on nerve and heart alone. When they dropped exhausted in the gutters, doctors revived them with strychnine and they struggled on. Their hoses burned, the engine fuel gave out. Helmets baked to their heads. Rubber coats shredded from their backs. The courageous fire horses collapsed in their harness.

That forenoon, in a bursting spray of sparks, the fire jumped Van Ness Avenue and attacked the bell tower and gilded cross of Saint Mary's Cathedral. Hundreds of refugees who had sought sanctuary in the great nave poured screaming into the street. While the cross burned brighter and brighter, the Reverend Charles Ramm climbed into the tower and with an ax chopped away the blazing timbers. From a vantage point in Jefferson Square, the lady novelist saw him; he was a tiny figure at the tower peak, grimly hacking "with the constrained small movement of a mechanical toy."

But he had saved the church and stopped the fire. Angrily it turned to its shortened front. Most of the flamboyant Nob Hill villas and châteaux had been built in the 1870s by the railroad giants and the silver kings; these were the solider middle-class mansions of a second generation of nabobs, the later merchants and burghers.

Along this stretch of boulevard, the time had come for the showdown. Here the fire fighters came to grips with the monster at last.

They smothered it with flame and blasted it with dynamite. They drowned it in salt water pumped two miles from the bay, and flailed it with blankets and brooms and sticks and their bare hands in a reeling struggle that endured long after the sun had set. In the smoke and turmoil and flaming confusion of the battle, five blocks of homes on the east side of Van Ness were put to the back-firing torch; on the west side of Van Ness, five blocks of homes were dynamited.

One small flame, bright yellow and wriggling with evil life, raced to the far side of Franklin, the next street west. Groggy firemen converged on it. A brief, desperate struggle and it was dead.

Maimed and crippled, harried by a rising west wind, the fire wheeled back to the north and east as if it were now its turn to seek an escape. The line along Van Ness held fast. At the avenue's end, by the docks of Fort Mason, the fighters cut off the flames and drove them down to the bay and the soaring white streams that feathered from the nozzles of the swarming fireboats.

But back up the sides of Russian Hill, the fire front went sweeping up over the high, brown-shingled houses that for 30 and 40 years had looked down upon Alcatraz and the bay. Many of their inhabitants, hoping for a miracle that would spare their homes, had stayed with them. Now they, too, fled for their lives.

Others, with homes in hilltop open spaces, had a chance to fight back. One man, believing everything lost, dipped the American flag on his roof-top staff three times in a gesture of defiance, and prepared to flee. Fort Mason troops, taking it for an Army signal, rushed up the hill to the rescue and saved the house with buckets of wet sand.

While nearby homes went up like kindling wood, "Humphrey's Castle," a turreted landmark on Russian Hill's north ridge, was saved when its owner and son wet down its shingles with squirting seltzer bottles and three cases of Roederer's champagne.

As Friday ended, the flame banners flared skyward from the narrow alleys of the foreign quarters that nestled against the base of Telegraph Hill. They rippled with a strange lazy ease up the rocky eastern slopes of the hill, through the ramshackle rookeries and unsavory deadfalls of the Barbary Coast. Higher still, swarthy Neapolitan fishermen fought the conflagration for their rose-grown cottages. Barrels of sharp red Chianti and zinfandel were aging in their cellars from the fall crush, but what was wine if you lost a home to drink it in? Swinging wine-soaked blankets, they drove the fire from their roofs and porches, and bested it in the last, most spirited revolt of all.

Hour after hour along the waterfront that night, 30 tugs tied to the smoking piers threw their streams into the flames. Now at last they had it cornered. The scene was one of wild disorder and excitement. Firemen, staggering with weariness but sensing the finish, lowered their helmets against the searing heat and carried their nozzles time and again toward the savage flames, then, with warning shouts, fell back in retreat. Walls crashed to earth and sent the flames shooting skyward amid geysers of snapping sparks.

Then, at the end of an endless dawn, the life went out of the fire. Suddenly it flickered lower. And all at once, there at the foot of the smoke-black cliffs, in the foggy daybreak with the gulls wheeling and crying overhead, it was all over.

When the firemen grasped what had happened and what they had done, they sank to the streets beside their engines. The tugs kept their strong white streams arching into the smoldering expanse of embers, but their whistles shrieked, and climbed, and joined in a long shrill blast of triumph.

Moments later, jaunty victory notes broke out over the camps from Army bugles, and brought the refugees laughing and cheering and weeping for joy from their tents and blanket rolls. In another hour the whole world knew that San Francisco's ordeal had ended. . . .

As the April sun broke through the mist that morning, a band of San Franciscans picked their way through the ruins. They had come to look at what was left.

As far as they could see, the city—four fifths of her—lay destroyed.

A footpath led them down Market Street. On every side loomed tottering walls, piles of rubble, twisted skeletons of steel, incinerated shells of buildings open to the sky, and, where the city had proudly crowned her hills, mile upon mile of—nothing.

Acrid yellow smoke drifted slowly across the desolate scene. A brooding silence hung in the air. The men and women might have been travelers, exploring the remains of a long-perished race, a long-dead civilization.

But the curious thing was, they did not see, really, the ashen waste. They saw instead the rocklike mint, still standing as it was when its valiant crew stumbled choking into the street, their battle won. Two blocks west, they saw the imposing post office and federal court building; the quake had battered it and the fire had scarred it, but men had stood fast and fought for it, and it had come through.

Down in the devastated streets of the Gold Rush town, the Montgomery Block, erected in the '50s, rose solid and fortress-like among the wreckage. And there was the building that the son of the pioneer had saved with the spirit of '49. On Russian Hill were the homes, scorched but intact, that resolute men had snatched from disaster. To the cliffs of Telegraph Hill clung the cottages the fishermen would not yield.

The San Franciscans took off their coats and rolled up their sleeves.

"Let's go," they said. "Let's get started."

The bricks in Market Street were still hot, and blistered their hands. But they could not wait. Bending over, they began to clear away the rubble, and if at that moment they had looked up, they might have seen the phoenix—the mythical golden bird, with the shimmering golden wings.

Somewhere near the city's heart, it must have risen from the ashes. On immortal wings it must have flown triumphantly toward the sun, higher and higher into the sky, until it was a shining speck, until it disappeared.

A Visit with Mr. Fitz and Nashua

John McNulty

John McNulty loved people and horses, and wrote tenderly of both. Best remembered for his stories of life on New York's Third Avenue in the days when the shadow of the Elevated cast an aura of perpetual twilight over the saloons beneath, McNulty occasionally went forth to do an out-of-town reporting job—in this case about a remarkable race-horse and trainer who, at eighty-one, stood clearly at the top of his profession.

March 30, 1956

IT WAS MODERATELY EARLY, ABOUT TEN past, quarter past seven on a smartly chilly morning, and three of us were standing in front of a horse in Stall 45, Barn A, at the Hialeah Racetrack in Florida. The three of us were:

(1) Mr. James E. Fitzsimmons, eighty-one-year-old race-horse trainer, and probably the best man at his trade in the United States. However, "best" and all other superlatives are doled out only with the utmost caution at the race track.

(2) Alfred Robertson, forty-seven-year-old groom, who has been in the employ of Mr. Fitzsimmons since 1927, with the exception of a couple of years when he was doing a hitch with the Coast Guard—and even then he was riding horses on patrol on islands near Cape Hatteras.

(3) Myself—a reporter and aging horse player on a small scale. I love horses but I am not a horse lover, because as James G. Thurber, the writer, says: a horse lover is one horse who loves another horse.

The horse in the stall, a big, strong bay with nervously alert ears and a tiny star and a tiny trickle of a blaze a little way down his nose, was Nashua, who on December 15th last was sold to Leslie Combs II, of Lexington, Kentucky, and six other men for $1,251,200. This is the equivalent of 625,600 bets of two dollars each, enough to last any horse player, no matter how devout he is, pretty near a lifetime.

Mr. Fitzsimmons, who hereinafter shall be called "Mister Fitz" because that is what he is most respectfully called wherever racing people gather, was there because he is the trainer of Nashua, and has been all Nashua's life, which is now in its fourth year. Robertson, who hereinafter shall be called "Al," was there because he is Nashua's personal groom, who is with Nashua all day long. The horse is never alone. Another man, Jim Driscoll, stays by his stall all night.

I was there because on the day Nashua's sale was announced I said to the delicatessen man on my corner in New York, "It must be a terrible responsibility to have charge of a horse worth more than $300,000 a leg. Anything could happen." I wondered what it would be like to be around him and his family—of humans, that is—and I arranged to go down to Florida and try to find out.

"How's he acting, Al?" asked Mister Fitz.

"He's doing real good," said Al. "He slept good and he ate good, and a little while ago when I was bandaging his legs for his gallop, why, he leaned over and took my hat off and waved it around in his teeth, just for the pure hell of it, Mister Fitz. He's beginning to feel real good, after the farm. He got lonesome for the race track out on the farm, like the rest of us."

"He's playful," Mister Fitz told me. "But sometimes his idea of having fun is r'arin' up in his stall and that ain't good. Dangerous."

Strolling up to us came a dog who, Al said, was Susie. She is a small, old, round, black-and-white dog who used to be a fox terrier in the old days, and she comes over from the barn of Alfred G. Vanderbilt to get bones Al brings to her from the trailer where he lives. There is plenty to eat at Vanderbilt's, but Susie has taken a fancy to Nashua, and Nashua to Susie, and so she comes over. The horse arched his neck and leaned over, so Al opened the half door to let Nashua nuzzle Susie's back with his nose.

Mister Fitz stroked Nashua's nose and said, "I got twenty-three other horses here to train. I got to go out with a set now."

At the race track, a "set" is a group of horses, usually four to eight, going out on the track for exercise under the supervision of one trainer.

Mister Fitz walked away toward his car and the track itself. He walks with considerable difficulty, but with a remarkable agility and determination, sometimes using one aluminum crutch. Arthritis has practically immobilized the upper part of his spine, pushing his head down and forward, so that his posture, walking or standing, is a most awkward one.

As Mister Fitz moved away, John Fitzsimmons came along, with a newly opened letter in his hand. John, who hereinafter shall be called Johnny Fitz, is sixty-two, one of Mister Fitz's six children, five sons and a daughter, and it is Johnny Fitz who takes care of the voluminous paper work of the stable.

"Hey, Pop!" Johnny Fitz yelled. "More fan mail for the horse!" (Hereinafter Nashua will mostly be known as "the horse" because that's how his human family refers to him.)

Mister Fitz stopped and turned his whole body round to look at Johnny Fitz. The arthritis makes it impossible for him to turn his neck. He took the letter Johnny gave him. Mister Fitz's clear, young, blue eyes shone and he smiled happily as he read the letter. He handed the letter to me.

"All these years, must be sixty years I'm training, I never had nice little kids write to me before about one of my horses!" he said. "Some of them write right to the horse himself. He gets letters every day, doesn't he, Johnny?"

The letter was from a fourteen-year-old girl from Wyoming, a girl with the uncommonly beautiful name of Milady Suppes. She was staying with her folks at nearby Pompano Beach. Her last paragraph said:

"If you could find time to answer this letter and tell me if I can come to the barn and when it would be o.k. to see Nashua, that would be just fine. I really would like to pet him if I could, but if it's against any rules or regulations, I would be satisfied just to stand there and look for awhile."

"Write to that little girl, Johnny," Mister Fitz said to his son. "Tell her she can come over and see the horse."

Mister Fitz hustled away in his laborious but uncomplaining way, and I went back to Stall 45 to talk with Al. And also to "stand there and look for awhile."

"What's his day like?" I asked Al.

"Well, start with his breakfast; that's about half past three in the morning," Al said. "He'll eat about three quarts of oats for breakfast, then he'll have a nap, usually lying down, sometimes drowsing on his feet a couple hours.

"I get him ready about seven, seven thirty, bandaging up all his legs for his gallop about half past eight. Right now, he's only galloping. Mister Fitz will decide when to start running him fast for his works.

"After about two miles or so of galloping, well, naturally, he has to be walked around for an hour or more, cooling him off gradually. Then I take the bandages off and make him comfortable, and he has lunch at half past ten. That's about four quarts of oats, and I chop up five or six carrots in them, making a tasty lunch.

"He's sure to go to sleep after lunch, and supper is half past four. That's his big meal, about six quarts of oats, with five or six more carrots in them. Then, of course, there's hay to munch on betweentimes. Maybe twenty to twenty-five pounds a day, timothy hay, clover hay and a flake or two of alfalfa. Take a real hot day, he'll drink about fifteen gallons of water, but ordinary weather, why, ten gallons will do.

"He gets special water, what they call Mountain Valley water, shipped all the way from Hot Springs, Arkansas. It's a mineral water. The horse is what we call a good doer. That means he eats good."

Bill McCleary came up to the stall, in jodhpurs, boots, a white sweater and a white cap. He used to be a jumping-horse rider, and now he's the one who rides the horse during all his exercise periods. Originally from Flatbush, Brooklyn, Bill is of Irish descent, and he's fifty-nine now. The Fitzsimmons barn is a sure-enough Irish barn; there are more blue eyes and more Irish brogues around there than you can shake a shillelagh at.

"Doesn't it ever scare you, Bill, when you're riding him at his exercise or his works that you got a million and a quarter dollars' worth of horse under you?" I asked.

"No, not a-tall, not a-tall," said Bill. "I knew him before he was rich. I broke him in when he was a baby, and he knows who's boss. We get along good. I never think how rich he is. He's a horse."

Bill, the fifty-nine-year-old "boy," swung up on the horse, Al walked along beside them, holding a shank fastened to his bridle, another "boy," about fifty, on a pony named Francis, joined them, and they walked to the "gap," the break in the fence that leads to the track, and Nashua was ready for his gallop. Along the way, as he passed, other men and boys, with or without horses, stopped in their tracks and watched.

"That's him," they'd say, not mentioning any name. "That's him all right."

And they, too, would "stand there and look for awhile."

When a horse gets to the point where he receives letters from little girls from Wyoming, he comes pretty near being a national idol, a star like Marlon Brando. As I walked to join Mister Fitz at the trackside rail, near the clubhouse turn, I thought of the events, first sporting, then tragic, which had flashed the name of Nashua onto the newspaper front pages the world over.

To begin with, he is an animal of royal blood indeed. His sire, Nasrullah, now sixteen years old and living at the Claiborne Farm in Paris, Kentucky, where the most distinguished mares come to visit his court, is estimated to be worth $1,700,000, or $448,800 more than himself. His dam, Segula, was sold in January for $126,000. Her dad, by the way, was Johnstown, who was trained by Mister Fitz, and thus Mister Fitz had charge of Nashua's granddaddy, on his mother's side. Mister Fitz is indeed an old family friend of the horse.

Last year the horse was a sensation of the sports pages, and especially in defeat. That was when, as the favorite, he was beaten in the Kentucky Derby by Swaps, an excellent race horse from California. Then, on August 31st, at Washington Park in Chicago, Nashua defeated Swaps by six and one half lengths for $100,000, winner-take-all, in a match race between the two horses only.

Later on in my visit, I asked Mister Fitz about those two races, and here's what he said:

"It only goes to show how things work out. We were terribly disappointed losing the Derby, but we got beat fair and square. No excuses. Some of my grandchildren were at the Derby and they were crying after it was over, they had been so sure the horse was a dead cinch to win. I didn't do any crying, because I know nothing is a dead cinch until it's over.

"Anyway, it goes to show. If we hadn't got beat in the Derby there wouldn't have been any match race, and the way it turned out, why, I never wanted so much in my life to win a race as I did that one and the horse win it for me."

Well, Derby, match race and all, the horse was chiefly on the sports pages still, until tragedy moved him out to Page One.

On October 30th, William Woodward, Jr., who had inherited the horse from his father, William Woodward, when the banker died in 1953, was accidentally shot to death by his wife, Ann, who mistook him for a nighttime prowler in their home at Oyster Bay, Long Island.

Everybody wondered what would become of the horse, who would train him, and so forth. The Hanover Bank, handling the Woodward estate, said sealed bids for Nashua (and other horses Woodward owned) would be opened December 15th, and the highest bidder would get the horse.

Mr. Combs's bid of $1,251,200 won the horse for him. The price for about 1,200 pounds of horseflesh is the largest in the world's history.

I thought of all these things (including the dates even) on my walk to "Mister Fitz's place." It's a fact that at every major race track where Mister Fitz goes—Hialeah, Saratoga, Aqueduct (his home track), everywhere—there is a certain place by the rail set aside as "Mister Fitz's place" and everybody knows it. There's no sign or reservation, race-trackers simply know the spot, and they'll say, if he isn't around, "Don't stand there; that's Mister Fitz's place."

He was standing in his place when I got there. An orderly row of straight-up Australian pine trees bordered the rail, at the clubhouse turn, and Mister Fitz was swaying between two of the trees. He had a hand on each of two trees and was swaying back and forth between them. "Exercising," he said when I came along. "Got to keep my blood moving around, with this back I got. Got to exercise as much as I can every time I can."

He stopped exercising and leaned on the rail, putting his "third leg," the aluminum crutch, against the rail. He looked across the track, away to the far turn about a half mile away. Those blue eyes are remarkable. Except for reading, he wears no glasses. He spotted the horse away over there, although there must have been 30 other horses scattered around the track, galloping, jogging, walking or running fast.

"There's the horse," he said, pointing to the white sweater and white cap of Bill McCleary, dimly visible so far away. "Looks like he wants to run. I won't let him though. Not yet. He'll get to running in a week or so."

Other people's horses, with other people's "boys" up on them, would come by, walking back. Invariably, the boy'd manage to steer over near us, and yell cheerfully, "Morning, Mister Fitz!" And he'd answer back, usually by name. Once he added, to a boy on a dark brown colt: "Who's that you got there, Willie?" The boy answered: "This is the one they got from Australia, Mister Fitz."

"Oh, I knew I didn't know that feller," said Mister Fitz.

Every now and then, a couple of horses, running fast, would come by, making the triple-beat, the "clud-clud-a-clud" on the softish track that to a man bitten by the horse bug is the sweetest sound in the world. Every now and then, some dainty two-year-old filly would come mincing by, stepping tiptoe like some sixteen-year-old girl ballet dancer, and maybe wiggling her behind by way of caprice, the way that a mischievous ballet dancer might do, too.

How many thousand such mornings has Mister Fitz spent, I thought, and how serenely happy they have made him be!

Well, we watched the horse gallop, and Bill McCleary, passing on his return, hollered from the horse's back that "he's feeling good, he wants to run." Mister Fitz took up his third leg, Johnny Fitz joined us, and we hustled to the car to go back to the barn and wait for the horse.

"I'll drive, Johnny," said Mister Fitz to his son. And he did, adroitly, bad back or no bad back.

"I like to do everything for myself that I possibly can do for myself," Mister Fitz told me as he drove along. "Keeps a man young. I do my own washing and ironing, too."

At the barn, Mister Fitz keenly looked over the horse's legs, which is the first thing any horseman, young or old, does when his horse comes off the track, and he found them fine. Al threw a blanket over the horse, and Bill McCleary, on foot, started walking him around in a circle, along with other horses of the set.

This process has the picturesque name of "walkin' hots." It is one of the lowliest, yet one of the most necessary of stable tasks, because few trainers think a hot horse can be put back in a sometimes drafty stall without cooling him off first.

The horse walked around for an hour or more, was put in his stall, little Susie came over for a visit and the horse nuzzled her. Al gave the horse his lunch, and Mister Fitz, Johnny Fitz and I went back to the Fitzsimmons home, a kind of cute, small, white house on Northwest 42d Street, about 15 minutes' ride from the track. It is one of Mister Fitz's three homes he owns—two in New York, this one in Florida.

The minute we went through the door,

Mister Fitz went over and turned on the television. "It'll be Godfrey, this hour," he said. "That Godfrey seems like a nice feller. He likes horses. Maybe that little bit of a Japanese girl that ran a dead heat with that big strong piano player in the Talent Scouts will be on. She got a real nice voice."

Before the others of us could hardly get our coats off, Mister Fitz had gone into the kitchen, lighted the gas stove, and started things. He peeked out the kitchen door at me, and grinned.

"I got to make some lunch for you and the children," he said, and ducked back into the kitchen. The children he meant are the sixty-two-year-old Johnny Fitz and the sixty-year-old Jimmy Fitz, who works around the stable and who would be in shortly.

The lunch Mister Fitz made so quickly that day was hamburg, fried onions, little boiled potatoes, string beans and peach shortcake, with whipped cream he whipped up himself. At lunch, under my questioning, we got to talking about training.

"There's no miracle stuff to it, Mc," Mister Fitz said to me. "Listen. No trainer can put anything into a horse that the good Lord hasn't put there already. There's lots of good trainers. All a good trainer can do is bring out what's in a horse, that's all. The bad trainers can spoil what's in a horse, though.

"Listen," he said again. "The beauty of this racing game is nobody can corner it, no matter how many million dollars he got. No matter how much brains he got either. Because nobody can look at a yearling or a baby two-year-old and tell what's inside the horse. He can look good—good legs, good chest, good head, all that. But inside, nobody knows.

"You can't see what's inside—lungs, heart, brains," he went on.

"You think race horses got much brains?" I asked.

"They got brains enough to do what they're supposed to do, run fast and make the other guy quit. And you can't see inside, some other thing, determination or whatever that other thing is, I don't know what to call it."

"Would you call it courage, maybe?" I asked.

"Maybe, but courage sounds like something with the band playing," Mister Fitz said. "It's something you got without any band playing. Something that makes you able to keep going just one little bit more, no matter how your legs hurt or your lungs hurt or everything in your brains makes you want to quit, you had enough, keep going just a little bit more and make the other guy quit, not you. Make the other guy quit, not *ever* you, Nashua got it, I don't know what to call it."

"He certainly has shown that," I said. "Would you say he's the best horse you ever had, Mister Fitz?"

"I don't like to say anything is the best anything," was his answer. "I've had some good horses before this. Nashua's a real good horse, I say."

Twenty-six years ago, in 1930, Gallant Fox won the Triple Crown of racing for Mister Fitz and for his boss, Mr. Woodward. The Triple Crown consists of the Kentucky Derby, the Preakness at Pimlico, and the Belmont, at Belmont Park, the three traditionally great races for three-year-olds.

"Is he as good as Gallant Fox?" I asked, boldly. I say "boldly" because through the years, Gallant Fox has been pretty well accepted as Mister Fitz's favorite horse.

"Foolishness!" he said. "Foolishness! Nobody knows. Only way in the world to tell which is better would be have them race each other, and that can't be done. It's the same as those arguments could Jack Dempsey lick Joe Louis when both of them were at their best. Foolish talk, waste of time!"

While we were at it, I asked another question: "Do you ever bet on the horses, Mister Fitz?"

"Sure, I bet five dollars sometimes, for pure devilment," he answered, laughing. "My idea is betting a few dollars for devilment is all right. Betting on horses to make money is downright foolishness. Devilment's all right."

After lunch, and before Mister Fitz had his nap, he and I watched television some more and talked. Johnny Fitz was busy at the stable books in another room, Jimmy Fitz was busy tidying up and running the carpet sweeper around. There are no women around the house. The families of both sons are back around New York, and the men live in the small white house together, fending for themselves, with Mister Fitz doing a great deal of the fending. He likes to do so. Mister Fitz's wife, Jenny, to whom he was married since he was seventeen, died six years ago.

What he does watching the TV is sit in a big chair, with an electric vibrator propped against his back, and he sometimes sits there for hours, watching any old thing that comes on the 17-inch screen—a modest, simple screen, like everything else around Mister Fitz in person.

"People keep complicating things up," he said to me one minute. "There ain't any need to."

"You said Arthur Godfrey liked horses; how about yourself?" I asked him another minute. "When do you think you began to like horses?"

"I must have got the horse bug when I was six or seven years old," he said. "Perhaps it was when I used to be driving my father home in the vegetable wagon." He told me his father was a huckster, back in Sheepshead Bay, in New York, where Mister Fitz was born July 23, 1874. He has a 16-room house there still, one he bought years ago, and one that used to be chock full of children playing when Mister Fitz's children were young and then later when the grandchildren were young. Mister Fitz has 17 grandchildren and 19 great-grandchildren.

When he was six or seven, Mister Fitz used to ride to town with his father, in the huckster wagon. Sometimes when his father had had a jolly and tiring day with his customers and friends, the little boy would drive the wagon home.

"I was horse-crazy all right," he said. "I loved that driving home when I was a kid." He adjusted the electric vibrator at his back a little, and I asked him if his back hurt. "Ain't I lucky?" he answered. "Never hurts a bit. And I see some of these poor old fellers around here with arthritis and I guess they're in pain all the time. I always been lucky anyway. Like with my bosses. One thing, my bosses certainly have spent plenty of money keeping me in good horses."

That led to my asking just how he got the word that Mr. Combs, his new boss, was going to keep him as Nashua's trainer after he bought the horse.

"He called me on the telephone from Kentucky the minute they told him his bid won out," Mister Fitz said. "He asked me if I'd be willing to go on training the horse and I said I would be glad to do it.

I liked the horse. And he said all right. Next day I got a letter from him airmail. Hey, Johnny, show that letter to Mc here, will you? That nice letter from Mr. Combs."

Johnny Fitz brought a letter from the next room. In it Mr. Combs said he hoped Mister Fitz would go right on as always, and do things his own way. Then a paragraph said: "*I have known you ever since I was a little boy, and I certainly appreciate your doing this favor for me.*"

I asked Mister Fitz about his contract with Mr. Combs. He looked startled. "Contract?" he said. "I never had a contract in my life. I don't believe in them. Contracts mean that perhaps it'll wind up with two people supposed to be working together and not liking each other but trying to go on just because there's a contract. I never had a contract with Mr. Woodward and I worked for him thirty-one years. No contract with young Mr. Bill either, or with Mrs. H. C. Phipps, who has the Wheatley Stable I train for, or for young Mr. Ogden Phipps, her son, that I train for, too. No contracts. Don't believe in them. The other people say they'll do certain things and I say I'll do certain things and that's all there is to it. No need complicating things up."

Mister Fitz explained that he trains horses "by the day," and that goes for Nashua, too. It means he charges so much a day, I didn't ask him how much, and for that he provides the training, the care, the feeding, and so on. That's his regular fee, and he also gets 10 per cent of the winnings of each horse in his care. In the case of Nashua alone—as I figured quickly in my head—that would be $94,541.50 for 1954 and 1955, and that's to say nothing of the percentage of winnings from all the other horses. Pretty good going for a man who likes to do his own washing and ironing, in order to keep life simple, the way he wants it to be.

After a while, Mister Fitz went and had his nap, and that evening the supper he cooked for us was fried chicken, mashed turnips, some string beans that had been left over, some hot biscuits and lots of butter, and some chopped-up canned fruit.

The TV and the vibrator after supper for a while, in that haphazardly happy little home on 42d Street. Maybe it was during a lull in Red Skelton or maybe it was in between Westerns, I forget what it was, but Mister Fitz talked a little bit more about training.

"Thing is, that's the horse's business, running," he said. "Running, that's his business he's on earth for. There comes a time when he simply got to get at his business, running. He feels like he just plain *got* to run, that's all. Well, part of my job is to train him so he'll feel exactly that way, crazy to run, at exactly the right time, at exactly the time they go to the post. Sometimes I do it, sometimes I don't, no denying that. But give me twenty-five more years and I'll have a pretty good holt on this horse-training business."

The next morning, the horse showed that he was getting at "the business he's on earth for."

Because the moment Bill McCleary got up on Nashua, ready to go out on the track for his exercise, Bill said:

"I can feel him today, Mister Fitz! He's itchin' to run."

"Let him run a mile," said Mister Fitz (a decision he'd probably made, to himself, the night before). "But not too fast, not too fast."

A few minutes later, we were at "Mister Fitz's place" at the trackside. The horse had jogged around a bit, while Mister Fitz exercised by swaying between his two pet trees.

Then, looking up the track a long way, Johnny Fitz, standing near his father, said, "Get ready, Pop, get ready!"

Mister Fitz let go of the trees, swung to the rail, and he automatically flicked out his huge, split-second stop watch, which he carries in his topcoat pocket, at the end of a braided shoestring. The gesture of taking it out was as natural, as automatic, as that of a sage old doctor flicking out his stethoscope.

"Get ready, Pop," Johnny Fitz said again. "*Bing!*"

The "*bing!*" meant that the horse had started his run, far up the track. Mister Fitz's blue eyes were peering intently up the track at the horse, and I knew his alert fingers had started the watch for the timing.

The horse rushed by, going at a pretty good clip. The good loud snorts of his nostrils hit our ears, a sound you don't hear in the afternoon at the races, because the roar of the crowd muffles it. Smoothly, while everyone in sight watched him, Nashua moved around the oval. McCleary was nearly standing up in the stirrups, holding him in, as at last he began to slow down.

"Fifty and a fifth," said Mister Fitz calmly. "Good. Nice and slow but good." He meant the horse had run a mile in one minute, fifty and one fifth seconds. Horsemen seldom mention the minute in speaking of speeds. For a first-time run after merely galloping, 1:50 1/5 really was good. Of course, in a race, good horses run a mile in 1:36, around there, but this was no race.

"I had all I could do to hold him in," McCleary said when he rode back to us and Mister Fitz's eyes had run over the horse and found him good.

I began to understand better what Mister Fitz meant when he said that his job was to get him so he'll be "just crazy to run, at exactly the right time."

The right time Mister Fitz had in mind that particular morning was late in the afternoon of February 18th, the time of the Widener mile-and-a-quarter race, the race the horse was being trained for.

Every few days, Mister Fitz explained to me, the horse would be allowed to run a little, ever so little, faster, with intervals of gallops. All in the hopes that the great moment would come the instant the Widener field would flash out of the starting gate.

That moment came at 20 minutes and 30 seconds past five o'clock on the afternoon of February 18th. Of the nine horses in the race, Nashua was third coming out of the gate. When they had gone three quarters of a mile, he was fourth. Then, under the superb jockey, Eddie Arcaro, he showed he really was "just crazy to run." For, almost at the finish of the mile and a quarter, he was barely in front when Vanderbilt's Social Outcast came at him with a furious rush and seemed about to beat him. But Nashua summoned from somewhere within him that "little bit more" that Mister Fitz had talked about. He won by the length of his head. Again, Mister Fitz had done his work well.

The victory added $92,600 to the horse's lifetime earnings, making his total $1,038,015, or $47,745 behind Citation's all-time record of $1,085,760. Out of the $92,600, Mister Fitz got $9,260, and jockey Arcaro the same amount. Nashua got four carrots, nearly 20 cents' worth, when he got back to his stall.

"Are you doing any celebrating tonight?" I asked Mister Fitz when I talked to him an hour and a half after the race.

"About all I figure to do tonight is mix that pancake batter for tomorrow's big Sunday breakfast," he said. "You know, half buckwheat, half regular pancake flour. I do that every Saturday night because I like it to stand in the icebox overnight. Makes it better."

Mister Fitz was taking victory in his stride, in keeping with the greatest of racing maxims—"Win as though you were used to it, lose as though it didn't matter."

His serenity after so great a triumph was also in keeping with what I had learned about him during my visit. That is, that 81 years, naturally, have brought to Mister Fitz both good fortune and bad. Simplicity and directness enable him to enjoy the good breaks with an easygoing air and to put up peacefully with the bad ones. I do wish I could learn that way of living with Mister Fitz someday. Perhaps years from now, say at the time when he gets "a real good holt on this horse-training business."

Terror at Webb's Landing

Frank Harvey

In this novelette, Charles Capehart Morrison II, whose father's business was baling money in Wall Street, whose taste ran to bright red sports cars, whose seventeenth birthday was coming up tomorrow, seemed fair game for a trio of kidnappers.

April 13, 1956

THE SUN HAD SET BUT THE SKY WAS STILL pink with afterglow, and the live-oak jungle to the west of Daytona Beach looked like something snipped out of black paper with sharp scissors. Charles Capehart Morrison II, who would be seventeen years old tomorrow, was sneaking a cigarette behind the thick hedge on the lawn of the house his mother had rented for the month. And he was watching Diane coming down the beach.

He did not know Diane's last name. All he knew was that she was staying at a nearby tourist court, had a terrific shape, brown hair braided in two pigtails, a cute little snub nose and a soft-looking mouth. Diane was always surrounded by a ring of craggy-jawed lifeguard types, and she didn't know Charles Capehart Morrison II was alive.

Now, as Charles watched Diane kick up bright skitters of spray as she moved through the tidewash, he felt he couldn't stand it. He wanted to pick up something and break it, or yell with all his might, or get in a car and drive a hundred miles an hour.

Beyond the hedge Charles could hear Tracy, the family chauffeur, working in the garage. Tracy was working silently except for an occasional clink of the wrench, not singing, as he usually did. Tracy had a rich velvety voice when he sang, and he had been with the Morrisons three months, somewhat longer than most chauffeurs lasted. Charles knew why Tracy wasn't singing this evening and he felt a stab of vicious happiness. This afternoon Charles had tried to get Tracy to buy him a fifth of whisky; Tracy had refused and Charles had threatened to get him fired. Not that he really intended to, but he had talked mean and tough, as if he meant it. And he *could* get Tracy fired, if he wanted to. Charles could wrap his mother around his finger.

He heard the screen door at the side of the house open and slam, and he quickly flipped his half-smoked cigarette toward the beach. Normally he might have gone on smoking until his mother arrived, just to see how she'd react, but tonight, with his birthday coming up, he was thinking about his big deal.

Charles had been working on the deal ever since he and his mother had said good-by to his father in Morristown, New Jersey, three weeks ago. He had laid the groundwork very carefully, pointing out that it had been more than a year since his suspension from Bradytown Academy, and that, after all, the headmaster had taken him back. He dropped in the fact that he hadn't teased for a single present since the motorboat. Then he mentioned the Commando, very casually, almost as an afterthought. He did not say anything about the car's speed or horsepower. Instead, he concentrated on its artistic appearance. The car had a flame-red plastic body, airplane-type pants on the front wheels, white leather upholstery, and fins on the rear fenders. The price was $5,100.

Now, on the eve of his seventeenth birthday, all the groundwork had been pretty well laid. He'd been through phase one, where his mother said no, definitely no!; phase two, where he badgered her until she went to bed with a sick headache; and phase three, where he gave her the silent treatment. Now he was in the warm, mellow, closing phase, and he could almost feel the keys to the Commando jingling in his pocket.

The Money Machine, of course, would kick up a rumpus—but Charles's mother could handle that. The Money Machine was his father, a pretty rough old character, when you came right down to it. You couldn't slip any quick deals past him. For a guy who spent all his time down in Wall Street baling up money, he knew an amazing lot. . . .

"Charles! Oh, Charley!"

Charles got up from behind the hedge. His mother was standing on the lawn looking at the beach. She was forty-six, but she looked like a girl. She was slim and smoothly tanned and wore a simple white dress. Her one concession to age was a blue tint in her smartly clipped poodle cut.

Charles made a low wolf whistle, which he had been rehearsing mentally for this moment as a sort of kickoff for the closing phase of the Commando deal. "Cool," he said appreciatively.

His mother smiled. "Oh—you're over there, Charley."

He walked over to her, grinning. "Got a kiss for a real gone kid?"

She smiled, and he pecked at her cheek, holding his breath so she wouldn't smell the cigarette. As he drew away he caught sight of Diane, looking tiny and isolated, far down the beach. There was a quick pinch in his stomach. Maybe, if he started walking now, he could catch up with her and somehow get into a conversation. Or maybe she'd decide to go for a dip and be taken with a cramp, and he could save her.

Charles had been a lifeguard at camp for two summers, and in prep school he'd been captain of the swimming team. Even the coach at the academy, who hated him and had got him suspended, had said Charles was a crackerjack swimmer. But, heck—Charles didn't need the coach to tell him he could swim. He could swim.

"I'm driving up to the Bath and Tennis Club," Charles's mother said. "Anything I can bring you?"

Charles grinned. "Not from the B and T," he said, "unless they happen to have a Commando lying around."

His mother started to frown, then smiled at him. Charles smiled back. The campaign had clicked.

As soon as his mother left, Charles trotted down to the beach. Haze had crept in from the sea, and the beach was luminous in the fading light.

By the time Charles passed Judge Byrd's cottages, it was dark, but the beach was almost as familiar to him at night as it was in the daytime. He took runs after supper, sometimes down as far as the north turn of the NASCAR race track. Sometimes he didn't get back until after midnight. His mother had objected at first, but of course it hadn't done any good.

Charles kept watching for Diane in the glow from the headlights on passing cars, but he did not see the girl. Probably some rich handsome guy in a convertible had picked her up.

A car passed him, rolling slowly toward the inlet. Charles watched the beach in front of its headlights, but without hope. Diane was gone. He wouldn't see her tonight.

Ahead of him the car's taillights glowed brighter suddenly and the car slowed. Charles glanced through the rear window. A woman was driving and she was alone. As Charles watched her, her head silhouetted in the window, she suddenly sagged to the right, pulled herself erect, then sagged again. The car stopped.

Charles hesitated. All his life he'd been taught to stay away from strange automobiles. It was part of the training every rich kid had drilled into him from the day he was born.

He walked past the car, looking out of the corner of his eye, and listening. Nothing happened. He stopped and looked back. He could see nothing but the blaze of the headlights. Maybe the woman in the car was really sick. He hesitated, then turned and trotted back. It was a woman, all right, although he couldn't see her very well in the dim light of the dashboard. He said, "Hello. Hello in there . . ."

The woman did not answer. She acted rather drunk but Charles could not smell any liquor. There was a queer smell in the car that he couldn't quite place, very faint. She tried to reach her throat with one hand. The hand seemed very heavy. It fumbled a moment and fell back into her lap. This woman was sick all right. Charles twisted the door handle and got in, pushing the woman across the seat. "Just take it easy," he said. "I'll have you in the hospital in five minutes."

"Hospital," the woman said. "Yes . . ."

He slammed the door and was reaching for the starter button when he heard a faint sound behind him. He started to turn. An arm went around his neck and locked. A man's voice said, "Okay, Lora—give it to him."

A rag full of ether suddenly shut the air away from his mouth and nose. He fought it frantically, holding his breath, but the arm was like a vise. Then he had to breathe and he took in great lungfuls of the ether fumes.

A woman's voice said, "I thought we'd need the gun . . . I thought the little slob was going to pass us by . . ."

His face was pressed against something scratchy. It was dark and he felt horribly sick at his stomach. Somewhere a radio was playing. He tried to speak but something held his mouth tightly shut. Then he realized where he was: on the floor in the back of a moving car. His mouth was taped, his legs were fastened together and his wrists were handcuffed behind his back.

Suddenly a man's voice said, "Come on Lora—come *on!*"

A woman's voice said, "We're doing forty, honey."

"I know we're doing forty. The speed limit's fifty."

"Tommy. Please. We can't be picked up now."

"They'll be throwing up a road block any minute," the man said.

"We checked all through that, honey," the woman said patiently. "We know this kid walks on the beach at night. Nobody ever checks up. Relax, sweetie."

"Don't call me sweetie."

"I'm sorry," the woman said.

There was a ridge in the middle of the car floor, running from front to back. It was the drive-shaft housing. It cut into Charles's side whenever the car went over a bump.

"Tommy," the woman said. "Let's run through it one more time."

"Run through what?"

"The phone call."

The man said, "Look—you think I'm a moron or something?"

"Please, honey. It's terribly important. You know that."

"All right. *All right!*"

There was a pause. Then Charles heard the man's voice, grudging and angry: "I call from a pay phone at some drugstore. I tell the kid's mother right off the bat that we've got him and we're not kidding. If she calls the cops at any time she won't get back a kid, she'll get a corpse. Then I give her the details. Three hundred thousand dollars in twenties, and no runs of serial numbers. She puts the money in a barracks bag and drives up Alternate Route One from Daytona Beach at eleven o'clock this coming Friday night. She comes alone and she holds her speed at forty-five. She follows the ocean to the pier at Flagler Beach, turns left and goes across to Bunnel, and back down U.S. One to Daytona. It's around fifty miles. Should take about an hour. She drives with her dimmers on and she has a red flashlight strapped inside the windshield on the right side. It's lighted—so we know who's coming."

"Fine, Tommy. Go ahead."

"I show a red light," the man said. "I flash it low on the side of the road. When the kid's mother sees it she slows down, drops out the cash, and keeps going. If there's any other traffic on the road we don't show our light—she drives back home and we try again the next night. We keep trying until we can make the pickup without traffic. If there's any funny business—anyone with her in the car—we kill the kid."

The woman said, "And don't forget. Make it tough."

"Don't worry," Tommy said.

One of them turned up the volume on the car radio and a girl's voice was singing an oldie, one of Charles's favorites, but now he scarcely heard it. For a while it was dark; then swatches of light flared into the car from overhead and Charles knew they were in a town.

The car stopped and Charles saw the red reflection of a stop light. A girl's voice, right beside the car, said gaily: "Oh, no you don't, Peggy Johnson. He's my date . . ." Charles screamed against the tape; a muffled mooing sound came out. The stop light turned green and the car moved forward. Charles heard the man say, "Take the next left, Lora."

A hand reached back and tightened on Charles's throat, pinning his head savagely to the floor. Red mists accumulated like smoke in his head. They grew steadily darker and went through brown into deep black . . .

The next morning Lora Matthews was fixing her nails in front of the mirror on the dressing table. She felt good. Tommy had made the phone call last night. He'd talked to the kid's mother and he'd put it to her straight. There was no fear of that woman running to the police. Lora held up her hands. I do have pretty hands, she thought.

Tommy Snyder had noticed her hands that first night when he brought her home from Dave French's Hacienda—the night she'd won $6,100 at blackjack. Tommy had said, "Mrs. Matthews, you have the hands of a model." Tommy was Dave French's floor manager, which was a nice name for bouncer. He'd driven her back to her hotel with the $6,100—just to make sure nobody molested her on the way. It was one of the services of the club.

Tommy looked like Marlon Brando in the movies and he had a trick of looking at you as if he just might suddenly pick up a beer bottle and smash you across the face with it. It made Lora go all hot inside when Tommy looked at her that way.

Lora was thirty-four. Before her divorce she had been married to a butler. They'd been a "couple" on a rich broker's estate in Connecticut. Lora hated the rich. She thought they were slobs, all of them. The broker and his wife had pulled some pretty rare deals—they turned the thermostat down on the furnace when they went out on a winter evening, they drained the swimming pool during vacation, and after a party they poured out any champagne that was left so the servants wouldn't get a taste for it.

Lora's husband just shrugged off those things. But they bothered Lora.

She didn't think it was stealing to take her employer's things out of the attic of the guesthouse, where they were in storage, and sell them in New York. It was just payment for the oil burner and the champagne and the swimming pool and all the rest of it. And so the detective came as a complete surprise. Lora was selling a vase at the time. The man was going to give her forty dollars for it. The vase cost Lora more than forty dollars. It cost her three years in a women's penitentiary. They proved she'd been stealing consistently over a period of months, and her employers hired a smart tough lawyer and insisted on the maximum penalty. The rich had kicked Lora Matthews when they had a chance. In prison, Lora vowed that someday she was going to kick back.

Seeing that item in the Daytona Beach paper about Mrs. Morrison and her son—coupled with the fact that Lora had pretty well run through the $6,100—made Lora think about the kidnaping. The idea had appalled her a little at first but she had got used to it—and she had plenty pushing her. One thing was Tommy: she was nuts about Tommy. And Tommy liked her—Lora could tell.

Tommy also liked money. He mentioned the bar on Coquina Drive on their second date. He told her how he could buy in for $5,000, run it himself, and bring a lot of the gang from the Hacienda over. In two years he'd be smoking dollar cigars and raking in the cash. And Lora would be right there to help him spend it.

Tommy didn't come right out and ask Lora for a loan, but she knew he thought she had most of the $6,100 she'd won at the Hacienda. That was what made it so tough. She didn't have most of the $6,100, and she did not intend for Tommy to find it out.

She built up the mention of the kidnaping very carefully. She got Tommy a little drunk and then she told him how strong, tough, smart and capable he was. Finally she said it was a shame that a man of Tommy's ability should have to fool around a place like the Hacienda—or any cheap bar—when he could be handling big money.

Then she casually mentioned the kidnaping, and Tommy balked. He didn't want any part of anything like that, he said, but by two thirty in the morning they were in Lora's apartment making plans. Lora knew of a cabin for rent on the road to New Smyrna, very isolated. They could go there and sign up for two weeks as Mr. and Mrs. Snyder, tourists from New York. They could stay in the cottage a while and let the landlord, who lived half a mile away on the highway, get used to seeing them come and go. They could spend enough time to case the Morrison house and the habits of the kid and his mother and the servants . . .

Finally Tommy said, "How much did you say we could get?"

"Three hundred thousand."

"Give me another drink," Tommy said. "For three hundred thousand I'd roller-skate through hell barefoot."

Lora gave him the drink. Then she gave him a kiss. The next day Tommy quit his job at the Hacienda and bought a second-hand car, and they rented a cottage on the New Smyrna road.

Now, sitting in that cottage, Lora capped the bottle of nail polish and put it in the dresser drawer. She did not notice the tapping at the door at first because the radio was playing dance music. When the music stopped, the tapping came quite clearly.

Lora sat perfectly still until the announcer was through with the commercial and the music had started again. Then she ran to the clothes closet, grabbed the .38 off the hat shelf and stuck it into the pocket of her housecoat. Then she ran back into the living-room and stood behind the closet door.

"Yes?" she called. "Who's there?"

"Mr. Ellis," a quavery voice said. "The landlord, Mrs. Snyder."

"Mr. Ellis," Lora called out. "You caught me in the bathtub."

"I'm sorry," the voice said.

There was a pause in the radio music. Lora gripped the gun. If the kid made one of his mooing sounds right at this moment. . . .

"I hate to bother you, Mrs. Snyder," the old man called. "I know you're on vacation, but my brother-in-law is coming tomorrow from De Land to help me put the shingles back on the roof, the ones the hurricane tore off last year. It won't take long, ma'am."

From the bedroom Lora heard the squeak of bedsprings and a heavy thud. The radio was blaring loudly again however, and she was reasonably sure the old man hadn't noticed it. But she had to get rid of him now, very fast, before the music stopped. She called: "All right, Mr. Ellis. Tomorrow will be just fine."

"All right," the old man said. "We'll be here at two—if my brother-in-law gets in from De Land. I hope I haven't bothered you."

Lora's fingers tightened on the gun. Keep talking, Granddad, she thought, and wind up with a bullet in you!

"'By, Mr. Ellis," she called. "I've got to run now."

The song on the radio was in its chorus. Lora ran across the room, jerked the bedroom door open and knelt down beside the gangling boy who lay gagged on the floor beside the bed. She pressed the muzzle of the .38 against his right cheek, and whispered: "Make a sound, buster. Go ahead!"

The boy's eyes glared up at her. The anouncer's hearty gabbling stopped and the music began again. Lora waited, then whispered to the boy, "I'm going to tell you something, junior. I wouldn't mind killing you. If you try any more tricks like rolling off that bed, you get it. Clear?"

The boy's head bobbed up and down with difficulty, and she could see tears in his eyes. She went out, closed the door behind her, and went to look out the bathroom window at the stoop. The old man had gone.

After the redheaded woman left, Charles Morrison lay thinking about her eyes. They'd been hot and crazy-looking. She hadn't been kidding when she said she wouldn't mind killing him.

Suddenly Charles couldn't hold it in any longer. He began to cry, the tears he'd cried when he was a little boy. He shook all over, and made whimpering sounds. He did not hear the car drive in. The first he knew that the man named Tommy had come home was the sound of the woman's voice, calling, "Honey, what kept you so long?"

The man's voice was louder than it had been last night, and not so tense.

"We're in, baby. We've got it made."

There was a pause. Then the woman said sharply, "You've been drinking."

The sound of her voice made Charles shiver. "Carl Hall got drunk," she went on, her voice flat and quiet. "Carl Hall and Bonnie Heady were doing fine until Hall went into that bar in St. Louis and got drunk."

"I'm not drunk, Lora," Tommy insisted. "I tell you it's in the bag. The kid's mother hasn't made a peep. There's nothing in the papers. Everything's quiet in town."

"Don't drink again, Tommy. Not till after the pickup. Understand?"

"Listen, who are you trying to tell—"

The man's voice broke off short, and then he spoke again, his voice low: "Put that gun down, baby."

"I love you Tommy," the woman said. "But I'm not winding up like Bonnie Heady. Not for you or anyone. Is that clear?"

"Sure, baby. Sure, it's clear."

"While you were out living it up," Lora said, "I had a caller." And she told Tommy about the landlord wanting to repair the roof. "We can't have the kid here in the house while they're working," she went on. "The walls are so thin you can hear a pin drop anywhere in the house."

"I'll go over," Tommy said. "I'll tell the old guy not to disturb us."

"You can't. It would look funny, after me telling him to come. It would be something he'd remember later. We can't do anything that anybody will remember later. Once the lid comes off this deal, they'll be looking for us in every state of the Union. And don't forget—once we take the kid across a state line the FBI get into the act."

Irritation was back in the man's voice when he spoke: "So we don't take the kid across any state lines, just keep it between us and the cracker Florida cops. Is that what you have in mind?"

There was a pause. Then the woman said, almost casually, "You might say that's what I have in mind, Tommy. We'll have to get rid of the kid."

The man said instantly, "Look, Lora, we agreed there'd be none of that."

"We agreed you wouldn't drink—"

"Never mind my drinking. I don't go for murdering kids in cold blood. I like dough, but not that well."

"You don't have to do it," Lora said. "I'll take care of it."

"Don't be a fool!" Tommy said. "If you mention that once more—"

"Okay, honey—sorry," Lora said soothingly. But Charles did not think she sounded convinced.

Charles heard footsteps then. The door to his room opened and the man called Tommy stood there. His shoulders filled the doorway. He wore a pale-yellow sport shirt and white slacks. His forearms were tanned and corded with muscles. He said, "Hey, the kid rolled off the bed."

Charles saw the redheaded woman squeeze into the doorway beside the man. He hadn't realized how little she was. She barely reached the man's shoulder. She said, "Junior, here, is a smart little operator. He's the type that rolls off beds when people are around to hear him. But we had a little heart-to-heart talk and he's promised to be a good boy from now on."

Tommy bent and propped Charles against the bed. The woman, standing in the doorway with her hands behind her, said, "I've been thinking, Tommy. With those two old geezers coming here tomorrow, this joint is getting crowded. We've got to get out of here."

"We can't get out of here," Tommy said. "There's no place to go."

Lora looked at him. She said, "I'll take the kid in the car. I'll head south and hole up and wait. You make the pickup. When you've got the money you can join me."

Charles wanted to scream. He wanted to yell to Tommy that if Lora got him in the car alone, it wouldn't be just kidnaping—it would be murder.

Tommy said, "I need the car for the pickup." He looked at Lora. "Besides, I don't trust you with the kid."

Lora sneered. "What's the matter? Getting soft, Tommy?"

Charles saw the big man flex his fingers, lightly. The woman saw it too. She swung an arm out from behind her and pointed her ice pick toward him. "Take it easy, Tommy," she said.

Tommy loked at Lora steadily. Then he said, "Look. You pointed a gun at me a little while ago. Now you got that ice pick. I'm telling you something. Put it down. I'm a big dumb guy maybe, but I mean what I say."

The woman's eyes narrowed and Charles thought for an instant she was going to spring at the man. Then, very slowly, she lowered the pick. Tommy said, "Gimme it. Handle first."

Lora handed him the pick. "Don't push me around," Tommy said. He laid the pick on the dresser. "There is one place we can go," he said. "It's over back of Palatka. Dave French took some of the New York crowd in there fishing one time and asked me to come along to help. It's called the Oklawaha swamp, and it's a hell of a place. Used to be a stand of cypress. Now it's a thick jungle."

"Honey," Lora said, and her voice was low, almost pleading, "how can we live in a swamp?"

"There's an old hermit back there. Name of Webb. He sells bait to fishermen. We could stay in his shack."

"How would we get there?"

"We'd drive as far as we could, then take the boat. I remember there's a boat back there on one of the feeder streams. It's a community deal. Anyone who goes in uses the boat and then brings it back to the same spot."

"Suppose somebody is already using the boat."

"It's a chance we'd have to take—but it's not a big one. People don't go in there very often." Tommy rubbed his hand over his mouth. "The more I think about it, the better I like it," he said. "After we pick up the dough we can burn the old man's boat, row out of the swamp in the community boat and take off. The old guy and the kid would be stuck. By the time somebody found them we'd be safe."

"All right," Lora said. "But what about the landlord?"

"I'll go over as soon as it's dark," Tommy said. "I'll pay him off and tell him I got a wire from New York. They want me back there right away. I'm real blue about it too." Tommy winked. Lora winked back.

After dark Lora cooked eggs and bacon on the hot plate and made coffee. Tommy and Lora ate. Charles was lying on the living-room floor now, and they didn't offer him anything to eat but he didn't mind. The smell of the food made him feel sick.

Lora washed the dishes and Tommy went out to the landlord's house. When he was gone, Lora went into the bedroom and Charles heard her rummaging around in a closet. The door was ajar. Charles saw Lora take out a large coil of wire and put it into a suitcase. Next she put in a small plastic object that he did not recognize. Then she put in a .38 revolver, packed some clothes over the lot, closed the bag and locked it. Charles could see a .38 lying on top of the radio. That meant there were two. Charles wondered if Tommy knew that Lora had a gun of her own.

Finally Tommy came back, grinning. It was all set, he said. The landlord was even looking forward to having them in his cabin when they came to Florida for their vacation next year.

"How about that?" Tommy said.

He packed his clothes while Lora double-checked the cabin to make sure they hadn't left any evidence. Then Tommy took Charles out to the car, put him on the floor of the back seat and tucked a blanket over him. When they drove past the landlord's cottage, both Lora and Tommy leaned out and waved and shouted good-by. It was all very friendly and normal.

After a very long time, Tommy turned off the smooth road onto a rough surface and drove very carefully and slowly. Vegetation of some kind scraped the car on both sides. Even traveling in low gear, dead slow, the car bucked on its springs and at times Charles could hear the gurgle of water around the wheels.

Finally Tommy stopped the car. The weeds were too high in front, he said; he couldn't see where he was going. In the morning it would be a cinch. In the morning they'd find the boat without any trouble. Tommy seemed in good spirits, now they were in the swamp. They were safe now, he said. From the look of the weeds, nobody had been in here for months. He took the tape off Charles's mouth and ankles. "Take a good yell, kid," he said. "You probably need it."

"I won't yell," Charles said. "Please—will you take the handcuffs off? Just for a little while?"

Tommy laughed. "All the comforts of home, hey, kid?"

But he unlocked the handcuffs and let Charles rub the circulation back into his wrists before he put him in the front seat and fastened his left hand to the steering column. Charles would have thanked him if Lora had not been there. If he ever got out of this, he'd remember Tommy. He'd also remember Lora . . .

Tommy and Lora were in the back

seat together now, smoking cigarettes and talking in whispers. They'd rolled up the windows to keep out the mosquitoes. The smoke was thick in the closed car and it was very hot. Charles was very tired. Presently his mind sank toward sleep, and the sounds of the swamp grew faraway and dim.

Tommy woke Charles in the pre-dawn, released him from the steering column, and they went away from the car into the swamp a little distance. Tommy had lost his easy mood of the night. His eyes were hooded and his face was creased with sleep. Charles did not speak while they completed their toilet, and Tommy said nothing.

Lora was sitting in the front seat of the car when they returned. She had combed her hair and put on lipstick, but her eyes were puffy, and the lines in her face were etched clearly now.

Tommy put Charles in the back seat and cuffed his hands together. Then Tommy got into the driver's seat.

Lora held up the leather wallet. She said, "You dropped this on the floor last night."

"Oh," Tommy said. "Thanks." He put the wallet in his pocket.

Lora said, "Who is Iris Parks?"

Tommy turned and faced Lora. "You went through my wallet."

"How else would I know it was yours? It might have belonged to junior."

Tommy didn't speak.

"I must say she's pretty," Lora said. "And from what she wrote on her picture, she isn't exactly neutral on the subject of Tommy Snyder."

"Look, baby," Tommy said. "That picture was in my wallet long before I met you. It doesn't mean anything."

Lora laughed shortly.

"You don't believe it?" Tommy said.

"Oh, certainly I believe it. I know you wouldn't lie to me, dearest." From the back seat Charles could see her face as she looked at Tommy. Her lips were smiling, but her eyes were like the eyes of a snake. "Since you don't care about her any more," Lora said, "I know you won't mind telling me if she lives around here."

"I wouldn't mind," Tommy said. "But I'm not going to."

Lora bit her lip. Her face was dirty white under her tan. She said, "All right, Tommy, if that's how you feel."

"That's how I feel," Tommy said.

They drove through the grass and entered a forest of jack pines. The air smelled of turpentine and the ground was matted with red needles.

They passed the site of an ancient abandoned logging camp and entered the swamp. It was like moving into a green tunnel. The car was drenched with a bright rain of dew.

Tommy parked the car in a palmetto clump near the rowboat landing, well hidden from the road. Lora locked their bags in the trunk and Tommy bailed out the boat. His yellow shirt was soaked by the time he had the boat floating and a push pole ready.

"Okay now, kid," he said to Charles. "You sit in front. Lora, you in the middle. I'll stand in back and pole."

Lora said, "Wait. I'll be back."

She ran to the car. In a moment she reappeared, carrying the handle from the bumper jack. "There just might be snakes in this lovely place," she said.

For once, Charles had to agree with Lora. The swamp certainly looked snaky. The stream was so narrow that vegetation slithered over Charles's shoulders as they moved along.

Gradually the channel grew wider. They passed through sunlit glades between jackstraw piles of abandoned cypress logs. The mosquitoes were gone now but the sun was very hot and Charles realized how hungry he was. He had not eaten anything for thirty hours. His stomach felt hollow, and specks swam before his eyes.

The boat entered a long stream choked with bonnets and purple water hyacinth. "Almost there," Tommy said. "Another half hour should do it."

"It can't be too soon for me," Lora said. "This place gives me the creeps."

They left the water hyacinths and, where the ground rose a few feet above the water, passed between high walls of pines. Suddenly they rounded a bend and emerged into a deep, wide river. The boat immediately sagged with the current and Tommy had to thrust powerfully with the pole.

"Give me your scarf, Lora," Tommy said. "I want to mark this entrance. Otherwise we may miss it going out. There are dozens of little channels along this river."

Lora unknotted her scarf and Tommy tied it tightly and carefully to an overhanging branch. Then he stood up and began poling the boat upstream. It was hard work. The river's surface was smooth as glass. You could not tell there was a current unless you looked at the grass on the bottom. The sun was now very hot. Tommy had to keep wiping the sweat from his eyes. Finally he beached the boat and sat down.

"Look, Tommy," Lora said. "I hate to bring this up—but you said, almost an hour ago, that we'd be there in half an hour."

"Yeah," Tommy said. "I know."

"You sure there is really an old man back here?"

"Last October there was. He had a landing up a creek to the right. There was a little wooden sign nailed to a tree to mark the turn. I've been looking for it."

"That's great, "Lora said. "You've been looking for it. That's fine."

They were silent for a while. Tommy was resting, breathing heavily, looking at the river. "What are you thinking about, honey?" Lora said finally. "About Iris Parks? That girl whose picture was in your wallet?"

Tommy turned slowly away from the river and looked at Lora, and his eyes crinkled. "You happy here, Lora?"

Lora frowned. "What do you mean?"

"I mean, if you're not happy here, you can leave. You can swim back."

"That's a real bright remark."

"That's no bright remark," Tommy said. "That's how it is."

Lora turned away without speaking and Charles did not look at her face. He didn't want to see it. He hoped Tommy knew what he was doing. Tommy was big and he could break your back with his bare hands if he got mad. But he had to be mad. Lora was different. Lora could shoot you or stick an ice pick into you—for kicks.

Finally Tommy stood up and began to pole methodically upstream. His dark face had gone flushed. Fifteen minutes passed. A channel, choked with hyacinths, opened on the right. There did not seem to be any freeway through it. They had almost passed it when Charles saw the little wooden sign. The words had been burned on it with an iron: *Webb's Landing*.

"There's the sign," Tommy said.

"How far through this flower bed does old buddy live?" Lora asked.

Without answering, Tommy poled the boat powerfully into the mat of hyacinths. The boat moved out of the sunshine past some jack pines on a little mound of dry earth. It slid under a canopy of wild-grape vines, which seemed to be a dead end. Then Charles saw open water through the hanging tendrils of vine. Tommy thrust powerfully with his pole, and the boat shot out into a large basin of deep black water. Across the basin was a boat landing made of palm pilings, and a sun-bleached cabin roofed with palm thatching. At the edge of the dock, an old man was sitting in a chair fishing. Tommy called: "Hi there, Mr. Webb. Remember me?"

The old man's face was like leather and his hair was white. He reeled in a bright-colored wooden plug and set his steel rod and reel in a little stand beside him. He said, "Hello. What do you folks want? Bait?"

Charles wanted to scream a warning to the old man. But Lora Matthews was facing forward, and her eyes were on him. He saw that she was holding the flat steel jack handle in her right hand out of sight of the old man.

The boat bumped the dock. Charles's manacled hands came up involuntarily in an effort to keep his balance and the steel handcuffs glinted in the sun. The old man said, "Hey, what—"

Charles saw Lora rise, sure-footed and catlike, and swing the jack handle around viciously in a wide arc. He heard the bar strike something with a *whunk,* heard an agonized gasp from above, and then the old man fell heavily onto the dock.

Lora raised the jack handle to strike again, but Tommy had her arm. He jerked the handle away from her. "Okay, baby," he said. "*Okay.*"

"Oh . . ." The old man's voice was a moan. "My leg—you broke it—"

The next minutes were a nightmare to Charles. Lora and Tommy climbed out of the boat onto the dock and Tommy pulled Charles out after him. Instinctively Charles reached out to the old man, lying quiet on the dock in the sun, and Lora jerked him back with such force that he fell backward onto the dock. He could not take his eyes off the old man, seeing the tear in the corduroy trousers and the leg beginning to bleed where the skin had been torn.

Tommy manacled Charles's right wrist to the casing of a little iron pump the old man had installed at the edge of the dock to pull up water for cleaning his fish. Tommy and Lora lifted the old man and put him in the chair he'd been sitting in.

Lora stood there looking down at the old man without expression, while Tommy ransacked the cabin for food.

"Go ahead and fish," Lora said to the old man. "You've got your rod right there in the rack. Catch us a mess of trout." She chuckled as if she had said something funny.

Tommy laughed a little too. He'd found a bottle of whisky inside the cabin, and he'd been drinking.

Lora did not drink. She had found a can of beans in the shack and had opened it and was spooning the beans into her mouth. For the first time she seemed happy and content.

The old man's face was flushed now, and Charles saw him squeezing his eyes tightly at intervals, and tightening the muscles around his mouth. Charles had taken first aid in camp. He knew what had happened: the old man had been in shock. Now the shock was wearing off and the pain in his leg was getting through to him.

Tommy Snyder had drunk a lot from the bottle very fast and his voice had become loud and jovial. He said, "Mr. Webb —hey, Mr. Webb! I want-cha know I'm sorry. Wasn't necessary hit your leg. Mistake, Mr. Webb. Does it hurt? Bet it hurts like hell. Tell you what. We'll fix up a splint for that leg."

He bent down in front of the old man. "Lemme look at it, dad."

"Get away from me!" the old man cried.

Charles hadn't noticed Lora leave, but now he saw her come out of the cabin lugging a five-gallon can. She called, "Hey, Tommy—want to have a little fire? This is kerosene. Remember what you said about burning the old guy's boat?"

"Oh," Tommy said. "Burn the boat. Oh, sure. But not now, baby. Burn the boat anytime. Have a little drink!"

"There's a glass inside the shack, honey," Lora said. "Get it for me?"

"Right," Tommy said. . . .

When Tommy went into the shack, Lora swung the kerosene can to the edge of the dock, tipped it and let the kerosene cascade into the bottom of the old man's rowboat. Then she let the can fall back on its bottom, took her cigarette lighter from her pocket, snapped it and dropped it into the boat. There was a soft puff and the boat was enveloped with a bright rush of fire.

Tommy stepped out onto the dock with a water glass partly filled with whisky. He stood for a moment, staring stupidly at the fire. Then he lunged toward the woman. "You asked for it!" he snarled. "Now you get it!"

Charles did not know how Lora happened to have Tommy's gun in her pocket. Tommy had laid it down in the shack, probably, when he started drinking, and forgotten it. Charles heard himself cry out a warning to Tommy, but it was too late. Lora shot Tommy Snyder in the stomach. He stumbled and angled toward the edge of the dock, and the momentum of his body carried him over into the water.

When Tommy came up there was blood in the water around him, and his eyes were not drunken now but sober and terribly clear. Charles saw Lora hold the .38 down near Tommy's upturned face and fire it.

Charles was watching the woman in horror. He did not see old man Webb take his steel casting rod out of the stand beside him, but then he heard the small scream of the reel and saw the bright flash of the plug along the dock. The plug passed a few inches behind the woman's head, then snapped back savagely in mid-air, as the old man snubbed the reel with his thumb. The woman screamed and lost her balance, dropping the gun. Then, as the old man set the hooks, she lunged headlong into the water.

For an instant the dock hid her and Charles saw the old man's pole bend nearly double; then the woman had broken the line and was scrambling into her own boat and pushing away from the dock. Her cheek was bloody but the plug was gone.

The kerosene fire had died down, but the wooden portion of the rowboat was burning above the water line. In the center of the basin, Lora's boat lost the impetus of her frantic shove and stopped. She put her hand to her face, brought it down, and stared at the blood on her fingers. Then she looked back toward the dock, her expression quite calm, and slowly her lips drew tight across her teeth in a grim smile. In horror, Charles followed the direction of her gaze.

"Mr. Webb," he whispered. "She's going to burn us alive. . . ."

Lora Matthews stared at the half-filled can of kerosene which stood on the dock where she had left it. Then she crouched in the bottom of the boat and began paddling rapidly with her hands.

"The gun!" old man Webb called suddenly. "Get the gun, boy!"

Charles turned wildly. Then he saw the .38. It was lying on the dock where Lora had dropped it. He reached for it with his left hand, straining at the handcuff that held his right wrist.

"Your foot!" the old man called. "Try your foot! Quick!"

Charles swung his body out flat on the dock, hands toward the pipe, feet toward the gun. He pointed his toe and strained for it. The motion made him lose sight of what he was doing. He felt his toes strike something. He stopped straining and looked again. He'd kicked the gun out of his range.

He saw Lora Matthews working furiously now, trying to speed the boat toward the dock.

"Mr. Webb!" he screamed.

He felt the dock shake. He twisted and stared. The old man was out of his chair, pulling himself along with his hands, dragging his broken leg. His eyes were squinted nearly shut, and between each forward hitch he fell flat on the dock. Then he lifted himself up and took another hitch.

Lora was almost there. She was standing up in the boat. Charles looked wildly for something to pick up and throw at her. He saw nothing. Then old man Webb hunched his body forward and very carefully put his hand on the gun. Charles wanted to shout with relief.

Now Mr. Webb was on his belly and had the gun in both hands, aimed directly at Lora. "All right," he said, his voice curiously soft and expressionless, "that's far enough, ma'am."

Lora Matthews sat down and watched old man Webb. Somehow the whole situation seemed unreal to Charles. It did not seem possible that anyone and anything could really stop Lora.

"The boat pole is floating over by the outlet," old man Webb said. "You paddle over there with your hands and get it. Then get out of here."

Shoot her! Charles's mind screamed. Shoot her while you still have a chance.

When Lora still did not move, the old man cried, "Git! Do it quick. I ain't going to be able to hold myself much longer and I want to kill you awful bad."

Lora Matthews knelt down then and began paddling with her hands toward the outlet. When the boat moved out of sight, Mr. Webb laid the gun down carefully, crooked his arm under his face and lay still. . . .

The sunlight gradually faded. The shadow of the canopy of vines crept slowly across the surface of the pool.

Charles heard a mosquito's thin singing in his ears. He had, for some time, been watching with morbid fascination a pale-yellow blob of cloth floating in the brown water. It was a sport shirt. There was trapped air inside it and it ballooned above the surface like part of a pair of water wings. Beneath the yellow blob the body of Tommy Snyder was dimly visible under the surface of the water. Charles had not looked at the body at first. But now he was watching it, hoping it would float close to the dock. Tommy had the key to the handcuffs in his pocket.

Charles examined the handcuffs: one cuff was around his right wrist; the other was fastened to the two-inch casing under the pump head. He spit on his wrist, tucked his thumb tightly into his palm and tried to pull his hand free. It was no good.

Charles could see a can of baked beans on a shelf inside the old man's shack. When he looked at them he could feel his stomach convulse slightly and saliva thicken in his mouth. "Mr. Webb," he said softly.

The old man did not move.

Charles felt panicky. Was the old man —was he dead? Charles shouted, "Mr. Webb! Wake up!"

The old man stirred and opened his eyes. He peered at Charles but he did not seem to see him. "Mr. Webb," Charles said as calmly as he could. "Hand me the gun."

The old man raised his head off his arms. He peered at Charles carefully. "Oh," he said. "Hello, son."

"Throw me the gun, Mr. Webb. I have to use it to get this handcuff off."

Webb gripped the gun barrel with his left hand and drew it close to his body. Then he straightened his arm. The gun slid along the planking, bounced across a crack, and came to rest within Charles's reach. The old man let his head down on his arms. "Be careful . . . ," he said.

Charles held the gun in his hand for a long time, looking at it and at the handcuff in the fading light. He had never realized how large the bore of a .38 was, or how strong real handcuffs were. The only chance was to fire at the metal eyes that fastened the links to the cuffs. But if the bullet richocheted wrong it could very well go off the eyelet into his own body.

The alligator came from the direction of the river. Charles heard it first in the hyacinth bed; then he saw something black moving smoothly toward the yellow shirt.

Charles pointed the revolver at the shape, then lowered it. He had only two bullets. He might need them both if the thing passed Tommy and tried to get him or the old man. The alligator stopped swimming and lay quietly in the water, then disappeared. For a moment nothing happened. Then the body in the yellow shirt was gone. Charles shuddered, and his fingers on the gun relaxed.

The alligator broke the surface of the water with a mighty rolling splash, and then thrashed into the hyacinths. On the far bank, in the darkness, it stopped. A subdued wrenching and tearing sound began . . . .

Charles pulled the handcuffs taut, put the gun against the links and squeezed the trigger. There was a dynamite roar in the dusk, something clubbed his wrist savagely, and then he found himself sprawling on his back ten feet from the pump. He held up his wrist. It was bloody and the cuff still was on it, but the link had been broken. He was free!

He glanced at the old man, who apparently was unconscious again, hesitated, and then ran into the shack and began to eat voraciously whatever he could find—a can of beans, sliced pineapple, condensed milk.

When he was through eating he found a lantern and lighted it with one of the old man's kitchen matches. On a tiny workbench lay four or five fishing plugs in various stages of construction. Several were still in the whittling stage, and the one that had caught Charles's eyes was hanging up to dry: a vivid yellow body with black polka dots and a black head.

A low moaning sound from outside made Charles hold his breath. He went out at once, feeling guilty. The old man was still lying exactly as he had been, on his stomach, with his head on his arm, but his breathing had changed. His breath came smoothly for a while, then seemed to choke up, and he gasped and shivered. And then the breathing smoothed out again.

Charles knew first aid from his work in camp. One of the first rules was not to move a person with a broken bone unless you first secured the bone with a splint. Vaguely he recalled something about traction—pulling the leg out so the broken edges of bone wouldn't injure the nerves and tissue. You had to have a special apparatus for that. You needed two people, one to pull and one to bandage.

Charles felt a twinge of unreasoning anger. He had been through enough. He was so tired he could barely stand up, his hand and arm were beginning to ache from the bullet bruise, and the mosquitoes were buzzing around his face and bare hands. Charles went into the shack. The bed looked very soft. He wanted to lie on it, just for a minute, but he knew if he lay down he wouldn't get up. He took the lantern outside and set it on the dock so he could see what he was doing. He brought a blanket from the bed and tucked it around the old man so there would be no place for mosquitoes to enter. He peered at the old man's head, resting on his arms. It seemed to be in a comfortable position. But he had to protect the old man's face and hands.

Charles carried the lantern back into the shack and looked for mosquito netting, but there was none. It's probably okay, Charles thought. He's probably been bitten a million times. He's probably immune.

He sat down on the edge of the bed and started taking off his shoes. He had both shoes off and was starting on his socks when he stopped. In his stocking feet he dragged the kitchen table out onto the dock and placed it over the old man's head. Then he brought a bed sheet out, draped it like a tent, and weighted it down around the edges with some chunks of firewood he found stacked at the corner of the shack. He paused and looked at his handiwork. He said, "Good night, Mr. Webb. Pleasant dreams."

The sun was high when Charles awoke. The sun did not wake him—it was the old man groaning. Charles sat up in bed, feeling sore and stiff. He looked at his injured wrist. The handcuff was still on it and the knuckles of his hand were swollen and caked with dried blood. He got up and stepped out on the dock. He almost screamed.

Somehow the old man had rolled over and pulled the sheet loose, and one side of the table was completely open. His face was horribly swollen and blotched with mosquito bites, and when he breathed, little bubbles rose and burst on his lips. Charles did not want to look at the old man's leg, but he had to look. He pulled back the blanket very gently. Then he replaced the blanket and ran back into the shack and fell face down on the bed.

He sobbed into the pillow, holding it against his face to muffle the sound. His body shook. A thought kept pounding in his head: I slept . . . I slept . . .

After a while he sat up on the bed. He

didn't know much about first aid but he was sure of this: old man Webb no longer needed just a traction splint—he needed a doctor, a hospital, blood. He needed them now, today. If he did not get them today he might never need them again. If I'd acted like a man instead of like a crummy kid, Charles thought bitterly, if I'd stayed awake and checked that sheet— The bites the old man had taken were no joke, even for a man in top shape. In his weakened condition, when he needed all his reserve strength to stand the pain in his leg, the mosquito bites might tip the scale.

Charles looked out the doorway of the shack. The water was empty and peaceful. There was no sign of Tommy Snyder's body. The kerosene can still stood on the edge of the dock where Lora had left it.

Charles took off his trousers and socks; then he went outside and carefully rearranged the sheet around the old man's head and weighted it in such a way that Webb would scarcely be able to touch it, even if he moved. Charles poured all of the rest of the kerosene out of the can, found the cap and screwed it on tight. He tossed the can into the water, slipped in beside it, and pulled his body over it. The can sank almost out of sight and stabilized, keeping his body afloat. He gave the can a hard push across the pool and struck out after it.

It was late afternoon when he drifted out of the mouth of the Oklawaha into the broad sweep of the St. Johns River. He thought it was a lake. He did not know how long it had been since he had stopped swimming and merely floated, supported by the can.

He had swum beautifully in the beginning, pushing the can along ahead of him in the current; after he made himself stop thinking of jaws rising up under him from the depths, he reveled in the clean power of the six-beat crawl. Gradually the crawl slowed and turned into a side stroke. He went ashore several times and lay among the bonnets and his chest heaved, and gradually the leaden feeling drained out of his arms and legs.

He hadn't gone ashore now, however, for a long time—not since he'd almost put his hand on a snake that had been lying on a log.

Now Charles had stopped worrying about snakes or alligators. He was mainly concerned with keeping his mouth and nose out of the water. He kept slipping down, and each time it was harder to get his head clear. He thought: I must hold onto this can. No matter what happens I must hold this can . . .

"Grab his shoulders, Ed," a faraway voice said. "I'll get his hips."

Hands pulled at him.

"Watch it, Ed!" the voice said sharply. "You wanta upset the boat?"

Charles lay on the bottom of the boat, feeling the motor driving it somewhere; and then sometime later, a voice said, "Son? Can you hear me, son?"

He said, "Yes. I can hear you." With a great effort he drew himself up. He said, "Please, sir, will you get me to a telephone —quick?"

The two men carried him up a winding pathway through some palmettos and into a sandy yard where there were some people sitting on the porch of a house.

Then Charles was sitting in a room holding an old-fashioned upright telephone in his hand. He got the operator and placed a call to his mother's house in Daytona Beach. Then, suddenly, he heard his mother's voice, sounding tired and remote: "Hello? This is Mrs. Morrison."

He said, "Hello, Mom."

The wire hummed emptily. Then his mother's voice came to him, kind of wild and crazy, "Charley! Are you safe? Where are you?"

"I'm all right," he said. "I'm safe. I'm in a farmhouse in a town called—" He stopped, and somebody said, "Welaka. The Culpepper house in Welaka."

"Mother, I'm in Welaka. At the Culpepper house in Welaka."

His mother said, "Your dad's here, Charley. He wants to talk to you."

Charles heard his father's voice: "Hello, Charley? Are you alone?"

"How do you mean?"

"Are they—"

"Oh—the kidnapers! No, Dad. I'm in this farmhouse and—"

"Charley—" Mr. Morrison said, and then Charles heard his father's voice break. The wire hummed for an instant, and Charles heard a deep breath. Then his father's voice came back, normal and strong. "Okay, Charley," his father said. "Let's have it, son."

Charles talked fast and tried not to leave any of it out. He told about Tommy and Lora, and swimming out of the swamp. He said that old man Webb was in the swamp alone, told what he needed and how if he didn't get it tonight it would probably be too late. He said, "Dad, Mr. Webb saved my life. You'll get on it right away, won't you?"

His father said, "Yes, I'll get on it, Charles. Now tell me again where you are."

Twelve minutes after Charles hung up, he heard the sirens. It was like a movie. He heard the sirens get louder and louder, saw the headlights careening through the dark. The cars skidded hard as they stopped in the dust outside the Culpepper house, and men in uniform piled out and ran up the steps. The first thing they did when they saw him was unlock the single handcuff and remove it from his wrist. Charles started telling them about old Mr. Webb, but they interrupted. "Never mind the old man now, son," one trooper said. "We know he needs help. It's on its way from Daytona Beach. We've got another job to do. Steady down now, son. Help us."

"What can I do?"

"This is Friday night," the trooper said. "Your mother is expected to deliver three hundred thousand dollars in twenty-dollar bills to some one between eleven and twelve tonight, somewhere on the road above Daytona Beach. Our job is to pick up that person."

Charles had forgotten about the pickup of the ransom money. He had forgotten it was to be on Friday night. He hadn't even realized that today was Friday. He told the police all he knew about the instructions Tommy had given his mother by telephone.

"We know that, son." the trooper said. "Where did they say they'd be waiting?"

"They didn't say," Charles said, "and it isn't 'they' anymore. It's just Lora." And he told them how an alligator had got Tommy's body. "Lora's got a gun," Charles went on. "I don't know what you're going to do, but you'd better be awful careful."

"Don't worry, kid," the trooper said. "We'll take care of it. Now, you wait here for your folks—they're on their way from Daytona Beach with doctors and hospital equipment and rescue boats. . . ."

When the rescue boats reached the hyacinth bed at the mouth of Webb's Creek, it was quite dark. Charles was in a boat with his father. He wore trousers and a jacket borrowed from one of the Culpepper sons, and his face was smeared with mosquito lotion. The motors bogged down in the hyacinth bed. One boat had oars and was able to make it through with the doctor and two interns. Charles and his father had to wait until someone could wade ashore and cut a pole. It was after eleven o'clock before they reached the landing.

The doctor had worked fast. He and the interns had rigged a small mosquito-netting tent under a battery of portable lights. The old man was lying inside it on a stretcher. He was getting a blood transfusion from a bottle that stood on a bench beside him.

When the doctor heard Charles and his father climb onto the dock, he stared blindly out of the spotlights. He said, "Is that you, Morrison?"

"Yes, it is." Charles's father said. "How's the patient, doctor?"

The doctor smiled and the light flashed on his teeth. "He's not feeling very chipper right this minute, but I think he'll come around. These swamp characters are tough old boys. They take an awful lot of killing."

At eleven thirty Lora was crouched in the palmetto scrub beside U.S. Route 1, on the outskirts of Daytona Beach. Everything was ready. She had placed the red flashlight beside the road and positioned it to shine in the face of anyone approaching in a car from the north. She had attached two long wires to the light and stretched them back into the palmettos. When Lora touched the tips of the wires together, a dull red glow lighted the margin of the concrete road. The wires were a precaution in case the Morrison woman tried to cross her up and brought police along. If the police fired at the red light, Lora would fire at the police. She had her own .38, which she had left behind in the trunk of the car when they went into the swamp, and it was fully loaded.

Now, kneeling among the palmettos, Lora went over the getaway plan once more. As soon as the Morrison woman dropped the cash Lora would pick it up, go to her car, which was hidden on an adjacent side road, and drive toward the beach. A mile away was a large dump with a good hiding place for the money and the gun. This way, even if an alarm were out and radio cars stopped her on her way to town there wouldn't be a scrap of proof.

The plan was foolproof. If the Morrison woman had tipped off the police, Lora would simply leave the money in the dump until the roadblocks were lifted. This wouldn't take long; resort highways were too heavily traveled to be tied up by a continuing roadblock. As soon as she dared, Lora would pull the money out of its hiding place and head north. In two days she'd be lost in New York City.

Now she began to watch traffic carefully. There was only an occasional car. Her luck was holding. Lora felt a crazy excitement rising inside her.

At five minutes to twelve a car entered the straightaway, driving slowly, and Lora cocked the .38. She picked up the two wires to the signal light. The car came slowly toward her, and Lora had to strain to see the red light in the windshield. She moved the tips of the wires into contact, saw the dull red glow of the signal light on the pavement, and crouched low, aiming her revolver at the darkness above the car's headlights.

The car suddenly stopped dead. The

roadside around the red signal light was bathed in blinding brightness. Lora fired instantly, and heard the shattering of glass and a man's voice yell, "To the right, Frank! In the scrub!"

Someone slipped out of the side door of the car. Lora shot at him, heard a grunt of pain, and saw a man flounder into the palmettos. Then the spotlight hit her.

The Reising gun stuttered once from the back seat of the car. Lora Matthews was dead before her body touched the ground.

For four days everything was very hectic. The Morrisons' lawn was trampled by reporters and littered with flash bulbs, and crowds of curious people came and stood on South Atlantic Avenue and looked at the house. What they expected to see, Charles couldn't quite figure out.

On the fourth morning after his escape, both old man Webb and the cop who'd been shot by Mrs. Matthews were reported out of danger. On the fifth morning, Charles's father tossed a paper on the breakfast table. The headline read: *JUNIOR CHAMBER OF COMMERCE PLANS ANNUAL MISS DIXIE CONTEST*.

Charles's father leaned back and lighted a cigar. He said, "The situation is back to normal. Beautiful girls, bless them, have pushed the Morrisons off the front page at last."

Charles's mother said, "I told your dad about the little red car you want."

Charles looked up from his plate. "Yes, Mom?"

"He says it's up to you. You've been pretty wonderful, Charles. We're awfully proud of you. If you want the car, you may have it—as a birthday present."

Charles looked at his father. His father grinned. "That's right, Charley."

Charles wanted it. There wasn't a guy in the world with red blood in his veins who wouldn't want that sleek little sweetheart. He opened his mouth to tell his parents that he certainly appreciated it, and he wanted the Commando very much. He got out the first part, about appreciating it, but the second part came out crazy. Completely crazy. He somehow was saying that he didn't care so much about the car now, as much as he thought he had, and maybe later, when he got hold of some money he'd earned himself, he'd think more about it.

His mother was looking at him with open amazement. She made him feel like a darned fool. He said, "Look—I *do* want the car! Don't think I've flipped my lid or anything. It's just that . . ." Nobody said anything. "I think I'll take a walk on the beach if nobody minds."

He got up and started out. At the door he looked back. His mother was staring bewilderedly at his father. But his father didn't seem bewildered; he was grinning.

Charles walked down past the hedge. Tracy, the family chauffeur, was working on the car. He was whistling. He stopped whistling and said, "Charley, there's a girl down on the beach. She wants to know if you're coming down this morning."

Charles felt his body go weak and empty. He looked at the beach. Diane was sitting on a blanket. She had lovely legs, two pigtails and a cute snub nose. He took a deep breath and swallowed. Then he walked slowly down the path through the hedge.

When he reached her he said, "Hello there. Somebody said you might be looking for me."

Diane looked up at him. Her eyes were brown and very bright and shy—but not *too* shy. She said, "You're the boy who swam out of the swamp to save that old man's life, aren't you?"

Charles said, "Yeah."

Diane looked at him and Charles felt his knees begin to tremble. "My name is Diane Frazier," she said. "I live up the beach a little way. I was wondering—I mean, if it wouldn't be too much trouble, I was wondering if you could teach me that special crawl stroke you use. The one they mentioned in the newspapers."

Charles was very careful to keep his voice calm and controlled, and he sternly repressed a desire to leap into the air and clap his heels together. He said, "I guess I could find time to teach you that stroke, Diane. Sure. Why not?"

Five Desperate Hours in Cabin 56

Cornelius Ryan

It's a newspaperman's job to get the spot news against today's or tomorrow morning's deadline; a magazine reporter, with greater leeway, can cover a story in depth. Cornelius Ryan, Collier's *reporter, aided by a half dozen members of the staff, undertook a focus-down on the events in one cabin of the Andrea Doria from the time she collided with the Swedish Liner Stockholm until she sank five hours later—and produced a story that had the jolting impact of spot news when it reached the newsstands a month later.*

September 28, 1956

EDITOR'S NOTE: AT 11:10 O'CLOCK ON THE night of July 25th, the impossible happened. Two transatlantic passenger liners, equipped with radar and all the other electronic aids of modern navigation, collided in the open ocean. The prow of the 12,165-ton Swedish liner Stockholm, less than 12 hours out of New York with 750 passengers and crew bound for Scandinavia, knifed 30 feet into the starboard side of Italy's 29,100-ton Andrea Doria, inbound from the Mediterranean with 1,706 passengers and crew. The scene: 45 miles south of Nantucket Island.

Within minutes, the greatest sea-rescue operation in history was under way. As the Andrea Doria slowly heeled over to starboard, lifeboats from the damaged but still navigable Stockholm and at least 15 other ships that had responded to the two ships' SOS—among them the French liner Ile de France—began ferrying the stricken Italian vessel's passengers and crew to safety. Within five hours, all survivors but the captain and a handful of volunteers had been taken off. Sometime after dawn, they, too, left—and almost exactly 11 hours after the collision, the Andrea Doria went down. The final count of those who had been aboard showed: 1,661 rescued, 45 dead or missing. Five crewmen aboard the Stockholm also had died or were missing.

Millions of words already have been published about the collision and its aftermath. But the most dramatic story of all has never, until now, been told. It is the story of what happened in first-class Cabin 56 on the Upper Deck of the Andrea Doria after the Stockholm's bow plowed into the Italian liner and crumpled the cabin to matchwood.

Primarily, it focuses on four people: an American chiropractor and his wife, returning from a European trip for which they had planned and saved 12 years; another woman passenger (Mrs. Camille Cianfarra, wife of the eminent New York

Times foreign correspondent), who was hurled into their cabin by the impact of the collision, and a cabin-class dining-room steward whose greatest ambition had been to be assigned to first-class passengers.

The story of the next five hours in the lives of these people makes a true narrative of heroism and horror, terror and tragedy more incredible than fiction.

* * *

Ahead lay Cannes and the voyage back home to the United States. Dr. Thure C. Peterson and his attractive wife, Martha, relaxed as their hired, chauffeur-driven limousine swung onto the coast road and rolled swiftly through the tropical scenery of the French Riviera.

Peterson turned to his wife. "Marty," he said, "we're nearly there."

The ocean voyage would be the first for both of them and Peterson wondered, as he idly watched the white, pink and russet-colored villas flash by, if he'd be seasick on the elegant Andrea Doria.

A month before, the Petersons had flown to Sweden to visit the birthplaces of their parents—a trip for which they had planned and saved since 1944. They had toured Denmark and Switzerland—and now, ahead, were nine days at sea on Italy's most luxurious liner.

Mrs. Peterson was excited about the voyage, but her husband was a little disappointed. He and Marty had planned a trip through Italy prior to boarding the Doria. But they had lost a week because Peterson, an internationally known chiropractor and president of the Chiropractic Institute of New York, had been invited to give a series of lectures before European chiropractors who were meeting in Switzerland. He had tried, without success, to switch their reservations to the Doria's sister ship, the Cristoforo Colombo, due to sail from Genoa 13 days later.

But he had been able to get plane reservations. Back in Zurich, Peterson had tentatively booked two seats on a flight leaving a week later and scheduled to arrive in New York July 26th. Marty was against flying home. From the very beginning she had set her heart on the ocean voyage. "Darling," she had said, "let's forget the Italian tour altogether—you're all tired out after the Switzerland lectures anyway. And we're not as young as we used to be. The voyage home will give you a good chance to rest up."

Peterson had to agree that Marty was probably right. They weren't as young as they used to be—he was fifty-seven, Marty was fifty-five; and reluctantly he had to admit that that nine-day rest sounded good.

So it was a few minutes before five that afternoon—July 17th—that Thure and Martha Peterson, with ten pieces of baggage, two raincoats, two cameras and two first-class tickets which had cost them $1,040, boarded the graceful Andrea Doria at Cannes. "Well," said Marty gaily, as they climbed on board, "we made it—didn't we?"

From the moment the Petersons came on board they were swallowed up in the gleaming world of the 29,100-ton luxury liner. At the top of the stairs on the Upper Deck and to the right was their cabin: Number 56. It had twin beds, separated by a wide built-in chest. One bed ran beneath the twin portholes, the other against a blond, veneered paneled wall which backed an elevator shaft. There were two low beige upholstered chairs and a thick carpet on the floor. At the portholes and the baggage closet in the entrance hall were beige and maroon plaid curtains.

After a quick look around the cabin, Marty hurried over to one of the portholes. She was disappointed to find that, being only five feet three inches tall, she couldn't see out of it. Her husband had no such trouble—he is a big man, over six feet tall and weighing more than 200 pounds.

"Well, which bed do you want?" Peterson asked his wife.

Marty hesitated for a moment, then walked over to the bed against the inside wall which backed up the elevator shaft.

"This one," she said.

It was some time before their luggage was brought up. When it arrived they began to unpack. Marty had come well prepared. She had a different evening dress for nearly every night aboard ship. But like a good housewife, with one eye on the budget, she'd shopped for the materials herself, had the gowns made by a dressmaker friend in their home town, Upper Montclair, New Jersey. In the midst of her unpacking, she took out several of the dolls she'd bought for her granddaughters in each of the countries the Petersons had visited.

Then she carefully rewrapped them and put them away. She thought that her daughters, June and Peggy, would be pleased with all the things she'd bought for her five grandchildren.

Their minor duties finished, the Petersons left their cabin and walked up one flight of steps to the Promenade Deck and entered the first-class cocktail lounge. The hurry was over, the voyage had finally begun.

Three decks below the Promenade Deck a wiry, 48-year-old crewman named Giovanni Rovelli lay asleep. Within eight days, this cabin-class waiter from Genoa and first-class passenger Peterson of New Jersey were to be bound together as men are only in war or catastrophe.

Gino occupied the upper berth in one of the three double-decker bunks in the sparsely furnished six-man crew cabin. On the afternoon before, while the ship still lay in Genoa, he and his wife Pina, and their seven-year-old son, Gianni, had visited the shrine of the Madonna of the Mountain, which overlooks the harbor of Genoa. As always, the last hours before a sailing were difficult. Gino hated to leave his family and their four-room apartment on the Via Carlotta Benettini in Genoa. But the sea has always been more than just a job to Gino. As he has told Pina many times: "When the soul is brought to the sea, there she stays."

When Gino woke up, he glanced at his watch and carefully washed and dressed. Then he hurriedly made his way to the cabin-class dining room. For him, the voyage meant 12 to 15 hours a day of hard work.

The next morning the Doria arrived at Naples; two days later it stopped briefly at Gibraltar. The Petersons, who had wondered about their next-door neighbors, saw that a family, boarding at Gibraltar, had Cabins 54 and 52. These new passengers were Camille Cianfarra, the New York Times correspondent in Spain; his wife, Jane; their eight-year-old daughter, Joan, and Cianfarra's step-daughter, Linda Morgan, fourteen. The Petersons never did find out who occupied Cabin 58, on the other side of them.

By the time the Doria reached the Atlantic and began its 101st crossing, the Petersons had made many new friends and were enjoying every minute of the trip. They even had met the Doria's fifty-eight-year-old captain Piero Calamai on the bridge and he had shown them the radar. They could clearly see the outlines of the Azores which they were passing. The voyage was everything they had hoped for—until the afternoon of July 25th.

On that day, the Doria's last day out of New York, Peterson noticed the first wisps of fog about 2:00 P.M.; by 4:30 P.M., he could hardly see the water through the portholes. "This could delay us," he told Marty.

Gino, too, had noticed the fog. Just be-before he went upstairs to serve at dinner, he told one of his cabinmates, Menotti Calligaris: "I don't like that mist. It was like this on the San Miguel on the Oslo run one time. We rammed the Binna coming down the fiord. She sank in 15 minutes."

Menotti turned on Gino angrily: "To hell with you and your presentiments."

The Petersons entered the first-class dining room a little after eight. They had a leisurely dinner. To celebrate their last night on board, they ordered a half bottle of champagne. Throughout the meal of roast beef, mixed salad and fresh fruit, they heard the muted bass notes of the foghorn.

They decided to turn in early. When they entered their cabin at 10:30 P.M., they found that the maid had put Peterson's bathrobe (he slept nude) on Marty's bed. Her white pleated nylon nightgown lay on the bed nearest the portholes.

"Marty, do you want to switch beds for the final night?" Peterson asked his wife.

"No—you keep that one, I'll stay where I am," she told him.

Peterson locked the door. Marty undressed, got into bed and picked up a book she had bought in Denmark.

"I haven't got a darn' thing to read," he told her. He took off his glasses, put his watch on the chest and turned out his light. It was just before eleven. The last thing he heard before dropping off to sleep was Marty's voice: "I can't keep my eyes open." Her reading light went out.

At about the same time, Gino went below to his cabin on A Deck, got ready for bed and climbed into his bunk. He worked for a little while on his hobby: algebra. After about 20 minutes, he removed his glasses and glanced at his ancient watch, hanging on a chain from a pipe just above his head. It was 10:50 P.M. Gino switched off his bunk light.

Like a great city, the Andrea Doria was slowly quieting down for the night. The mist that had become fog had thickened and, like felt, padded the onward rush of the ship as she slipped through the night. In the ballroom some people were still dancing. Elsewhere, passengers listened to music, strolled the decks or took leave of their shipboard acquaintances over nightcaps in the various bars. But many, like Gino and the Petersons, had already retired. In Cabins 54 and 52 the Cianfarras had gone to bed.

The occupants of Cabin 58, whom the Petersons had never seen, were not in bed. They were two priests, Fathers John Dolciamore and Richard Wojcik, of Chicago, and they were sitting in a quiet corner of the Promenade Lounge playing Scrabble.

The liner Stockholm plowed into the starboard side of the Andrea Doria at 11:10 P.M.

The first thing Peterson was conscious of was the sight of the Stockholm's bow passing through his cabin. The white prow seemed dark, almost gray, as it ripped into the side of the Doria. He was conscious of a hard, heart-stopping thud, the noise of the ripping plates and churning debris falling all about him. Then he felt himself moving through space. Naked, half-stunned, covered by falling debris, just before he lost consciousness he realized that he was trapped.

Two decks below, Gino awoke to see his watch spinning crazily on its chain. He and his friend, Menotti, sat up in their bunks. A white-jacketed steward rushed into the cabin and took a life jacket from beneath his bunk. Stupefied, Gino and Menotti watched him.

"What's happened?" asked Gino.

"We're going down," the steward replied, and left the room.

Menotti looked at Gino. "*Al diavolo!*" he said in hushed, incredulous tones. "It's impossible."

Menotti and Gino hurriedly dressed.

Thinking that the noise had been caused by a boiler explosion and seeing smoke in the corridor, Gino made his way to the fire station near his quarters. From other hurrying crewmen he learned the truth—the Andrea Doria had collided with another vessel; it was shipping water fast. Already it was listing 20 degrees.

The two priests, Fathers Dolciamore and Wojcik, had been shaken by the crash. But they scrambled out of their chairs and made their way through dazed groups of passengers who were beginning to gather in the lounge. As quickly as they could, they descended the stairs to Cabin 58, next door to the Petersons' room, passing many passengers streaming up from below.

Father Wojcik opened the door, switched on the light and picked up the life jackets from the baggage closet in the hallway. Quickly he glanced about the room and saw that one side of the partitioning wall between their cabin and Number 56 had buckled inward. The furniture had been disarranged and the bed under the portholes was covered with debris. He switched off the light, and he and Father Dolciamore rushed upstairs to the Promenade Deck.

They left, thinking the room was empty.

When Peterson came to, he found he could not move. Naked, in total darkness, he discovered he was lying on a bunk buried in debris. He wasn't sure how long he had been there. He called out to his wife: "Marty, Marty, are you all right?"

Everything was silent. The ship's engines had stopped, there was no movement or noise in the cabin or from outside—only the sound of water lapping gently against something below him. Then he heard a muffled moan somewhere off in the distance. "Marty, Marty," he called again, "are you all right?"

There was a faint reply. "My legs," Marty moaned. "They're caught."

"Don't move," yelled Peterson. "Just don't move. Help will be coming."

There was another pause, and in the closeness of the room the silence was accentuated. Marty said suddenly: "There seems to be someone here with me."

Peterson began the slow and painful job of extricating himself. Because his arms were free, he could push away the planking, plasterboard, torn mattresses and splintered furniture that covered him. And by heaving his muscular shoulders and torso from side to side, he was able to twist his way out. All the while, he kept reminding his wife not to move. She answered him calmly. But he could not understand why her voice seemed so far away. Bleeding from the head and with the muscles of his back, chest and abdomen badly wrenched, he staggered to his feet.

He stood for a moment in the darkness

trying to get his bearings. But there was something wrong. The layout of the cabin seemed to be reversed. He could not find his wife or her berth. They had disappeared. He called to her again.

She replied, "I'm here, over here."

He found a light switch, pressed it, but nothing happened. The ship's regular lighting system had failed. In the darkness, he began to feel his way toward his wife's voice, but he encountered only debris and furniture—and then the blank finality of a wall. The voice seemed to come from the other side of it.

Unable to go farther, he headed in the general direction of the door. Feeling his way, he found the washbasin and clothes closet were not where they should have been. Suddenly it dawned on him. *He was not in his own cabin.* He reached the door and wrenched it open. He stumbled out of the darkness into the carpeted corridor, which gleamed duskily under the amber emergency lights. The number on the cabin door was 58.

Peterson saw nobody in the corridor. He stood there gasping, his body streaked with dirt, his feet bleeding from the slivers of glass on which he had trod.

The familiarity of the surroundings gave him momentary relief. Then he tried the door to Cabin 56, his own cabin. It was locked, but the bottom panel had been stove in. On hands and knees he crawled through. It, too, was in darkness. As he slowly felt his way, his hand suddenly brushed against the coldness of a dead face. From beyond it and slightly to his right, behind an impassable pile of wreckage, he heard the voices of his wife and another woman. Directly in front of him, through chinks in the debris, he could just make out the outlines of a large gaping hole and somewhere below, as in the bottom of a well, water.

He returned to Cabin 58, frantically hoping that he could force a way to the trapped women from that side. Even in the darkness, by sense of feel alone, he was able to visualize roughly the triangular prison which contained them. One side of the prison was formed by the wall of the elevator shaft that separated the hallways leading into Cabins 56 and 58. A second side was a wall of twisted plates and wreckage forming the rim of the gaping hole, and the third was what remained of the partition between Cabins 56 and 58. To Peterson, the two imprisoned women were actually trapped on a triangular tongue with its tip leaning toward the sea—for the deck was already tilting crazily toward the water. For all he knew, the wreckage and the imprisoned women might at any moment slide into the nothingness of the gash made by the prow of the colliding ship.

Again, guided by his wife's voice, he made his way toward the base of the triangle—the partially demolished wall that separated Cabin 56 from 58. He found that although the partition was securely attached to the ceiling, it was loose at the bottom. Working his fingers beneath it at floor level, he pulled it toward him with all his strength. He levered it up about 18 inches.

Holding the partition with one hand, he maneuvered first his right shoulder, then his left under its edge. He paused for a moment for breath. His eyes were growing accustomed to the darkness, but also from somewhere light was being reflected into the area where the women were trapped. Inch by inch, he wriggled beneath the loose partition. He could just make out the outlines of the debris when suddenly he saw the whiteness of his wife's upturned face directly in his path. Behind and above her was the shadowy figure of another woman. Both of the women were grotesquely twisted in the wreckage.

"Marty," he said.

His wife answered: "Mrs. Cianfarra is with me."

"Don't move," he said to the two women. "I'll go for help."

"My husband was in the other cabin," said Mrs. Cianfarra. "I think he's dead."

It suddenly dawned on Peterson that the body he had touched in the hallway of Number 56 a few minutes earlier was that of Mr. Cianfarra. (He learned later that one of Mrs. Cianfarra's two daughters in Cabin 52—Joan—also had been killed. The other, Linda, was miraculously thrown onto the intruding prow of the Stockholm and was rescued.)

By the feeble reflected light and by feel, Peterson took stock of the situation. Mrs. Peterson was lying on her back, with her body arching up and around the corner of the elevator shaft. Her body must have been almost touching Cianfarra's. Piles of wreckage covered the lower part of her body and that of Cianfarra; a shattered wall had fallen across them. Next to Mrs. Peterson, and a little above her, and almost touching her was Mrs. Cianfarra, partly sitting, partly standing—almost in the crouch of a skier—in the wreckage. Her legs were caught and twisted beneath her.

Although both women in their torn nightgowns were trapped and badly injured, they were calm; there was no hysteria. "I'm going for help," Peterson told them. He crawled back into Cabin 58. The partition swung down behind him with a thud.

It wasn't until he opened the door leading to the lighted corridor that he realized that he was still naked. Reaching to his right, he yanked the beige and maroon plaid curtain from the cabin's baggage closet and wrapped it around his middle like a sarong. He stepped into the corridor and headed for the stairs that led to the Promenade Deck directly above.

Gino had already reached the Promenade Deck. With the first-class headwaiter, Pietro Nanni, he was handing out life jackets and showing passengers how to slide across the sloping deck in a sitting position from the up-tilted port side to the starboard. It was now eleven thirty—the crash had occurred only 20 minutes before.

Into this scene of confusion stumbled Peterson, his massive, begrimed body covered only by the draped curtain. He began asking for help, but there was misery everywhere; everybody had his own problem.

Then a slender young man, twenty-five-year-old Raymond Waite, a seminarian at St. Charles Seminary in Philadelphia, stepped forward and said, "I'll help you if I can, but I don't know if I'm much good."

Peterson led the way down to Cabin 58. He lifted the partition and in the same manner as before crawled back into Cabin 56.

"Marty, I've got someone to help."

"Don't bother about me," his wife said. "Help Mrs. Cianfarra first."

"Oh, if only I could free my legs," Mrs. Cianfarra said.

Peterson knew that he had to get Mrs. Cianfarra free first. She was almost on top of Mrs. Peterson. Working in the darkness, he and Waite tried to move the wreckage pinning Mrs. Cianfarra, but it wouldn't budge. Without a light of some sort, the task seemed impossible. After a few minutes they crawled back under the partition into Cabin 58.

"Is there any other way I can be of help?" Raymond Waite said.

Peterson, thinking that the young man in clerical clothes was a priest, told him that Cianfarra, who he believed was Catholic, lay dead in the hallway of Cabin 56.

As Waite picked his way out of Cabin 58, Peterson added: "There's one other thing, could you please find me a pair of pants?"

As he left, Waite stopped a minute beside Cianfarra to recite the Act of Contrition. Then he went in search of the Doria's chaplain, Monsignor Sebastiano Natta, to administer the last rites.

Peterson crawled back to his wife and Mrs. Cianfarra and told them to hang on—he was going after help again.

As he crossed the corridor, he heard, coming from the hallway of Cabin 56, a priest saying: "*Ego te absolvo ab omnibus censuris et peccatis. . . .*" ("I absolve you from all censures and sins. . . .") Peterson slowly climbed toward the Promenade Deck again.

It was on the stairs that he ran into Gino and Pietro Nanni, their arms full of life jackets.

"I need help," he told them. "My wife and another woman are trapped." The three of them rushed down to the cabin.

For the first time, because Nanni had a flashlight, Peterson saw the jungle of debris and wreckage that he had been wandering through since the crash. Nanni held the light as Peterson lifted the partition for Gino to crawl beneath. Peterson followed him, taking the light from Nanni. Since there was only room for Peterson and Gino in the tangled wreckage, Nanni left them and went to help other passengers.

With the flashlight, Peterson was able to examine both women carefully. From the lack of sensation in the lower part of Mrs. Peterson's body and the manner in which she was bent around the corner of the elevator shaft, Peterson realized that her back and legs were probably broken. Her head was hanging downward, unsupported, about two feet off the floor. Her shoulders, upper body and arms were all that could be seen.

Mrs. Cianfarra was less seriously injured. But her hair was matted with blood from head injuries and her face was lacerated. She was jammed in an almost upright position, and it was clear that at least one leg was twisted and broken. That leg was securely held, not only by the bulk of the debris but by twisted bed springs. Although the women were bearing their injuries bravely, it was obvious that both were in great pain. Peterson left Gino behind and went in search of a doctor.

Crouching by the women, Gino began to lift off the lighter pieces of planking and the jagged sheets of hard laminated plywood panels. But he realized that to raise the heavier partitions he needed a jack. Shortly after midnight, he, too, left the women, reassuring them as he crawled under the partition that he'd be back. "I won't leave you," he told them.

He made his way to the Promenade Deck and headed for the paint locker, which he believed was in an open area near the bow. Hanging onto the handrail, he slowly made his way forward along the listing deck. But when he reached the open area he slipped and cut his leg on a stanchion. He sat for a moment to get his breath, then removed his shoes and threw them over the side. He found that he could walk better in his bare feet.

There was no jack in the paint locker.

He was returning when he saw a man in white overalls. "For God's sake," he said, "where can I get a jack?"

"I don't know," the man replied.

Gino hurried back downstairs. In Peterson's absence, he didn't want to remain too long away from the women.

Peterson had found two doctors on the Promenade Deck. He pleaded for medical help. "Do you have any morphine?" he asked.

"No," he was told.

"What do you mean?" he demanded.

"There's plenty down in the reception room," he was informed, "but we can't get to it now—we're too busy."

"Please," begged Peterson, "please get it as fast as you can."

Because of all the confusion, Peterson decided the best person to help him was the captain. He started the long climb from the Promenade Deck to the bridge on the Sun Deck, three levels above. The liner was now listing so badly that he almost had to haul himself up the 65 stairs to the bridge.

The captain, busy giving orders, seemed quite calm in spite of the catastrophe and he even remembered Peterson's name.

Peterson asked for "some experienced help." The captain assured him he would get it. He left the bridge and began the even more difficult climb downstairs. By the time he got back to Cabin 58, it was 12:30 A.M.

The Doria was now listing more than 30 degrees to starboard and in the four-foot triangular prison where the women were trapped, Gino was finding it difficult to work and also keep his balance. But he had been able to push a lot of debris into the gaping hole and the sea behind Mrs. Cianfarra. Also he had propped up the edge of the partition with a block of wood.

Together, Gino and Peterson succeeded in freeing Mrs. Cianfarra's right leg. The other remained entangled in the bed-springs.

Gino and Peterson wriggled beneath the partition to discuss their next move. The young seminarian, Raymond Waite, suddenly appeared with a pair of black pants belonging to his traveling companion, Father Paul Lambert. The pants were large: size 48. Peterson tore a strip of cloth from his sarong and used it as a belt. He thanked Waite and said, "Thank God, I'm alive."

The seminarian corrected him. He said: "*Thank God*. You're alive." Then he hurried off. Gino and Peterson crawled back into Cabin 56.

Mrs. Peterson was in much greater agony than before; so was Mrs. Cianfarra.

"Help is coming, Marty. The captain has said so," he told her.

For the first time his wife seemed to despair. "Darling," she said, "how will they ever get me out of here? Why don't you save Mrs. Cianfarra and yourselves?"

Gino said, "Take it easy, we won't leave you. We'll get you out."

Impatient for the morphine, Peterson returned to Cabin 58. Where were the doctors? He was about to look for medical help again when one of them arrived. Peterson showed him where the women were. The doctor made no move.

As calmly as he could, Peterson said, "Fix a double injection. I'll give it to them myself."

"The needle should be sterilized," the doctor warned.

"To hell with sterilization at a time like this," Peterson barked. "Give me the hypodermic."

Quickly, he crawled on his belly under

the partition and injected first his wife and then Mrs. Cianfarra in their left arms.

Feverishly Peterson and Gino then began trying to free Mrs. Cianfarra's other leg. But it soon became apparent that physical strength was not enough. They needed tools.

Gino, frustrated, summed up the situation. "We need wire cutters, scissors, pliers —anything to cut the mattresses and the bed springs. And we must get a jack to lift the debris off your wife."

Where could they get them? There was one place Peterson knew he could get wire cutters—the radio shack behind the captain's bridge. Once more he set out for the Sun Deck. As he crawled out, he took the empty syringe with him and placed it upside down in a cigarette-disposal cup.

His journey up the stairs was much tougher this time. He had to pull himself up, step by step, to the Sun Deck. And the red marbled covering on each landing was as slippery as a polished dance floor. Peterson was the only one on the staircase. The whole ship seemed to be enveloped in a cloak of silent expectancy.

In the wireless room, the radio officer was working at top speed. To reach him Peterson had to slide across the floor because of the list.

"Where can I find some wire cutters?" Peterson asked.

Surprised, the officer looked up. "I can't leave here. But there's a drawer of tools somewhere around. Help yourself."

Peterson had no difficulty in finding them. Several drawers had slid open because of the deck's slant, and in one he found two pairs of cutters. As he left the cabin, the radio officer was bent over his key. And although Peterson had no idea what messages were going out, at approximately that time, 1:12 A.M., the Doria was messaging into the night, NEED MORE LIFEBOATS.

Meanwhile, Gino had made his way to the deck below and there in the darkened galleys he found a large carving knife. He climbed back up to the Promenade Deck and from a nurse got a bone saw and several pairs of scissors. He returned to Cabin 56 almost at the same time as Peterson.

They began to work in shifts—one holding the flashlight and supplying the makeshift tools, while the other cut the mattresses and clipped the bed springs which held Mrs. Cianfarra captive. Both women by now were extremely weak—more than two hours had passed since the collision.

The men worked rapidly, urgently; in this silent microcosm of tragedy neither had time to dwell on the nightmarish possibility that at any moment the liner might capsize and take them all down.

Peterson cut through the last bed spring. All that held Mrs. Cianfarra now was a heavy length of ragged paneling. It passed directly over the instep of her left foot. Gino said to Mrs. Cianfarra: "This is going to hurt, but we must move it to get you out."

Mrs. Cianfarra said: "Go ahead."

Mrs. Cianfarra, her eyes closed, said nothing as the jagged edge of the paneling tore across her foot. Then, suddenly, she was free.

Gino backed up to her, placed her left arm over his shoulder and told her to hang on—she couldn't use the other arm, it hung limp. Then, carrying her piggyback fashion, he inched over to the partition. There he dropped to all fours. Easing her under the partition, Gino placed her on a blanket which Peterson had spread in the hallway of Cabin 58. It had taken them one hour and fifty minutes to free Mrs. Cianfarra.

Now they had to carry her along the sloping corridor and up 16 stairs to the Promenade Deck without injuring her further. They knew they could not do it alone.

Peterson headed for the Promenade Deck once more to recruit help. Three male passengers and a crewman returned with him. As the men stooped over Mrs. Cianfarra, Peterson warned them to be careful about her right shoulder and left leg. But because the ship was listing so badly they had difficulty holding onto the corners of the blanket and one accidentally grabbed Mrs. Cianfarra's right shoulder as the blanket slipped. She screamed—the first time she had cried out since her ordeal began. Finally, Gino and the four other volunteers got her up to the starboard side of the Promenade deck.

Gino went with the men; Peterson returned to his wife. For the first time since the collision they were alone together.

He tried to boost her morale by telling her that with Mrs. Cianfarra free, her release from the pinioning wreckage was only a matter of time. But in his heart he had doubts—and so had she.

She said: "Even if I get out of here, I'll be a hopeless cripple the rest of my life. I don't want to live like that. Why don't you save yourself?"

Lightheartedly Peterson tried to dismiss her fears: "Nonsense. We'll get you out of here—a jack will do the trick."

Up on the Promenade Deck, Gino was frantically searching for that jack. He ran from one end of the deck to the other, yelling at the sailors manning the many lifeboats which now dotted the water off the leaning starboard side of the Doria. He even gestured wildly and went through the motions of working a jack.

Off in the distance he could see the brilliantly lit Ile de France. The time was 2:30 A.M. and the Andrea Doria was being abandoned rapidly.

Almost in tears from sorrow and exhaustion, Gino finally caught the attention of a U.S. Coast Guard officer helping survivors into the lifeboats. "I must have a jack—a big jack," he cried. "There's a woman—she's trapped. We must get it quick."

The officer semaphored with a flashlight into the darkness.

Gino returned to Cabin 58. He whispered to Peterson that he had talked with an "American officer" about the jack, but shrugging his shoulders, added: "Maybe, like the others, he thought I was crazy. Maybe he didn't understand. You must go to the captain again."

Peterson agreed.

"I'll stay with Mrs. Peterson and do what I can," Gino assured him.

Peterson made the long, arduous trip to the bridge again. But the captain was elsewhere.

At least, Peterson thought, as he slowly made his way down the dangerously angled staircase, he'd get more morphine. Searching for a doctor, he was seen by Mr. and Mrs. Sigmund Morey, of New York, whom he had met earlier in the voyage. Peterson looked exhausted ("like a wild man") and they begged him to pause and take a drink. He stayed long enough only to take a swallow of blackberry brandy, then resumed his search. Eventually he found two doctors helping injured passengers into lifeboats. One told him, "We're terribly short of morphine. We must keep all we can for the seriously wounded."

After hours of holding himself emotionally in check, Peterson loosed his anger. "In God's name," he thundered. "Don't you think my wife is seriously wounded?"

He got the morphine.

A few minutes later, as he was injecting it into his wife, she said, "Darling, I'll never make it. Why don't you save yourself?"

Peterson decided to try to see the captain again. Tired, but terribly determined, he climbed the sloping stairway to the bridge. This time the captain was there—still calm, but trying to solve hundreds of problems all at once. "I must get a disaster crew," Peterson told him.

The captain ordered a deck officer to go down with Peterson. The officer took a fire ax with him, and together they returned to Cabin 58. While Gino went up on the Promenade Deck to see if the jack had arrived, Peterson asked the officer to try to remove the partition. But the impact of the ax against the springy, veneered plywood brought a shower of debris down on Mrs. Peterson. She cried out. Dr. Peterson crawled under the partition to help her. The officer, meanwhile, went around to the hallway of Cabin 56—and tried to chop through the debris on that side. Again wreckage began falling on and around Mrs. Peterson. Dr. Peterson yelled out for him to stop. He never saw the officer again.

The terrible agony she was suffering suddenly caused Marty to say quietly: "Can't you please put me out of my misery?"

Once more her distraught husband tried to console her and begged her to "hang on." He said: "I'm going up to see if the jack has arrived—I'll be back."

Peterson knew as he climbed the stairs that the situation was nearly hopeless. When he got to the deck he found it almost empty. Gino met him and together they stood waiting for the jack. Neither of them said anything. And then Gino heard a voice coming from a lifeboat below them. It said: "Are you the fellow who was looking for a jack?"

The sailor in the lifeboat threw them a line and slowly they began hauling a 150-pound jack with a six-foot-long handle up the liner's sloping side. The jack was so heavy that every few minutes they had to stop and secure the rope around a post—near the spot where Marty used to sit reading during the warm Mediterranean afternoons.

It took the two men a full 15 minutes to get the jack onto the deck and to the top of the stairway. The liner was now listing more than 40 degrees. Sitting, kneeling and squatting, they manhandled the jack down the staircase to the doorway of cabin 58. Both were so exhausted that they sat for a moment. Gino said to Dr. Peterson, "I wonder how much time we have left."

Peterson decided to ask the captain. When he reached the bridge for the fifth time, Peterson said, "My wife is still trapped. Will you be honest with me—how much time do we have left? An hour, a half-hour?"

The captain's face showed great weariness and strain as he answered, "There's no immediate danger." Peterson returned to his wife.

When he got back, he saw that Gino had placed cushions across Mrs. Peterson's body to protect her from the jack's pressure. The jack had to be used horizontally with its base against the corner of the elevator wall to lever away the wreckage pinning her down. But the handle of the jack was too long.

Peterson went out into the corridor, found the ax that the deck officer had used, and chopped through a bar that had held towels in one of the nearby bathrooms. This makeshift lever worked.

Suddenly and quietly, his wife said, "Oh, darling, I think I'm going. I'm going."

Peterson held one end of the jack as Gino began to pump the handle. The wreckage began to move. But it was too late. Gino's hand accidentally brushed Mrs. Peterson's face. It was cold. He looked down and saw that blood was trickling from her mouth. "Doctor," said Gino, "I think your wife's dead."

Peterson bent over his wife, placing his ear over her heart. After a few seconds, he raised his head and lifted the eyelid of her right eye. For a long time he held the wrist of her left hand searching for a pulse. Then, still holding her hand, his eyes on her upturned face, he said, "Marty's dead."

"Why couldn't it have been me?" cried Gino. "I'm nobody."

The time was ten minutes after four; the nightmare in Cabin 56 had lasted exactly five hours.

Gino saw Peterson kiss his wife on the lips and say, "Good-by, darling." Peterson gently removed a pearl ring from her left hand. Together he and Gino covered her with pillows and cushions and crawled out under the partition. As the sea began to enter the cabin, Dr. Peterson kicked the wooden brace which had been holding up the edge of the partition. The panel snapped back into place.

Gino said: "Is there anything I can do for you?" Peterson asked him if he could find his passports and maybe his pants. Then he slipped the pearl ring over the little finger of his left hand. This was the only possession of Marty's he could take with him.

Somehow, in all the debris Gino found the pants and the passports. They were in Cabin 58.

Then he and Gino went to the Promenade Deck and climbed down a rope into a lifeboat—the next to the last one to leave the Doria.

As the boat pulled away, Peterson's eyes remained on the gash which had been Cabin 56. Suddenly, unable to control himself longer, he burst into tears.

Contents of the Dead Man's Pocket

Jack Finney

The span of this story is a few minutes in one man's life—and the distance he covered in those minutes was a few steps—but it took no more than that for Jack Finney to develop one of the greatest suspense stories ever written.

October 26, 1956

At the little living-room desk Tom Benecke rolled two sheets of flimsy and a heavier top sheet, carbon paper sandwiched between them, into his portable. *Interoffice Memo*, the top sheet was headed, and he typed tomorrow's date just below this; then he glanced at a creased yellow sheet, covered with his own handwriting, beside the typewriter. "Hot in here," he muttered to himself. Then, from the short hallway at his back, he heard the muffled clang of wire coat hangers in the bedroom closet, and at this reminder of what his wife was doing he thought: Hot, hell—guilty conscience.

He got up, shoving his hands into the back pockets of his gray wash slacks, stepped to the living-room window beside the desk and stood breathing on the glass, watching the expanding circlet of mist, staring down through the autumn night at Lexington Avenue, eleven stories below. He was a tall, lean, dark-haired young man in a pullover sweater, who looked as though he had played not football, probably, but basketball in college. Now he placed the heels of his hands against the top edge of the lower window frame and shoved upward. But as usual the window didn't budge, and he had to lower his hands and then shoot them hard upward to jolt the window open a few inches. He dusted his hands, muttering.

But still he didn't begin his work. He crossed the room to the hallway entrance and, leaning against the doorjamb, hands shoved into his back pockets again, he called, "Clare?" When his wife answered, he said, "Sure you don't mind going alone?"

"No." Her voice was muffled, and he knew her head and shoulders were in the bedroom closet. Then the tap of her high heels sounded on the wood floor and she appeared at the end of the little hallway, wearing a slip, both hands raised to one ear, clipping on an earring. She smiled at him—a slender, very pretty girl with light brown, almost blonde, hair—her prettiness emphasized by the pleasant nature that showed in her face. "It's just that I hate you to miss this movie; you wanted to see it too."

"Yeah, I know." He ran his fingers through his hair. "Got to get this done though."

She nodded, accepting this. Then, glancing at the desk across the living room, she said, "You work too much, though, Tom—and too hard."

He smiled, "You won't mind though, will you, when the money comes rolling in and I'm known as the Boy Wizard of Wholesale Groceries?"

"I guess not." She smiled and turned back toward the bedroom.

At his desk again, Tom lighted a cigarette; then a few moments later as Clare appeared, dressed and ready to leave, he set it on the rim of the ash tray. "Just after seven," she said. "I can make the beginning of the first feature."

He walked to the front-door closet to help her on with her coat. He kissed her then and, for an instant, holding her close, smelling the perfume she had used, he was tempted to go with her; it was not actually true that he had to work tonight, though he very much wanted to. This was his own project, unannounced as yet in his office, and it could be postponed. But then they won't see it till Monday, he thought once again, and if I give it to the boss tomorrow he might read it over the weekend . . . "Have a good time," he said aloud. He gave his wife a little swat and opened the door for her, feeling the air from the building hallway, smelling faintly of floor wax, stream gently past his face.

He watched her walk down the hall, flicked a hand in response as she waved, and then he started to close the door, but it resisted for a moment. As the door opening narrowed, the current of warm air from the hallway, channeled through this smaller opening now, suddenly rushed past him with accelerated force. Behind him he heard the slap of the window curtains against the wall and the sound of paper fluttering from his desk, and he had to push to close the door.

Turning, he saw a sheet of white paper drifting to the floor in a series of arcs, and another sheet, yellow, moving toward the window, caught in the dying current flowing through the narrow opening. As he watched, the paper struck the bottom edge of the window and hung there for an instant, plastered against the glass and wood. Then as the moving air stilled completely the curtains swinging back from the wall to hang free again, he saw the yellow sheet drop to the window ledge and slide over out of sight.

He ran across the room, grasped the bottom edge of the window and tugged, staring through the glass. He saw the yellow sheet, dimly now in the darkness outside, lying on the ornamental ledge a yard below the window. Even as he watched, it was moving, scraping slowly along the ledge, pushed by the breeze that pressed steadily against the building wall. He heaved on the window with all his strength and it shot open with a bang, the window weight rattling in the casing. But the paper was past his reach and, leaning out into the night, he watched it scud steadily along the ledge to the south, half plastered against the building wall. Above the muffled sound of the street traffic far below, he could hear the dry scrape of its movement, like a leaf on the pavement.

The living room of the next apartment to the south projected a yard or more farther out toward the street than this one; because of this the Beneckes paid seven and a half dollars less rent than their neighbors. And now the yellow sheet, sliding along the stone ledge, nearly invisible in the night, was stopped by the projecting blank wall of the next apartment. It lay motionless, then, in the corner formed by the two walls—a good five yards away, pressed firmly against the ornate corner ornament of the ledge, by the breeze that moved past Tom Benecke's face.

He knelt at the window and stared at the yellow paper for a full minute or more, waiting for it to move, to slide off the ledge and fall, hoping he could follow its course to the street, and then hurry down in the elevator and retrieve it. But it didn't move, and then he saw that the paper was caught firmly between a projection of the convoluted corner ornament and the ledge. He thought about the poker from the fireplace, then the broom, then the mop—discarding each thought as it occurred to him. There was nothing in the apartment long enough to reach that paper.

It was hard for him to understand that he actually had to abandon it—it was ridiculous—and he began to curse. Of all the papers on his desk, why did it have to be this one in particular! On four long Saturday afternoons he had stood in supermarkets counting the people who passed certain displays, and the results were scribbled on that yellow sheet. From stacks of trade publications, gone over page by page in snatched half hours at work and during evenings at home, he had copied facts, quotations and figures onto that sheet. And he had carried it with him to the Public Library on Fifth Avenue, where he'd spent a dozen lunch hours and early evenings adding more. All were needed to support and lend authority to his idea for a new grocery-store display method; without them his idea was a mere opinion. And there they all lay, in his own improvised shorthand—countless hours of work—out there on the ledge.

For many seconds he believed he was going to abandon the yellow sheet, that there was nothing else to do. The work could be duplicated. But it would take two months, and the time to present this idea, damn it, was *now,* for use in the spring displays. He struck his fist on the window ledge. Then he shrugged. Even though his plan were adopted, he told himself, it wouldn't bring him a raise in pay—not immediately, anyway, or as a direct result. It won't bring me a promotion either, he argued—not of itself.

But just the same, and he couldn't escape the thought, this and other independent projects, some already done and others planned for the future, would gradually mark him out from the score of other young men in his company. They were the way to change from a name on the payroll to a name in the minds of the company officials. They were the beginning of the long, long climb to where he was determined to be, at the very top. And he knew he was going out there in the darkness, after the yellow sheet fifteen feet beyond his reach.

By a kind of instinct, he instantly began making his intention acceptable to himself by laughing at it. The mental picture of himself sidling along the ledge outside was absurd—it was actually comical—and he smiled. He imagined himself describing it; it would make a good story at the office and, it occurred to him, would add a special interest and importance to his memorandum, which would do it no harm at all.

To simply go out and get his paper was an easy task—he could be back here with it in less than two minutes—and he knew he wasn't deceiving himself. The ledge, he saw, measuring it with his eye, was about as wide as the length of his shoe, and perfectly flat. And every fifth row of brick in the face of the building, he remembered—leaning out, he verified this —was indented half an inch, enough for the tips of his fingers, enough to maintain balance easily. It occurred to him that if this ledge and wall were only a yard aboveground—as he knelt at the window staring out, this thought was the final confirmation of his intention—he could move along the ledge indefinitely.

On a sudden impulse, he got to his feet, walked to the front closet and took out an old tweed jacket; it would be cold outside. He put it on and buttoned it as he crossed the room rapidly toward the open window. In the back of his mind he knew he'd better hurry and get this over with before he thought too much, and at the window he didn't allow himself to hesitate.

He swung a leg over the sill, then felt for and found the ledge a yard below the window with his foot. Gripping the bottom of the window frame very tightly and carefully, he slowly ducked his head under it, feeling on his face the sudden change from the warm air of the room to the chill outside. With infinite care he brought out his other leg, his mind concentrating on what he was doing. Then he slowly stood erect. Most of the putty, dried out and brittle, had dropped off the bottom edging of the window frame, he found, and the flat wooden edging provided a good gripping surface, a half inch or more deep, for the tips of his fingers.

Now, balanced easily and firmly, he stood on the ledge outside in the slight, chill breeze, eleven stories above the street, staring into his own lighted apartment, odd and different-seeming now.

First his right hand, then his left, he carefully shifted his finger-tip grip from the puttyless window edging to an indented row of bricks directly to his right. It was hard to take the first shuffling sideways step then—to make himself move —and the fear stirred in his stomach, but he did it, again by not allowing himself time to think. And now—with his chest, stomach, and the left side of his face pressed against the rough cold brick—his lighted apartment was suddenly gone, and it was much darker out here than he had thought.

Without pause he continued—right foot, left foot, right foot, left—his shoe soles shuffling and scraping along the rough stone, never lifting from it, fingers sliding along the exposed edging of brick. He moved on the balls of his feet, heels lifted slightly; the ledge was not quite as wide as he'd expected. But leaning slightly inward toward the face of the building and pressed against it, he could feel his balance firm and secure, and moving along the ledge was quite as easy as he had thought it would be. He could hear the buttons of his jacket scraping steadily along the rough bricks and feel them catch momentarily, tugging a little, at each mortared crack. He simply did not permit himself to look down, though the compulsion to do so never left him; nor did he allow himself actually to think. Mechanically—right foot, left foot, over and again—he shuffled along crabwise, watching the projecting wall ahead loom steadily closer. . . .

Then he reached it and, at the corner —he'd decided how he was going to pick up the paper—he lifted his right foot and placed it carefully on the ledge that ran along the projecting wall at a right angle to the ledge on which his other foot rested. And now, facing the building, he stood in the corner formed by the two walls, one foot on the ledging of each, a hand on the shoulder-high indentation of each wall. His forehead was pressed directly into the corner against the cold bricks, and now he carefully lowered first one hand, then the other, perhaps a foot farther down, to the next indentation in the rows of bricks.

Very slowly, sliding his forehead down the trough of the brick corner and bending his knees, he lowered his body toward the paper lying between his outstretched feet. Again he lowered his fingerholds another foot and bent his knees still more, thigh muscles taut, his forehead sliding and bumping down the brick V. Half squatting now, he dropped his left hand to the next indentation and then slowly reached with his right hand toward the paper between his feet.

He couldn't quite touch it, and his knees now were pressed against the wall; he could bend them no farther. But by ducking his head another inch lower, the top of his head now pressed against the bricks, he lowered his right shoulder and his fingers had the paper by a corner, pulling it loose. At the same instant he saw, between his legs and far below, Lexington Avenue stretched out for miles ahead.

He saw, in that instant, the Loew's theater sign, blocks ahead past Fiftieth Street; the miles of traffic signals, all green now; the lights of cars and street lamps; countless neon signs; and the moving black dots of people. And a violent instantaneous explosion of absolute terror roared through him. For a motionless instant he saw himself externally—bent practically double, balanced on this narrow ledge, nearly half his body projecting out above the street far below—and he began to tremble violently, panic flaring through his mind and muscles, and he felt the blood rush from the surface of his skin.

In the fractional moment before horror paralyzed him, as he stared between his legs at that terrible length of street far beneath him, a fragment of his mind raised his body in a spasmodic jerk to an upright position again, but so violently that his head scraped hard against the wall, bouncing off it, and his body swayed outward to the knife edge of balance, and he very nearly plunged backward and fell. Then he was leaning far into the corner again, squeezing and pushing into it, not only his face but his chest and stomach, his back arching; and his finger tips clung with all the pressure of his pulling arms to the shoulder-high half-inch indentation in the bricks.

He was more than trembling now; his whole body was racked with a violent shuddering beyond control, his eyes squeezed so tightly shut it was painful, though he was past awareness of that. His teeth were exposed in a frozen grimace, the strength draining like water from his knees and calves. It was extremely likely, he knew, that he would faint, to slump down along the wall, his face scraping, and then drop backward, a limp weight, out into nothing. And to save his life he concentrated on holding onto consciousness, drawing deliberate deep breaths of cold air into his lungs, fighting to keep his senses aware.

Then he knew that he would not faint, but he could not stop shaking nor open his eyes. He stood where he was, breathing deeply, trying to hold back the terror of the glimpse he had had of what lay below him; and he knew he had made a mistake in not making himself stare down at the street, getting used to it and accepting it, when he had first stepped out onto the ledge.

It was impossible to walk back. He simply could not do it. He couldn't bring himself to make the slightest movement.

The strength was gone from his legs; his shivering hands—numb, cold and desperately rigid—had lost all deftness; his easy ability to move and balance was gone. Within a step or two, if he tried to move, he knew that he would stumble clumsily and fall.

Seconds passed, with the chill faint wind pressing the side of his face, and he could hear the toned-down volume of the street traffic far beneath him. Again and again it slowed and then stopped, almost to silence; then presently, even this high, he would hear the click of the traffic signals and the subdued roar of the cars starting up again. During a lull in the street sounds, he called out. Then he was shouting "*Help!*" so loudly it rasped his throat. But he felt the steady pressure of the wind, moving between his face and the blank wall, snatch up his cries as he uttered them, and he knew they must sound directionless and distant. And he remembered how habitually, here in New York, he himself heard and ignored shouts in the night. If anyone heard him, there was no sign of it, and presently Tom Benecke knew he had to try moving; there was nothing else he could do.

Eyes squeezed shut, he watched scenes in his mind like scraps of motion-picture film—he could not stop them. He saw himself stumbling suddenly sideways as he crept along the ledge and saw his upper body arc outward, arms flailing. He saw a dangling shoestring caught between the ledge and the sole of his other shoe, saw a foot start to move, to be stopped with a jerk, and felt his balance leaving him. He saw himself falling with a terrible speed as his body revolved in the air, knees clutched tight to his chest, eyes squeezed shut, moaning softly.

Out of utter necessity, knowing that any of these thoughts might be reality in the very next seconds, he was slowly able to shut his mind against every thought but what he now began to do. With fear-soaked slowness, he slid his left foot an inch or two toward his own impossibly distant window. Then he slid the fingers of his shivering left hand a corresponding distance. For a moment he could not bring himself to lift his right foot from one ledge to the other; then he did it, and became aware of the harsh exhalation of air from his throat and realized that he was panting. As his right hand, then, began to slide along the brick edging, he was astonished to feel the yellow paper pressed to the bricks underneath his stiff fingers, and he uttered a terrible, abrupt bark that might have been a laugh or a moan. He opened his mouth and took the paper in his teeth, pulling it out from under his fingers.

By a kind of trick—by concentrating his entire mind on first his left foot, then his left hand, then the other foot, then the other hand—he was able to move, almost imperceptibly, trembling steadily, very nearly without thought. But he could feel the terrible strength of the pent-up horror on just the other side of the flimsy barrier he had erected in his mind; and he knew that if it broke through he would lose this thin artificial control of his body.

During one slow step he tried keeping his eyes closed; it made him feel safer, shutting him off a little from the fearful reality of where he was. Then a sudden rush of giddiness swept over him and he had to open his eyes wide, staring sideways at the cold rough brick and angled lines of mortar, his cheek tight against the building. He kept his eyes open then, knowing that if he once let them flick outward, to stare for an instant at the lighted windows across the street, he would be past help.

He didn't know how many dozens of tiny sidling steps he had taken, his chest, belly and face pressed to the wall; but he knew the slender hold he was keeping on his mind and body was going to break. He had a sudden mental picture of his apartment on just the other side of this wall—warm, cheerful, incredibly spacious. And he saw himself striding through it, lying down on the floor on his back, arms spread wide, reveling in its unbelievable security. The impossible remoteness of this utter safety, the contrast between it and where he now stood, was more than he could bear. And the barrier broke then, and the fear of the awful height he stood on coursed through his nerves and muscles.

A fraction of his mind knew he was going to fall, and he began taking rapid blind steps with no feeling of what he was doing, sidling with a clumsy desperate swiftness, fingers scrabbling along the brick, almost hopelessly resigned to the sudden backward pull and swift motion outward and down. Then his moving left hand slid onto not brick but sheer emptiness, an impossible gap in the face of the wall, and he stumbled.

His right foot smashed into his left anklebone; he staggered sideways, began falling, and the claw of his hand cracked against glass and wood, slid down it, and his finger tips were pressed hard on the puttyless edging of his window. His right hand smacked gropingly beside it as he fell to his knees; and, under the full weight and direct downward pull of his sagging body, the open window dropped shudderingly in its frame till it closed and his wrists struck the sill and were jarred off.

For a single moment he knelt, knee bones against stone on the very edge of the ledge, body swaying and touching nowhere else, fighting for balance. Then he lost it, his shoulders plunging backward, and he flung his arms forward, his hands smashing against the window casing on either side; and—his body moving backward—his fingers clutched the narrow wood stripping of the upper pane.

For an instant he hung suspended between balance and falling, his finger tips pressed onto the quarter-inch wood strips. Then, with utmost delicacy, with a focused concentration of all his senses, he increased even further the strain on his finger tips hooked to these slim edgings of wood. Elbows slowly bending, he began to draw the full weight of his upper body forward, knowing that the instant his fingers slipped off these quarter-inch strips he'd plunge backward and be falling. Elbows imperceptibly bending, body shaking with the strain, the sweat starting from his forehead in great sudden drops, he pulled, his entire being and thought concentrated in his finger tips. Then suddenly, the strain slackened and ended, his chest touching the window sill, and he was kneeling on the ledge, his forehead pressed to the glass of the closed window.

Dropping his palms to the sill, he stared into his living room—at the red-brown davenport across the room, and a magazine he had left there; at the pictures on the walls and the gray rug; the entrance to the hallway; and at his papers, typewriter and desk, not two feet from his nose. A movement from his desk caught his eye and he saw that it was a thin curl of blue smoke; his cigarette, the ash long, was still burning in the ash tray where he'd left it—this was past all belief—only a few minutes before.

His head moved, and in faint reflection

from the glass before him he saw the yellow paper clenched in his front teeth. Lifting a hand from the sill he took it from his mouth; the moistened corner parted from the paper, and he spat it out.

For a moment, in the light from the living room, he stared wonderingly at the yellow sheet in his hand and then crushed it into the side pocket of his jacket.

He couldn't open the window. It had been pulled not completely closed, but its lower edge was below the level of the outside sill; there was no room to get his fingers underneath it. Between the upper sash and the lower was a gap not wide enough—reaching up, he tried—to get his fingers into; he couldn't push it open. The upper window panel, he knew from long experience, was impossible to move, frozen tight with dried paint.

Very carefully observing his balance, the finger tips of his left hand again hooked to the narrow stripping of the window casing, he drew back his right hand, palm facing the glass, and then struck the glass with the heel of his hand.

His arm rebounded from the pane, his body tottering, and he knew he didn't dare strike a harder blow.

But in the security and relief of his new position, he simply smiled; with only a sheet of glass between him and the room just before him, it was not possible that there wasn't a way past it. Eyes narrowing, he thought for a few moments about what to do. Then his eyes widened, for nothing occurred to him. But still he felt calm: the trembling, he realized, had stopped. At the back of his mind there still lay the thought that once he was again in his home, he could give release to his feelings. He actually *would* lie on the floor, rolling, clenching tufts of the rug in his hands. He would literally run across the room, free to move as he liked, jumping on the floor, testing and reveling in its absolute security, letting the relief flood through him, draining the fear from his mind and body. His yearning for this was astonishingly intense, and somehow he understood that he had better keep this feeling at bay.

He took a half dollar from his pocket and struck it against the pane, but without any hope that the glass would break and with very little disappointment when it did not. After a few moments of thought he drew his leg up onto the ledge and picked loose the knot of his shoelace. He slipped off the shoe and, holding it across the instep, drew back his arm as far as he dared and struck the leather heel against the glass. The pane rattled, but he knew he'd been a long way from breaking it. His foot was cold and he slipped the shoe back on. He shouted again, experimentally, and then once more, but there was no answer.

The realization suddenly struck him that he might have to wait here till Clare came home, and for a moment the thought was funny. He could see Clare opening the front door, withdrawing her key from the lock, closing the door behind her and then glancing up to see him crouched on the other side of the window. He could see her rush across the room, face astounded and frightened, and hear himself shouting instructions: "Never mind how I got here! Just open the wind—" She couldn't open it, he remembered, she'd never been able to; she'd always had to call him. She'd have to get the building superintendent or a neighbor, and he pictured himself smiling and answering their questions as he climbed in. "I just wanted to get a breath of fresh air, so—"

He couldn't possibly wait here till Clare

came home. It was the second feature she'd wanted to see, and she'd left in time to see the first. She'd be another three hours or— He glanced at his watch; Clare had been gone eight minutes. It wasn't possible, but only eight minutes ago he had kissed his wife good-by. She wasn't even at the theater yet!

It would be four hours before she could possibly be home, and he tried to picture himself kneeling out here, finger tips hooked to these narrow strippings, while first one movie, preceded by a slow listing of credits, began, developed, reached its climax and then finally ended. There'd be a newsreel next, maybe and then an animated cartoon, and then interminable scenes from coming pictures. And then, once more, the beginning of a full-length picture—while all the time he hung out here in the night.

He might possibly get to his feet, but he was afraid to try. Already his legs were cramped, his thigh muscles tired; his knees hurt, his feet felt numb and his hands were stiff. He couldn't possibly stay out here for four hours, or anywhere near it. Long before that his legs and arms would give out; he would be forced to try changing his position often—stiffly, clumsily, his co-ordination and strength gone—and he would fall. Quite realistically, he knew that he would fall; no one could stay out here on this ledge for four hours.

A dozen windows in the apartment building across the street were lighted. Looking over his shoulder, he could see the top of a man's head behind the newspaper he was reading; in another window he saw the blue-gray flicker of a television screen. No more than twenty-odd yards from his back were scores of people, and if just one of them would walk idly to his window and glance out. . . . For some moments he stared over his shoulder at the lighted rectangles, waiting. But no one appeared. The man reading his paper turned a page and then continued his reading. A figure passed another of the windows and was immediately gone.

In the inside pocket of his jacket he found a little sheaf of papers, and he pulled one out and looked at it in the light from the living room. It was an old letter, an advertisement of some sort; his name and address, in purple ink, were on a label pasted to the envelope. Gripping one end of the envelope in his teeth, he twisted it into a tight curl. From his shirt pocket he brought out a book of matches. He didn't dare let go the casing with both hands but, with the twist of paper in his teeth, he opened the matchbook with his free hand; then he bent one of the matches in two without tearing it from the folder, its red-tipped end now touching the striking surface. With his thumb, he rubbed the red tip across the striking area.

He did it again, then again, and still again, pressing harder each time, and the match suddenly flared, burning his thumb. But he kept it alight, cupping the matchbook in his hand and shielding it with his body. He held the flame to the paper in his mouth till it caught. Then he snuffed out the match flame with his thumb and forefinger, careless of the burn, and replaced the book in his pocket. Taking the paper twist in his hand, he held it flame down, watching the flame crawl up the paper, till it flared bright. Then he held it behind him over the street, moving it from side to side, watching it over his shoulder, the flame flickering and guttering in the wind.

There were three letters in his pocket and he lighted each of them, holding each till the flame touched his hand and then dropping it to the street below. At one point, watching over his shoulder while the last of the letters burned, he saw the man across the street put down his paper and stand—even seeming, to Tom, to glance toward his window. But when he moved, it was only to walk across the room and disappear from sight.

There were a dozen coins in Tom Benecke's pocket and he dropped them, three or four at a time. But if they struck anyone, of it anyone noticed their falling, no one connected them with their source, and no one glanced upward.

His arms had begun to tremble from the steady strain of clinging to this narrow perch, and he did not know what to do now and was terribly frightened. Clinging to the window stripping with one hand, he again searched his pockets. But now—he had left his wallet on his dresser when he'd changed clothes—there was nothing left but the yellow sheet. It occurred to him irrelevantly that his death on the sidewalk below would be an eternal mystery; the window closed—why, how, and from where could he have fallen? No one would be able to identify his body for a time, either—the thought was somehow unbearable and increased his fear. All they'd find in his pockets would be the yellow sheet. *Contents of the dead man's pockets,* he thought, *one sheet of paper bearing penciled notations—incomprehensible.*

He understood fully that he might actually be going to die; his arms, maintaining his balance on the ledge, were trembling steadily now. And it occurred to him then with all the force of a revelation that, if he fell, all he was ever going to have out of life he would then, abruptly, have had. Nothing, then, could ever be changed; and nothing more—no least experience or pleasure—could ever be added to his life. He wished, then, that he had not allowed his wife to go off by herself tonight—and on similar nights. He thought of all the evenings he had spent away from her, working; and he regretted them. He thought wonderingly of his fierce ambition and of the direction his life had taken; he thought of the hours he'd spent by himself, filling the yellow sheet that had brought him out here. *Contents of the dead man's pockets,* he thought with sudden fierce anger, *a wasted life.*

He was simply not going to cling here till he slipped and fell; he told himself that now. There was one last thing he could try; he had been aware of it for some moments, refusing to think about it, but now he faced it. Kneeling here on the ledge, the finger tips of one hand pressed to the narrow strip of wood, he could, he knew, draw his other hand back a yard perhaps, fist clenched tight, doing it very slowly till he sensed the outer limit of balance, then, as hard as he was able from the distance, he could drive his fist forward against the glass. If it broke, his fist smashing through, he was safe; he might cut himself badly, and probably would, but with his arm inside the room he would be secure. But if the glass did not break, the rebound, flinging his arm back, would topple him off the ledge. He was certain of that.

He tested his plan. The fingers of his left hand clawlike on the little stripping, he drew back his other fist until his body began teetering backward. But he had no leverage now—he could feel that there would be no force to his swing—and he moved his fist slowly forward till he rocked forward on his knees again and could sense that his swing would carry its greatest force. Glancing down, however, measuring the distance from his fist to the glass, he saw that it was less than two feet.

It occurred to him that he could raise his arm over his head, to bring it down against the glass. But, experimenting in slow motion, he knew it would be an awkward girl-like blow without the force of a driving punch, and not nearly enough to break the glass.

Facing the window, he had to drive a blow from the shoulder, he knew now, at a distance of less than two feet; and he did not know whether it would break through the heavy glass. It might; he could picture it happening, he could feel it in the nerves of his arm. And it might not; he could feel that too—feel his fist striking this glass and being instantaneously flung back by the unbreaking pane, feel the fingers of his other hand breaking loose, nails scraping along the casing as he fell.

He waited, arm drawn back, fist balled, but in no hurry to strike; this pause, he knew, might be an extension of his life. And to live even a few seconds longer, he felt, even out here on this ledge in the night, was infinitely better than to die a moment earlier than he had to. His arm grew tired, and he brought it down and rested it.

Then he knew that it was time to make the attempt. He could not kneel here hesitating indefinitely till he lost all courage to act, waiting till he slipped off the ledge. Again he drew back his arm, knowing this time that he would not bring it down till he struck. His elbow protruding over Lexington Avenue far below, the fingers of his other hand pressed down bloodlessly tight against the narrow stripping, he waited, feeling the sick tenseness and terrible excitement building. It grew and swelled toward the moment of action, his nerves tautening. He thought of Clare—just a wordless, yearning thought—and then drew his arm back just a bit more, fist so tight his fingers pained him, and knowing he was going to do it. Then with full power, with every last scrap of strength he could bring to bear, he shot his arm forward toward the glass, and he said, "*Clare!*"

He heard the sound, felt the blow, felt himself falling forward, and his hand closed on the living-room curtains, the shards and fragments of glass showering onto the floor. And then, kneeling there on the ledge, an arm thrust into the room up to the shoulder, he began picking away the protruding slivers and great wedges of glass from the window frame, tossing them in onto the rug. And, as he grasped the edges of the empty window frame and climbed into his home, he was grinning in triumph.

He did not lie down on the floor or run through the apartment, as he had promised himself; even in the first few moments it seemed to him natural and normal that he should be where he was. He simply turned to his desk, pulled the crumpled yellow sheet from his pocket and laid it down where it had been, smoothing it out; then he absently laid a pencil across it to weight it down. He shook his head wonderingly, and turned to walk toward the closet.

There he got out his topcoat and hat and, without waiting to put them on, opened the front door and stepped out, to go find his wife. He turned to pull the door closed and the warm air from the hall rushed through the narrow opening again. As he saw the yellow paper, the pencil flying, scooped off the desk and, unimpeded by the glassless window, sail out into the night and out of his life, Tom Benecke burst into laughter and then closed the door behind him.

Drawn by James Montgomery Flagg
January 19, 1907

August 24, 1907

PICTURESQUE AMERICA

FROM A CAR WINDOW

DRAWN BY E. W. KEMBLE

The Liquor Dealer: *His Supports and His Burdens*

Drawn by BOARDMAN ROBINSON

May 2, 1908

The Inventions of Professor Lucifer G. Butts, A.K. By Rube Goldberg

THE MASSIVE INTELLECT OF PROFESSOR BUTTS EVOLVES A SIMPLE APPLIANCE FOR PUTTING POSTAGE STAMPS ON ENVELOPES.

BOSS (A) SNEEZES. SNOZZLEHOUND (B), FRIGHTENED OUT OF A SOUND SLUMBER, RUNS OUT OF THE OFFICE, UPSETTING HATRACK (C) AND BREAKING ICE WATER CONTAINER (D). WATER (E) IS SPILLED INTO TROUGH (F) AND IS THEN CONVEYED TO BUCKET (G).

THE WEIGHT OF THE WATER IN BUCKET CAUSES STRING (H) TO COMPRESS NUT-CRACKER (I) WHICH SQUEEZES BULB ON MEDICINE-DROPPER (J) AND MOISTENS POSTAGE STAMP (K)

STENOGRAPHER (L), ABOUT TO GO OUT TO LUNCH, HEARS THE SPLASHING OF WATER ON SEVERAL OCCASIONS DURING THE OPERATION OF THE APPARATUS. SHE THINKS IT IS RAINING AND PICKS UP HER UMBRELLA (M), WHICH PULLS BACK SMALL HOOK (N), CAUSING SPRING (P) TO THROW PADDLE (O) OVER ON ENVELOPE (Q) AND PRESS MOISTENED STAMP IN PLACE.

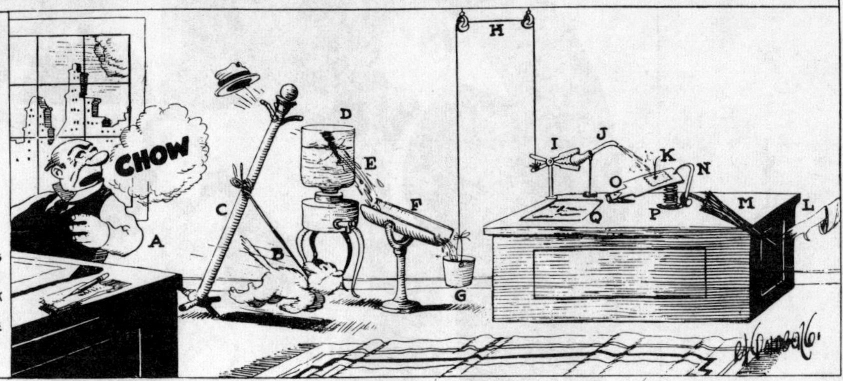

January 26, 1929

"Go 'round the block again and make sure you cop me a big red one when we pass next time!" *Adolph Schus*

October 22, 1932

"May I have the 'Help Wanted' section after you, sir?"

Lawrence La Riar

November 26, 1932

"Why don't you boys figure out something different to give Kennesaw for his birthday? You gave him a bath last year"

REAMER KELLER

October 2, 1937

"Pardon me—sorry—my fault—excuse me—pardon me!"

RICHARD DECKER

November 12, 1938

March 30, 1940

"'Peter Piper picked a peck of pickled peppers.' Now you fan me a while!"

GEORGE LICHTY

"It's the latest—a V-8"

AL KAELIN

October 19, 1940

January 4, 1941

"Oh! Oh! I wouldn't care to be in the devil's shoes this morning!"

IRVING ROIR

February 8, 1941

January 2, 1943

"All I got this year was neckties!" BILL KING

"Pssst—alternately, Shultz!" VIRGIL PARTCH

January 16, 1943

"Watch out, everybody—the plate's hot!"

April 17, 1943

"Ah hates short'nin' bread, Mammy"

June 2, 1945

"Sorry we can't give you a wider choice . . . there's a war on, you know"

HERB WILLIAMS

June 16, 1945

"Now just speak slowly and carefully, Oscar, and tell us how this thing occurred"

NED HILTON

October 28, 1945

"It's a switch! He's going over the falls with a barrel in him!"

BO BROWN

June 8, 1946

"Saith who?"

CHARLES PEARSON

June 29, 1946

January 11, 1947

"It's great having you home again, Kilroy.
Sit down and tell us where you've been"

March 29, 1947

"Double Martini" VIRGIL PARTCH

September 13, 1947

"Oh, no, I think you dance very well for a horse" IRWIN CAPLAN

September 27, 1947

March 20, 1948

"... and I'm breaking off our engagement, so you can come over and take back your toad" GERALD GREEN

May 15, 1948

FRANK B. MODELL

April 16, 1954

"Thanks a lot"

ROWLAND WILSON

April 30, 1954

CHARLES E. MARTIN

November 24, 1955

"We must be ever alert, my boy! This fox we're after is clever as they come"

EARLE LEVENSTEIN

November 23, 1956